W9-DBG-654

# TODO
# ANDALUCIA

HUELVA

CORDOBA

JAEN

SEVILLA

GRANADA

ALMERIA

CADIZ

MALAGA

editorial escudo de oro, s.a. Palaudarias, 26 - 08004 Barcelona - España

*La Maestranza, la famosa plaza de toros de Sevilla.*

# SEVILLA

En estas páginas, intentaremos mostrar todo el esplendor, diversidad, misticismo y peculiaridad que la región merece.

Empezamos nuestro recorrido por Sevilla, la ciudad más importante de Andalucía, una de las ciudades más bellas del mundo.

Esto es Andalucía, la tierra preferida durante mucho tiempo por viajeros y turistas de todo el mundo.

*La Torre del Oro y el Guadalquivir.*

*Vista general de la catedral, en la que se puede admirar el armonioso conjunto gótico.*

*Entrada al Patio de los Naranjos por la Puerta del Perdón.* ▷

*Los «Seises» de la catedral sevillana tienen el privilegio de cantar y bailar delante del Santísimo y en honor de la Inmaculada.*

*La sacristía mayor muestra la exuberancia del plateresco.*

La provincia sevillana se halla situada en la depresión del Guadalquivir, limita al Norte con Sierra Morena y al Sur con las estribaciones del sistema Penibético.

Justo en el margen izquierdo de ese viejo río, *Betis* para los romanos, se encuentra la antigua *Hispalis* capital de la *Bética*.

Privilegiada geográfica y climatológicamente, de ella diría Ortega y Gasset que es la «ciudad de los reflejos».

A estas características naturales se le suman las fachadas de sus casas enjalbegadas de blanco, los balcones repletos de flores, sus patios, a caballo entre romanos y orientales pero por encima de todo andaluces, y sus innumerables monumentos.

Conqusitada por César, se convirtió en capital romana de la *Bética*. Capturada por los árabes bajo el mando de Muza (año 712), será llamada *Ixbilia* y llegará a ser una de las ciudades más importantes de Al Andalus hasta su reconquista por Fernando III en el año 1248.

Tras el descubrimiento de América, en ella se cen-

*Sepulcro de Cristóbal Colón, obra de Arturo Mélida.*

tralizó el comercio colonial, erigiéndose como metrópoli del Nuevo Mundo.

Fernando VII trasladaría a esta ciudad el gobierno durante la invasión francesa (1823).

Por Sevilla han pasado, pues, civilizaciones milenarias, tartesos, fenicios, romanos, vándalos, árabes y castellanos. Todos ellos han dejado sus huellas en los monumentos que la adornan, en el paisaje, en el espíritu y en la propia atmósfera indefinible que tiene esta ciudad y que inspiraría a Velázquez, Murillo, Juan de Mesa, Zurbarán, Bécquer, Merimée, Rossini, etc.

Cuenta la leyenda que el río Guadalquivir fue creado expresamente para Sevilla pero, aunque tal información sería difícil de demostrar, lo que nadie discute es que en Sevilla se concentran una serie de maravillas artísticas indiscutiblemente construidas para honrar a la capital sevillana.

A pie de río, se levanta la Torre del Oro como defensa del puerto y se dice que fue llamada así porque estaba recubierta de mosaicos dorados. Su planta dodecagonal fue construida en 1220 y la linterna se le añadió en el siglo XVIII.

Esta torre y la Giralda constituyen los dos monumentos más singulares de Sevilla.

La Giralda está asentada sobre piedras romanas aunque su construcción data de 1184. Entre 1558 y 1568, Hernán Ruiz, arquitecto cordobés, la coronó con un cuerpo compuesto por veinticinco campanas y una enorme estatua de la Fe, llamada popularmente «Giraldillo».

En la actualidad, la Giralda complementa la majestuosa catedral sevillana. Erigida sobre el emplazamiento de la mezquita mayor de Sevilla, fue consagrada como catedral cristiana en 1248.

De la antigua mezquita, hoy únicamente queda el Patio de los Naranjos que fue el antiguo sahn.

Por sus dimensiones, la catedral es la tercera más grande del mundo cristiano, después de la de San Pedro de Roma y de la de San Pablo de Londres.

Está compuesta por cinco naves góticas y un gran crucero que alberga la capilla mayor, presidida por

*El Patio de las Doncellas, en los Reales Alcázares, desde donde las mujeres veían pasar a los embajadores.*

*El Patio del Yeso, en los Reales Alcázares, de origen almohade.*

uno de los retablos más espléndidos de la cristiandad (1482-1525), obra de Pieter Dancart y de Jorge y Alejo Fernández. La reja que cierra esta capilla (1518-1533) fue realizada por fray Francisco de Salamanca y otros artistas.

En la maravillosa sillería del coro, trabajaron Nufro Sánchez y Dancart.

Una obra de gran majestuosidad es el sepulcro de Cristóbal Colón, realizado por Arturo Mélida (1891). Las sacristías encierran tesoros inapreciables, entre ellos y en la mayor: el tenebrario, candelabro de 1559, la custodia de Juan de Arfe (1587), el crucifijo de márfil de Alonso Cano (siglo XVII), el *Descendimiento* de Pedro de Campaña y las tablas Alfonsinas (relicario de 1280). En la de los cálices: el Cristo de la Clemencia, talla de Martínez Montañés (1604) y pinturas de Murillo, Valdés Leal, Zurbarán, Ribera, etc. Las bibliotecas (Capitular y Colombina) conservan impresos y manuscritos de gran valor.

La Capilla Real (1550-1575), plateresca, se encuentra en el ábside. En su interior, los nichos con los sepulcros de Alfonso X el Sabio y de su madre; al pie del altar mayor, una riquísima urna de plata en la que se veneran los restos del rey San Fernando y en la cripta, los féretros del rey Don Pedro el Cruel y de Doña María de Padilla. Entre los tesoros de la Capilla Real destacan los ornamentos litúrgicos y la espada de San Fernando.

*El Salón de
Embaja-
dores o
«salón de la
media
naranja», en
los Reales
Alcázares
de Sevilla.*

*Cruz de la Cerrajería, en pleno barrio de Santa Cruz.*

Además, la catedral guarda un incalculable número de tesoros artísticos en esculturas, pinturas, orfebrería, rejas y vidrieras.

Los Reales Alcázares de Sevilla son la principal muestra de arquitectura civil de la ciudad.

De sus orígenes almohades resta el Patio del Yeso, de planta rectangular con arquerías y una alberca central.

Todos los moradores que por él pasaron dejaron su huella en algún que otro rincón, pero básicamente el alcázar que hoy podemos admirar es el que construyera el rey Don Pedro el Cruel, reformado posteriormente por los Reyes Católicos y por Carlos V.

Destacaremos el Patio de las Doncellas, que constituye la más hermosa muestra de patio mudéjar de la arquitectura española.

Entre los salones los más importantes son el de Embajadores y el dormitorio de los reyes moros. Este último, a la derecha del Patio de las Doncellas, tiene unas bellísimas puertas. En el Salón de Embajadores todo es magnífico: el zócalo de azulejos, las puertas, el artesonado, la cúpula, etc.

En la planta alta resaltamos el llamado Oratorio de los Reyes Católicos, con una singularísimo altar recubierto de azulejos policromos.

Capítulo aparte constituyen sus jardines, de traza árabe, mudéjar y renacentista, todos ellos adornados con caprichosas fuentes y surtidores.

Otros edificios civiles son: el Archivo General de Indias, o Casa Lonja, los planos de su construcción se deben a Juan de Herrera y se datan a finales del siglo XVI. El Archivo General de Indias atesora la principal documentación sobre el descubrimiento y conquista de América, legajos, mapas, cartas, etc.

La Casa de Pilato, su construcción se inicia a finales del siglo XV y fue finalizada al regresar su propietario, el primer marqués de Tarifa, de un viaje a Jerusalén, quien aportaría a la construcción esa mezcla de estética islámica y renacentista. Su nombre se debe a que en un principio se creyó que el palacio era un reproducción del Pretorio de Jerusalén. Posee un

La plaza de la Virgen de los Reyes, típicamente sevillana.

La arena de la Maestranza sevillana.

Detalle del pintoresco barrio de Triana.

El pescado frito, crujiente y delicioso, es uno de los aperitivos mas populares.

Sevilla, durante la Feria de Abril, se engalana con los
espléndidos trajes típicos.

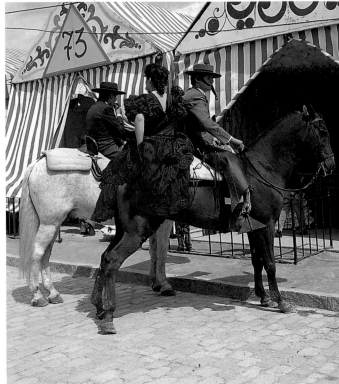

*La plaza de España, colofón del Parque de María Luisa.*

bellísimo patio renacentista con una elegante fuente sostenida por cuatro delfines. En los ángulos, a modo de ornamento, imponentes estatuas representando a Minerva.

Resaltamos en este apartado de arquitectura civil, el Ayuntamiento, que es una gran muestra del plateresco español, el Palacio de San Telmo, de estilo barroco y la Fábrica de Tabacos, convertida en la actualidad en Universidad y considerado como el monumento más grande de España después del Escorial.

*En un antiguo monasterio mercedario se alberga el Museo de Bellas Artes.*

*La Casa de Pilato, mezcla de estética árabe y renacentista.*

*Museo Arqueológico situado en un pabellón de la plaza de América.*

*Pabellón mudéjar del recinto de la Exposición Iberoamericana, actualmente Museo de Artes y Costumbres Populares.* ▷

*Palacio de San Telmo, obra de Leonardo de Figueroa.*

En cuanto a museos, Sevilla cuenta con un importante Museo de Bellas Artes, instalado en un antiguo monasterio mercedario. En su excelente pinacoteca figuran obras de Pacheco, Zurbarán, Murillo, Valdés Leal, etc. En uno de los pabellones de la plaza de América, en pleno Parque de M.ª Luisa, se alberga el Museo Arqueológico, con abundantes piezas de gran interés entre las que destacamos la «Diana Cazadora», el «Mercurio», un busto de Trajano y el tesoro del Carambolo, de orígenes tartesos.

Por Sevilla, uno ha de pasearse entre sus callejas, barrios y jardines y si lo puede hacer en Semana Santa o durante la Feria de Abril mucho mejor.

De los jardines del alcázar ya hemos hablado pero a estos hay que sumárseles los de Catalina Ribera, justo bordeando las murallas del alcázar, los de Murillo y sobre todo los del Parque de María Luisa y los de las Delicias, estos últimos recorren todo el margen del Guadalquivir.

En el Parque de María Luisa se levantan las edificaciones de la Exposición Iberoamericana con las plazas de América y de España. Los jardines se planearon según el estilo británico pero, posteriormente, fueron rehechos por Forestier, quien proyectaría el sinfín de azulejería, albercas y surtidores.

Se dice que Sevilla huele a azahar y donde mejor puede comprobarse es en el barrio de Santa Cruz. A este barrio podremos entrar bien por el propio alcázar, bien desde el callejón de Santa Marta.

En este barrio se concentró, tras la Reconquista, la

judería. En el siglo XVI, conseguirá parte de su fisonomía actual, ampliando las fachadas, protegiendo las ventanas con rejas y celosías y construyendo amplios patios. En el siglo XIX, se consolida el estilo del barrio con la colocación de grandes cancelas que permitirán a los transeuntes admirar los patios desde la calle.

Entre el laberinto de callejuelas, aparecen algunas cuajadas de vitalidad y leyenda: Vida, Agua, Pimienta, Gloria y Jamerdana. Salpicando su urbanismo, placitas como la de Doña Elvira o la de Santa Cruz en la que encontramos la Cruz de la Cerrajería, original filigrana de hierro construida en el siglo XVIII, donde fue enterrado Murillo.

Desde el siglo XVI, Sevilla celebra la Semana Santa con todo el fervor religioso que tal acontecimiento litúrgico se merece.

El sevillano se organiza en cofradías o hermandades

*El Archivo General de Indias, o también llamado Casa Lonja.*

*El «paso» de Nuestro Padre Jesús de la Pasión.*

las cuales expresan su devoción por medio de las procesiones de los «pasos», en los que se representan diferentes escenas de la Pasión. Las tallas acostumbran a ser verdaderas obras de arte de imagineros como Martínez Montañés, Juan de Mesa, etc. Los cofrades o hermanos, ataviados con túnicas y capirotes, acompañan a los «pasos» que, gracias a la habilidad de los «costaleros», se desplazan al ritmo que marcan los clarines y tambores, sólo deteniéndose cuando suena el canto desgarrador de la «saeta».

*Caravana de peregrinos camino del Rocío.*

*Semana Santa sevillana: Ntra. Sra. de la Hiniesta.* ▷

*Murallas romanas de la Macarena.*

Todo el fervor religioso de los sevillanos se viste de fiesta y color para celebrar la Feria de Abril. Una zona de la ciudad se dedica a recinto ferial y sobre él se colocan centenares de casetas donde se bebe y baila al ritmo de las alegres sevillanas.

Por las improvisadas callejuelas desfilan caballerías adornadas con campanillas y cascabeles y las jóvenes luciendo sus mejores batas de cola.

Pero no abandonemos Sevilla sin probar el exquisito sabor de su «pescaíto frito» o de sus «tapas», tomadas a voleo en cualquier bar o taberna y siempre regadas con el vino de las vecinas tierras gaditanas.

*Vista parcial de Carmona.*

*Vista general de la Alhambra.*

# GRANADA

La ciudad de Granada se halla espléndidamente emplazada. Ocupa una extensa y fértil llanura y tres colinas: la del Sacromonte, la del Albaicín y la de la Alhambra, separada de las anteriores por las aguas del río Darro. Como telón de fondo se alza, majestuosa, la blancura de Sierra Nevada.

El origen de la ciudad se asocia a una primitiva población fundada por una tribu ibérica: los túrdulos. En el siglo V a.C. aparece citada por Hecateo de Mileto con el nombre de *Elibyrge.* Ya en ese período se acuñan monedas, en las que se muestran alegorías al Sol, práctica esta que continuará bajo la dominación de los romanos, los cuales levantan su ciudad, *Iliberri,* entre los barrios de la Alcazaba y del Albaicín. Aunque los árabes someten Granada por la fuerza de las armas será, sin embargo, gracias a ellos que la ciudad alcance su época de máximo esplendor, especialmente a partir de 1238 con la fundación de un emirato nazarita de cuya suntuosidad y magnificencia nos hablan los hermosos edificios y los soberbios jardines que han llegado hasta nuestros días. En

*Puerta de la Justicia, del siglo XIV, abierta en una torre de las murallas de la Alhambra.*

Jardín y torre de Machuca, así llamados porque aquí vivió el arquitecto de tal nombre, artífice del palacio de Carlos V.

Sala del Mexuar, destinada originariamente a la administración de justicia.

*Patio del Mexuar: fachada del Cuarto Dorado.*

*Patio del Mexuar: fachada del Palacio de Comares.*

1492, la metrópoli es reconquistada por los Reyes Católicos que, al igual que sus sucesores, muestran un especial interés en continuar embelleciéndola. Se crea la urbe moderna y en torno a la catedral surgen espléndidos monumentos renacentistas, barrocos y neoclásicos.
De entre todas las edificaciones que adornan la ciudad sobresale, sin duda, el prodigio arquitectónico de la Alhambra.

*Detalle del mosaico del Salón del Mexuar.*

*El Patio de los Arrayanes o de la Alberca constituía el núcleo central de las actividades oficiales.*

*Detalle del mosaico que decora el Patio de los Arrayanes.*

Fue levantada en la colina que los árabes llamaban Asabica —por Alhamar, fundador de la dinastía nazarí—, y finalizada por sus sucesores Yusuf I y Mohamed V, a quienes corresponden la mayoría de las construcciones que han llegado hasta nosotros.

Asentada en una antigua fortaleza, consta de la Alcazaba, reconstruida por Alhamar, y de la Casa Real o Palacio de los reyes moros de Granada, donde residían los monarcas árabes.

El nombre de la Alhambra procede de «calat-alhamrá» (castillo rojo) y hace referencia al tono rojizo de la arcilla de los muros, aunque el cronista Aben Aljatib explique ese color como consecuencia de haberse efectuado la reedificación de la antigua fortaleza de noche, al resplandor rojizo y fantástico de las antorchas.

La Alhambra sorprende por la sobriedad de su exterior que en nada anticipa los tesoros que su interior esconde. Para llegar a ellos, se debe atravesar la Puerta de la Justicia, del siglo XIV, que presenta un gran arco de herradura y en la clave una mano grabada en mármol, talismán para algunos contra el mal de ojo y para otros, emblema de los cinco preceptos alcoránicos: ayuno, oración, limosna, peregrinación a la Meca y creencia de la unidad de Dios. La entrada actual del palacio nos conduce a la Sala del Mexuar, destinada originariamente a la administración de justicia y convertida más tarde en capilla cristiana. Al fondo, tiene un reducido oratorio desde el que se divisa una excelente vista del Albaicín.

En el lado norte del Patio del Mexuar, aparece el pórtico de tres arcos que precede a la pieza conocida como el «Cuarto Dorado», obra de Mohamed V según consta en una de las inscripciones. A continuación se pasa al gran Patio de los Arrayanes que muestra dos lados con pórticos de siete arcos semicirculares, mayor el central, sostenidos sobre columnas de gran riqueza; los otros dos son más largos y sencillos. Hay un estanque en el centro, bordeado de mirtos, con pilas de mármol en sus extremos. Tras el

*Entrada a la
Torre de
Comares
por el Patio
de los
Arrayanes.*

*Vista parcial
del Patio de
los
Arrayanes.*

Vista del Salón de Embajadores. Exhibe magníficas piezas de yesería y azulejos en las paredes.

Patio de los Leones, construido por Mohamed V en el siglo XIV.

*Sala de los Abencerrajes, de gran preciosismo decorativo.*

pórtico norte se encuentra la Sala de la Barca que precede al salón del trono y que debió ser utilizada como lugar de espera para las audiencias reales que se celebraban en el Salón de Embajadores, en la contigua Torre de Comares. Este salón, el mayor del palacio, fue escenario de las grandes recepciones y se cuenta que en él se acordó entregar Granada a los Reyes Católicos. Exhibe magníficas piezas de yesería y azulejos en las paredes y un excelente artesonado de cedro tallado en el techo.

Del Patio de los Arrayanes, cruzando la Sala de los Mocárabes, se entra en el conocido Patio de los Leones, que toma su nombre de los doce leones que sostienen la fuente central. La rusticidad del conjunto

*Decoración de la bóveda de la Sala de los Abencerrarjes.*

*Pinturas del techo de la Sala de los Reyes, donde se representan los diez primeros reyes nazaritas.*

contrasta con las líneas elegantes y delicadas de la galería que lo rodea y que se sostiene sobre unas finas columnas de mármol blanco.

El patio se comunica con fastuosas dependencias como la Sala de los Abencerrajes, la de los Reyes o la de las Dos Hermanas.

La primera recibe este nombre en recuerdo de los caballeros de esta familia que, según la tradición, fueron degollados en este aposento. Sus cabezas fueron amontonadas en la fuente central, por lo que la voz popular asegura que son de sangre de Abencerrajes las manchas de óxido de hierro que se observan en la excelente pila de mármol. La sala conserva unos capiteles pintados de azul, de buen esculpido y notable pureza de estilo, y una espléndida cúpula de mocárabes.

Las alcobas de la Sala de los Reyes, que posiblemente fueron dormitorios reales, presentaban bóvedas recubiertas de pinturas que, por su estilo, se atribuyen a algún artista cristiano de finales del siglo XIV o principios del XV.

*Sala de los Reyes, también llamada Sala de la Justicia.*

Sala de las Dos Hermanas, llamada así por las dos losas gemelas de su pavimento.

Mirador de Daraxa, de paredes esmaltadas y cinceladas como si se tratasen de joyas.

Sala del Reposo, así
denominada porque
todo en ella induce al
descanso.

Detalle de la Sala del
Reposo.

En la alcoba central aparecen los diez primeros reyes de la dinastía nazarí; en las restantes alcobas, escenas de caza, torneos, juegos e historias de amor. La Sala de las dos Hermanas se cubre con una maravillosa cúpula de mocárabes, que por su perfección es digna de compararse con la bóveda celeste, según rezan las inscripciones que recubren las paredes. Una puerta comunica con la Sala de los Ajimeces; esta estancia y el llamado Mirador de Daraxa, que se encuentra a continuación, formaban parte de los aposentos reservados a la sultana. Ambos presentan una decoración exquisita y refinada.

Desde el jardín de Daraxa, se puede visitar el Patio de la Reja y la Sala de los Baños.

La restauración de los Baños Reales, llevada a cabo en el siglo XIX, recuperó los colores oro, azul, verde y rojo primitivos y nos permite imaginar las tonalidades que originariamente tuvo el palacio.

*Jardines del Partal.*

*Patio de la Acequia, en el palacio del Generalife.*

En la zona este del alcázar, se encuentran los Jardines del Partal, que forman terrazas hasta llegar a la torre de las Damas, con un primoroso pórtico, «partal» en árabe, de cinco arcos por el que se accede a una sala de hermosa techumbre y a un mirador que ha preservdo una gran parte de sus yeserías. Desde sus ventanas se ve el río Darro y el Sacromonte.

Ya en el exterior de la Alhambra, pero estrechamente vinculado a ella, se halla el Generalife, residencia veraniega de los soberanos nazaritas, rodeado de exuberantes jardines con delicados surtidores y fuentecillas.

Se llega al palacio, construido en el siglo XIV, a través del paseo de los Cipreses y el de las Adelfas. El edificio consta de dos pabellones unidos entre sí por el patio de la Acequia, por cuyo centro corre un largo canal en el que desembocan las aguas de múltiples surtidores. Lo delimitan una galería con arcadas y los muros de la residencia construida en el siglo XVI.

Antes de abandonar la Alhambra, es obligado visitar el palacio de Carlos V, que el Emperador mandó construir a Pedro Machuca en 1526. Aunque ofrece un notable contraste con la edificación árabe, es realmente digno de admirar su depurado estilo renacentista. Su gran patio, de 30 metros de diámetro, es uno de los más bellos del Renacimiento español. El palacio alberga el Museo de Arte Hispano-musulmán. De entre las edificaciones cristianas de la ciudad, destaca la Capilla Real. Fue erigida por orden de los Re-

Un ángulo
del Patio de
la Acequia.

*Fachada oeste del Palacio de Carlos V.*

yes Católicos, quienes deseaban ser sepultados en Granada, en estilo gótico florido.

Su planta es de cruz latina y el crucero queda cerrado por una excelente reja dorada, obra del maestro Bartolomé de Jaén. Sobresalen las valiosas tallas y figuras flamencas, el retablo del altar mayor y los sepulcros de los Reyes Católicos y sus hijos.

La primitiva portada gótica de la capilla, dentro de

*Museo de Arte Hispanomusulmán: pila de mármol, probablemente de finales del siglo X aunque lleva una inscripción de 1305.*

*Patio circular del Palacio de Carlos V, mide 30 m de diámetro y ostenta columnas dóricas en el pórtico y jónicas en la parte alta.*

*El llamado «Jarrón de la Alhambra», conservado en el Museo de Arte Hispanomusulmán. Se trata de un jarrón vidriado de 1,32 m de alto, pieza clave de la cerámica hispanomusulmana.*

Vista aérea de la catedral de Granada, considerada como una de las más importantes iglesias renacentistas de España.

Fachada y crestería de la Capilla Real, erigida por mandato de los Reyes Católicos. Las obras se iniciaron en 1506.

*Capilla mayor de la catedral, obra de Diego de Siloé.*

*Tríptico de la Pasión de Dierick Bouts, en la Capilla Real.*

*Mausoleo de los Reyes Católicos, en la Capilla Real.* ▷

*Restos de los Reyes Católicos, en la cripta de la Capilla Real.*

*La corona, el cetro y el cofrecito de Isabel la Católica y la espada de Don Fernando.*

*Fachada principal de la cartuja.*

la catedral, está decorada con los escudos de los Reyes Católicos.

La catedral es uno de los templos renacentistas más destacados. Sus obras comenzaron en 1518 y concluyeron definitivamente en 1704. La fachada principal, barroca, es una obra maestra de Alonso Cano (1667). En su interior sobresale la capilla mayor, de planta circular y equilibradas proporciones.

En 1506, se inició la construcción del monasterio de la Cartuja, situado en la carretera de Alfacar. Su sacristía es un ejemplo señero del barroco español, estilo utilizado también en la ornamentación del Sancta Sanctorum, obra realizada por Francisco Hurtado a principios del siglo XVII.

Merece visitarse el Albaicín, antiguo barrio moro que conserva, en general, su aspecto típico original y su

Detalle del claustro
de la cartuja.

Detalle de la
sacristía, recinto
barroco construido
entre 1726 y 1764.

Artístico coro de
legos de la cartuja. El
templo fue acabado
en el siglo XVII,
consta de una sola
nave y lo
ornamentan yeserías
barrocas realizadas
por Francisco Díaz de
Rivero.

*Vista panorámica del Albaicín.*

*Típica casa de inspiración morisca.*

antiguo trazado urbano. Sus calles trepan por la colina que se levanta frente a la Alhambra, delimitadas por casas de recuerdo morisco y los célebres «cármenes» o jardines.

Desde la plaza de San Nicolás se disfruta de una impresionante vista de la Alhambra, el Generalife y la ciudad baja.

A mitad de la Cuesta del Chapiz, parte el camino del Sacromonte que, a medida que asciende hacia la montaña, se va poblando de cuevas donde se baila la zambra gitana, al son de las palmas y las guitarras. El lugar ideal para adquirir un recuerdo de la ciudad es, sin duda, la Alcaicería que, en otros tiempos, había sido el mercado árabe de la seda y que se ha reconstruido siguiendo la disposición original.

*Vista de la Fuente del Triunfo.*

*Nuestra Señora de las Angustias, patrona de Granada, cuya imagen se venera en la iglesia de mismo nombre.*

*Monumento a Isabel la Católica y a Cristóbal Colón, realizado por Mariano Benlliure.*

Bailes típicos en una de las cuevas del Sacromonte.

La Alcaicería, antiguo mercado musulmán de la seda reconstruido según el plano original.

La Carrera del Darro, una de las más antiguas y pintorescas vías granadinas.

*Vista de Málaga con la plaza de toros en primer término y, al fondo, el puerto.*

# MALAGA

La capital malagueña, la «Ciudad del Paraíso» del poeta Aleixandre, ocupa un lugar privilegiado en la desembocadura del Guadalmedina, cara al Mediterráneo y a los pies de la colina de Gibralfaro.

Su excelente situación geográfica explica la diversidad de pueblos que la han visitado: fenicios, griegos, cartagineses, romanos,... Bajo el dominio árabe se convirtió en el puerto del reino de Granada y en una de las más significadas ciudades andaluzas. Reconquistada por los Reyes Católicos en 1487, Málaga ha sabido preservar esa significación a lo largo de los siglos hasta convertirse en nuestros días en una moderna ciudad, capital de la Costa del Sol, gracias al auge turístico del que disfruta.

De la riqueza de la historia malagueña da fe su patrimonio monumental, en el que destaca la catedral. El templo, realizado según los planos de Diego de Siloé, es una edificación renacentista con portada barroca que se levantó por iniciativa de los Reyes Católicos sobre una antigua mezquita.

Las obras se iniciaron en 1528 y concluyeron en el siglo XVIII, aunque la torre de la derecha quedó inacabada.

*Vista aérea de la catedral.*

En su interior, sobresalen las capillas de Santa Bárbara, con un hermoso retablo gótico, y la de Nuestra Señora de los Reyes que conserva, reconstruido, un retablo de Pedro de Mena con las estatuas orantes de los Reyes Católicos realizadas en madera policromada. También es obra de Pedro de Mena gran parte de las sillerías del magnífico coro, cuyas figuras destacan por su naturalidad y sencillez.

Otros templos de interés son la iglesia del Sagrario, con portada gótica y retablo mayor del siglo XVI, procedente de Becerril de Campos (Palencia); la de Santiago, donde fue bautizado Picasso, con una excepcional torre mudéjar; las iglesias de San Pedro y Santo Domingo, de estilo barroco; el templo de San Pablo, neogótico, y el Santuario de la Virgen de la Victoria, fundado por los Reyes Católicos y reconstruido en estilo barroco a finales del siglo XVII. Su interior guarda una magnífica Dolorosa, obra de Pedro de Mena, y la impresionante cripta, panteón de los condes de Buenavista, del siglo XVII. En el templo se venera la imagen de la Virgen de la Victoria, patrona de la ciudad, talla gótica del siglo XV.

En la calle Alcazabilla, se encuentra la entrada principal de la Alcazaba que, construida en el siglo XI, fue la antigua residencia de los gobernadores árabes de Málaga.

La fortaleza posee tres muros concéntricos; en su interior hay tres patios con bellas albercas moriscas y en el edificio de la Puerta de Granada está instalado el Museo Arqueológico de la ciudad. Desde lo alto

Interior de
la catedral.
El templo
ha sido
declarado
monumento
nacional.

Patio de la Alcazaba malagueña, antigua residencia de los gobernadores árabes.

Vista del castillo de Gibralfaro.

«El Cenachero», en la Plaza de la Marina, obra de Jaime F. Pimentel.

Iglesia de San Pablo, de estilo neogótico.

Iglesia de Santiago, donde fue bautizado el pintor Pablo Ruiz Picasso.

Imagen de Santa María de la Victoria, patrona de la ciudad, talla gótica del siglo XV.

Una de las «pandas» que participan en las fiestas de «Los Verdiales».

Aspectos típicos de Málaga.

de las murallas se disfruta de magníficas vistas de la bahía.

La Alcazaba se comunica con el castillo de Gibralfaro por un pasadizo entre las murallas. Los orígenes del castillo se remontan a tiempos fenicios, aunque los restos más notables corresponden a la época árabe.

El castillo exhibe frondosos jardines, está rodeado de un atractivo paisaje y desde sus murallas se divisa una excelente panorámica de la ciudad, sus montañas y la bahía.

Otros lugares clave de la capital malagueña son la plaza de la Merced, donde se encuentra la casa natal del gran genio de la pintura, Pablo Ruiz Picasso, y el popular pasaje de Chinitas.

Muy cerca de la catedral se extiende el paseo del Parque, en terrenos ganados al mar. En sus avenidas, crece un amplio y variado complejo floral, subtropical en gran parte, y con algunas especies únicas en Europa. El Parque comunica por uno de sus extremos, y tras cruzar la plaza de la Marina, donde se alzan las estatuas al Cenachero y al Jazminero, con el bello paseo de la Alameda.

*El popular Pasaje de Chinitas, lugar de encuentro en el siglo XIX y hoy lleno de solera y recuerdos.*

*Semana Santa malagueña: llegada de la cofradía de los estudiantes, fundada en el siglo XVI.*

*Imagen de la Virgen de la Amargura.*

Ya lejos del centro urbano, se encuentra la barriada típica de El Palo, antiguo poblado de pescadores donde hoy se puede saborear el «pescaíto frito» o cualquier otra deliciosa especialidad en alguno de sus animados bares playeros.

Málaga es rica en tradiciones y fiestas. Una de las celebraciones más populares es la de «Los Verdiales», en la que se ejecutan cantes y bailes considerados por algunos incluso más antiguos que el cante flamenco.

En Semana Santa, Málaga entera vive llena de emoción los actos solemnes: la liberación de un preso que cada Miércoles Santo concede la imagen del Naza-

*Desfile procesional de la Semana Santa.* ▷

Vista aérea del
Bajondillo, una de las
extensas playas de la
localidad de
Torremolinos, a
12 km de Málaga.

Vista de
Benalmádena-Costa.

*Playa de Fuengirola.*

reno; la procesión del Jueves Santo, con el Cristo de la Buena Muerte y la Virgen de la Amargura; el paso de las cofradías, alguna tan antigua como la de los Estudiantes, formada en el siglo XVII...

La costa malagueña forma, junto a la de las provincias de Granada y Almería, la internacionalmente conocida Costa del Sol.

De clima templado y escasas lluvias, con una gran variedad paisajística, el litoral malagueño está jalonado por amplias playas, calas semiocultas y poblaciones en las que el visitante hallará excelentes instalaciones hoteleras y un variado abanico de entretenimientos y diversiones.

En la costa occidental de la provincia se encuentra Torremolinos y sus extensas playas. Casi como una

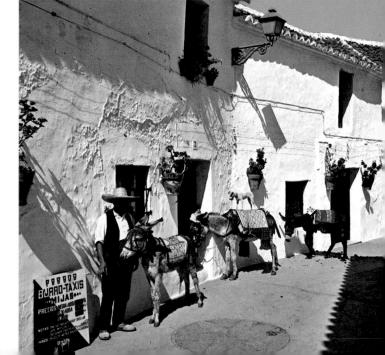

*Típicos burros-taxi de Mijas.*

*Vista parcial de Puerto Banús.*

prolongación de esta localidad está Benalmádena-costa con su gran parque de atracciones.

Fuengirola se extiende por una larguísima playa. De esta población parte la carretera que conduce a la pintoresca Mijas. Nuevamente en el litoral, llegamos a la cosmopolita Marbella y la lujoso Puerto Banús. En Estepona convive el moderno paseo marítimo con el antiguo núcleo de pescadores.

Dejando momentáneamente la costa, se llega al pueblo blanco de Casares y a Ronda, una de las poblaciones andaluzas más interesantes. Antequera es un importante centro monumental, con obras renacentistas y barrocas. Nuevamente en la costa, encontramos la extensa playa de Torre del Mar y Nerja, un enclave verdaderamente privilegiado.

*Vista de Marbella.*

Estepona: jardines y Museo Marítimo.

Vista del Puerto de la Duquesa, en Manilva.

Ronda. El Puente Nuevo y el tajo del río Guadalevín, que divide el casco urbano.

Vista general de Casares.

Vista aérea de Antequera.

La playa del Faro, en Torre del Mar.

El «Balcón de Europa» en Nerja.

*Vista del puente romano de Córdoba.*

# CORDOBA

do a la civilización europea con grandes personajes como Maimónides, Averroes, Aben Hazam, etc.

En el año 1236, fue conquistada por Fernando III el Santo. Fue también corte temporal de los Reyes Católicos y en ella Isabel la Católica decidió apoyar la aventura de Colón.

Córdoba es en la actualidad una ciudad monumental, en la que el arte se esconde en cada rincón: callejuelas, patios, plazas, etc.

A Córdoba se la conoce entre otras cosas por su mezquita, pero además son dignos de mención sus viejos barrios árabe y judío y sus nobles mansiones. El arte califal en Occidente tiene su máxima representación en la mezquita de Córdoba. Sus orígenes como mezquita musulmana se remontan al siglo VIII

La provincia de Córdoba está situada en el centro de Andalucía y el Guadalquivir la cruza de Este a Oeste, separando la sierra al Norte y la campiña al Sur. Córdoba fue hace diez siglos la capital de la España musulmana y además de convertirse en la ciudad más grande del orbe llegó a ser el mayor centro cultural e intelectual del mundo conocido, contribuyen-

En la mezquita
cordobesa destaca su
gran bosque
laberíntico de
columnas.

A través de las
columnas se adivina
el mihrab, orientado
en dirección a la
Meca.

Exterior de la
mezquita.

y como catedral cristiana al año 1236. En ella se combinan exquisitamente dos culturas, dos mundos. La mezquita musulmana acabó de construirse a finales del siglo X, cuando Almanzor era el primer ministro del Califa Hixam II. Se edificó sobre una catedral visigótica. La mezquita está constituida por un fascinante laberinto de columnas de franjas rojiblancas y verdes.

Uno de los rasgos más importantes de la mezquita es el mihrab, desde donde los fieles musulmanes dirigían sus oraciones. Es una habitación de planta octogonal rematada por una maravillosa cúpula, un laborioso trabajo en su arquería y valiosísimos mosaicos, regalo del Emperador Constantino VII al califa Alhaquem II. En la mezquita musulmana también se concentran otras obras artísticas de gran valor, de maestros como Valdés Leal, Pedro de Córdoba, Alonso Cano, etc.

Justo en el centro de la mezquita, se halla enclavada la catedral cristiana, cuya construcción se inició en el año 1523 durante el reinado de Carlos V, aunque se concluyó en 1776 con la realización del coro

*Zona del mihrab y las naves de Alhakem II.*

*Vista lateral
del mihrab.*

y púlpitos. En ella cohabitan diferentes estilos arquitectónicos: renacentista, con reminiscencias ojivales, plateresco, herreriano y barroco.

Hemos de destacar su retablo mayor, realizado en mármol rojo y adornado con pinturas de Palomino, los púlpitos churriguerescos construidos por el escul-

*Perspectiva del coro y crucero de la catedral.*

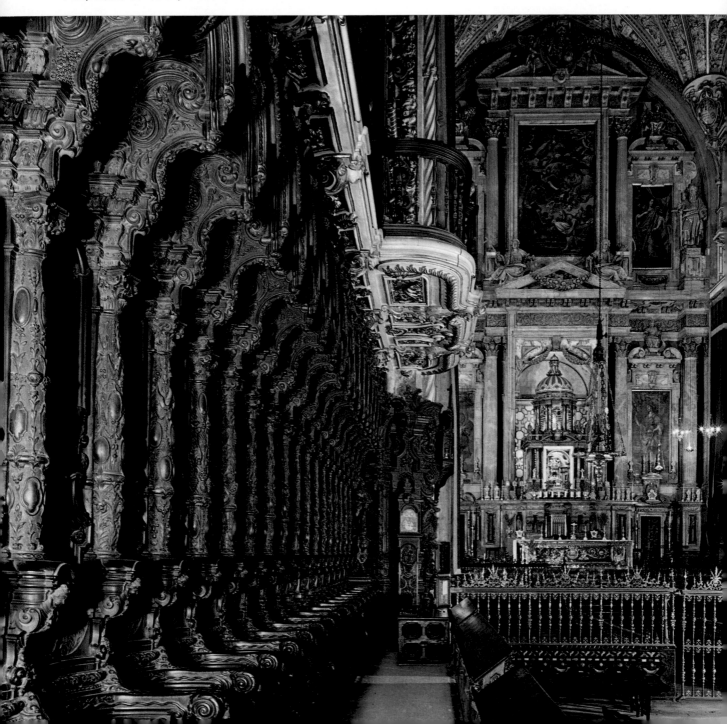

*Púlpito del
Evangelio
de la
catedral
cordobesa.*

Foto superior: estatua de Maimónides, importante filósofo y médico judío.

Foto inferior: estatua de Averroes, filósofo hispanoárabe.

Puerta del Puente y, a la derecha, el monumento llamado el «Triunfo de San Rafael».

Estatua del poeta árabe cordobés Aben Hazam.

tor francés Michel de Verdiguier y el bellísimo coro. Alrededor de la mezquita, se suceden toda una serie de capillas cristianas: la de Nuestra Señora de la Concepción, la de San Pedro, la de San Lorenzo, etc. Saliendo por la Puerta del Perdón entramos en el Patio de los Naranjos. Por la Puerta de los Deanes encontramos la Portada de San Jacinto y a continuación el Palacio Espiscopal, donde residieron gobernadores visigodos.

Uno de los mejores ejemplos de arquitectura militar del siglo XIV es el Alcázar de los Reyes Cristianos, construido en 1328 a instancias de Alfonso XI. Cons-

Los jardines del alcázar, cuyo origen se remonta a Abderramán II.

Monumento erigido en honor al rey cristiano Alfonso X el Sabio, quien residiría en Córdoba.

Vista de un ángulo de los jardines del alcázar. ▷

*La plaza del Potro, con su fuente construida en 1557, y la fachada del Museo de Bellas Artes.*

*Fachada del Museo de Arte Cordobés y Taurino.*

ta de tres torres: la de los Leones, la de la Alianza y la del Río y en su interior alberga una importante colección de mosaicos y un rico sarcófago romano. En la Judería encontramos la sinagoga datada en el siglo XIV y con una importante obra de estuco. Cuenta también Córdoba con una magnífica serie de iglesias, en las que se fusionan diferentes estilos, e importantes museos, en los que se recogen las mejores muestras de diferentes artistas y del folklore cordobés.

◁ *Monumento a Séneca, en la Puerta de Almodóvar.*

PLAZUELA
DE
MAIMONIDES

*Rincón muy característico de Córdoba, en el que se alza el Cristo de los Faroles.*

*La calleja o callejón de las Flores, una de las calles más típicas de la ciudad de Córdoba.*

*Típicos patios cordobeses, con sus muros encalados y un sinfín de floridas macetas.*

*El pueblo cordobés celebra con gran fervor la Semana Santa sacando sus «pasos» en solemne procesión.*

Foto superior:
estatua ecuestre del
Gran Capitán, en la
plaza de las
Tendillas.
Foto inferior:
monumento a
Manolete, hijo ilustre
de la ciudad.

El Museo Julio
Romero de Torres
alberga uno de los
mejores cuadros de
ese artista cordobés:
«El poema de
Córdoba».

Vista general y detalle de la plaza de la Corredera.
Foto inferior: una de las actividades artesanas más
típicas de Córdoba, el repujado.

La gastronomía cordobesa ofrece platos tan característicos como el estofado de rabo de toro o el «pastelón».

*Vista aérea de la catedral jiennense.*

# JAEN

Se encuentra enclavada en el centro de Andalucía, entre Córdoba y Granada, al pie de la Sierra de Jabalcuz.

Los árabes la llamaron *Geen*, camino o lugar de paso de caravanas y tradicionalmente se la ha llamado la «Puerta de Castilla».

Jaén conserva una interesantísima parte vieja de clara influencia árabe.

◁ *Medina Azahara o el Versalles cordobés del siglo X.*

El monumento más importante de la ciudad es su catedral, edificada sobre el solar de la antigua mezquita. En ella se encuentran elementos góticos, platerescos, renacentistas y barrocos.

Se empezó a edificar en 1550 y comenzó la obra Andrés de Vandelvira, a quien le sucedería su discípulo Alonso Barba. No se levantó la fachada principal ni se cerraron las bóvedas hasta la época barroca.

La fachada principal está flanqueada por dos torres gemelas, decoradas por bajorrelieves y esculturas de Pedro Roldán. La fachada se abre en balaustrada con estatuas de San Fernando, los grandes doctores de la Iglesia y los Evangelistas.

El interior está diseñado según planta de cruz latina.

*Fachada principal de la catedral de Jaén, obra de Vandelvira.*

*Dos aspectos del interior de la catedral: la grandiosidad del conjunto catedralicio y el coro de una gran riqueza ornamental.*

Las tres naves terminan en bóvedas que se sostienen sobre macizas columnas corintias.
En medio de la nave central, está el coro que tiene un magnífico testero y sillería de los siglos XV y XVI.

Paso de Jesús
Nazareno, de la
Semana Santa
jiennense.

Dos aspectos del
interior de la
catedral, el altar
mayor y la sala
capitular, a la que se
accede desde la
capilla de Santiago.

*Monumento a Bernardo López García, en la alameda.*

*Puerta del Angel.*

En la capilla mayor se conserva, resguardada en un relicario de piedras preciosas, la reliquia del Santo Rostro considerada como una de las sábanas con la que la Verónica limpió el rostro de Cristo.

El museo catedralicio está instalado en la cripta de la sacristía. La catedral atesora valiosas muestras de arte, entre ellas obras del maestro Bartolomé, de Alonso Cano, de Martínez Montañés, etc.

Adosado a la catedral se encuentra el templo del Sagrario, del siglo XVIII, obra del arquitecto Ventura Rodríguez.

Otras iglesias de interés son la de la Magdalena; la iglesia de San Andrés, mudéjar, que conserva reminiscencias judías que la hacen parecer una sinagoga; la Capilla de la Purísima, aneja a la anterior, que exhibe una pintura sobre tabla de la Virgen del Pó-

pulo y una obra cumbre del maestro Bartolomé, la reja de hierro dorado; el convento de Carmelitas Descalzas, en el que se puede admirar el manuscrito del «Cántico espiritual» de San Juan de la Cruz; la iglesia de San Ildefonso, con fachadas gótica, renacentista y barroca; el monasterio de Santa Clara, uno de los más antiguos de Jaén y en el que todavía se conserva una apreciadísima imagen de Cristo de bambú, posiblemente de escuela quiteña, y el colegio de Santo Domingo, que antaño fuera convento y palacio árabe, morada de San Fernando y sede de la Inquisición. Posee en su fachada una excelente obra de Vandelvira y un hermoso claustro con columnas toscanas.

Destacaremos el Museo Provincial, en el que se guarda la portada de la iglesia de San Miguel, de Vandel-

Dos vistas de la calle Bobadilla Alta
(Barrio de San Juan).
El barrio de la Magdalena, en la carretera de Martos.
Portada del Convento de Santo Domingo.

*Vista de la plaza de las Batallas.*

*Sarcófago paleocristiano de Martos, conservado en el
Museo Provincial.
Castillo de Santa Catalina.*

vira, el «toro ibérico» de Porcuna y otras valiosas
obras.

En la ciudad también se alzan interesantes edificaciones civiles que nos muestran la importancia his-
tórica de Jaén. Perdiéndose por sus callejuelas es-
trechas, pavimentadas con guijarros, descubriremos
numerosas mansiones y palacios que contrastan ad-
mirablemente con las encaladas casas de tejados púr-
puras: los palacios de los Vilches, los Vélez, los Uri-
be y los restos mudéjares del palacio del Condestable y, dominándolo todo, el castillo de Santa Catalina, hoy Parador Nacional, erigido por el rey Alhamar
y reconstruido por Fernando III. Desde él se puede
admirar la espléndida panorámica que se extiende
desde Sierra Morena a Sierra Nevada.

Parte de las murallas que descienden del castillo y
que rodearon la antigua ciudad, todavía se conservan: los torreones de la calle del Obispo, la torre en
la casa del Conde Torralba y el arco de San Lorenzo
son buenos ejemplo.

A unos 50 km de Jaén se encuentran Ubeda y Baeza, ambas verdaderas muestras de arte y de historia.
Baeza reúne en sus monumentos todos los movi-
mientos artísticos desde el románico al renacimiento. La catedral con muestras de mudéjar, gótico y
renacentista; la iglesia de Santa Cruz, románica; la
iglesia románica y de interior mudéjar del Salvador;
la de San Andrés, renacentista.

Baeza mantiene un admirable conjunto de edificios
públicos, su primitiva Casa Consistorial, gótica, su

*Baeza: vista parcial y Antigua Carnicería.*

antigua Universidad, la antigua cárcel, la antigua carnicería, su alhondiga, y palacios góticos como los de Jabalquinto y Montemar.

Muy cerca de Baeza, Ubeda a la que se le ha llamado «la Salamanca de Andalucía», por la categoría de sus monumentos, como la Sacra Capilla del Salvador, renacentista, la iglesia de Santa María de los Reales Alcázares, gótico-mudéjar, etc.

Y, sobre todo, un sinfín de palacios renacentistas: del Deán Ortega, del Condestable Dávalos, el del Marqués de Mancera, el de la Rambla y, como construcción civil más destacable, el Hospital de Santiago, de mediados del siglo XVI.

Pero no nos despidamos de la provincia jiennense sin pasear por las callejuelas del barrio de intramuros de Ubeda.

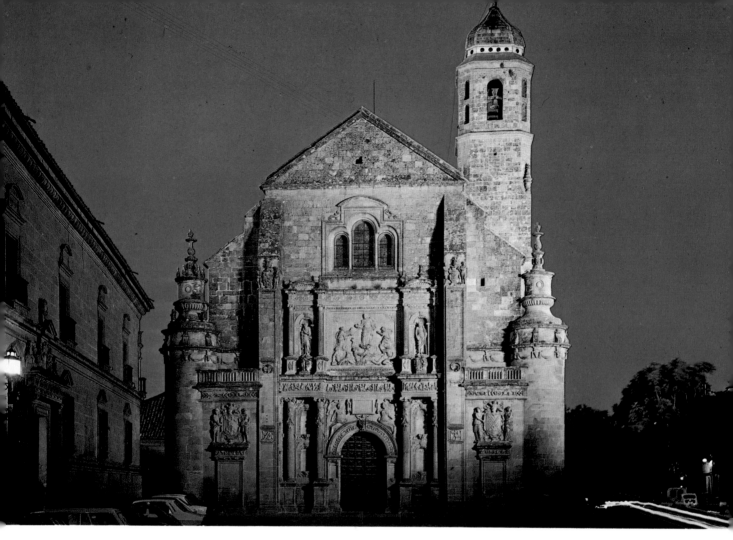

*Ubeda: Sacra Capilla del Salvador.*

*Típica fiesta de la «capea», en Torreperogil.*

*Vista aérea de Bailén.*

*Vista general del barrio de la Chanca.*

# ALMERIA

Emplazada en la bahía de su nombre, Almería es una ciudad luminosa, protegida de los vientos del interior por sus montañas de tonalidades ocres, que refleja el azul intenso que aquí adquieren las aguas mediterráneas.

Su fundación se remonta a los tiempos prehistóricos; después, fue lugar de contacto con las culturas del Mediterráneo oriental y posteriormente visitada por cartagineses, romanos y árabes, quienes la llamaron «Espejo del mar».

Reconquistada por los Reyes Católicos en 1484, la ciudad conserva testimonios de su protagonismo histórico. Uno de ellos, la Alcazaba, domina la capital con su imponente mole.

La fortaleza debió ser construida por Abderramán III en el siglo X, con capacidad para más de 20.000 hombres. Su planta es irregular y se distribuye en tres recintos escalonados. La torre del homenaje tiene dos portadas góticas con el escudo de los Reyes Católicos, realizadas en el siglo XV.

Desde sus adarves se disfruta de una excelente panorámica de la ciudad y su puerto.

*Foto superior: calle típica de Alcalá la Real.*
*Foto inferior: Vista de Quesada.*

La Alcazaba, con las cuevas del pintoresco barrio de la Chanca a sus pies.

La sillería del coro de la catedral almeriense fue realizada por Juan de Orea en estilo plateresco.

Sepulcro de fray Diego Fernández de Villalán, en una de las capillas laterales.

*Vista parcial de la zona portuaria de Almería.*

La antigua muralla, de la que se conservan algunos tramos, la une por el barranco de la Joya con el cerro de San Cristóbal, donde subsisten algunos torreones del castillo del mismo nombre.

A los pies de la Alcazaba se encuentra la Chanca, el popular barrio de pescadores donde las casas, en muchos casos cuevas excavadas en la colina, alternan en sus fachadas el blanco con los más llamativos colores.

La catedral almeriense sorprende por su aspecto de fortaleza. Construida en el siglo XVI, su arquitectura defensiva intentó preservarla de los ataques piratas que la capital padecía en aquella época. A pesar de su severidad externa, posee dos portadas de una gran elegancia ornamental.

El interior, amplio, se divide en naves góticas con capillas laterales; una de ellas alberga el magnífico sepulcro del obispo que impulsó la edificación del templo, Fernández de Villalán; otras guardan valiosas obras de Salzillo, Alonso Cano, Murillo y Ribera. También destacan el altar mayor y los púlpitos, la sillería del coro, plateresca, y el trascoro, del siglo XVIII, decorado con estatuas de alabastro.

Almería es una ciudad que vive de cara al mar; buena prueba de ello es su puerto, donde alternan las barcas de pesca con embarcaciones de gran tonelaje en las que se exportan las abundantes cosechas de flores y frutas almerienses.

En las proximidades de la zona portuaria, merecen visitarse los jardines del Malecón, el barrio del Mue-

Los jardines del
Malecón en las
proximidades del
puerto.

Vista del barrio del
muelle de San Pedro.

*Detalle del puerto de Almería.*

*Vista de la playa de Aguadulce, en la carretera a Málaga.*
*Rodaje de una película ambientada en el Oeste americano, en el desierto de Tabernas.*
*Fachada de la ermita de Nuestra Señora de la Salud.*

lle de San Pedro, así como la plaza de la Puerta de Purchena, la plaza Vieja o la de la Virgen del Mar, etc. La capital posee, además, alrededores interesantes con playas como las de Aguadulce o Roquetas del Mar.

Almería es una provincia repleta de contrastes que van desde la fertilidad del campo de Dalias hasta el paisaje desértico de las proximidades de Tabernas, donde en más de una ocasión se han rodado películas ambientadas en el Oeste americano. Tabernas conserva los restos del castillo donde pernoctó Isabel la Católica durante el sitio de Almería.

Las casas colgadas de Sorbas se encaraman sobre una colina rocosa, aislada por una cañada que actúa a modo de foso natural.

Níjar conserva una artesanía original: sus cerámicas de origen fenicio y sus tejidos, llamados jarapas, realizados con tiras de diferentes telas.

Mojácar forma un hermoso y singular núcleo, con sus blancas casas apiñadas en un cerro.

Carboneras es un pueblo de pescadores situado en una extensa playa. En Vélez Blanco se encuentra el castillo señorial de los Vélez; en Laujar, población cargada de historia, nace el río Andarax en un bello paraje...

Vista general de Sorbas, enclavado en una auténtica fortaleza natural.

Detalle de Níjar, de innegables reminiscencias árabes.

Mojácar constituye un hermoso y singular conjunto, con sus blancas casas agrupadas en un cerro, en las estribaciones de la sierra Alhamilla.

Casa-escultura de André Bloc, en Carboneras.

En Mojácar se han mantenido algunas influencias árabes, como se refleja en ciertos detalles de los atavíos populares que lucen las mujeres mojaqueras.

Vista de Vélez Blanco, con el castillo señorial del marquesado de los Vélez, que conoció su máximo apogeo en la época de los Reyes Católicos.

Vista de Laujar de Andarax donde nace, rodeado de bellos parajes, el río Andarax.

*Vista aérea de Cádiz.*

# CADIZ

Cádiz, la «tacita de plata», ciudad marinera magníficamente emplazada, es una de las capitales andaluzas de mayor atractivo.

Tres veces milenaria, la *Gadir* fenicia es la población más antigua de la Península y, posiblemente, de todo Occidente.

La ciudad atesora dentro de sus murallas del siglo XVIII, de las que conserva algunos tramos, ricos monumentos entre los que destaca la catedral, considerada como el edificio más importante de la capital.

De estilo neoclásico, su construcción la inició el arquitecto Acero en el siglo XVIII y no fue concluida definitivamente hasta mediados del siglo XIX.

En el museo catedralicio se guarda una preciosa colección de orfebrería en la que sobresale, entre otras piezas de gran valor, la custodia del «Millón», llamada así por el considerable número de piedras preciosas que la adornan.

Cádiz está engalanada por un sinnúmero de bellos paseos, playas y jardines. En la plaza de la Constitu-

*La Puerta de Tierra, flanqueada por los dos patronos de Cádiz, San Servando y San Germán.*

*Perspectiva de las alamedas de Apodaca y del Marqués de Comillas.*

*Fachada de la catedral de Cádiz.*

Tres puntos claves en la historia de Cádiz: el monumento a las Cortes, la casa de la Aduana y el muelle transatlántico.

Una calle típica de Cádiz.

ción se levanta la Puerta de Tierra, una de las cinco de las que disponía la muralla. En la conocida plaza de San Juan de Dios, está el Ayuntamiento, edificio neoclásico; en la de España, el monumento a las Cortes de Cádiz y, por fin, la ciudad se asoma al océano

El buque-escuela «Juan Sebastián Elcano» arribando al puerto de Cádiz.

Vista del puente construido sobre la bahía gaditana.

Los carnavales de Cádiz han sido declarados de Interés Turístico. Las calles de la ciudad se llenan de algarabía, canciones y humor en un alarde de ingenio, colorido y vistosidad sin igual.

*Jerez de la Frontera: castillo de San Marcos.*

*Monumento al General Primo de Rivera.* ▷

por las alamedas de Apodaca y del Marqués de Comillas, espléndido jardín que se prolonga hasta el Parque Genovés.

De arraigada tradición marinera, la urbe mantiene una señalada actividad pesquera; posee un importante puerto mercantil y al sur de la bahía se divisa la blancura de las salinas de San Fernando.

En febrero, Cádiz celebra sus afamados carnavales que han sido declarados de Interés Turístico.

No existe en Cádiz pueblo que no merezca ser visitado: desde los de la sierra, de blancas casas, hasta los costeros, pasando por los que componen la fértil ruta del vino.

Jerez de la Frontera debe su nombre a sus prestigiosos vinos, que pueden catarse en las bodegas loca-

les. Posee también una gran rirqueza monumental con hermosas casas señoriales e iglesias, como las de Santiago, San Mateo, San Marcos, la Colegiata, etc. La deslumbrante población de Vejer, asentada en un promontorio calizo, conserva su trazado árabe en el que sobresale la iglesia parroquial, levantada sobre la planta de una antigua mezquita.

Algeciras ocupa un lugar estratégico en la bahía de su nombre, a tan sólo 25 km de la costa africana. Población cosmopolita, con un gran tránsito de viajeros, posee destacados monumentos, como la iglesia de la Palma, e importantes restos arqueológicos.

La Línea de la Concepción es una ciudad moderna que cierra por el este la bahía de Algeciras y hace frontera con Gibraltar.

Vista parcial del conjunto arquitectónico de Vejer de la Frontera.

Vista de la Línea de la Concepción y, al fondo, el peñón de Gibraltar.

Iglesia parroquial de Algeciras, donde se venera la imagen de la Virgen de la Palma.

Diversos aspectos de la cultura vinícola. En la llamada
«ruta del vino» gaditana se incluye, además de Jerez
de la Frontera, a Trebujena, Sanlúcar de Barrameda,
Chipiona, Rota y El Puerto.

*La popular plaza de las Monjas, en Huelva.*

# HUELVA

Es la provincia más occidental de Andalucía. Su zona litoral denominada la Costa de la Luz se extiende desde la desembocadura del Guadiana, en la frontera con Portugal, hasta Tarifa, en el estrecho de Gibraltar.

En la actualidad es uno de los litorales más preciados turísticamente por sus grandes extensiones de arena, sus pinares y el tipismo de sus pueblos de pescadores: Ayamonte, Isla Cristina, Lepe, Matalascañas o Punta Umbría.

Su zona montañosa no tiene tampoco nada que despreciar: Aracena, Cortegana, Jabugo son nombres llenos de color y sabor.

En el centro de la provincia, Huelva, capital maravillosamente enclavada en la encrucijada de los ríos Tinto y Odiel.

Huelva se levanta a orillas del mar ofreciéndonos sus calles, rincones, plazas... como la tranquila plaza de San Pedro, con la iglesia del mismo nombre y el monumento al arcipreste Don Manuel González García, donde se concentraba antaño el consejo de la villa, y la plaza de las Monjas, uno de los puntos de encuentro más acogedor de Huelva.

*Vista aérea del muelle.*

*Vista de la alameda de Sundheim.*

En 1755, Huelva sufrió un terrible terremoto que la destruyó casi por completo, sin embargo, conserva tres iglesias de gran interés: la Merced, la Concepción y San Pedro.

La primera es también la catedral y fue construida en el siglo XVIII. Conserva una talla del Cristo de Jerusalén, del siglo XII, y una bella imagen de la Virgen de la Cinta, de Montañés.

La más popular de Huelva es la iglesia de la Concepción, construida en el siglo XVI y reedificada tras el terremoto.

La iglesia de San Pedro es la más antigua y se cons-

*La iglesia de San Pedro, situada en la plaza del mismo nombre, es la más antigua de Huelva. Edificada sobre los restos de una mezquita mora, conserva todavía trazas mudéjares. El campanario es del año 1772.*

*Vista aérea de Punta Umbría.*

truyó donde había una mezquita conservando, todavía, trazos mudéjares.

Huelva siempre se ha distinguido por sus empresas
marinas, pero sin duda fue el Descubrimiento la que
más prestigio le ha dado a su historia.

Sus instalaciones portuarias son, hoy en día, escenario de una gran actividad comercial minera y pesquera. Justo al borde de la zona portuaria, se extiende el paseo de las Palmeras, que es como un oasis
en medio del bullicio del puerto.

En el estuario del río Tinto se encuentra Palos de la

*Vista de la ría y del muelle de Punta Umbría.*

*Vista aérea del monumento a Colón, en la Punta del Cebo, en la confluencia del Tinto y el Odiel.*

*El convento de Santa María de la Rábida.*

Frontera, el punto geográfico desde el cual partió Colón a las Indias. En la confluencia del Tinto y del Odiel, en la Punta del Cebo, se levanta el monumento a Colón. La gran estatua blanca fue esculpida por Gertrudis Whitney y fue un regalo de Norteamérica a España.

La ruta de los lugares colombinos ha de pasar obligatoriamente por Moguer, Palos y el monasterio de Santa María de la Rábida.

De Moguer eran los tres primeros marineros que se alistaron en las carabelas y de Moguer es también el gran poeta Juan Ramón Jiménez. Palos es por antonomasia «la tierra de toda empresa del Descubrimiento». Por la puerta de San Jorge, llamada «de los novios» salieron Colón y los Pinzones, el 3 de agosto de 1492.

La víspera de su partida Colón había estado orando toda la noche, en el convento de la Rábida, por el éxito de su empresa.

El convento aunque de construcción muy sencilla es interesante: fachada gótica, luminoso claustro, importantes frescos de Vázquez Díaz y una pequeña iglesia gótico-mudéjar.

El día de Pentecostés miles de romeros onubenses, gaditanos y sevillanos peregrinan al Santuario de la Virgen del Rocío, en Almonte, para rendirle tributo a la «Blanca Paloma». Es un acontecimiento de gran tradición y que goza de inmensa popularidad.

Diferentes vistas del monasterio de la Rábida: sala
capitular, con frescos de Vázquez Díaz, sala de las
primeras conferencias de Colón y la capilla del Sagrario
donde, se conserva la imagen de Nuestra Señora de
los Milagros.

*La popular romería del Rocío.*

*Detalle del Coto de Doñana.*

*Vista de Gibraleón, con el río Odiel en primer término.*

*Vista general de Aroche.*

*Las salinas de Isla Cristina.*

*El castillo de Almonaster la Real.*

*Plaza del Ayuntamiento, en Ayamonte.*

# Indice

## Colección TODO EUROPA

| | Español | Francés | Inglés | Alemán | Italiano | Catalán | Holandés | Sueco | Portugués | Japonés | Finlandés |
|---|---|---|---|---|---|---|---|---|---|---|---|
| 1 ANDORRA | ● | ● | ● | ● | ● | ● | | | | | |
| 2 LISBOA | ● | ● | ● | ● | ● | | | | ● | | |
| 3 LONDRES | ● | ● | ● | ● | ● | | | | | ● | |
| 4 BRUJAS | ● | ● | ● | ● | | | ● | | | | |
| 5 PARIS | ● | ● | ● | ● | ● | | | | | ● | |
| 6 MONACO | ● | ● | ● | ● | | | | | | | |
| 7 VIENA | ● | ● | ● | ● | ● | | ● | | | ● | |
| 8 NIZA | ● | ● | ● | ● | | | | | | | |
| 9 CANNES | ● | ● | ● | ● | | | | | | | |
| 10 ROUSSILLON | ● | ● | ● | ● | | | ● | | | | |
| 11 VERDUN | ● | ● | ● | ● | | | | | | | |
| 12 LA TORRE DE LONDRES | ● | ● | ● | ● | | | | | | | |
| 13 AMBERES | ● | ● | ● | ● | ● | | ● | | | | |
| 14 LA ABADIA DE WESTMINSTER | ● | ● | ● | ● | | | | | | | |
| 15 ESCUELA ESPAÑOLA DE EQUITACION DE VIENA | ● | ● | ● | ● | ● | | | | | | |
| 16 FATIMA | ● | ● | ● | ● | ● | | | | ● | | |
| 17 CASTILLO DE WINDSOR | ● | ● | ● | ● | ● | | | | | ● | |
| 18 LA COSTA DE OPALO | | ● | ● | | | | | | | | |
| 19 LA COSTA AZUL | ● | ● | ● | ● | | | | | | | |
| 20 AUSTRIA | | ● | ● | ● | ● | | | | | | |
| 21 LOURDES | ● | ● | ● | ● | | | | | | | |
| 22 BRUSELAS | ● | ● | ● | ● | ● | | ● | | | | |
| 23 PALACIO DE SCHÖNBRUNN | ● | ● | ● | ● | ● | | ● | | | | |
| 24 RUTA DEL VINO DE OPORTO | ● | ● | ● | ● | ● | | | | ● | | |
| 25 CHIPRE | | ● | ● | ● | | | | ● | | | |
| 26 PALACIO DE HOFBURG | ● | ● | ● | ● | ● | | | | | | |
| 27 ALSACIA | ● | ● | ● | ● | ● | | ● | | | | |
| 28 RODAS | | ● | ● | ● | | | | | | | |
| 29 BERLIN | ● | ● | ● | ● | | | | | | | |
| 30 CORFU | | ● | ● | ● | | | | | | | |
| 31 MALTA | | | ● | ● | ● | | | | | | |
| 32 PERPIÑAN | | ● | | | | | | | | | |
| 33 ESTRASBURGO | ● | ● | ● | ● | ● | | | | | | |
| 34 MADEIRA | ● | ● | ● | ● | ● | | | | | | |
| 35 LA CERDANYA - CAPCIR | | ● | | | | ● | | | | | |

## Colección ARTE EN ESPAÑA

| | Español | Francés | Inglés | Alemán | Italiano | Catalán | Holandés | Sueco | Portugués | Japonés | Finlandés |
|---|---|---|---|---|---|---|---|---|---|---|---|
| 1 PALAU DE LA MUSICA CATALANA | ● | ● | ● | ● | | ● | | | | ● | |
| 2 GAUDI | ● | ● | ● | ● | ● | | | | | ● | |
| 3 MUSEO DEL PRADO I (Pintura Española) | ● | ● | ● | ● | ● | | | | | ● | |
| 4 MUSEO DEL PRADO II (Pintura Extranjera) | ● | ● | ● | ● | ● | | | | | | |
| 5 MONASTERIO DE GUADALUPE | ● | | | | | | | | | | |
| 6 CASTILLO DE XAVIER | ● | ● | ● | ● | | | | | | ● | |
| 7 MUSEO DE BELLAS ARTES DE SEVILLA | ● | ● | ● | ● | ● | | | | | | |
| 8 CASTILLOS DE ESPAÑA | ● | ● | ● | ● | | | | | | | |
| 9 CATEDRALES DE ESPAÑA | ● | ● | ● | ● | | | | | | | |
| 10 CATEDRAL DE GERONA | ● | ● | ● | | | | | | | | |
| 11 GRAN TEATRO DEL LICEO DE BARCELONA | ● | ● | ● | ● | ● | ● | | | | | |
| 12 ROMANICO CATALAN | ● | ● | ● | ● | | | | | | | |
| 13 LA RIOJA: TESOROS ARTISTICOS Y RIQUEZA VINICOLA | ● | ● | ● | | | | | | | | |
| 14 PICASSO | ● | ● | ● | ● | ● | | | | | | |
| 15 REALES ALCAZARES DE SEVILLA | ● | ● | ● | ● | ● | | | | | | |
| 16 PALACIO REAL DE MADRID | ● | ● | ● | ● | ● | | | | | | |
| 17 REAL MONASTERIO DE EL ESCORIAL | ● | ● | ● | ● | ● | | | | | | |
| 18 VINOS DE CATALUÑA | ● | | | | | | | | | | |
| 19 LA ALHAMBRA Y EL GENERALIFE | ● | ● | ● | ● | ● | | | | | | |
| 20 GRANADA Y LA ALHAMBRA (MONUMENTOS ARABES Y MORISCOS DE CORDOBA, SEVILLA Y GRANADA) | ● | | | | | | | | | | |
| 21 REAL SITIO DE ARANJUEZ | ● | ● | ● | ● | ● | | | | | | |
| 22 REAL SITIO DE EL PARDO | ● | ● | ● | ● | ● | | | | | | |
| 23 CASAS REALES | ● | ● | ● | ● | ● | | | | | | |
| 24 PALACIO REAL DE SAN ILDEFONSO | ● | ● | ● | ● | ● | | | | | | |
| 25 SANTA CRUZ DEL VALLE DE LOS CAIDOS | ● | ● | ● | ● | ● | | | | | | |
| 26 EL PILAR DE ZARAGOZA | ● | ● | ● | ● | | | | | | | |

## Colección TODO ESPAÑA

| | Español | Francés | Inglés | Alemán | Italiano | Catalán | Holandés | Sueco | Portugués | Japonés | Finlandés |
|---|---|---|---|---|---|---|---|---|---|---|---|
| 1 TODO MADRID | ● | ● | ● | ● | ● | | | | | ● | |
| 2 TODO BARCELONA | ● | ● | ● | ● | ● | ● | | | | | |
| 3 TODO SEVILLA | ● | ● | ● | ● | ● | | | | | ● | |
| 4 TODO MALLORCA | ● | ● | ● | ● | ● | | ● | | | | |
| 5 TODO LA COSTA BRAVA | ● | ● | ● | ● | ● | | | | | | |
| 6 TODO MALAGA y su Costa del Sol | ● | ● | ● | ● | ● | | | | | | |
| 7 TODO CANARIAS — Gran Canaria, Lanzarote y Fuerteventura | ● | ● | ● | ● | ● | | ● | ● | | | |
| 8 TODO CORDOBA | ● | ● | ● | ● | ● | | | | | ● | |
| 9 TODO GRANADA | ● | ● | ● | ● | ● | | | | | ● | |
| 10 TODO VALENCIA | ● | ● | ● | ● | ● | | | | | | |
| 11 TODO TOLEDO | ● | ● | ● | ● | ● | | | | | ● | |
| 12 TODO SANTIAGO | ● | ● | ● | ● | ● | | | | | | |
| 13 TODO IBIZA y Formentera | ● | ● | ● | ● | ● | | | | | | |
| 14 TODO CADIZ y su Costa de la Luz | ● | ● | ● | ● | ● | | | | | | |
| 15 TODO MONTSERRAT | ● | ● | ● | ● | ● | ● | | | | | |
| 16 TODO SANTANDER y Cantabria | ● | ● | ● | ● | ● | | | | | | |
| 17 TODO CANARIAS — Tenerife, La Palma, Gomera, Hierro | ● | ● | ● | ● | ● | | ● | ● | | | ● |
| 18 TODO ZAMORA | ● | ● | ● | ● | ● | | | | | | |
| 19 TODO PALENCIA | ● | ● | ● | ● | ● | | | | | | |
| 20 TODO BURGOS, Covarrubias y Santo Domingo de Silos | ● | ● | ● | ● | ● | | | | | | |
| 21 TODO ALICANTE y Costa Blanca | ● | ● | ● | ● | ● | | | | | | |
| 22 TODO NAVARRA | ● | ● | ● | ● | ● | | | | | | |
| 23 TODO LERIDA, provincia y Pirineos | ● | ● | ● | ● | ● | ● | | | | | |
| 24 TODO SEGOVIA y provincia | ● | ● | ● | ● | ● | | | | | | |
| 25 TODO ZARAGOZA y provincia | ● | ● | ● | ● | ● | | | | | | |
| 26 TODO SALAMANCA y provincia | ● | ● | ● | ● | ● | | | | ● | | |
| 27 TODO AVILA y provincia | ● | ● | ● | ● | ● | | | | | | |
| 28 TODO MENORCA | ● | ● | ● | ● | | | | | | | |
| 29 TODO SAN SEBASTIAN y Guipúzcoa | ● | | | | | | | | | | |
| 30 TODO ASTURIAS | ● | ● | ● | ● | | | | | | | |
| 31 TODO LA CORUÑA y Rías Altas | ● | ● | ● | ● | | | | | | | |
| 32 TODO TARRAGONA y provincia | ● | ● | ● | ● | | | | | | | |
| 33 TODO MURCIA y provincia | ● | ● | ● | | | | | | | | |
| 34 TODO VALLADOLID y provincia | ● | ● | ● | ● | | | | | | | |
| 35 TODO GIRONA y provincia | ● | ● | ● | | | | | | | | |
| 36 TODO HUESCA y provincia | ● | ● | | | | | | | | | |
| 37 TODO JAEN y provincia | ● | ● | ● | | | | | | | | |
| 38 TODO ALMERIA y provincia | ● | ● | ● | | | | | | | | |
| 39 TODO CASTELLON y su Costa del Azahar | ● | ● | ● | | | | | | | | |
| 40 TODO CUENCA y provincia | ● | ● | ● | | | | | | | | |
| 41 TODO LEON y provincia | ● | ● | ● | | | | | | | | |
| 42 TODO PONTEVEDRA, VIGO y Rías Bajas | ● | ● | ● | | | | | | | | |
| 43 TODO RONDA | ● | ● | ● | | | | | | | | |
| 44 TODO SORIA | ● | | | | | | | | | | |
| 45 TODO HUELVA | ● | ● | ● | | | | | | | | |
| 46 TODO EXTREMADURA | ● | | | | | | | | | | |
| 47 TODO GALICIA | ● | ● | ● | | | | | | | | |
| 48 TODO ANDALUCIA | ● | ● | ● | ● | | | | | | | |
| 49 TODO CATALUÑA | ● | ● | ● | ● | ● | ● | | | | | |
| 50 TODO LA RIOJA | ● | ● | ● | ● | | | | | | | |

## Colección TODO AMERICA

| | Español | Francés | Inglés | Alemán | Italiano | Catalán | Holandés | Sueco | Portugués | Japonés | Finlandés |
|---|---|---|---|---|---|---|---|---|---|---|---|
| 1 PUERTO RICO | ● | | ● | | | | | | | | |
| 2 SANTO DOMINGO | ● | | ● | | | | | | | | |
| 3 QUEBEC | | ● | ● | | | | | | | | |
| 4 COSTA RICA | ● | | ● | | | | | | | | |

## Colección TODA AFRICA

| | Español | Francés | Inglés | Alemán | Italiano | Catalán | Holandés | Sueco | Portugués | Japonés | Finlandés |
|---|---|---|---|---|---|---|---|---|---|---|---|
| 1 MARRUECOS | ● | ● | ● | ● | ● | | | | | | |
| 2 EL SUR DE MARRUECOS | ● | ● | ● | ● | ● | | | | | | |
| 3 TUNICIA | | | ● | ● | | | | | | | |

# ANDALUCIA

PORTUGAL

BADAJOZ

CIUDAD REAL

ALBACETE

MURCIA

Belacazar
Hinojosa del Duque
Pozoblanco
Fuenteovejuna
Peñarroya Pueblonuevo
La Carolina
Villanueva del Arz.
Villacarrillo
Rosal
Jabugo
Cazalla de la Sierra
Montoro
Andujar
Bailen
Linares
Ubeda
Cazorla
Aracena
Santa Olalla
Constantina
CORDOBA
JAEN
Baeza
Jodar
Nerva
Posadas
Baena
Martos
Vélez Blanco
Valverde del Camino
Tocina
Lora del Río
Montilla
Cabra
Alcalá la Real
Baza
Huescar
La Palma del Condado
Carmona
Ecija
Aguilar de la Frontera
Puente Genil
Lucena
Priego
Guadix
Huércal-Overa
HUELVA
SEVILLA
Alcalá de Guadaira
Montefrío
Cuevas de Almanzora
Vera
Almonte
Coria
Dos Hermanas
Marchena
Monterío
GRANADA
Garruc
Mojaca
Ayamonte
sla Cristina
Punta Umbria Moguer
Los Palacios
Osuna
Loja
Tabernas
Sorbas
Carbonera
Palos de la F.
PARQUE
Utrera
Morón de la Frontera
Antequera
SIERRA NEVADA
Berja
ALMERIA
COSTA
Torre de la Higuera
DOÑANA
Montellano
Olvera
Vélez
Málaga
Alhama de Granada
Orjiva
CABO DE GATA
DE
Sanlucar de Barrameda
Ronda
MALAGA
Almuñécar
Albuñol
Adra
Roquetas
Chipiona
Arcos de la Frontera
Coin
Nerja
Motril
COSTA DE ALMERIA
LA LUZ
Puerto de Sta. María
Jerez de la Frontera
SERRANIA
Alhaurin
Torremolinos
Puerto Real
DE RONDA
Fuengirola
CADIZ
Marbella
COSTA DEL SOL
San Fernando
Vejer de la F.
San Roque
MAR MEDITERRANEO
Algeciras
Gibraltar
ESTRECHO DE GIBRALTAR
Tarifa
Ceuta

ESCALA GRAFICA
0   10   20   30   40   50 km.

Texto, fotografías, diseño y reproducción: EDITORIAL ESCUDO DE ORO, S.A.
Reservados los derechos de reproducción y traducción, totales o parciales.
Copyright de la presente edición sobre fotografías y texto literario: © EDITORIAL ESCUDO DE ORO, S.A. -
1.ª Edición, Noviembre 1989 - I.S.B.N. 84-378-1348-4 - Dep. Legal B. 38261-1989

Impreso en la C.E.E.
FISA · Escudo de Oro, S.A.

S0-ADK-995

## POST INDUSTRIAL

| 40 | 1945 | 1950 | 1955 | 1960 | 1965 | 1970 | 1975 | 1980 | 1985 | 1990 | 1995 | 2000 | 2003 | 2005 |
|---|---|---|---|---|---|---|---|---|---|---|---|---|---|---|

| | | | 1954-Brown v. Board of Education | | 1965 Watts riot | | | | | Rodney King arrest & LA riot | | Colin Powell Sec. of State | Univ. of Mich. AA cases | Condoleeza Rice becomes Sec. of State |

→  ← URBAN UNDERCLASS → ← INCREASING CLASS DIFFERENTIATION →

**on**

| | Termination | | | | | 1972-Trail of Broken Treaties | 1975-CERT | | | | Number of Indians reaches 2 million | | | |

RED POWER & PAN TRIBALISM   DEVELOPMENT OF RESERVATIONS AND ASSIMILATION →

| Zoot Suit Riots | Operation Wetback | | Cuban immigration | N E W | P O L | | | Marielitos | | Proposition 187 in California | | 2004 Hispanic Americans become largest minority group | | 2005 President Bush proposes Guest Worker Program |

CHICANISMO

**EASES**

I C
M Y
M
I
G
R
A
T
I
O
N

IMMIGRATION INCREASES, URBAN POVERTY, ETHNIC ENCLAVES, ASSIMILATION

| Token immigration from China | | | | | | | 1982- Vincent Chin murder | | | | | | | |

IMMIGRATION INCREASES, URBAN POVERTY, ETHNIC ENCLAVES, ASSIMILATION

ETHNIC REVIVAL

World War II

← ASSIMILATION →

## FLUID COMPETITIVE

FOURTH EDITION

# Race, Ethnicity, Gender, and Class

*To Pat*

*"Grow old  along with me the best is yet to be . . ."*

(Robert Browning)

FOURTH EDITION

# Race, Ethnicity, Gender, and Class

## The Sociology of Group Conflict and Change

## Joseph F. Healey

*Christopher Newport University*

WARNER MEMORIAL LIBRARY
EASTERN UNIVERSITY
ST. DAVIDS, PA  19087-3696

PINE FORGE PRESS
An Imprint of Sage Publications, Inc.
Thousand Oaks • London • New Delhi

5—5—6

E 184 .A1 H415 2006
Healey, Joseph F., 1945-
Race, ethnicity, gender,
and

Copyright © 2006 by Pine Forge Press.

All rights reserved. No part of this book may be reproduced or utilized in any form or by any means, electronic or mechanical, including photocopying, recording, or by any information storage and retrieval system, without permission in writing from the publisher.

*For information:*

Pine Forge Press
Sage Publications Company
2455 Teller Road
Thousand Oaks, California 91320
E-mail: order@sagepub.com

Sage Publications Ltd.
1 Oliver's Yard
55 City Road
London EC1Y 1SP
United Kingdom

Sage Publications India Pvt. Ltd.
B-42, Panchsheel Enclave
Post Box 4109
New Delhi 110 017  India

Printed in the United States of America

**Library of Congress Cataloging-in-Publication Data**

Healey, Joseph F., 1945-
Race, ethnicity, gender, and class : the sociology of group conflict and change / Joseph F. Healey.—4th ed.
      p. cm.
Includes bibliographical references and index.
ISBN 1-4129-1521-X (cloth : acid-free paper)
    1. Minorities—United States. 2. Ethnicity—United States. 3. Racism—United States. 4. Group identity—United States. 5. Social conflict—United States. 6. United States—Race relations. 7. United States—Ethnic relations. 8. United States—Social conditions. I. Title.
E184.A1H415 2006
305.8′00973—dc22

                                                2005007992

This book is printed on acid-free paper.

05   06   07   08   10   9   8   7   6   5   4   3   2

| | |
|---|---|
| *Acquisitions Editor:* | Benjamin Penner |
| *Production Editor:* | Denise Santoyo |
| *Copy Editor:* | Catherine Chilton |
| *Interior Design:* | Gary Hespenheide |
| *Typesetter:* | C&M Digitals (P) Ltd. |
| *Indexer:* | Kathy Paparchontis |
| *Cover Designer:* | Michelle Lee Kenny |

## ABOUT THE AUTHOR

**Joseph F. Healey** is Professor of Sociology at Christopher Newport University in Virginia. He received his PhD in Sociology and Anthropology from the University of Virginia. An experienced, innovative teacher of numerous race and ethnicity courses, he has written articles on minority groups, the sociology of sport, social movements, and violence, and he is also the author of *Statistics: A Tool for Social Research* (7th ed., 2004).

## ABOUT THE PUBLISHER

**Pine Forge Press** is a new educational publisher, dedicated to publishing innovative books and software throughout the social sciences. On this and any other publications, we welcome your comments and suggestions.

Please call or write us at:

**Pine Forge Press**
A Sage Publications Company
2455 Teller Road
Thousand Oaks, CA 91320
(805) 499-4224
E-mail: sales@pfp.sagepub.com

Visit our new World Wide Web site, your direct link to a multitude of on-line resources:

http://www.sagepub.com/pineforge

Only when lions have historians will hunters cease to be heroes.

*African Proverb*

Not everything that is faced can be changed, but nothing can be changed until it is faced.

*James Baldwin*

# Contents

# Preface

Of all the challenges confronting the United States today, those relating to minority groups continue to be among the most urgent and the most daunting. Discrimination and racial inequality are part of our national heritage and—along with equality, freedom, and justice—prejudice and racism are among our oldest values. Minority group issues penetrate every aspect of society, and virtually every item on the national agenda—welfare and health-care reform, crime and punishment, safety in the streets, the future of the family, even defense spending, foreign policy, and the war on terrorism—has some connection with dominant-minority relations.

These issues will not be resolved easily or quickly. Feelings are intense, and controversy and bitter debate are at least as common as dispassionate analysis and calm reason. As a society, we have little hope of resolving these dilemmas unless we confront them openly and honestly; they will not disappear, and they will not resolve themselves.

This textbook contributes to the ongoing discussion by presenting information, raising questions, and probing issues. My intent is to help students increase their fund of information, improve their understanding of the issues, and clarify their thinking regarding matters of race and ethnicity. This text has been written for undergraduate students—sociology majors and nonmajors alike. It makes minimal assumptions about students' knowledge of history or sociological concepts, and the material is presented in a way that students will find accessible and coherent.

For example, *a unified set of themes and concepts is used throughout the text.* The analysis is consistent and continuous, even as multiple perspectives and various points of view are examined. The bulk of the conceptual framework is introduced in the first six chapters. These concepts and analytical themes are then used in a series of case studies of minority groups in contemporary America and in an investigation of group relations in various societies around the globe. In the final chapter, main points and themes are summarized and reviewed, the analysis is brought to a conclusion, and some speculations are made regarding the future.

The analysis is in the tradition of conflict theory, but this text does not aspire to be a comprehensive statement of that tradition. Other perspectives are introduced and applied, but no attempt is made to give equal attention to all current sociological paradigms. The text does not try to explain everything, nor does it attempt to include all possible analytical points of view. Rather, the goals are (a) to present the sociology of minority group relations in a way that students will find understandable as well as intellectually challenging and (b) to deal with the issues and tell the stories behind the issues in a textbook that is both highly readable and a demonstration of the power and importance of thinking sociologically.

Although the text maintains a unified analytical perspective, *students are also exposed to a wide variety of perspectives on a number of different levels.* For example, clashing points of view are presented in the "Current Debates" at the end of almost every chapter. The debates focus on an issue taken from the chapter but present the views of scholars and analysts from a variety of disciplines and viewpoints. Without detracting from the continuity of the main analysis, these debates reinforce the idea that no one has all the answers (or for that matter, all the questions). The debates can be used to stimulate discussion, bring additional perspectives to the classroom, and suggest topics for further research.

In addition, every chapter (except the last two) includes at least one "Narrative Portrait" recounting the personal experiences and thoughts of a wide variety of people: immigrants, minority group members, journalists, sociologists, racists, and slaves, among others. These excerpts reinforce the analysis dramatically, memorably, and personally and are integrated into the flow of the chapters. Also, the experiences of minority groups and the realities of prejudice, racism, and discrimination are documented with photo essays throughout the text.

This text also *explores the diversity of experiences within each minority group, particularly gender differences.* Too often, minority groups (and the dominant group, for that matter) are seen by nonmembers as single, undifferentiated entities. The text acknowledges the variety of experiences within each group and, in particular, explores differences in the experiences of minority group males and females. The analysis explores the ways in which gender differences cut across ethnic and racial differences and stresses that these sources of inequality and injustice are independent of each other. Solving one set of problems (e.g., prejudice and racial discrimination) will not automatically or directly solve the other (e.g., sexism and gender inequalities).

This text focuses on the experiences of minority groups in the United States, but *a considerable amount of comparative, cross-national material has also been included.* A series of boxed inserts called "Comparative Focus" explores group relations in other societies, and chapter 12 analyzes group relations around the globe in terms of the conceptual framework developed in this text.

Finally, this text *stresses the ways in which American minority groups are inseparable from American society.* The relative success of this society is due no less to the contributions of minority groups than to those of the dominant group. The nature of the minority group experience has changed as the larger society has changed, and to understand America's minority groups is to understand some elemental truths about America. To raise the issues of race and ethnicity is to ask what it means, and what it has meant, to be an American.

## CHANGES IN THIS EDITION

- A new chapter has been added that consolidates coverage of contemporary immigrants and immigration issues. Chapter 11 presents new case studies (e.g., Arab Americans, Dominicans) along with selected case studies previously presented in the chapter on Hispanic Americans and Asian Americans. The chapter also covers issues of immigration, particularly the question of whether or not contemporary immigration is segmented.
- The treatment of gender, previously covered in separate boxed inserts, has now been incorporated into the flow of the chapters.
- All charts, graphs, and tables have been updated, and many new tables and graphs have been added.

- There is more coverage of mixed-race people, especially in Chapter 1.
- Many of the selections in the Current Debates have been updated, and some new topics have been added.
- "Questions for Review and Study" have been added to all chapters.
- Maps of the sending nations of immigrants have been added to Chapters 9, 10, 11, and 12.

All textbooks, even those with a single author's name on the title page, are profoundly collaborative efforts. This book has been shaped by 35 years of teaching minority relations and by the thoughts and reactions of hundreds of students. My approach to this subject has grown from years of "field testing" ideas, concepts, theories, and research and constant monitoring of what seemed to help the students make sense of the world they live in. I acknowledge and thank my students for their myriad contributions.

When I was a student, I had the good fortune of learning from faculty members who were both accomplished scholars and exceptionally dedicated teachers. Each of them contributed to my interest in and commitment to sociology, but two stand out in my memory as mentors and intellectual role models: Professors Edwin H. Rhyne and Charles S. Green. Dr. Rhyne encouraged me as a young scholar and quite literally introduced me to the world of ideas and the life of the mind. Later in my career, Dr. Green showed me what it means to be a professional scholar, a sociologist, and a teacher. Their influence on my life was profound, and I thank them deeply.

I am no less indebted to my colleagues Robert Durel, Michael Lewis, Marcus Griffin, Lea Pellett, Virginia Purtle, and Linda Waldron of Christopher Newport University. They have been unflagging in their support of this project, and I thank them for their academic, logistical, and intellectual assistance. I would also like to thank Lynn Maycroft for her help. I thank Jerry Westby and Ben Penner of Pine Forge Press for their invaluable assistance in the preparation of this manuscript and Steve Rutter, formerly of Pine Forge Press, for his help in the development of this project.

This text has benefited in innumerable ways from the reactions and criticisms of a group of reviewers who proved remarkably insightful about the subject matter and about the challenges of college teaching. I can no longer even estimate the number of points in the process of writing and research where the comments of the reviewers led to significant improvements in scholarship, clarity, and more meaningful treatments of the subject. The shortcomings that remain are, of course, my responsibility, but whatever quality this text has is a direct result of the insights and expertise of these reviewers. I thank the following people:

## First Edition Reviewers

A. Seals, Kentucky State University

Timothy Fiedler, Carroll College

Joseph J. Leon, California State Polytechnic University, Pomona

Donna Barnes, University of Wyoming

Ramona Ford, Southwest Texas State University

Seymour Leventman, Boston College

Anne Hastings, University of North Carolina, Chapel Hill

Nicole Grant, Ball State University

Charles Smith, Florida A&M

Min Zhou, University of California, Los Angeles

Raul Fernandez, University of California, Irvine

Audwin Anderson, University of South Alabama

Robert Williams, Jackson State University

Susan Takata, University of Wisconsin, Parkside

Ellen Rosengarten, Sinclair Community College

Wendy Ng, San Jose State University

Joyce Tang, City University of New York, Queens College

Michael Hodge, Georgia State University

Diana Torrez, University of Texas, Arlington

Gerald Rosen, California State University, Fullerton

Norma Burgess, Syracuse University

Maura I. Toro-Morn, Illinois State University

Steven Cornell, University of California, San Diego

Dennis Rome, Indiana University

Ray Hutchison, University of Wisconsin, Green Bay

Gerry R. Cox, Fort Hays State University

Kevin Delaney, Temple University

Carol Poll, Fashion Institute of Technology

Joni Fraser, University of California, Davis

## Second Edition Reviewers

Jeremy Hein, University of Wisconsin–Eau Claire

Linda Green, Normandale Community College

David Matsuda, Chabot College

Victor M. Rodriguez, Concordia University

Craig Watkins, University of Texas, Austin

Norma Wilcox, Wright State University

Luis Zanartu, Sacramento City College

JoAnn DeFiore, University of Washington

Min Zhou, University of California, Los Angeles

## Third Edition Reviewers

Rick Baldoz, University of Hawaii, Manoa

Jan Fiola, Minnesota State University, Moorhead

David Lopez, California State University, Northridge

Peggy Lovell, University of Pittsburgh

Gonzalo Santos, California State University, Bakersfield

Carol Ward, Brigham Young University

## Fourth Edition Reviewers

Samuel Leizear, West Virginia University

Gregory J. Rosenboom, University of Nebraska/Nebraska Wesleyan University

Herman DeBose, California State University, Northridge

Peggy A. Shifflett, Radford University

Debbie Storrs, University of Idaho

Carol Ward, Brigham Young University

Celestino Fernandez, University of Arizona

Abby Ferber, University of Colorado, Colorado Springs

Earl Wright, University of Central Florida

Norma Wilcox, Wright State University

# PART I

An Introduction to
the Study of Minority
Groups in the United States

**Chapter 1**
Diversity in the
United States: Questions and Concepts

**Chapter 2**
Assimilation and Pluralism

The United States is a nation of groups as well as individuals. These groups vary along a number of dimensions, including size, wealth, education, race, culture, religion, and language. Some of these groups have been part of American society since colonial days, and others have formed in the past few years.

How should all these groups relate to one another? Who should be considered American? Should we preserve the multitude of cultural heritages and languages that currently exists and stress our diversity? Should we encourage everyone to adopt Anglo-American culture and strive to become more similar and unified? Should we emphasize our similarities or celebrate our differences? Is it possible to do both?

Questions of unity and diversity are among the most pressing to face the United States today. In this text, we analyze these and many other questions. Our goal is to develop a broader, more informed understanding of the past and present forces that have created and sustained the groups that compose U.S. society. Part I introduces many of the important questions, concepts, and themes that will be developed and explored in later chapters.

## WHAT IS PUBLIC SOCIOLOGY?

The 2004 Annual Conference of the American Sociological Association called for "public sociology," a sociology that is engaged in the community, the society, and the world. Although not all sociologists would endorse a call for activism and involvement, the study of American race relations will, for many people, stimulate an impulse to address social problems directly and personally. To facilitate that involvement, we have developed a number of projects for students that will lead them into their communities and provide them with the possibility of making a positive difference in the lives of others. The projects will be presented in the introductions to the parts of this book, and each will be keyed to the material covered in the chapters that follow. The assignments, as stated here, should be regarded as outlines and suggestions, and it is quite likely that participants will have to improvise and respond to unanticipated challenges as they arise. Nonetheless, these assignments will allow students to bridge the (sometimes large) gap between the classroom and the community and to develop and practice their own public sociology. Each assignment could be the basis for a semester-long project for individual or teams of students.

The first public sociology assignments, which follow, will lead students to confront diversity in their community through two different avenues: schools and soup kitchens. In the first assignment, it is very likely that students will discover that diversity is increasing in the local school system at a rate that reflects the national trends discussed in Chapter 1 and presented in Exhibit 1.1. The challenges of educating a diverse population are analyzed at various places throughout the text, including the Current Debate at the end of Chapter 2.

Homelessness can affect any group, not just minorities. However, the realities of institutional discrimination (see Exhibit 1.3) and the legacies of American racism and inequality mean that minority groups are likely to be overrepresented in the soup kitchen, along with other more vulnerable populations: women and children and recent immigrants. We explore these patterns of poverty throughout the text and especially in the case study chapters (7–12).

# Assignment 1
## Revealing Diversity in the United States in Your Local School

The United States is inherently diverse despite the domination of one or more groups over others. The diversity can be seen in ethnic composition, national origin, religious affiliation, and gendered behavior. However, this diversity is not always obvious nor are its historical roots apparent. In this assignment, you will choose a local school and, working with its staff, take the lead in creating a 20-year portrait of diversity. The school may use this information to assess how well it has addressed its multicultural education needs.

### Step 1

Locate a school in your community. It may be public, private, or religious, but should be at least 20 years old.

### Step 2

Create your draft research design. You will want to decide what diversity variables you think will be important for an accurate picture of your community and the school it serves. All categories, such as Asian, White, Hispanic, and so on, include a great deal of diversity within them. If, for example, there is a large Latino population locally, perhaps you will want to discern the diversity within the larger ethnic category (for example, Puerto Rican, Cuban, Mexican, Brazilian) to create a more accurate portrait.

Once you know your variables, decide where you will get data to explore them. Local information is often made more compelling when compared to another data set, so you may want to get data on your variables from the U.S. Census or your particular state's databook (a compilation of census and vital statistics available through the state's official Web site). After preliminary exploration of data, you will be ready to discuss the project with a school.

### Step 3

Meet with the school principal or other appropriate administrator to discuss your interest in conducting this assignment. Review your research design and rationale together and modify according to input. A key aspect of this research is that the school should agree that there is a need for the diversity portrait and participate as key stakeholders. If the school does not agree, you will need to decide if another school would provide a better subject population, and you may need to approach the school district administrator (in a public system) for suggestions on likely candidates. Once you find a school that understands the need and accepts the terms, you will work with school staff to locate enrollment records and begin compiling your data.

### Step 4

As data is compiled, you will begin packaging it in an easily understood portrait. Programs such as Microsoft Excel can present clear and accessible tables and charts of data showing ethnic and gender (or your other variables) enrollment trends for the 20-year study period. Periodically meet with your stakeholders to review the growing findings or areas of difficulty and obtain feedback, revising data collection methods and presentation as needed until you complete data collection and charting for the chosen variables.

### Step 5

Review all of your charts and tables of data. Consider the patterns you see among the data and the gaps that reveal themselves. Now write an executive summary describing these patterns and gaps and the overall portrait of diversity at the school for the past 20 years. Include in your report each of your charts with brief (one or two paragraph) summaries of what they seem to mean.

### Step 6

Present your findings to the school, providing them with electronic copies of all data files and charts and one master hard copy. You have now provided them with the necessary data to begin assessing how to best address the multicultural education needs of their student body. Thank them for allowing you to work with them and ask them to share with you in the future the curriculum innovations they implement as a result of the data.

### Step 7

Congratulate yourself for hard work well done!

*Note:* This project was inspired by the fine demographic work conducted by Susan M. Cheng and T. Linh Ho. Their publication, though much larger in scope than your final report, may be helpful in visualizing your project.

SOURCE: Cheng, Susan M., and Ho, T. Linh. 2003. *A Portrait of Race and Ethnicity in Hawaii: An Analysis of Social and Economic Outcomes of Hawaii's People.* Honolulu: Pacific American Research Center. Retrieved April 15, 2005, from http://www.thepaf.org/Research/Portrait_I.pdf

# Assignment 2
## Diversity in a Soup Kitchen

The homeless population in the United States is often an invisible population. Many people pretend not to see them on the streets asking for loose change, offering to work for food, or simply sitting quietly reading the newspaper in the local public library on a cold winter day. Nonetheless, they are an important population to understand because they are the most vulnerable in many ways to cutbacks in social services. This assignment is designed to assist a soup kitchen better understand the diversity of social backgrounds their patrons bring to the table.

### Step 1

Locate one or more soup kitchens serving the homeless and contact their representative, asking if you may make an appointment with them to discuss a school research project. Many soup kitchens are run by religious organizations, maybe even by one with which you participate, and may be approached through a ministry liaison. This will be your choice. When you meet the ministry staff or other representative, discuss your interest in conducting a series of oral histories and interviews with homeless patrons. Share with them your basic research design (as described here) and explore with them the potential to better understand the diversity of cultural backgrounds the homeless bring to the soup kitchen. Try to discover if such information is welcome and valued as a means to provide an environment that is not culturally alien and more than a place to get a warm meal and be safe for an evening, among other things. Be open to changing aspects of your research design to meet the soup kitchen's particular needs and interests.

### Step 2

Set up a schedule to volunteer at the soup kitchen. To better understand the perspective of those serving the homeless, one should walk a mile in their shoes, so to speak. Volunteer at the soup kitchen for a minimum of 3 weeks regularly to get a feel for the rhythm of the facility, discern patterns among the behaviors of the patrons, and get to know a few of the patrons while serving them from the food line and while wiping down tables afterward and chatting casually with those remaining behind. To successfully get to know others, one must build rapport and share a bit of oneself, and wiping tables, sweeping floors, and otherwise not staying behind the food-service counter is critical to this end.

### Step 3

After volunteering regularly for a minimum of 3 weeks, you will probably know a few of the patrons by name and they will know you. Now is the time to design a survey instrument to get general background information on the soup kitchen's clientele. Write a survey form that asks questions about life history and vital statistics. Questions may include the following:

- Are you married, divorced, widowed, or single?
- Do you have any children?
- How old are you?
- How long have you lived in this town?
- What town did you last live in?
- What is your ethnic background?
- Who was your last employer and how long were you employed with them?
- How long have you been homeless?

Discuss your survey with the soup kitchen staff and solicit feedback and input on its design. To be useful to them, it must include information they can use that you may not have thought of.

### Step 4

Conduct a pretest of your survey instrument. Before conducting interviews with a fairly large number of informants, conducting a pretest on a small sample is usually a good idea. Approach the few (four to six individuals at most) patrons that you have gotten to know over the past weeks and ask them if you may interview them. Explain what you are doing as a student and how you hope the information may help the soup kitchen serve its visitors best. Assuming they agree, administer your survey. Review your results reflectively to discern questions that seem irrelevant and include questions in the revised survey to tap information you did not think of initially. Share the revised survey with the soup kitchen staff, revising as needed.

### Step 5

Administer your survey to as many patrons as possible, but do not include the initial sample used for the pretest. You may get other staff to assist you if they are able and willing. Compile your responses using a spreadsheet software program such as Microsoft Excel. You will need to think creatively to discover the patterns that are likely to exist in your data. Such patterns may involve amount of time homeless, general proximity of last residence, ethnic composition, gender, age, or marital status. Part of the wonder of social science is discovering the patterns, so spend some time perusing the data rather than giving them a cursory overview.

### Step 6

Conduct oral history interviews. By this point you will have been a regular volunteer for approximately 6 weeks at the soup kitchen, know several patrons by name, and know a fair amount of information about the clientele as a whole. Now is the time to explore the depth of the population with a small sample of oral histories. Oral histories of any worth generally require a fair amount of rapport with an informant, so your best bet is to approach the patrons you first interviewed for the pretest. Ask them if you may obtain an oral history from them, and assuming they agree, begin. The first stage is to get a general portrait of their life in their own words. Your informant should lead the conversation with you providing encouragement—focus on active listening. This should be followed by questions derived from the patterns you discovered in your survey in Step 5, and in this conversation, you are in the lead.

### Step 7

Organize your two kinds of data: quantitative survey and qualitative personal history. Review the two sets, exploring the patterns and meanings that emerge. Write an executive summary of approximately six pages that describes and explains the patterns in your data. Share this with the soup kitchen staff. This data may be useful in ensuring that their community outreach activities are targeted efficiently and giving them baseline information on their clientele's backgrounds. Ask the staff to share with you in the future the changes they make based on the data you collected.

### Step 8

Congratulate yourself for rewarding work well done, and do not forget to occasionally visit the soup kitchen: You are likely to brighten the day of the informants you once served.

**1**

# Diversity in the United States

## Questions and Concepts

WHAT DOES IT MEAN TO BE AN AMERICAN? IS THE UNITED STATES SPLINTERING INTO separate racial and ethnic groups? Is there a limit to the amount of diversity we can tolerate? Should the number of immigrants entering the United States be reduced? Should Spanish become an official second language? Should multiculturalism be a part of the public school curriculum? Should Black History Month be celebrated by everyone?

These questions are crucial, but they are not new. They have been debated in one form or another over and over in our past, and continuing controversies about race, immigration, and language suggest that these questions are far from settled. We are a nation of immigrants, and we have been arguing, often passionately, about exclusion and inclusion and unity and diversity since the infancy of American society. Every member of our society is in some sense an immigrant or the descendant of immigrants. Even Native Americans "immigrated" to this continent, albeit thousands of years ago. We are all from someplace else, with roots in another part of the globe. Some came here in chains; others came on ocean liners, on 747s, or on foot. Some arrived last week and others have had family here for centuries. Each wave of newcomers has in some way altered the social landscape of the United States. As many have observed, American society is continually becoming and permanently unfinished.

Our immigrant heritage and cultural diversity have made us a nation of both groups and individuals. Some of us feel intensely connected to the groups to which we belong and identify closely with our heritage. For others, the group connection is tenuous and distant. Either way, our group memberships influence our lives and perceptions. They help to shape who we are and how we fit into the larger society.

# SIX AMERICAN STORIES

To illustrate the influences of our connections with others who share our heritage, consider the life stories of six Americans. Each represents millions of others, and each exemplifies a part of what it means to be an American.

Kim Park is a 24-year-old immigrant from Korea. He arrived in New York City about 3 years ago to work in his uncle's grocery store. Kim typically works a 14-hour shift every day, 7 days a week. His duties include stocking and cleaning, and he operates the register when necessary. He is also learning how to do the bookkeeping. Instead of wages, Kim receives room and board and some spending money.

Kim is outgoing and gregarious. His English is improving rapidly, and he practices it whenever possible. He has twice enrolled in English language classes, but the demands of his job prevented him from completing the courses. On a third occasion, he was turned away because the course was already filled and there was no money to hire additional teachers. Eventually, Kim wants to become a U.S. citizen, bring his siblings to America, get married and start a family, and take over the store when his uncle retires. The store is located in a neighborhood that is changing in ethnic composition. Many different minority groups have called this neighborhood home over the years. During the late 1950s, the area was almost exclusively Jewish. The Jewish residents have since died or moved out, and they were followed by a mixture of African Americans, Puerto Ricans, and Asians.

Not far from Kim's store is the apartment building where Shirley Umphlett spent much of her childhood. In search of work, her family moved to New York from Alabama in the 1920s. Both her grandfather and father were construction workers, but because most labor unions and employers discriminated against African Americans, they had limited access to the better paying, more stable jobs and were often unemployed. Shirley's mother worked as a housekeeper in a large downtown hotel to help meet family expenses. Shirley did well in school, attended college on scholarship, and is now a successful executive with a multinational corporation. She is in her 40s, is married with two children, and is career oriented and ambitious. At the same time, she is committed to helping other African Americans and poor Americans. She and her spouse are volunteers in several community action programs and maintain memberships in three national organizations that serve and represent African Americans.

Shirley's two children attend public school. One of their teachers is Mary Ann O'Brien, a fourth-generation Irish Catholic. Mary Ann's great-grandparents were born in Ireland and came to New York as young adults in the 1880s. Her great-grandfather found work on the docks, and her great-grandmother worked as a housekeeper before her marriage. They had seven children and 23 grandchildren. Mary Ann keeps in touch with more than 50 of her cousins, most of whom live within an hour of New York City. Each successive generation of Mary Ann's family tended to do a little better educationally and occupationally. Mary Ann's father was a fireman, and her sister is a lawyer. Mary Ann does not think much about her Irish ancestry. She does attend Mass regularly, mostly because she likes the ritual and the connection with tradition. She has a vague interest in Ireland and admits she goes a little crazy on St. Patrick's Day, but otherwise her energies are completely focused on her family and her job.

In one of her fourth-grade classes, Mary Ann took a liking to a young Native American student named George Snyder. George was born on a reservation in upstate New York, but his family moved to the city when he was a baby. The unemployment rate on the reservation often exceeded 50%, and George's father thought that the city would offer a better chance for work.

Mary Ann and George kept in touch after he left elementary school, and George stopped by occasionally for a chat. Then, when George was in high school, his father was laid off, and the family returned to the reservation. Shortly thereafter, George became rebellious, and his grades began to slip. He was arrested for shoplifting and later for selling drugs, spent some time in a state correctional facility, and never finished school. The last time Mary Ann saw him, she tried to persuade him to return to school but got nowhere. She pointed out that he was still young and told him that there were many things he could do in the future, that life was full of opportunities. He responded, "What's the use? I'm an Indian with a record—I've got no future."

George's parole officer is Hector Gonzalez. Hector's parents came to the United States from Mexico. Every year, they crossed the border to join the stream of agricultural migrant laborers and then returned to their village in Mexico at the end of the season. With the help of a cousin, Hector's father eventually got a job as a cabdriver in New York City, where Hector was raised. Hector's mother never learned much English but worked occasionally in a garment factory located in her neighborhood. Hector thinks of himself as American but is very interested in his parents' home village back in Mexico, where most of his extended family still lives. Hector is bilingual and has visited the village several times. His grandmother still lives there, and he calls her once a month.

Hector worked his way through college in 7 years. After 10 years as a parole officer, he is becoming increasingly burned out and discouraged, especially about young men like George. "There are no jobs in the city, no real opportunities. What's the point of working with these guys if all they have the chance to do is hustle dope?"

Hector rents an apartment in a building owned by a corporation headed by William Buford III. The Bufords have been a part of New York's high society for generations. The family invests the bulk of its fortune in real estate and owns land and buildings throughout the New York metropolitan area. The Bufords have a three-story luxury townhouse in Manhattan but rarely go into town, preferring to spend their time on their rural Connecticut estate. William Buford attended the finest private schools and graduated from Harvard University. At age 57, he is semiretired, plays golf twice a week, vacations in Europe, and employs a staff of five to care for himself and his family. He has little interest in the history of his family but knows that his ancestors came to America from England. Family legend has it that a distant relative played an important role in the Revolutionary War, but no one in his family has ever bothered to investigate this claim.

These six individuals belong to groups that vary along some of the most consequential dimensions within our society—ethnicity, race, social class, gender, and religion—and their lives have been shaped by these affiliations (some more than others, of course). Similarly, our group memberships affect the ways others perceive us, the opportunities available to us, the way we think about ourselves, and our view of American society and the larger world. They affect our perception of what it means to be American.

# THE INCREASING VARIETY OF AMERICAN MINORITY GROUPS

Our group memberships also shape the choices we make in the voting booth and in other areas of social life. We face important decisions that will affect our lives and the lives of countless millions, and we need to contemplate these choices systematically and thoroughly. We also need to be aware that members of different groups will evaluate these decisions in different ways. The issues will be filtered through the screens of divergent experiences, group histories, and present situations. The debates over which direction our society should take are unlikely to be meaningful or even mutually intelligible without some understanding of the variety of ways of being American.

These choices about the future of our society are especially urgent because we are at present in a period of increasing diversity, largely due to high rates of immigration. Over the past three decades, the number of immigrants arriving in the United States each year has increased from less than 300,000 to over a million and includes groups from all over the globe (U.S. Department of Homeland Security, 2003, p. 3).

Can our society deal successfully with this diversity of cultures, languages, and races? Concerns about increasing diversity are compounded by other long-standing minority issues and grievances that remain unresolved. For example, charts and graphs presented in Chapters 7 through 12 show persistent gaps in income, poverty rates, and other measures of affluence and equality between minority groups and national norms. In fact, in many ways, the problems of African Americans, Native Americans, Hispanic Americans, and Asian Americans today are just as formidable as they were a generation ago.

As one way of gauging the dimensions of diversity in our nation, consider the changing makeup of U.S. society. Exhibit 1.1 presents the percentage of the total U.S. population in each of five groups. Before examining the data in the exhibit, consider the groups themselves and the labels used to designate them. All of these categories are arbitrary; none of these groups have clear or unambiguous boundaries. Two people within any of these categories might be as different from each other as any two people selected from different categories. The people included in a category may share some general physical or cultural traits, but they will also vary by social class, religion, gender, and in thousands of other ways. People classified as "Asian and Pacific Islander" represent scores of different national and linguistic backgrounds (Japanese, Samoans, Vietnamese, Pakistanis, and so forth), and "American Indian or Alaska Native" includes people from hundreds of different groups. These categories appear frequently in government reports and in the professional literature of the social sciences, but they are arbitrary conventions and should never be mistaken for unchanging or "natural" divisions between people.

**EXHIBIT 1.1**  Groups in American Society (Percentage of Total Population)

|  | Actual | | Projected | |
|---|---|---|---|---|
|  | 1980 | 2000 | 2025 | 2050 |
| Non-Hispanic Whites | 81 | 71 | 62 | 53 |
| African Americans | 11 | 12 | 13 | 13 |
| American Indian or Alaska Native | < 1 | < 1 | < 1 | < 1 |
| Asian and Pacific Islanders | 2 | 4 | 6 | 9 |
| Hispanic Americans | 6 | 12 | 18 | 24 |
| **Total Population** | 226,564,000 | 275,306,000 | 337,814,000 | 403,686,000 |

SOURCE: U.S. Bureau of the Census (2000g).

In the exhibit, the relative sizes of the groups are presented for 1980 and 2000, and group sizes are estimated for two different future dates. Note how the increasing diversity of U.S. society is reflected in the declining predominance of Non-Hispanic whites from 1980 through the middle of the 21st century. Asian and Pacific Islander populations are projected to increase dramatically over the next five decades, more than doubling their proportion of the total population. Hispanic Americans will also double their relative size. In fact, in the summer of 2002, Hispanic Americans surpassed African Americans and became the largest minority group in the United States (U.S. Bureau of the Census, 2003a). African and Native Americans are expected to increase in numbers but remain at roughly their present proportional share of the population.

The projections into the future are merely educated guesses, but they presage profound change for the United States. Within the next five decades, the total percentage of minority group Americans is projected to increase from less than 30% to almost 50%. Our society will grow more diverse racially, culturally, and linguistically. The United States will become less white, less European, and more like the world as a whole. Some see these changes as threats to traditional white middle-class American values and lifestyles. Others see them as providing an opportunity for other equally attractive and legitimate value systems to emerge.

Even though the categories in Exhibit 1.1 are broad, they still provide no place for a number of groups. For example, where should we place Arab Americans and recent immigrants from Africa? Although these groups are relatively small in size (about 1 million people each, according to the 2000 census), there is no clear place for them in the classification scheme used in Exhibit 1.1. Should Arab Americans be classified as "Asian"? Should recent immigrants from Africa be placed in the same category as African Americans? Of course, there is no particular need to have a category for every single group, but we should recognize that classification schemes like the one used in this exhibit (and in many other contexts) have limited utility and application.

A further problem with the type of classification schemes used in Exhibit 1.1 will become increasingly apparent in the years to come: There are no categories for the growing number of mixed-race individuals. The number of "mixed" Americans is relatively small today (about 2% of the population in the 2000 census) but is likely to increase rapidly because of the growing number of marriages across group lines. The number of these marriages has increased more than 10 times over since 1960 and almost doubled between 1990 and 2000 (U.S. Bureau of the Census, 2005, p. 48). Clearly, the greater the number of mixed marriages, the greater the number of mixed Americans: One study estimates that 21% of the population will claim membership in this category by 2050 (Smith & Edmonston, 1997, p. 119).

These changes and complications do not lessen the importance of the continuing issues that separate the larger society and its myriad minority groups. What kind of society are we becoming? What should it mean to be American? In the past, opportunity and success have been far more available to white Anglo-Saxon Protestant males than to members of other groups. Most of us, even the favored males such as William Buford III, would agree that this definition of American is far too narrow, but how inclusive should the definition be? Should we stress unity or celebrate diversity? How wide can the limits be stretched before national unity is threatened? How narrow can they be before the desire to preserve cultural and linguistic diversity is unjustly and unnecessarily stifled?

These first few paragraphs have raised a lot of questions. The purpose of this book is to help you develop some answers and some thoughtful, informed positions on these issues. You should be aware from the beginning that the questions addressed here are complex and that the answers we seek are not obvious or easy. Indeed, there is no guarantee that we as a society will be able or willing to resolve all the problems of intergroup relations in the United States. However, we will never make progress in this area unless we confront the issues honestly and with an accurate base of knowledge and understanding. Certainly these issues will not resolve themselves or disappear if they are ignored.

In the course of our investigation, we will rely on sociology and other social sciences for concepts, theory, and information. Chapters 1 and 2 introduce and define many of the ideas that will guide our investigation. Part II examines prejudice and discrimination, and Part III explores how relations between the dominant group and minority groups have evolved in American society. Part IV analyzes the current situation of U.S. minority groups. In the final section of the book, we explore group relations in several other societies around the globe and see what conclusions we can glean from our investigations and how they might shape the future.

## WHAT IS A MINORITY GROUP?

Before we can begin to sort out the issues, we need common definitions and a common vocabulary for discussion. We begin with the term **minority group**.[1] Taken literally, the mathematical connotation of this term is a bit misleading, because it implies that minority groups are small. In reality, a minority group can be quite large and can even be a numerical majority of the population. Women, for example, are sometimes considered to be a separate minority group, but they form a numerical majority in the U.S. population. In South Africa, as in many nations created by European colonization, whites are a numerical minority (less than 30% of the population), but despite recent changes, they remain the most powerful and affluent group.

Minority status has more to do with the distribution of resources and power than with simple numbers. The definition of minority group used in this book is based on Wagley and Harris (1958). According to this definition, a minority group has five characteristics:

1. The members of the group experience a pattern of disadvantage or inequality.

2. The members of the group share a visible trait or characteristic that differentiates them from other groups.

3. The minority group is a self-conscious social unit.

4. Membership in the group is usually determined at birth.

5. Members tend to marry within the group.

We will examine each of the defining characteristics here and, a bit later, we will return to examine the first two—inequality and visibility—in greater detail, because they are the most important characteristics of minority groups.

The first and most important defining characteristic of a minority group is *inequality;* that is, some pattern of disability and disadvantage. The nature of the disability and the degree of disadvantage are variable and can range from exploitation, slavery, and **genocide** (the extermination of the group) to slight irritants such as a lack of desks for left-handed students or a policy of racial exclusion at an expensive country club. (Note, however, that you might not agree that the irritant is slight if you are a left-handed student awkwardly taking notes at a right-handed desk or if you are a golf aficionado who happens to be African American.)

Whatever its scope or severity, whether it extends to wealth, jobs, housing, political power, police protection, or health care, the pattern of disadvantage is the key characteristic of a minority group. Because the group has less of what is valued by society, the term *subordinate group* is sometimes used instead of minority group. The pattern of disadvantage is the result of the actions of another group, often in the distant past, that benefits from and tries to sustain the unequal arrangement. This group can be called the core group or the **dominant** group. The latter term is used most frequently in this book because it reflects the patterns of inequality and the power realities of minority group status.

The second defining characteristic of a minority group is some *visible trait* or characteristic that sets members of the group apart and that the dominant group holds in low esteem. The trait can be cultural (language, religion, speech patterns, or dress styles), physical (skin color, stature, or facial features), or both. Groups that are defined primarily by their cultural characteristics are called **ethnic minority groups**. Examples of such groups are Irish Americans and Jewish Americans. Groups defined primarily by their physical characteristics are **racial minority groups**, such as African Americans or Native Americans. Note that these categories can overlap. So-called ethnic groups may have (or may be thought to have) distinguishing physical characteristics (for example, the stereotypical Irish red hair or Jewish nose), and racial groups commonly have (or are thought to have) cultural traits that differ from the dominant group (for example, differences in dialect, religious values, or cuisine).

These distinguishing traits set boundaries and separate people into distinct groups. The traits are outward signs that identify minority group members and help to maintain the patterns of disadvantage. The dominant group has (or at one time, had) sufficient power to create the distinction between groups and thus solidify a higher position for itself. These markers of group membership are crucial: Without these visible signs, it would be difficult or impossible to identify who was in which group, and the system of minority group oppression would soon collapse.[2]

It is important to realize that the characteristics that mark the boundaries between groups usually are not significant in and of themselves. They are selected for their visibility and convenience, and objectively, they may be quite trivial and unimportant. For example, scientists have concluded that skin color and other so-called racial traits have little scientific, evolutionary, medical, or biological importance. As we shall see, skin color is an important marker of group membership in our society because it was selected during a complex and lengthy historical process, not because it has any inherent significance. These markers become important because we attribute significance to them.

A third characteristic of minority groups is that they are *self-conscious social units,* aware of their differentiation from the dominant group and of their shared disabilities. This shared social status can provide the basis for strong intragroup bonds and a sense of solidarity and can lead to views of the world that are quite different from those of the dominant group and other minority groups. For example, public opinion polls frequently show vast differences between dominant and minority groups in their views of the seriousness and extent of discrimination in American society. Exhibit 1.2, for example, shows the percentage of nationally representative samples of whites and blacks who agree that "blacks are treated the same as whites in my local community" (Gallup, 2001). The chart shows that African Americans are much more pessimistic in their perception of

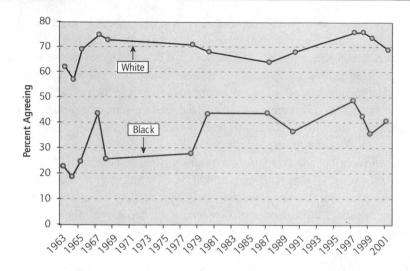

**EXHIBIT 1.2** Percentage of Whites and Blacks Agreeing That Blacks are Treated the Same as Whites in Their Local Community, 2001

racial fairness and that this racial gap is dramatic and persistent—on the order of 30% to 40%—although there may have been a slight narrowing in the more recent time period.

A fourth characteristic of minority groups is that in general, membership is an **ascribed status,** or a status that is acquired at birth. The trait that identifies minority group membership typically cannot be easily changed, and minority group status is usually involuntary and for life.

Finally, minority group members tend to *marry within their own groups.* This pattern can be voluntary, or the dominant group can dictate it. In fact, only a generation ago in America, interracial marriages were against the law in many states. State laws against **miscegenation** were declared unconstitutional in the late 1960s by the U.S. Supreme Court (Bell, 1992).

This is a lengthy definition, but note how inclusive it is. Although it encompasses "traditional" minority groups such as African Americans and Native Americans, it also could be applied to other groups (with perhaps a little stretching). For instance, women arguably fit the first four criteria and can be analyzed with many of the same concepts and ideas that guide the analysis of other minority groups. Also, gay and lesbian Americans; Americans with disabilities; left-handed Americans; the aged; and very short, very tall, or very obese Americans could fit the definition of minority group without much difficulty. Although we should not be whimsical or capricious about matters of definition, it is important to note that the analyses developed in this book can be applied more generally than you might realize at first and may lead to some fresh insights about a wide variety of groups and people.

## THE PATTERN OF INEQUALITY

As I mentioned earlier, the most important defining characteristic of minority group status is inequality. As documented in Chapters 7 through 12, minority group membership can affect access to jobs, education, wealth, health care, and housing. It is associated with a lower (often much lower) proportional share of valued goods and services and more limited (often much more limited) opportunities for upward mobility.

**Stratification**, or the unequal distribution of valued goods and services, is a basic feature of society. Every human society, except perhaps the simplest hunter-gatherer societies, is stratified to some degree; that is, the resources of the society are distributed so that some get more and others less of whatever is valued. Societies are divided into horizontal layers (or strata), often called **social classes**, which differ from one another by the amount of resources they command. Many criteria (such as education, age, gender, and talent) may affect a person's social class position and his or her access to goods and services. Minority group membership is one of these criteria, and it has had a powerful impact on the distribution of resources in the United States and many other societies.

This section begins with a brief consideration of theories about the nature and important dimensions of stratification. It then focuses on how minority group status relates to stratification. During the discussion, I identify several concepts and themes used throughout this book.

## Theoretical Perspectives

Sociology and the other social sciences have been concerned with stratification and human inequality since the formation of the discipline in the 19th century. An early and important contributor to our understanding of the nature and significance of social inequality was Karl Marx, the noted social philosopher. Half a century later, a sociologist named Max Weber, a central figure in the development of the discipline, critiqued and elaborated on Marx's view of social inequality. Here, we will also consider the views of Gerhard Lenski, a contemporary sociologist whose ideas about the influence of economic and technological development on social stratification have considerable relevance when comparing societies and understanding their evolution.

**Karl Marx.** Although best known as the father of modern communism, Karl Marx was also the primary architect of a political, economic, and social philosophy that has played a major role in world affairs for nearly 150 years. Marxism is a complex theory of history and social change in which inequality is a central concept and concern.

Marx argued that the most important source of inequality in society was the system of economic production. More specifically, he focused on the **means of production**, or the materials, tools, resources, and organizations by which the society produces and distributes goods and services. In an agricultural society, the means of production include land, draft animals, and plows. In an industrial society, the means of production include factories, commercial enterprises, banks, and transportation systems, such as railroads.

All societies include two main social classes that struggle over the means of production. One class owns or controls the means of production, and in the case of an industrial society, Marx called this elite or ruling class the **bourgeoisie**. The other class is the working class, or the **proletariat**. Marx believed that conflict between these classes was inevitable and that the ultimate result of this class struggle would be the victory of the working class, followed by the creation of a utopian society without exploitation, coercion, or inequality: in other words, a classless society.

Marxism has been extensively revised and updated over the past century and a half. Still, modern social science owes a great deal to Marx's views on inequality and his insights on class struggle and social conflict. As you shall see, Marxism remains an important body of work and a rich source of insight into group relations in industrial society.

Max Weber. One of Marx's major critics was Max Weber, a German sociologist who did most of his work around the turn of the 20th century. Weber thought that Marx's view of inequality was too narrow. Whereas Marx saw social class as a matter of economic position or relationship to the means of production, Weber noted that inequality was more complex than this and included dimensions other than just the economic. Individuals could be members of the elite in some ways but not in others. For example, an aristocratic family that has fallen on hard financial times might belong to the elite in terms of family lineage but not in terms of wealth. To use a more contemporary example, a major figure in the illegal drug trade could enjoy substantial wealth but be held in low esteem otherwise.

Weber expanded on Marx's view of inequality by identifying three separate stratification systems. First, economic inequality is based on ownership or control of property, wealth, and income. This is similar to Marx's concept of class, and in fact, Weber used the term *class* to identify this form of inequality.

A second system of stratification revolves around differences in **prestige** between groups, or the amount of honor, esteem, or respect given to us by others. Class position is one factor that affects the amount of prestige enjoyed by a person. Other factors might include family lineage, athletic ability, and physical appearance. In the United States and other societies, prestige is affected by the groups to which people belong, and members of minority groups typically receive less prestige than members of the dominant group. The difference between prestige and class can be illustrated by Shirley Umphlett, one of the six Americans introduced earlier. As a minority group member with an economically rewarding career, she is ranked higher on one dimension of stratification (class or control of property, wealth, and income) but lower on another (status or amount of prestige).

Weber's third stratification system is **power**, or the ability to influence others, have an impact on the decision-making process of society, and pursue and protect one's self-interest and achieve one's goals. One source of power is a person's standing in politically active organizations, such as labor unions or pressure groups, which lobby state and federal legislatures. Some politically active groups have access to great wealth and can use their riches to promote their causes. Other groups may rely more on their size and their ability to mobilize large demonstrations to achieve their goals. Political groups and the people they represent vary in their abilities to affect the political process and control decision making; that is, they vary in the amount of power they can mobilize.

Typically, these three dimensions of stratification go together: Wealthy, prestigious groups will be more powerful (more likely to achieve their goals or protect their self-interest) than low-income groups or groups with little prestige. It is important to realize, however, that power is a separate dimension: Even very impoverished groups have sometimes found ways to express their concerns and pursue their goals.

Gerhard Lenski. Gerhard Lenski is a contemporary sociologist who follows Weber and distinguishes between class (or property), prestige, and power. Lenski expands on Weber's ideas, however, by analyzing stratification in the context of societal evolution or the **level of development** of a society (Nolan & Lenski, 2004). He argues that the nature of inequality (the degree of inequality or the specific criteria affecting a group's position) is closely related to **subsistence technology**, the means by which the society satisfies basic needs such as hunger and thirst. A preindustrial agricultural society relies on human and animal labor to generate the calories necessary to sustain life. Inequality in this type of society centers on control of land and labor because they are the most important means of production at that level of development.

In a modern industrial society, however, land ownership is not as crucial as ownership of manufacturing and commercial enterprises. At the industrial level of development, control of capital is more important than control of land, and the nature of inequality will change accordingly.

The United States and other societies have recently entered still another stage of development, often referred to as *postindustrial society.* In this type of society, economic growth is powered by developments in new technology, computer-related fields, information processing, and scientific research. It seems fairly safe to speculate that economic success in the postindustrial era will be closely related to specialized knowledge, familiarity with new technologies, and education in general (Chirot, 1994, p. 88; see also Bell, 1973).

These changes in subsistence technology, from agriculture to industrialization to the "information society," alter the stratification system. As the sources of wealth, success, and power change, so do the relationships between minority and dominant groups. For example, the shift to an information-based, "hi-tech," postindustrial society means that the advantages conferred by higher levels of education will be magnified and that groups that have less access to schooling are likely to fall even lower in the stratification system.

## Minority Group Status and Stratification

The theoretical perspectives we have just reviewed raise three important points about the connections between minority group status and stratification. First, as already noted, minority group status affects access to wealth and income, prestige, and power. A society in which minority groups systematically receive less of these valued goods is stratified, at least partly, by **race** and ethnicity. In the United States, minority group status has been and continues to be one of the most important and powerful determinants of life chances, health and wealth, and success. These patterns of inequality are documented and explored in Part IV, but even casual observation of U.S. society will reveal that minority groups control proportionately fewer resources and that minority group status and stratification are intimately and complexly intertwined.

Second, although social classes and minority groups are correlated, they are separate social realities. The degree to which one is dependent on the other varies from group to group. Mary Ann O'Brien, the Irish American schoolteacher introduced at the beginning of this chapter, belongs to a group that today enjoys considerable **social mobility** or easy access to opportunities (although her ethnicity would have been a major impediment in the past). Although her ethnicity may not matter much these days, her gender can still be an extremely consequential factor in shaping her life chances. Many studies document the persistence of inequality in American society for all women and especially for minority women (e.g., see Browne, 1999).

Because social classes and minority groups are different dimensions, they can vary independently. Some minority group members can be successful economically, wield great political power, or enjoy high prestige even though the vast majority of their group languishes in poverty and powerlessness. Each minority group is internally divided by systems of inequality based on class, status, or power, and in the same way, members of the same social class may be separated by ethnic or racial differences.

The third point concerning the connections between stratification and minority groups brings us back to group conflict. Dominant-minority group relationships are created by struggle over the control of valued goods and services. Minority group structures (such as slavery) emerge so that the dominant group can control commodities such as land or labor, maintain its position in the stratification system, or eliminate a perceived threat to its well-being. Struggles over property, wealth, prestige, and power lie at the heart of every dominant-minority relationship. Karl Marx believed that all aspects of society and culture were shaped to benefit the elite or ruling class and sustain the economic system that underlies its privileged position. The treatment of minority groups throughout American history provides a good deal of evidence to support Marx's point.

## VISIBLE DISTINGUISHING TRAITS

In this section, we focus on the second defining characteristic of minority groups: the visible traits that denote membership. The marks of group membership that become important in a society reflect the outcomes of previous struggles between dominant and minority groups. A visible trait is selected as a convenient way for the dominant group to identify the minority group and maintain a boundary.

These marks, it should be stressed, are arbitrary. They are chosen as a result of a social process, not because they are important in any other sense. This point can be illustrated with the most socially visible marks of group membership in U.S. society: race and gender.

## Race

Race became a matter of concern in Western European history in relatively recent times. Beginning in the 1500s, Europeans came into continuous contact with the peoples of Africa, Asia, and the Americas and became more aware of and curious about the physical differences between people. Europeans also conquered, colonized, and sometimes destroyed the peoples and cultures they encountered. From the beginning, the European awareness of the differences between the races was linked to notions of inferior and superior (conquered vs. conquering) peoples. For centuries, the European tradition has been to see race in this political and military context and to intermix the biological realities with judgments about the relative merits of the various races.

Because of the way it developed, the European concept of race came to have both a biological and a social dimension. As a biological concept, race was seen as a set of fixed, unchanging, physical categories into which all people could be sorted. Investigations of race based on this approach focused on constructing typologies or taxonomies, systems of classification that were intended to provide a category for every race and every person. Some of these typologies were quite elaborate and included scores of races and subraces. For example, the "Caucasian" race was often subdivided into Nordics (blond, fair-skinned Northern Europeans), Mediterraneans (dark-haired Southern Europeans), and Alpines (those falling between the first two categories).

The major limitation of these taxonomies is that the dividing lines between the so-called racial groups are arbitrary and blurred. Contrary to the assumptions of the biological approach, there is no clear or definite point where, for example, "black" skin color stops and "white" skin color begins. The characteristics used to define race blend imperceptibly into each other, and one racial trait (skin color) can be blended with others (e.g., hair texture) in an infinite variety of ways. A given individual might have a skin color that is associated with one race, the hair texture of a second, the nasal shape of a third, and so forth. Many individuals fit into more than one racial category or none at all. Although people undeniably vary in their physical appearance, these differences do not sort themselves out in a way that permits us to divide people up like species of animals: The differences between the so-called races are not like the differences between elephants and butterflies. The ambiguity of race makes it impossible to establish categories that are not arbitrary, and the biological approach to race has been largely abandoned in the sciences.

The social conception of race, in contrast, retains a great deal of strength in everyday life. Race continues to be socially important and a significant way of differentiating among people. Race, along with gender, is one of the first things people notice about one another. In the United States, we tend to see race as a simple, unambiguous matter of skin color alone and to judge everyone as belonging to one and only one group, ignoring the realities of multiple ancestry and ambiguous classification.

To further illustrate the differences between the biological and social conceptions of race, consider skin color. Biologically, skin color is derived from melanin, a pigment that everyone except albinos has. The skin color associated with each "race" is a function of the amount of melanin in the skin, which in turn is thought to relate to climate and to the amount of sunlight characteristic of a given ecology. In areas with intense sunlight, at or near the equator, melanin acts as a screen and protects the skin against the ultraviolet rays of the sun that cause sunburn and, more significantly, skin cancer. Thus higher levels of melanin and darker skin colors are found in peoples who are adapted to equatorial ecologies. In peoples adapted to areas with less intense sunlight, the amount of melanin is lower, and skin color is therefore lighter. The lower concentration of melanin may also be an adaptation to a particular ecology. It maximizes the synthesis of vitamin D, which is important for the absorption of calcium and protection against disorders such as rickets. Thus the skin color (amount of melanin) of any group balances the need for vitamin D and the need for melanin to protect against ultraviolet rays (for more information, see Harris, 1988, pp. 98-114, and for a different view, see Vigilant, 1997). From a biological point of view, that is all there is to skin color. This most visible marker of minority group membership is a superficial and relatively unimportant biological trait. In the United States, race is a more a social than a biological reality, however, and skin color is regarded as a matter of great significance. It is important to realize that racial minority groups are creations of historical and social—not biological—processes (see Omi & Winant, 1986; Smedley, 1999). In other words, who belongs to which racial group is largely a matter of social definitions and traditions, not biology. Membership in ethnic minority groups is even more arbitrary and subjective than membership in racial minority groups. Ethnic groups are distinguished by characteristics that are less visible (language, religion, or customs) and even more subjective, arbitrary, and changeable than skin color.

## Gender

You have already seen that minority groups can be internally divided by social class and other factors. An additional source of differentiation is gender. Like race, gender has both a biological and a social component and can be a highly visible and convenient way of judging and sorting people. From birth, the biological differences between the sexes form the basis for different **gender roles,** or societal expectations about proper behavior, attitudes, and personality traits. In virtually all societies, including those at the advanced industrial stage, adult work roles tend to be separated by gender, and boys and girls are socialized differently in preparation for these adult roles. In hunter-gatherer societies, for example, boys train for the role of hunter, whereas

## Visualizing Race, Ethnicity, Gender, and Class by *Judith Friedman*

A person's race, ethnicity, social class, and gender make a great difference in the kind of life that person lives. Their impact can be difficult to recognize, however. This is especially true for individuals whose classifications together bring benefits, a good life. This textbook will help you see the impacts of race, ethnicity, gender, and class on individuals. It also will describe the struggles and victories of people in different social groups. This photo essay and the others in this textbook provide a visual complement to the text. They will encourage you to see more clearly how the material relates to your own life, and to see where you fit in the larger picture of United States society today.

This visual essay emphasizes ways that you can learn by just looking more carefully at the social world around you. Try this with the images above and below left. Which group would you feel free to join? What is it about this group that makes it seem more welcoming?

How do people show, without words, that other people are welcome? How can you, even without words, make a new coworker feel wanted and respected?

In the United States, people categorize others, even strangers, by race and ethnicity, but how is this done? Have you ever been surprised about a person's ethnic group membership after you got to know them? What clues did you use? Adding a person's last name may make you more confident about your classification choices. Women still do, however, change their name at marriage.

The United States population is increasingly diverse. You will be more aware of this if you live on the East Coast or the West Coast, but diversity in the rest of the country is increasing as well. For immigrants and their children, living in the United States can mean adopting parts of the general culture while retaining parts of their original culture. Decisions of what to retain and what to change can be especially difficult for those of college age, as adopting American customs can seem a sign of disrespect to their parents or group. What questions does each of the images here raise about what it means to be an American?

As you go through the other visual essays, look for connections among the images, and look for the ways the images clarify or expand ideas found in the text.

# Narrative Portrait

## The Social Construction of Racial Identity

*Traditionally, in the United States, race has been seen as a set of fixed, unchanging, unambiguous categories. Perhaps the most powerful example of this perception was the "one-drop rule" used to determine racial identity. Most commonly associated with the tradition of Southern racism, the rule was simple: Any trace of black ancestry—any drop of African American blood in your veins—meant that you were black.*

*In contrast to this rigid perception, the increasing cross-group marriages and growing numbers of "mixed race" individuals reminds us that race is subjective and negotiable, not fixed and permanent. That is, racial identity is a definition of self that is constructed during socialization and negotiated and developed in interaction with parents, siblings, peers, and others in the community. Race is not permanent or fixed and social conceptions can change independent of the biological realities. New racial categories can emerge as the social conception of race changes. For example, professional golfer Tiger Woods has (tongue in cheek) made up his own racial category—Cablasian—to acknowledge his Caucasian, Black, and Asian ancestry.*

*Although the newer, less rigid view of group membership may be growing in strength, the tradition of categorical thinking still has an enormous impact on the way people of mixed racial heritage are regarded by others and how they think about themselves and their place in the larger society. Some of these conflicts are illustrated in this selection from writer Lawrence Hill, the son of an African American father and a white mother. His parents were involved in the U.S. civil rights struggle in the 1950s and 1960s but opted to move to the more tolerant racial climate of Canada to raise their children. Hill was raised in a suburb of Toronto and rarely encountered other children of color. In the passage included here, he remembers some of the issues related to his multiracial status and the problem of finding a place for himself even in the mild Canadian racial atmosphere. He also reflects on the more certain racial identity of his parents, the difference between black and white racial identities, and he provides something of an outsider's view on U.S. race relations.*

### DEVELOPING A RACIAL IDENTITY

**Lawrence Hill**

As a child, my experience of race, including my racial identity, was shaded quite differently from that of my parents. They were both born and raised in the United States, and their racial identities were clearly delineated all their lives. The America of their youth and early adulthood was replete with laws that banned interracial marriages and upheld segregation in every domain of public life. . . . In the United States, there was never any doubt that my father was first and foremost a black man. Or that my mother was a white woman. And there is no question that, had my siblings and I been raised in the United States, we would have been identified . . . as black. . . .

When I was growing up, I didn't spend much time thinking about who I was or where I fit in. I was too busy tying my shoelaces, brushing my teeth, learning to spell, swinging baseball bats and shooting hockey pucks. But once in a while, just as my guard was down, questions of my own identity would leap like a cougar from the woods and take a bite out of my backside.

I found that race became an issue as a result of environmental factors. The average white kid growing up in a white suburb didn't have to think of himself as white. Gradually, my environment started talking to me and making me aware that I could never truly be white. There's nothing like being called "nigger" to let you know that you're not white.

Learning that I wasn't white, however, wasn't the same as learning that I was black. Indeed, for the longest time I didn't learn what I was—only what I wasn't. In the strange and unique society that was Canada, I was allowed to grow up in a sort of racial limbo. People knew what I wasn't—white or black—but they sure couldn't say what I was. . . .

These days, I think of the factors that contributed to my sense of identity, and of how malleable that sense of identity was and still is. There were days when I went straight from my exclusive, private boys' high school to family events populated by black relatives or friends. . . . I bounced back and forth between studying Latin . . . and revering black American cultural icons, but who exactly was I? . . .

Today in Canada, black people still contend with racism at every level of society. And yet, the way my children will define themselves, and be defined by others, remains up for grabs. Racial identity is about how you see yourself, about how you construct a sense of belonging, community, awareness and allegiance.

To this date, I have mostly seen myself as black. . . . My siblings and I learned early that you can have a white parent and still be considered black, but you can never have a black parent and be considered white. It ain't allowed. You'll be reminded of your "otherness" more times than you can shake a stick at it. This is one of the reasons why I self identify as black. Attempts at pleasant symmetry, as in "half-white, half-black," trivialize to my eye the meaning of being black. . . .

The suburb of [Toronto in which I was raised] became as suffocating for [me as the U.S. had been for my parents]. There were no blacks in my school, on my street. Because I looked so different from everyone else, I feared that I was ugly. I worried about having frizzy hair, big ears, a big nose and plump lips. When I looked in the mirror, I felt disgust. None of the people I admired looked the least bit like me. Listening to my father's [stories] . . . instilled in [me and my siblings] a measure of black pride. . . . I had to find . . . ways to connect [to Black traditions and cultural icons]. So I ate up every bit of black writing that I could find. Langston Hughes, Ralph Ellison, Richard Wright . . . James Baldwin. Eldridge Cleaver. . . . I read Alex Haley's Autobiography of Malcolm X, and had to struggle through the section of Malcolm X's life when he ardently believed that white people were the devil incarnate. I knew this to be false. My mother was white, and she was no devil.

Without knowing exactly what I was doing, I was forming my own sense of blackness and my own connection to the black Diaspora. . . . Slowly, I was developing a sense of myself. (Hill, 2001)

---

girls learn the skills necessary for successful harvesting of vegetables, fruit, and other foodstuffs. In advanced industrial societies, girls tend to learn nurturing skills that will help them take primary responsibility for the well-being of family and community members, and boys learn aggressiveness, which is considered necessary for their expected roles as leaders, combatants, and providers in a highly competitive society.

Gender roles and relationships vary across time and from society to society, but gender and inequality have usually been closely related, and men typically claim more property, prestige, and power. The societies of Western Europe and the United States, like most, have a strong tradition of **patriarchy**, or male dominance, throughout the social structure. In a patriarchal society, men have more control over the economy and more access to leadership roles in religion, politics, and other institutions. In these societies, women possess many characteristics of a minority group (namely, a pattern of disadvantage based on group membership marked by a physical stigma). Thus, women could be, and in many ways should be, treated as a separate minority group.

In this book, however, rather than discussing women as a separate group, I will focus on the divergent experiences of men and women within each minority group. This approach will permit us to analyze the ways in which race, ethnicity, gender, and class combine, overlap, and crosscut each other to form a "matrix of domination" (Hill-Collins, 1991, pp. 225-227). We will consider how the interests and experiences of females of different groups and classes coincide with and diverge from each other and from the men in their groups. For example, on some issues, African American females might have interests identical to white females and opposed to African American males. On other issues, the constellations of interests might be reversed. As you shall see, the experience of minority group membership varies by gender, and the way gender is experienced is not the same for every group.

History generally has been and is written from the standpoint of the "winners," that is, those in power. The voices of minority groups have generally been repressed, ignored, forgotten, or trivialized. Much of the history of slavery in America, for instance, has been told from the viewpoint of the slave owners. Slaves were kept illiterate by law and had few mechanisms for recording their thoughts or experiences. A more balanced and accurate picture of slavery began to emerge only in the past few decades, when scholars began to dig beneath the written records and memoirs of the slave owners and reconstruct the experiences of African Americans from nonwritten materials such as oral traditions and the physical artifacts left by the slaves.

However, our understanding of the experiences of minority groups is often based almost entirely on the experiences of minority group males alone, and the experiences of minority group females are much less well-known and documented. If the voices of minority groups have been hushed, those of female minority group members have been virtually silenced. One of the important trends in contemporary scholarship is to adjust this skewed focus and systematically incorporate gender as a factor in the minority group experience (Espiritu, 1997; Baca Zinn & Dill, 1994).

**Are Gender Roles Learned or Genetic?** The huge majority of social scientists regard race as a triviality, a social construction formulated in certain historical circumstances (such as the era of European colonialism) when it is needed to help justify the unequal treatment of minority groups. What about gender? Is it also merely a social creation designed by men to rationalize their higher status, or do the commonly observed gender differences (e.g., men are more aggressive, women more nurturing) have biological causes that are stronger and more controlling than those supposedly associated with race? Are men and women different because of nature (differences in biology and genetic inheritance) or because of nurture (differences in expectations and experience for boys and girls during childhood socialization)?

Needless to say, responses to these questions vary both in the scientific community and in the society at large. On one hand, some people (including most sociologists) argue that gender roles are entirely learned and that the commonly observed gender differences in adults are the results of the fact that society tracks boys and girls in different directions from the moment of birth and discourages "inappropriate" gender behaviors. Evidence for this point of view includes the malleable, open-ended nature of infants and the great range of behavioral and personality repertoires within each gender (e.g., some females are more aggressive than some males, and some males are more tender and nurturing than some females). Also, according to this view, the fact that "appropriate" behaviors for males and females vary from culture to culture and from time to time is taken as proof that there is no biological basis for gender roles because, if there were, gender roles would be fixed and permanent.

On the other hand, some believe that the behavioral differences between males and females are "hardwired" in our genetic code just as surely and permanently as the differences in reproductive organs. Sociologist Steven Goldberg, for example, argues that some gender characteristics are universal. He concludes that males are more aggressive and control leadership positions and the power structure in every single society about which we have information. Goldberg believes that this is so because men are predisposed to pursue status and dominance over other pleasures and rewards of life—safety, leisure time pursuits, and so on—and that this tendency is the result of biology and genetic inheritance, not socialization or learning (Goldberg, 1999, p. 54).

Still other scientists are pursuing a third possible approach to understanding gender differences that combines nature and nurture. In this view, genetic inheritance and socialization experiences work together in a variety of ways, some exquisitely subtle, to produce the commonly observed gender differences in adults. For example, sociologist Robert Udry (2000) reports the results of an investigation into the *combined* effects of biology and experience on the adult personalities of a sample of 351 women. He argues that one root of adult gender differences may lie in the biology of sex: specifically, the extent to which fetuses are exposed to the male hormone testosterone. Of course, male fetuses are exposed to much higher levels than females, and this prebirth experience, in Udry's view, is what makes males more responsive to postbirth learning experiences that stress aggression and toughness. Thus the biology of sex may predispose or sensitize males and females in very different ways and prepare them for differential socialization experiences.

Udry's research goes beyond this general difference between the sexes and asks if women who had been exposed to different levels of testosterone in the womb have different personality characteristics as adults. He found that the women in the study who had higher levels of prenatal testosterone exposure were more "masculine" in their behavior as adults and that this pattern persisted even for the women whose mothers had strongly encouraged them to become more feminine when they were children (Udry, 2000, p. 450). These and similar results led Udry to conclude that prenatal and postnatal experiences interact in complex ways to produce the differences that are seen as "typical" of men and women. Nature or biology sets limits and establishes tendencies but these potentials are then emphasized or minimized by nurture or experience, and it is the interaction between the two forces that produces the wide variation in, for example, aggressive or nurturing behaviors within the genders. Udry notes that these findings do not invalidate or refute explanations of gender differences that stress socialization or nurture. They do, however, require the recognition that biology sets some (very broad?) limits on the effects of gender socialization.

If Udry and (especially) Goldberg are correct, then gender is not an arbitrary social construct, at least not in the same way as race. However, it is important to recognize that this debate about the possible biological bases for gender roles is far from over. The research is limited in many ways and the evidence is open to a variety of interpretations. For example, Udry's sample was selected from a group of patients who happened to use a particular health-care facility, and his results cannot be generalized to larger or more diverse populations. Furthermore, scientific objectivity is often an issue when researching questions that can be so emotionally charged. Prejudicial sentiments and the pervasive sexism of the surrounding society can tinge and color even the most carefully crafted research project.

Where does that leave us? Can the view that adult gender roles are entirely learned be sustained? Must social scientists at least admit the possibility of biological influences? This issue will not be fully resolved for some time (if ever), but we can conclude by making the point that, if biology does play a role, it is to establish predispositions and tendencies. Gender does become a social construction like race when it is treated as a categorical, fixed difference and then used to deny opportunity and equality to women.

## KEY CONCEPTS IN DOMINANT-MINORITY RELATIONS

Whenever sensitive issues such as dominant-minority group relations are raised, the discussion turns to (or on) matters of prejudice and discrimination. We will be very much concerned with these subjects in this book, so we need to clarify what we mean by these terms. This section introduces and defines four concepts that will help you understand dominant-minority relations in the United States.

The book addresses how individuals from different groups interact, as well as relations among groups. Thus we need to distinguish between what is true for individuals (the psychological level of analysis) and what is true for groups or society as a whole (the sociological level of analysis). Beyond that, we must attempt to trace the connections between the two levels of analysis.

We also need to make a further distinction on both the individual and the group levels. At the individual level, what people think and feel about other groups and how they actually behave toward members of that group may differ. A person might express negative feelings about other groups in private but deal fairly with members of the group in face-to-face interactions. Groups and entire societies may display this same kind of inconsistency. A society may express support for equality in its official documents or formal codes of law and simultaneously treat minority groups in unfair and destructive ways. An example of this kind of inconsistency is the contrast between the commitment to equality stated in the Declaration of Independence ("All men are created equal") and the actual treatment of black slaves, Anglo-American women, and Native Americans at that time.

At the individual level, social scientists refer to the "thinking/feeling" part of this dichotomy as prejudice and the "doing" part as discrimination. At the group level, the term **ideological racism** describes the "thinking/feeling" dimension and **institutional discrimination** describes the "doing" dimension. Exhibit 1.3 depicts the differences among these four concepts.

## Prejudice

**Prejudice** is the tendency of an individual to think about other groups in negative ways, to attach negative emotions to those groups, and to prejudge individuals on the basis of their group memberships. Individual prejudice has two aspects: the cognitive, or thinking, aspect and the affective, or feeling, part. A prejudiced person thinks about other groups in terms of **stereotypes (cognitive prejudice)**, generalizations that are thought to apply to group members. Examples of familiar stereotypes include notions such as "women are emotional," "Jews are stingy," "blacks are lazy," "the Irish are drunks," and "Germans are authoritarian." A prejudiced person also experiences negative emotional responses to other groups (**affective prejudice**), including contempt, disgust, arrogance, and hatred. People vary in their levels of prejudice, and levels of prejudice vary in the same person from one time to another and from one group to another. We can say that a person is prejudiced to the extent that he or she uses stereotypes in his or her thinking about other groups or has negative emotional reactions to other groups.

EXHIBIT 1.3 Four Concepts in Dominant-Minority Relations

| | Level of Analysis | |
| --- | --- | --- |
| Dimension | Individual | Group or Societal |
| Thinking/feeling | Prejudice | Ideological racism |
| Doing | Discrimination | Institutional discrimination |

Generally, the two dimensions of prejudice are highly correlated with each other. However, they are also distinct and separate aspects of prejudice and can vary independently. One person may think entirely in stereotypes but feel no particular negative emotional response to any group. Another person may feel a very strong aversion toward a group but be unable to articulate a clear or detailed stereotype of that group.

# Discrimination

**Discrimination** is defined as the unequal treatment of a person or persons based on group membership. An example of discrimination is an employer who decides not to hire an individual because he or she is African American (or Puerto Rican, Jewish, Chinese, etc.). If the unequal treatment is based on the group membership of the individual, the act is discriminatory.

Just as the cognitive and affective aspects of prejudice can be independent, discrimination and prejudice do not necessarily occur together. Even highly prejudiced individuals may not act on their negative thoughts or feelings. In social settings regulated by strong egalitarian codes or laws (for example, restaurants and other public facilities), people who are highly bigoted in their private thoughts and feelings may abide by the codes in their public roles.

On the other hand, social situations in which prejudice is strongly approved and supported might evoke discrimination in otherwise unprejudiced individuals. In the Southern United States during the height of segregation or in South Africa during the period of state-sanctioned racial inequality, it was usual and customary for whites to treat blacks in discriminatory ways. Regardless of a person's actual level of prejudice, he or she faced strong social pressure to conform to the official patterns of racial superiority and participate in acts of discrimination.

# Ideological Racism

Ideological racism, a belief system that asserts that a particular group is inferior, is the group or societal equivalent of individual prejudice. These ideas and beliefs are used to legitimize or rationalize the inferior status of minority groups and are incorporated into the culture of a society and passed on from generation to generation during socialization.

Because it is a part of the cultural heritage, ideological racism exists apart from the individuals who inhabit the society at a specific time (Andersen, 1993, p. 75; See & Wilson, 1988, p. 227). An example of a racist ideology is the elaborate system of beliefs and ideas that attempted to justify slavery in the American South. The exploitation of slaves was "explained" in terms of the innate racial inferiority of blacks and the superiority of whites.

Distinguishing between individual prejudice and societal racist ideologies naturally leads to a consideration of the relationship between these two phenomena. We will explore this relationship in later chapters, but for now I can make what is probably an obvious point: People socialized into societies with strong racist ideologies are very likely to absorb racist ideas and be highly prejudiced. It should not surprise us that a high level of personal prejudice existed among whites in the antebellum American South or in other highly racist societies, such as South Africa. At the same time, we need to remember that ideological racism and individual prejudice are different things with different causes and different locations in the society. Racism is not a prerequisite for prejudice; prejudice may exist even in the absence of an ideology of racism.

## Institutional Discrimination

The final concept is the societal equivalent of individual discrimination. Institutional discrimination refers to a pattern of unequal treatment based on group membership that is built into the daily operations of society, whether or not it is consciously intended. The public schools, the criminal justice system, and political and economic institutions can operate in ways that put members of some groups at a disadvantage.

Institutional discrimination can be obvious and overt. For many years following the Civil War, African Americans in the American South were prevented from voting by practices such as poll taxes and rigged literacy tests. For nearly a century, well into the 1960s, elections and elected offices in the South were confined to whites only. The purpose of this blatant pattern of institutional discrimination was widely understood by African American and white Southerners alike: It existed to disenfranchise the African American community and keep it politically powerless.

At other times, institutional discrimination may operate more subtly and without conscious intent. If public schools use aptitude tests that are biased in favor of the dominant group, decisions about who does and who does not take college preparatory courses may be made on racist grounds, even if everyone involved sincerely believes that they are merely applying objective criteria in a rational way. If a decision-making process has unequal consequences for dominant and minority groups, institutional discrimination may well be at work.

Note that although a particular discriminatory policy may be implemented and enforced by individuals, the policy is more appropriately thought of as an aspect of the operation of the institution as a whole. Election officials in the South during segregation did not and public school administrators today do not have to be personally prejudiced themselves to implement these discriminatory policies.

However, a major thesis of this book is that both racist ideologies and institutional discrimination are created to sustain the positions of dominant and minority groups in the stratification system. The relative advantage of the dominant group is maintained from day to day by widespread institutional discrimination. Members of the dominant group who are socialized into communities with strong racist ideologies and a great deal of institutional discrimination are likely to be personally prejudiced and to routinely practice acts of individual discrimination. The respective positions of dominant and minority groups are preserved over time through the mutually reinforcing patterns of prejudice, **racism**, and discrimination on both the individual and the institutional levels. Institutional discrimination is but one way in which members of a minority group can be denied access to valued goods and services, opportunities, and rights (such as voting). That is, institutional discrimination helps to sustain and reinforce the unequal positions of racial and ethnic groups in the stratification system.

## Race and Sports

How real is race? Is it a matter of biology and genes and evolution or purely a social fiction arising from specific historical circumstances, such as American slavery? Does knowing people's race tell us anything important about them? Does it give any useful information about their character, their medical profiles, their trustworthiness, their willingness to work hard, or their intelligence? Does race play a role in shaping a person's character or his or her potential for success in school or on the job?

This debate about the significance of race and the broader question of "nature versus nurture" has been going on in one form or another for a very long time. One version of the debate has centered on the relationship between intelligence and race. One side of the debate argues that biological or genetic differences make some races more capable than other races. Most scientists reject this argument and maintain that there is no meaningful connection between race and mental aptitude (for the latest round of arguments in this debate, see Herrnstein & Murray, 1994; Jacoby & Glauberman, 1995).

Another manifestation of this debate centers on the relationship between race and sport. The fact is that, contrary to their general status as a minority group, African Americans dominate several different sports in the United States today. For example, African Americans are heavily overrepresented at the highest levels of achievement in basketball, football, track and field, and, to a lesser extent, baseball and soccer. From 1997 to 1998, African Americans were only 13% of the population but more than 75% of professional basketball players, two thirds of professional football players, and at least 15% of professional baseball and soccer players (Population Reference Bureau, 2000).

With Tiger Woods dominating professional golf, only the National Hockey League remains "white"

among professional sports. African Americans are more prominent among professional athletes—and especially among the very elite—than in virtually any other sphere of American life. Furthermore, the phenomenon is worldwide: In international track, athletes of African descent dominate both sprinting and long-distance running.

Why is this so? Has race played a role in establishing this pattern? Are people of African descent "naturally" better athletes? Are there social, cultural, and environmental forces at work here that produce this extraordinary dominance? One thing we do know, after so many decades of debate on this topic, is that there is no easy choice between nature and nurture; virtually every scholar agrees that explanations must include both genetic heritage and experience.

Journalist Jon Entine has recently argued the view that the dominance of black athletes in some sports is more biological: "Elite athletes who trace most or all of their ancestry to Africa are by and large better than the competition" (Entine, 2000, p. 4). Although Entine agrees that the racial performance gap in sports is partly due to cultural and environmental conditions (nurture), he argues that blacks are better athletes mainly because of a superior genetic heritage. The genetic differences are slight, but they are "crucial in competitions in which a fraction of a second separates the gold medalist from the also-ran" (Entine, 2000, p. 4). Specifically, blacks of West African heritage (which would include African Americans, whose ancestors were taken as slaves from this area) have a number of physiological traits that give them a decisive advantage in sprinting, leaping, and quick, explosive movements. These traits, in Entine's view, explain the dominance of blacks in certain sports (sprinting, basketball) and in certain positions (wide receiver in football) that capitalize on these abilities. Athletes of East African *descent, on the other hand, inherit a set of abilities that give them greater endurance and lung capacity, traits that, according to Entine, explain the dominance of East Africans (Kenyans, for example) in long-distance races on the international and Olympic levels. In the excerpt that follows, Entine summarizes the biological advantage of black athletes.*

*Writer Kenan Malik argues that Entine's argument is based on an arbitrary and uncritical view of race. He raises several questions and probes the weaknesses of some widespread assumptions about race.*

## The Dominance of Black Athletes is Genetic

### JON ENTINE

Since the first known studies of differences between blacks and white athletes in 1928, the data have been remarkably consistent: In most sports, African-descended athletes have the capacity to do better with their raw skills than whites. Let's summarize the physical and physiological differences known to date. Blacks with West African ancestry generally have relatively less subcutaneous fat on arms and legs and proportionally more lean body and muscle mass . . . bigger, more developed musculature in general, a longer arm span, faster patellar tendon reflex, greater body density, a higher percentage of fast-twitch muscles and more anaerobic enzymes, which can translate into more explosive energy. Relative advantages in these physiological and biomechanical characteristics are a gold mine for athletes who compete in . . . football, basketball, and sprinting. . . .

East Africa produces some of the world's best aerobic athletes because of a variety of bio-physiological attributes. Blacks from this region . . . have more energy-producing enzymes in the muscles and an apparent ability to process oxygen more efficiently, resulting in less susceptibility to fatigue; they have a slighter body profile and a larger lung capacity than whites or West Africans, which translates into greater endurance.

White athletes appear to have a physique between . . . West Africans and East Africans. They have more endurance but less explosive running and jumping ability than West Africans; they tend to be quicker than East Africans but have less endurance.

SOURCE: Entine, Jon. 2000. *Taboo: Why Black Athletes Dominate Sports and Why We're Afraid to Talk About It*. New York: Public Affairs. Pp. 268-269.

## The Argument for Genetic Differences is Deeply Flawed

### KENAN MALIK

What lies behind black domination of sport? The traditional liberal answer points the finger at social factors. Black people, so the argument goes, have been driven into sport because racism has excluded them from most areas of employment. Racism also makes blacks hungrier than whites for success. . . . Journalist Jon Entine dismisses [this] environmentalist theory of black athletic prowess as "political correctness." . . .

The liberal consensus, Entine argues, has served only to disguise the truth about the black domination of sport—which is that black people are built to run and jump. . . . [Entine and others argue] that it's time we put away our fears of talking about racial differences and face up to the facts of genetic diversity.

The view that black sportsmen and women have a natural superiority rests on the evidence of physiological research, largely into two groups of athletes: East African long-distance runners and West African sprinters.

East Africa, and Kenya in particular, is the powerhouse of middle- and long-distance running. . . . research suggests that the secret of such spectacular success lies in superior biology. Athletes of West African descent—and that includes most African Americans . . . have, on the other hand, a physique that is suited to . . . sprinting and jumping.

For Entine, such . . . differences demonstrate the natural superiority of black athletes. For Entine's critics, . . . the very search for such differences betrays a racist outlook. . . . The . . . problem with the "blacks are born to run" thesis is . . . that it is factually incorrect . . . It is certainly possible to divide humanity into a number of races . . . according to skin colour and body form. However, it is also possible to do it many other ways—using, for instance, blood group, lactose tolerance, sickle cell, or any other genetic trait. Genetically, each would be as valid a criterion as skin colour. The distribution of one physical or genetic characteristic is not necessarily the same as that of another. . . . The current division of the world into black, white, [and] Asian races is, in other words, as rooted in social convention as in genetics.

Entine rejects such criticisms as mere "semantics," but his own argument shows why it is not so. According to Entine, East Africans are naturally superior at endurance sports, West Africans at sprinting and jumping, and "whites fall somewhere in the middle." But if East and West Africans are at either end of a genetic spectrum of athletic ability, why consider them to be part of a single race, and one that is distinct from whites? Only because, conventionally, we use skin colour as the criterion of racial difference. . . .

Not only are genetic notions of population differences distinct from political concepts of race, but the physiology of human differences is not easy to interpret in sporting terms. Jon Entine suggests that West Africans have relatively slender calves compared to whites, and that this helps their sprinting ability. It is difficult to see how, because muscle power increases with cross-sectional area; smaller calves should make it harder, not easier, to excel in explosive sprinting events. . . .

It is true that athletes of West African descent living in North America, Western Europe and the Caribbean dominate many sports. But contemporary West Africans do not. This is the opposite of what one should expect if athletic ability were predominantly determined by genetics. In the United States, considerable intermixing between black and white has meant that the African American population embodies, on average, roughly 30 per cent of genes from populations of European descent. Hence, African Americans should be poorer athletes than West Africans. The reverse is true.

What all this suggests is that the relationship between sport, culture and genetics is much more complex than either liberal anti-racists or conservatives such as Entine . . . will allow. Athletic talent is at least in part inherited, and there are undoubted genetic differences between regional populations. . . . There is no reason to assume that all populations have physical characteristics equally suited to every athletic activity. But are blacks naturally better athletes than whites? Not necessarily. After all, how many African Pygmies have you ever seen climbing on to the winners' rostrum?

SOURCE: Malik, Kenan. September 18, 2000. "Yes, Nature Does Help to Explain African Sporting Success. If You Think That's Racist, Your Idea of Race is Wrong." *New Statesman,* 129: 13-18.

## Debate Questions to Consider

1. Is Entine using the social or biological definition of race? Is it racist to argue that blacks are "naturally" gifted? Is it appropriate for scientists to pursue the issue raised by Entine?

2. How strong are Malik's arguments? What does he mean when he questions the practice of grouping East and West Africans into the same race? What larger point is he making when he notes the absence of West Africans and Pygmies from the highest levels of sports competition?

3. If Entine is wrong, what social and environmental arguments might explain black dominance in sports? What is Malik implying when he says that these relationships are "more complex" than is commonly recognized?

- The United States faces enormous problems in dominant-minority relationships. Although many historic grievances of minority groups remain unresolved, our society is becoming increasingly diverse.

- The United States is a nation of immigrants, and many different groups and cultures are represented in its population.

- A minority group has five defining characteristics: a pattern of disadvantage, identification by some visible mark, awareness of its disadvantaged status, a membership determined at birth, and a tendency to marry within the group.

- A stratification system has three different dimensions (class, prestige, and power), and the nature of inequality in a society varies by its level of development. Minority groups and social class are correlated in numerous and complex ways.

- Race is a criterion widely used to identify minority group members. As a biological concept, race has been largely abandoned, but as a social category, race maintains a powerful influence on the way we think about one another.

- Minority groups are internally differentiated by social class, age, region of residence, and many other variables. In this book, I focus on gender as a source of variation within minority groups.

- Four crucial concepts for analyzing dominant-minority relations are prejudice, discrimination, ideological racism, and institutional discrimination.

- The public sociology assignments presented in the Introduction to Part I give you several opportunities to apply some of the concepts presented in this chapter. Studying diversity in a local school or in a soup kitchen will bring you face to face with the increasing diversity of U.S. society as well as some of the realities of inequality, discrimination, and racism.

### Study Site on the Web

Don't forget the interactive quizzes and other resources and learning aids at www.www.pineforge.com/healeystudy[4].

## For Further Reading

Allport, Gordon. 1954. *The Nature of Prejudice.* Reading, MA: Addison-Wesley. *(The classic work on individual prejudice.)*

Baca, Zinn, Maxine & Dill, Bonnie Thorton. 1994. *Women of Color in U.S. Society.* Philadelphia: Temple University Press. *(A wide-ranging collection of articles examining the intersecting forces of race, class, and gender in the United States.)*

Feagin, Joseph. 2001. *Racist America.* New York: Routledge. *(A passionate analysis of the pervasiveness of racism and antiblack prejudice in America.)*

Omi, Michael, & Winant, Howard. 1986. *Racial Formation in the United States from the 1960s to the 1980s.* New York: Routledge and Kegan Paul. *(An adept analysis of the social and political uses of race.)*

Smedley, Audrey. 1999. *Race in North American: Origin and Evolution of a Worldview.* Boulder, CO: Westview Press. *(An analysis of the origins of the American view of race.)*

Takaki, Ronald. 1993. *A Different Mirror: A History of Multicultural America.* Boston: Little, Brown. *(A highly readable look at minority groups and cultural diversity in American life.)*

## Questions for Review and Study

1. What kind of society should the United States strive to become? In your view, does the increasing diversity of American society represent a threat or an opportunity? Should we acknowledge and celebrate our differences, or should we strive for more unity and conformity? What possible dangers and opportunities are inherent in increasing diversity? What are the advantages and disadvantages of stressing unity and conformity?

2. What groups should be considered "minorities?" Using each of the five criteria included in the definition presented in this chapter, should gay and lesbian Americans be considered a minority group? How about left-handed people or people who are very overweight? Explain and justify your answers.

3. What is a social construction? How do race and gender differ in this regard? What does it mean to say "Gender becomes a social construction—like race—when it is treated as an unchanging, fixed difference and then used to deny opportunity and equality to women?"

4. Define and explain each of the terms in Exhibit 1.3. Cite an example of each from your own experiences. How does "ideological racism" differ from prejudice? Which concept is more sociological? Why? How does institutional discrimination differ from discrimination? Which concept is more sociological? Why?

## Internet Research Project

Additional information and a list of relevant Web sites are included in the Appendix (Internet Resources).

### A. Updating Data on Diversity

Update Exhibit 1.1, "Groups in American Society." Visit the Web site of the U.S. Census Bureau (http://www.census.gov) to get the latest estimates on the sizes of minority groups in the United States. Good places to begin the search for data include "Minority Links," "Statistical Abstract," and the list at "Subjects A to Z."

### B. How Does the U.S. Government Define Race?

In this chapter, I stressed the point that race is at least as much a social construction as a biological reality. Does the federal government see race as a biological reality or a social convention? Search the Census Bureau Web site for information on the federal definition of race. How was a person's race defined in the 2000 census? How does this differ from previous censuses? Who determines a person's race, the government or the person filling out the census form? Is this treatment of race based on a biological approach or a more arbitrary social perspective? Given the goals of the census (e.g., to accurately count the number and types of people in the U.S. population), is this a reasonable approach to classifying race? Why or why not?

### Notes

1. Boldface terms in the text are defined in the Glossary at the end of the book.
2. A partial exception to this generalization—the Burakumin in Japan—is covered in Chapter 10.

# 2

# Assimilation and Pluralism

THIS CHAPTER CONTINUES TO LOOK AT THE WAYS IN WHICH ETHNIC AND RACIAL GROUPS IN THE United States relate to one another. Two concepts, assimilation and pluralism, are at the core of the discussion. Each includes a variety of possible group relationships and pathways along which group relations might develop.

**Assimilation** is a process in which formerly distinct and separate groups come to share a common culture and merge together socially. As a society undergoes assimilation, differences among groups begin to decrease. **Pluralism**, on the other hand, exists when groups maintain their individual identities. In a pluralistic society, groups remain separate, and their cultural and social differences persist over time.

In some ways, assimilation and pluralism are contrary processes, but they are not mutually exclusive. They may occur together in a variety of combinations within a particular society or group. Some groups in a society may be assimilating as others are maintaining (or even increasing) their differences. As we shall see in Part IV, virtually every minority group in the United States has, at any given time, some members who are assimilating and others who are preserving or reviving traditional cultures. Some Native Americans, for example, are pluralistic. They live on or near reservations, are strongly connected to their heritage, and speak their native language. Other Native Americans are very much assimilated into the dominant society: They live in urban areas, speak English only, and know relatively little about their traditional cultures. Both assimilation and pluralism are important forces in the everyday lives of Native Americans and most other minority groups.

American sociologists have been very concerned with these processes, especially assimilation. This concern was stimulated by the massive immigration from Europe to the United States that occurred between the 1820s and the 1920s. Almost 40 million people crossed the Atlantic in that century, and a great deal of energy has been devoted to documenting, describing, and understanding the experiences of these immigrants and their descendants. These efforts have resulted in the development of a rich and complex literature that we can refer to as the "traditional"

POLITICAL CARICATURE No 2.

MISCEGENATION
OR THE MILLENNIUM OF ABOLITIONISM.

perspective on immigration. We will explore these perspectives on both assimilation and pluralism in the first two sections of this chapter and then briefly examine the current status of the descendants of these immigrants from Europe.

Next we will turn to contemporary (post-1965) immigrants and consider whether the concepts of the "traditional" perspective apply to these more recent experiences. These newest arrivals differ in many ways from the earlier wave of European immigrants, and theories based on the experiences of the latter will not necessarily apply to the former.

Finally, I note goals other than assimilation and pluralism and briefly consider the implications of these first two chapters for the exploration of intergroup relations. By the end of this chapter, you will be familiar with many of the concepts that will guide us throughout this text as we examine the variety of possible dominant-minority group situations and the directions our society (and the groups within it) can take.

## ASSIMILATION

We begin with assimilation because the emphasis in U.S. group relations has historically been on this goal rather than on pluralism. This section presents some of the most important sociological theories and concepts that have been used to describe and analyze assimilation in the United States.

## Types of Assimilation

Assimilation is a general term for a process that can follow a number of different pathways. One form of assimilation is expressed in the metaphor of the "**melting pot**," a process in which different groups come together and contribute in roughly equal amounts to create a common culture and a new, unique society. People often think of the American experience of assimilation in terms of the melting pot. This view stresses the ways in which diverse peoples helped to construct U.S. society and made contributions to American culture. The melting pot metaphor sees assimilation as benign and egalitarian, a process that emphasizes sharing and inclusion.

Although it is a powerful image in our society, the melting pot is not an accurate description of how American assimilation actually proceeded (Abrahamson, 1980, pp. 152-154). Some groups—especially the racial minority groups—have been largely excluded from the "melting" process. Furthermore, the melting pot brew has had a distinctly Anglocentric flavor: "For better or worse, the white Anglo-Saxon Protestant tradition was for two centuries—and in crucial respects still is—the dominant influence on American culture and society" (Schlesinger, 1992, p. 28). Contrary to the melting pot image, assimilation in the United States generally has been a coercive and largely one-sided process better described by the terms **Americanization** or **Anglo-conformity**. Rather than an equal sharing of elements and a gradual blending of diverse peoples, assimilation in the United States was designed to maintain the predominance of the English language and the British-type institutional patterns created during the early years of American society.

Under Anglo-conformity, immigrant and minority groups are expected to adapt to Anglo-American culture as a precondition to acceptance and access to better jobs, education, and other opportunities. Assimilation has meant that minority groups have had to give up their traditions and adopt Anglo-American culture. To be sure, many groups and individuals were (and continue to be) eager to undergo Anglo-conformity, even if it meant losing much or all of their heritage.

For other groups, Americanization created conflict, anxiety, demoralization, and resentment. We assess these varied reactions in our examination of America's minority groups in Part IV.

## The "Traditional" Perspective on Assimilation: Theories and Concepts

American sociologists have developed a rich body of theories and concepts based on the assimilation experiences of the immigrants who came from Europe from the 1820s to the 1920s, and we shall refer to this body of work as the *traditional* perspective on assimilation. As you will see, the scholars working in this tradition have made invaluable contributions, and their thinking is impressively complex and comprehensive. This does not mean, of course, that they have exhausted the possibilities or answered (or asked) all the questions. Theorists working in the pluralist tradition and contemporary scholars studying the experiences of more recent immigrants have questioned many aspects of traditional assimilation theory and have made a number of important contributions of their own.

**Robert Park.** Many theories of assimilation are grounded in the work of Robert Park. He was one of a group of scholars who had a major hand in establishing sociology as a discipline in the United States in the 1920s and 1930s. Park felt that intergroup relations go through a predictable set of phases that he called a "**race relations cycle.**" When groups first come into contact (through immigration, conquest, etc.), relations are conflictual and competitive. Eventually, however, the process, or cycle, moves toward assimilation, or the "interpenetration and fusion" of groups (Park & Burgess, 1924, p. 735).

Park argued further that assimilation is inevitable in a democratic and industrial society. In a political system based on democracy, fairness, and impartial justice, all groups will eventually secure equal treatment under the law. In an industrial economy, people tend to be judged on rational grounds—that is, on the basis of their abilities and talents—and not by ethnicity or race. Park believed that as American society continued to modernize, urbanize, and industrialize, ethnic and racial groups would gradually lose their importance. The boundaries between groups would eventually dissolve, and a more "rational" and unified society would emerge (see also Geschwender, 1978, pp. 19-32; Hirschman, 1983).

Social scientists have examined, analyzed, and criticized Park's conclusions for nearly 80 years. One frequently voiced criticism is that he did not specify a time frame for the completion of assimilation, and therefore his idea that assimilation is "inevitable" cannot be tested. Until the exact point in time when assimilation is deemed complete, we will not know whether the theory is wrong or whether we just have not waited long enough.

An additional criticism of Park's theory is that he does not describe the nature of the assimilation process in much detail. How would assimilation proceed? How would everyday life change? Which aspects of the group would change first?

**Milton Gordon.** To clarify some of the issues left unresolved by Park, we turn to the works of sociologist Milton Gordon, who made a major contribution to theories of assimilation in his book *Assimilation in American Life* (1964). Gordon broke down the overall process of assimilation into seven subprocesses; we will focus on the first three. Before considering these phases of assimilation, we need to consider some new concepts and terms.

| EXHIBIT 2.1 | Gordon's Stages of Assimilation |

| Stage | Process |
| --- | --- |
| 1. Acculturation (cultural assimilation) | The group learns the culture, language, and value system of the dominant group |
| 2. Integration (structural assimilation) | |
|    a. At the secondary level | Members of the group enter the public institutions and organizations of the dominant society |
|    b. At the primary level | Members of the group enter the cliques, clubs, and friendship groups of the dominant society |
| 3. Intermarriage (marital assimilation) | Members of the group intermarry with members of the dominant group on a large-scale basis |

SOURCE: Adapted from Gordon (1964), p. 71.

Gordon makes a distinction between the cultural and the structural components of society. **Culture** encompasses all aspects of the way of life associated with a group of people. It includes language, religious beliefs, customs and rules of etiquette, and the values and ideas people use to organize their lives and interpret their existence. The **social structure**, or structural components of a society, includes networks of social relationships, groups, organizations, stratification systems, communities, and families. The social structure organizes the work of the society and connects individuals to one another and to the larger society.

It is common in sociology to separate the social structure into primary and secondary sectors. The **primary sector** includes interpersonal relationships that are intimate and personal, such as families and groups of friends. Groups in the primary sector are small. The **secondary sector** consists of groups and organizations that are more public, task oriented, and impersonal. Organizations in the secondary sector are often very large and include businesses, factories, schools and colleges, and bureaucracies.

Now we can examine Gordon's earliest stages of assimilation, which are summarized in Exhibit 2.1.

1. *Cultural Assimilation, or Acculturation.* Members of the minority group learn the culture of the dominant group. For groups that immigrate to the United States, acculturation to the dominant Anglo-American culture may include (as necessary) learning the English language, changing eating habits, adopting new value systems, and altering the spelling of the family surname.

2. *Structural Assimilation, or Integration.* The minority group enters the social structure of the larger society. Integration typically begins in the secondary sector and gradually moves into the primary sector. That is, before people can form friendships with members of other groups (integration into the primary sector), they must first become acquaintances. The initial contact between groups often occurs in public institutions such as schools and workplaces (integration into the secondary sector). The greater their integration into the secondary sector, the more nearly equal the minority group will be to the dominant group in income, education, and occupational prestige. Once a group has entered the institutions and public sectors of the larger society, according to Gordon, integration into the primary sector and the other stages of assimilation will follow inevitably (although not necessarily quickly). Measures

of integration into the primary sector include the extent to which people have acquaintances, close friends, or neighbors from other groups.

3. ***Marital Assimilation****, or Intermarriage.* When integration into the primary sector becomes substantial, the basis for Gordon's third stage of assimilation is established. People are most likely to select spouses from among their primary relations, and thus, in Gordon's view, primary structural integration typically precedes intermarriage.

Gordon argued that acculturation was a prerequisite for integration. Given the stress on Anglo-conformity, a member of an immigrant or minority group would not be able to compete for jobs or other opportunities in the secondary sector of the social structure until he or she had learned the dominant group's culture. Gordon recognized, however, that successful acculturation does not automatically ensure that a group will begin the integration phase. The dominant group may still exclude the minority group from its institutions and limit the opportunities available to the group. Gordon argued that "acculturation without integration" (or Americanization without equality) is a common situation in the United States for many minority groups, especially the racial minority groups.

In Gordon's theory, movement from acculturation to integration is the crucial step in the assimilation process. Once that step is taken, all the other subprocesses will occur in due time. Gordon's idea that assimilation runs a certain course in a certain order echoes Park's conclusion regarding the inevitability of the process.

Forty years after Gordon published his analysis of assimilation, some of his conclusions have been called into question. For example, the individual subprocesses of assimilation that Gordon saw as linked in a certain order are often found to occur independently of one another (Yinger, 1985, p. 154). A group may integrate before acculturating or combine the subprocesses in other ways. Also, many researchers no longer think of the process of assimilation as necessarily linear or one-way (Greeley, 1974). Groups (or segments thereof) may "reverse direction" and become less assimilated over time, revive their traditional cultures, relearn the old language, or revitalize ethnic organizations or associations.

Nonetheless, Gordon's overall model continues to guide our understanding of the process of assimilation, to the point that a large part of the research agenda for contemporary studies of immigrants involves assessment of the extent to which their experiences can be described in Gordon's terms (Alba & Nee, 1997). In fact, Gordon's model will provide a major organizational framework for the case study chapters presented in Part IV of this text.

**Human Capital Theory.** Why did some European immigrant groups acculturate and integrate more rapidly than others? Although not a theory of assimilation per se, **human capital theory** offers one possible answer to this question. This theory argues that status attainment, or the level of success achieved by an individual in society, is a direct result of educational levels, personal values and skills, and other individual characteristics and abilities. Education is seen as an investment in human capital, not unlike the investment a business might make in machinery or new technology. The greater the investment in a person's human capital, the higher the probability of success. Blau and Duncan (1967), in their pioneering statement of status attainment theory, found that even the relative advantage conferred by having a high-status father is largely mediated through education. In other words, high levels of affluence and occupational prestige are not so much a result of being born into a privileged status as they are the result of the superior education that affluence makes possible.

Why did some immigrant groups achieve upward mobility more rapidly than others? Human capital theory answers questions such as these in terms of the resources and cultural characteristics of the members of the groups, especially their levels of education and familiarity with English. Success is seen as a direct result of individual effort and the wise investment of personal resources. People or groups who fail have not tried hard enough, have not made the right kinds of educational investments, or have values or habits that limit their ability to compete.

More than most sociological theories, human capital theory is quite consistent with traditional American culture and values. Both tend to see success as an individual phenomenon, a reward for hard work, sustained effort, and good character. Both tend to assume that success is equally available to all and that the larger society is open and neutral in its distribution of rewards and opportunity. Both tend to see assimilation as a highly desirable, benign process that blends diverse peoples and cultures into a strong, unified whole. Thus people or groups that resist Americanization or question its benefits are seen as threatening or illegitimate.

On one level, human capital theory is an important theory of success and upward mobility, and we will on occasion use the theory to analyze the experiences of minority and immigrant groups. On another level, the theory is so resonant with American "commonsensical" views of success and failure that we may tend to use it uncritically. A final judgment on the validity of the theory will be more appropriately made at the end of the text, but you should be aware of the major limitations of the theory from the beginning. First of all, as an explanation of minority group experience, human capital theory is not so much "wrong" as it is incomplete. In other words, it does not take account of all the factors that affect mobility and assimilation. Second, as we shall see, the assumption that U.S. society is equally open and fair to all groups is simply wrong. We will point out other strengths and limitations of this perspective as we move through the text.

## Assimilation Patterns

In this section, we will explore the patterns of assimilation followed by European immigrants and their descendants. These patterns have been well established by research conducted in the traditional perspective and are consistent with the model of assimilation developed by Gordon.

**The Importance of Generations.** People today—social scientists, politicians, and ordinary citizens—often fail to recognize the time and effort it takes for a group to become completely Americanized. For most European immigrant groups, the process took generations, and it was the grandchildren or the great-grandchildren (or even great-great-grandchildren) of the immigrants who finally completed acculturation and integration. Mass immigration from Europe ended in the 1920s, but the assimilation of some European ethnic groups was not completed until late in the 20th century.

Here is a rough summary of how assimilation proceeded for these European immigrants: The first generation, the actual immigrants, settled in ethnic neighborhoods, such as "Little Italy" in New York City, and made only limited movement toward acculturation and integration. They focused their energies on the network of family and social relationships encompassed within their own groups. Of course, many of them—most often the men—had to leave the neighborhood for work and other reasons, and these excursions required some familiarity with the larger society. Some English had to be learned, and taking a job outside the neighborhood is, almost by definition, a form of integration. Nonetheless, the first generation lived and died largely within the context of the "old country," which had been recreated within the new.

The second generation, or the children of the immigrants, found themselves in a position of psychological or social marginality: They were partly ethnic and partly American but full members of neither group. They were born in America but in households and neighborhoods that were ethnic, not American. They learned the old language first and were socialized in the old ways. As they entered childhood, however, they entered the public schools, where they were socialized into the Anglo-American culture.

Very often, the world the second generation learned about at school conflicted with the world they inhabited at home. For example, the old country family values often expected children to subordinate their self-interests to the interests of their elders and of the family as a whole. Marriages were arranged by parents, or at least were heavily influenced by and subject to their approval. Needless to say, these expectations conflicted sharply with American ideas about individualism and romantic love. Differences of this sort often caused painful conflict between the ethnic first generation and their Americanized children.

As the second generation progressed toward adulthood, they tended to move out of the old neighborhoods. Their geographic mobility was often motivated by social mobility. They were much more acculturated than their parents, spoke English fluently, and enjoyed a wider range of occupational choices and opportunities. Discriminatory policies in education, housing, and the job market sometimes limited them, but they were upwardly mobile, and in their pursuit of jobs and careers, they left behind the ethnic subcommunity and many of the customs of their parents.

The members of the third generation, or the grandchildren of the immigrants, were typically born and raised in nonethnic settings. English was their first (and often their only) language, and their values and perceptions were thoroughly American. Although family and kinship ties with grandparents and the old neighborhood often remained strong, ethnicity for this generation was a relatively minor part of their daily realities and their self-images. Visits on weekends and holidays and family rituals revolving around the cycles of birth, marriage, and death—these activities might connect the third generation to the world of their ancestors, but in terms of their everyday lives, they were American, not ethnic.

The pattern of assimilation by generation progressed as follows:

- The first generation began the process and was at least slightly acculturated and integrated.
- The second generation was very acculturated and highly integrated (at least into the secondary sectors of the society).
- The third generation finished the acculturation process and enjoyed high levels of integration at both the secondary and the primary levels.

Exhibit 2.2 illustrates these patterns in terms of the structural assimilation of Italian Americans (see chapter 12 for additional data on the assimilation of white ethnic groups). The educational and occupational characteristics of this group converge with those of white Anglo-Saxon Protestants (WASPs) as the generations change. For example, the percentage of Italian Americans with some college shows a gap of more than 20 points between the first and second generations and WASPs. Italians of the third and fourth generations, though, are virtually identical to WASPs on this measure of integration in the secondary sector. The other differences between Italians and WASPs shrink in a similar fashion from generation to generation.

**EXHIBIT 2.2**  Some Comparisons Between Italians and WASPs

| | WASPs* | Generation | | |
|---|---|---|---|---|
| | | First | Second | Third and Fourth |
| Percentage with some college | 42.4 | 19.0 | 19.4 | 41.7 |
| Average years of education | 12.6 | 9.0 | 11.1 | 13.4 |
| Percentage white collar | 34.7 | 20.0 | 22.5 | 28.8 |
| Percentage blue collar | 37.9 | 65.0 | 53.9 | 39.0 |
| Average occupational prestige | 42.5 | 34.3 | 36.8 | 42.5 |
| Percentage of "unmixed" Italian males marrying non-Italian females | — | 21.9 | 51.4 | 67.3 |

SOURCE: Adapted from Alba (1985), Tables 5–3, 5–4, and 6–2. Data are originally from the NORC General Social Surveys, 1975–1980, and the Current Population Survey, 1979. Copyright © 1985 Richard D. Alba.

*White Anglo-Saxon Protestants (WASPs) were not separated by generation, and some of the differences between groups may be the result of factors such as age. That is, older WASPs may have levels of education more comparable to first-generation Italian Americans than WASPs as a whole.

The first five measures of educational and occupational attainment in Exhibit 2.2 illustrate the generational pattern of integration (structural assimilation). The last comparison measures marital assimilation, or intermarriage. It displays the percentage of males of "unmixed," or 100%, Italian heritage who married females outside the Italian community. Note once more the tendency for integration, now at the primary level, to increase across the generations. The huge majority of first-generation males married within their group (only 21.9% married non-Italians). By the third generation, 67.3% of the males were marrying non-Italians.

Of course, this model of step-by-step, linear assimilation by generation fits some groups better than others. For example, immigrants from Northern and Western Europe (except for the Irish) were generally more similar, racially and culturally, to the dominant group and tended to be more educated and skilled. They experienced relatively easier acceptance and tended to complete the assimilation process in three generations or less. In contrast, immigrants from Ireland and from Southern and Eastern Europe were mostly uneducated, unskilled peasants who were more likely to join the huge army of industrial labor that manned the factories, mines, and mills. These groups were more likely to remain at the bottom of the American class structure for generations and to have risen to middle-class prosperity only in the recent past.

It is important to keep this generational pattern in mind when examining immigration to the U.S. today. It is common for newcomers to be criticized for their "slow" pace of assimilation, but their "progress" takes on a new aspect when viewed in the light of the time frame for assimilation followed by European immigrants. Especially with modern forms of transportation, immigration can be very fast. Assimilation, on the other hand, is by nature slow.

**Chains of Immigration.** Another noteworthy pattern in the immigration experience is the way in which immigrant groups tended to follow "chains" established and maintained by their members. Some versions of the traditional assimilation perspective (especially human capital theory) treat immigration and status attainment as purely individual (psychological) matters. To the contrary, scholars have demonstrated that immigration to the United States was in large measure a group (sociological) phenomenon. Immigrant chains stretched across the oceans and were held together by the ties of kinship, language, religion, culture, and a sense of common peoplehood (Bodnar, 1985; Tilly, 1990). The networks supplied information, money for passage, family news, and job offers.

Here is how chain immigration worked (and continues to work today): Someone from a village in, say, Poland, would make it to the United States. The successful immigrant would send word to the home village, perhaps by hiring a letter writer. Along with news and stories of his adventures, he would send his address. Within months, another immigrant from the village, perhaps a brother or other relative, would show up at the address of the original immigrant. After his months of experience in the new society, the original immigrant could lend assistance, provide a place to sleep, help with job hunting, and orient the newcomer to the area.

Before long, others would arrive from the village in need of the same sort of introduction to the mysteries of America. The compatriots would tend to settle close to one another, in the same building or on the same block. Soon, entire neighborhoods were filled with people from a certain village, province, or region. In these ethnic enclaves, the old language was spoken and the old ways observed. Businesses were started, churches or synagogues were founded, families were begun, and mutual aid societies and other organizations were formed. There was safety in numbers and comfort and security in a familiar, if transplanted, set of traditions and customs.

Immigrants often responded to U.S. society by attempting to recreate as much of their old world as possible. Partly to avoid the harsher forms of rejection and discrimination and partly to band together for solidarity and mutual support, immigrants created their own miniature social worlds within the bustling metropolises of the industrializing Northeast and the West Coast. These Little Italys, Little Warsaws, Little Irelands, Greektowns, Chinatowns, and Little Tokyos were safe havens that insulated the immigrants from the larger society and allowed them to establish bonds with one another, organize a group life, pursue their own group interests, and have some control over the pace of their adjustment to American culture. For some groups and in some areas, the ethnic subcommunity was a short-lived phenomenon. For others—Jews and especially the Chinese and Japanese—the neighborhood became the dominant structure of their lives, and the networks continued to function long after arrival in the United States.

## Variations in Assimilation

Assimilation is a complex process that is never exactly the same for any two groups. Sociologists have paid particular attention to the way that religion, social class, and gender shaped the overall patterns of European immigration in the late 1800s and early 1900s. They have also investigated the way in which immigrants' reasons for coming to this country have affected the experiences of different groups.

**Religion.** A major differentiating factor in the experiences of the European immigrant groups, recognized by Gordon and other students of American assimilation, was religion. Protestant, Catholic, and Jewish immigrants lived in different neighborhoods, occupied different niches in the workforce, formed separate networks of affiliation and groups, and chose their marriage partners from different pools of people.

One important study that documented the importance of religion for European immigrants and their descendants (and also reinforced the importance of generations) was conducted by sociologist Ruby Jo Kennedy (1944). She studied intermarriage patterns in New Haven, Connecticut, over a 70-year period ending in the 1940s and found that the immigrant genera- tion chose marriage partners from a pool whose boundaries were marked by ethnicity and religion. For example, Irish Catholics married other Irish Catholics, Italian Catholics married Italian Catholics, Irish Protestants married Irish Protestants, and so forth across all the ethnic and religious divisions she studied.

The pool of marriage partners for the children and grandchildren of the immigrants continued to be bounded by religion but not so much by ethnicity. Thus, later generations of Irish Catholics continued to marry other Catholics but were less likely to marry other Irish. As assimilation proceeded, ethnic group boundaries faded (or "melted"), but religious boundaries did not. Kennedy described this phenomenon as a **triple melting pot**: a pattern of structural assimilation within each of the three religious denominations. (Kennedy, 1944, 1952).

Will Herberg (1960), another important student of American assimilation, also explored the connection between religion and ethnicity. Writing in the 1950s, he noted that the pres- sures of acculturation did not affect all aspects of ethnicity equally. European immigrants and their descendants were strongly encouraged to learn English, but they were not so pressured to change their religious beliefs. Very often, their religious faith was the strongest connection between later generations and their immigrant ancestors. The American tradition of religious tolerance allowed the descendants of the European immigrants to preserve this tie to their roots without being seen as "un-American." As a result, the Protestant, Catholic, and Jewish faiths eventually came to occupy roughly equal degrees of legitimacy in American society.

Thus, for the descendants of the European immigrants, religion became a vehicle through which their ethnicity could be expressed. For many members of this group, religion and eth- nicity were fused, and ethnic traditions and identities came to have a religious expression. For example, Mary Ann O'Brien, the Irish American schoolteacher introduced in chapter 1, attends Mass partly as a family matter and partly as a religious devotion. She does not know much about the Irish culture of her immigrant ancestors or about the adjustments and changes they had to make to survive in the United States. What she does know is that they were Catholic and that by observing the rituals of the church in the present, she is honoring her connections to the past. It is not just that she is Irish-Catholic-American but that—for her and millions of others—being Catholic is part of being Irish in America.

**Social Class.** Social class is a central feature of social structure, and it is not surprising that it affected the European immigrant groups in a number of ways. First, social class combined with religion to shape the social world of the descendants of the European immigrants. In fact, Gordon (1964) concluded that U.S. society in the 1960s actually incorporated not three, but four melting pots (one for each of the major ethnic/religious groups and one for black Americans), each of which were internally subdivided by social class. In his view, the most significant struc- tural unit within American society was the "**ethclass**," defined by the intersection of the reli- gious,-ethnic, and social class boundaries (e.g., working-class Catholic, upper-class Protestant, etc.). Thus people were not "simply American" but tended to identify with, associate with, and choose their spouses from within their ethclasses.

Second, social class affected structural integration. The huge majority of the post-1880s European immigrants were working class, and because they "entered U.S. society at the bottom of the economic ladder, and . . . stayed close to that level for the next half century, ethnic history has been essentially working class history" (Morawska, 1990, p. 215; see also Bodnar, 1985). For generations, many groups of Eastern and Southern European immigrants did not acculturate to middle-class American culture but to an urban working-class, blue-collar set of lifestyles and values. Even today, ethnicity for many groups remains interconnected with social class factors, and a familiar stereotype of white ethnicity is the hard-hat construction worker (see chapter 12).

**Gender.** Anyone who wants to learn about the experience of immigration will find a huge body of literature incorporating every imaginable discipline and genre. The great bulk of this material, however, concerns the immigrant experience in general or is focused specifically on male immigrants. The experiences of female immigrants have been much less recorded and hence far less accessible. Now we are learning how different male and female immigration experiences sometimes were.

Many immigrant women came from cultures with strong patriarchal traditions and thus had much less access than the men to leadership roles, education, and prestigious, high-paying occupations. As was the case with slave women, the voices of immigrant women have been muted. The research that has been done, however, documents the fact that immigrant women played multiple roles both during immigration and during the process of adjusting to U.S. society. As would be expected in patriarchal societies, the roles of wife and mother were central, but immigrant women were involved in other activities as well.

In general, male immigrants tended to precede women, and it was common for the males to send for the women only after they had secured lodging, jobs, and a certain level of stability. However, women immigrants' experiences were quite varied, often depending on their original cultures.

In some cases, women were not only prominent among the "first wave" of immigrants but also began the process of acculturation and integration. During the 19th century, for example, a high percentage of Irish immigrants were young single women. They came to America seeking jobs and often wound up employed in domestic work, a role that permitted them to live "respectably" in a family setting. In 1850, about 75% of all employed Irish immigrant women in New York City worked as servants, and the rest were employed in textile mills and factories. As late as 1920, 81% of employed Irish-born women in the United States worked as domestics. Factory work was the second most prevalent form of employment (Blessing, 1980; see also Steinberg, 1981).

Because the economic situation of immigrant families was typically precarious, it was common for women to be involved in wage labor. The type and location of the work varied from group to group. Whereas Irish women were concentrated in domestic work and factories and mills, this was rare for Italian women. Italian culture had strong norms of patriarchy, and "one of the culture's strongest prohibitions was directed against contact between women and male strangers" (Alba, 1985, p. 53). Thus acceptable work situations for Italian women were likely to involve tasks that could be done at home: doing laundry, taking in boarders, and doing piecework for the garment industry. Italian women who worked outside the home were likely to find themselves in single-sex settings among other immigrant women. Thus women immigrants from Italy tended to be far less acculturated and integrated than those from Ireland.

Eastern European Jewish women represent a third pattern of assimilation. They were part of a flow of refugees from religious persecution, and most came with their husbands and children in intact family units. According to Steinberg (1981), "Few were independent bread-winners, and when they did work, they usually found employment in the . . . garment industry. Often they worked in small shops as family members" (p. 161).

It was common for the women of immigrant groups to combine work and home. "Peasant women were accustomed to productive work within the family economy. . . . Placing their highest priority on family needs, women stayed home whenever possible, shifting roles quickly according to family necessity" (Evans, 1989, p. 131). Compared to the men, immigrant women were more closely connected to home and family, less likely to learn to read or speak English or otherwise acculturate, and significantly more influential in preserving the heritage of their groups.

Younger, single, second-generation women tended to seek employment outside the home. They found opportunities in the industrial sector and in clerical and sales work, occupations that were quickly stereotyped as "women's work." Women were seen as working only to supplement the family treasury, and this assumption was used to justify a lower wage scale. Evans (1989) reports that in the late 1800s, "Whether in factories, offices, or private homes . . . women's wages were about half of those of men" (p. 135). These patterns of discrimination motivated women, both immigrant and native born, to join the labor movement (Evans, 1989; Seller, 1987; Wertheimer, 1979).

On a positive note, Seller (1987) rejects the stereotype of immigrant women as subservient, unassimilated preservers of the

"old ways" who were content to remain in the background. . . . They played a central role in both acculturation and immigration: Immigrant women built social, charitable, and educational institutions that spanned the neighborhood and the nation. They established day care centers, restaurants, hotels, employment agencies, and legal aid bureaus. They wrote novels, plays, and poetry. They campaigned for a variety of causes, from factory legislation to birth control, from cleaner streets to cleaner government. (Seller, 1987, p. 198)

**Sojourners.** Some versions of the traditional perspective and the "taken-for-granted" views of many Americans assume that assimilation is desirable and therefore desired. However, immigrant groups were highly variable in their interest in Americanization, a factor that greatly shaped their experiences.

Some groups were very committed to Americanization. Eastern European Jews, for example, came to America because of religious persecution and planned to make America their home from the beginning. They left their homeland in fear for their lives and had no plans and no possibility of returning. They intended to stay, for they had nowhere else to go. (The nation of Israel was not founded until 1948.) These immigrants committed themselves to learning English, becoming citizens, and familiarizing themselves with their new society as quickly as possible.

Other immigrants had no intention of becoming American citizens and therefore had little interest in Americanization. These **sojourners**, or "birds of passage," were oriented to the old country and intended to return once they had accumulated enough capital to be successful in their home villages or provinces. Because immigration records are not very detailed, it is difficult to assess the exact numbers of immigrants who returned to the old country (see Wyman, 1993). We do know, for example, that a large percentage of Italian immigrants were sojourners. It is estimated that although 3.8 million Italians landed in the United States between 1899 and 1924, around 2.1 million departed during the same interval (Nelli, 1980, p. 547). Sojourning was common among many groups, including the Chinese.

## The Blending of America: Mixed Race by *Jerome Krase*

It has been projected that over the next several decades, as American society becomes more culturally and linguistically diverse, the population of the United States will also look like the rest of the globe, that is, less white. As the population becomes more ethnically diverse it also seems to be becoming more racially "mixed." In my own lifetime the marriage of Italians and Slavs, even when both bride and groom were Roman Catholic, was looked upon somewhat as a "mixed marriage," and marriages between Jews and Gentiles were extremely unusual. Historically the most problematic forms of social integration or blending have been racial. For example, socially created racial categories like black and white (as well as even more arbitrary human colors of "yellow" for Asian and "red" for Indigenous Americans), despite the lack of a scientifically biological basis, were seen as fixed. The hierarchy of racism argued that just one drop of black blood would essentially contaminate an otherwise apparently "white" and allegedly also superior person. In fact, marriages between arbitrarily defined white and nonwhite races were illegal in many states. Following are a number of 19th-century illustrations which cast racial mixing, or miscegenation, as sinister and threatening to society.

Jack Johnson (pictured above) was the first African American heavyweight champion. There was a campaign of hatred and bigotry waged against him by whites who wished to regain the heavyweight title and who also resented his interracial relationships with women.

After his first interracial marriage and his defeat of several white hopefuls, Johnson was convicted in 1913 under contrived circumstances for violation of a federal law, the Mann Act. His life is the subject of a recent documentary film by Ken Burns "Unforgivable Blackness: The Rise and Fall of Jack Johnson."

Popular media reflected and in some cases helped the movement in the United States for racial equality. Films such as "Guess Who's Coming to Dinner?" (1967; see top right), which starred Sidney Poitier, presented the issue of interracial marriage, once a virtually taboo subject in mass media, in a humorous way. The opening of Hollywood for black movie stars ironically led to the decline of "race" films; a notable artistic and commercial industry of black writers, producers, directors, and actors which had resulted from segregation and discrimination.

Having stars like Sidney Poitier in leading roles side by side with white men and (once even more unthinkable) women have greatly enhanced the American movie industry.

Racially mixed gatherings and residential neighborhood integration continued to be unusual in the 1970s even after the many successes of the Civil Rights Movement. Organizations such as "National Neighbors" worked to bring groups together in successfully integrating neighborhoods. These and other efforts such as school integration led increasingly to scenes like that below of children as well as adults in Prospect-Lefferts-Gardens which was a National Neighbors member in the 70s.

Although It might seem that we have come a long way since the days when miscegenation was illegal, both interracial dating and interracial

as well as the Middle and Near East, also challenge the old racial categories as do the beautiful couple shown on this page below.

marriage continues to evoke hostility and, in too many cases, violence as well.

The US Census for the first time in 2000 included a "mixed race" category for self-identification which recognizes the sociological fact that race is subjective and negotiable, neither fixed nor permanent. Another sign of the times are interracial adoption websites such as http://interracial.adoption.com/Perhaps the strongest indication of the belated acceptance of interracial mixing in America today is the fact that some of the most celebrated idols of beauty and athletics could be called "Blended Americans." Finally, many of our newest immigrants and migrants to America are in one way or another "mixed," such as European-, Indigenous-, and African-blended Latinos. Actually, the United States Census Bureau has provided self-identified distinctions for "white" and "Nonwhite" Puerto Ricans. Other groups, such as those from South Asia

# PLURALISM

Sociological discussions of pluralism often begin with a consideration of the work of Horace Kallen. In articles published in the *Nation* magazine in 1915, Kallen argued that people should not have to surrender their culture and traditions to become full participants in American society. He rejected the Anglo-conformist, assimilationist model and contended that the existence of separate ethnic groups, even with separate cultures, religions, and languages, was consistent with democracy and other core American values. In Gordon's terms, Kallen believed that integration and equality were possible without extensive acculturation and that American society could be a federation of diverse groups, a mosaic of harmonious and interdependent cultures and peoples (Kallen, 1915a, 1915b; see also Abrahamson, 1980; Gleason, 1980).

Assimilation has been such a powerful theme in U.S. history that, in the decades following the publication of Kallen's analysis, support for pluralism remained somewhat marginalized. In more recent decades, however, interest in pluralism and ethnic diversity has increased, in part because the assimilation predicted by Park (and implicit in the conventional wisdom of many Americans) has not fully materialized. Perhaps we simply have not waited long enough, but as the 21st century begins, distinctions among the racial minority groups in our society show few signs of disappearing, and in fact, some members of these groups are questioning the very desirability of assimilation. Also, more surprising perhaps, is that white ethnicity maintains a stubborn persistence, although it continues to change in form and decrease in strength.

An additional reason for the growing interest in pluralism, no doubt, is the everyday reality of the increasing diversity of U.S. society, as reflected in Exhibit 1.1. Controversies over issues such as "English-only" policies, bilingual education, and welfare rights for immigrants are common and often bitter. Many Americans feel that diversity or pluralism has exceeded acceptable limits and that the unity of the nation is at risk (for example, visit http://www.us-english.org/, the home page of a group that advocates for English-only legislation).

Finally, interest in pluralism and ethnicity in general has been stimulated by developments around the globe. Several nation-states have disintegrated into smaller units based on language, culture, race, and ethnicity. Recent events in India, the Middle East, Eastern Europe, the former U.S.S.R., Canada, and Africa, just to mention a few, have provided dramatic and often tragic evidence of how ethnic identities and enmities can persist across decades or even centuries of submergence and suppression in larger national units.

In contemporary debates, discussions of diversity and pluralism are often couched in the language of **multiculturalism**, a general term for a variety of programs and ideas that stress mutual respect for all groups and for the multiple heritages that have shaped the United States. Some aspects of multiculturalism are controversial and have evoked strong opposition. In many ways, however, these debates merely echo a recurring argument about the character of American society, a debate which will be revisited throughout this text.

## Types of Pluralism

We can distinguish various types of pluralism by using some of the concepts introduced in the discussion of assimilation. **Cultural pluralism** exists when groups have not acculturated and each maintains its own identity. The groups might speak different languages, practice different religions, and have different value systems. The groups are part of the same society and might even live in adjacent areas, but in some ways, they live in different worlds. Many Native Americans are culturally pluralistic, maintaining their traditional languages and cultures and living on isolated reservations. The Amish, a religious community sometimes called the Pennsylvania Dutch, are also a culturally pluralistic group. They are committed to a way of life organized around farming, and they maintain a culture and an institutional life that is separate from the dominant culture (see Hostetler, 1980; Kephart & Zellner, 1994; Kraybill & Bowman, 2001).

Following Gordon's subprocesses, a second type of pluralism exists when a group has acculturated but not integrated. That is, the group has adopted the Anglo-American culture but does not have full and equal access to the institutions of the larger society. In this situation, called **structural pluralism**, cultural differences are minimal, but the groups occupy different locations in the social structure. The groups may speak with the same accent, eat the same food, pursue the same goals, and subscribe to the same values, but they may also maintain separate organizational systems, including different churches, clubs, schools, and neighborhoods. Under structural pluralism, the various groups practice a common culture but do so in different places and with minimal interaction across group boundaries. An example of structural pluralism can be found on any Sunday morning in the Christian churches of the United States. Not only are local parishes separated by denomination, they are also often identified with specific ethnic groups or races. What happens in the various churches—the rituals, the expressions of faith, the statements of core values and beliefs—is similar and expresses a common, shared culture. Structurally, however, this common culture is expressed in separate buildings and by separate congregations. Gordon's conclusion that U.S. society consisted of four separate melting pots, or subsocieties, differentiated by race, ethnicity, religion, and class illustrates one conception of structural pluralism.

A third type of pluralism reverses the order of Gordon's first two phases: integration without acculturation. This situation is exemplified by a group that has had some material success (measured by wealth or income, for example) but has not become Americanized (learned English, adopted American values and norms, etc.). Some immigrant groups have found niches in American society in which they can survive and occasionally prosper economically without acculturating very much.

Two different situations can be used to illustrate this pattern. An **enclave minority** establishes its own neighborhood and relies on a set of interconnected businesses, each of which is usually small in scope, for its economic survival. Some of these businesses serve the group, whereas others serve the larger society. The Cuban American community in South Florida and Chinatowns in many larger American cities are examples of ethnic enclaves. A similar pattern of adjustment, the **middleman minority**, also relies on small shops and retail firms, but the businesses are more dispersed throughout a large area rather than concentrated in a specific locale. Some Chinese American communities fit this second pattern, as do Korean American greengroceries and Indian American–owned motels (Portes & Manning, 1986). These types of minority groups are discussed further in Part IV.

The economic success of enclave and middleman minorities is partly due to the strong ties of cooperation and mutual aid within their groups. The ties are based, in turn, on cultural bonds that would weaken if acculturation took place. In contrast with Gordon's idea that acculturation is a prerequisite to integration, whatever success these groups enjoy is due in part to the fact that they have not Americanized. Kim Park, whom we met in the first chapter, is willing to work in his uncle's grocery store for room and board and the opportunity to learn the business. His willingness to forgo a salary and subordinate his individual needs to the needs of the group reflect the strength of his relationship to family and kin. At various times and places, Jewish,

Chinese, Japanese, Korean, and Cuban Americans have been enclaves or middleman minorities (see Bonacich & Modell, 1980; Kitano & Daniels, 2001).

The situation of enclave and middleman minorities, integration without acculturation, can be considered either a type of pluralism (emphasizing the absence of acculturation) or a type of assimilation (emphasizing a high level of economic equality). Keep in mind that assimilation and pluralism are not opposites but can occur in a variety of combinations. It is best to think of acculturation, integration, and the other stages of assimilation (or pluralism) as independent processes.

## THE TWILIGHT OF WHITE ETHNICITY?[1]

What lies ahead for white ethnic groups, the descendants of the 1820s-1920s immigration from Europe? We will explore this question further in chapter 12, but for now, we can use this question to introduce some additional useful concepts and bring our consideration of these groups to a close. The ongoing research on white ethnicity has sustained several opposed views of their future. Some researchers argue that white ethnic groups will persist; others find that, as functioning social entities, these groups are experiencing their last gasps.

The first viewpoint can be illustrated by two scholarly works. Sociologists Nathan Glazer and Daniel Moynihan argued, in the very influential work *Beyond the Melting Pot* (1970), that white ethnic groups retained a vital significance for their members despite massive acculturation over the decades. The authors based their conclusions on an analysis of both ethnic and racial minority groups in New York City and found that, although the groups changed form and function over time, they remained important social entities, valued by their members and showing no signs of disappearing. White ethnic groups in New York City helped to shape the self-image of their members and also provided a way to belong to the larger society. They linked members to one another through networks of mutual support and aid and served as a base of organization for political purposes and for relationships with other ethnic groups. Glazer and Moynihan concluded, "The point about the melting pot is that it did not happen" (p. 290).

A second important study of white ethnicity was conducted by sociologist Andrew Greeley (1974). He also found a great deal of evidence for the continuing existence and importance of white ethnic groups in American life. Greeley criticized the assumption that differences between groups would diminish over time in a simple, straightforward process of homogenization to the Anglo-American norm. He concluded that the sense of ethnicity or the strength of a person's identification with his or her ethnic group can vary from time to time and take on new dimensions. For example, Greeley used the term **ethnogenesis** to describe a process in which new minority groups can be formed from combinations of a variety of traditions, including Anglo-American traditions. He noted that, in the 1970s, there was "a deliberate and self-conscious attempt to *create* a 'Spanish speaking' ethnic group"; that "an American Indian group is *struggling to emerge*"; and that "in Chicago there is even an effort . . . to *create* an Appalachian white ethnic group" (Greeley, 1974, pp. 295-296, italics added). In all three examples, Greeley identifies situations in which single, unified, self-conscious groups could emerge in the future, even though they did not exist at the time he was writing. Greeley concludes that "ethnicity is not a residual social force that is slowly and gradually disappearing; it is, rather, a dynamic, flexible social mechanism that can be called into being rather quickly and transformed and transmuted to meet changing situations and circumstances" (1974, p. 301; see also Alba, 1990).

We should note that a process parallel to ethnogenesis can also occur with racial minority groups. Just as new ethnic groupings can emerge by combining different traditions, so can new "racial" groups arise from intermarriage. As I noted in chapter 1, people of mixed racial heritages will become increasingly more common in the future, and it is not inconceivable that new "racial" groups will form based on different combinations of ancestry and descent. Contrary to some theories of assimilation, increasing rates of intermarriage could lead to *more* minority groups, not fewer. The creation of racial groups independent of the traditional racial divisions based on skin color is also a striking illustration of the essentially social nature of race (see Chapter 1).

How long will the white ethnic identity documented by Glazer, Moynihan, and Greeley persist? Some analysts argue that white ethnic groups were particularly strong in the 1960s and 1970s (when Glazer, Moynihan and Greeley did their research) only as a reaction to the demands and claims advanced by African Americans and other peoples of color at that time. This point was argued, for example, by sociologist Steven Steinberg in his book *The Ethnic Myth* (1981). He contended that, by the 1960s and 1970s, white ethnicity had actually begun fading away and was temporarily revived only by the perceived need of white ethnic groups to defend their control of resources from the threats of racial minority groups. Steinberg predicted that white ethnicity would resume its slow decline after the tumultuous 1960s and 1970s and that the white ethnic groups would soon be fully assimilated.

More recently still, Gallagher (2001) reported a series of interviews that seem to confirm Steinberg's analysis. He interviewed 92 white ethnic respondents from all walks of life and found very little evidence or trace of ethnic identity. Only 13% of his respondents said that their ethnicity was an important part of their identity, a finding that supports Steinberg's 1981 prediction that ethnic identity would fade away. Gallagher also found—consistent with Steinberg's conclusions that ethnic identity can be a defensive reaction against the perceived threats of other groups—that his respondents often used their understanding of the struggles of their own ethnic ancestors as a device for criticizing and disparaging blacks and other racial minorities today. From the perspective of these respondents, their ancestors succeeded against odds just as formidable as those faced by African Americans today (a very dubious equation, as we shall see), and their (sometimes exaggerated) family tales of immigrant success were used as a rhetorical device for denigrating other groups: "My family came with nothing and succeeded, why can't blacks?"

What can we conclude? Clearly, white ethnic groups still played important roles in intergroup conflicts and remained viable and important social entities at least until late in the 20th century. Form and function changed, but new groupings appeared even as old ones declined in importance. Ethnic identity may have faded in importance, but it can still function as a rhetorical device for expressing disdain for other groups, especially African Americans. In the current era of multiculturalism and high rates of immigration, ethnicity is frequently celebrated, and people are encouraged to know and express their heritages. Pluralism is seen as sophisticated and progressive because it seems to be associated with increased tolerance for diversity and respect for all peoples and ways of life. Steinberg and Gallagher remind us that ethnicity can have a negative as well as a positive side: It may be the result of conflict and a disguise for expressing prejudice and denying opportunity to other groups.

# CONTEMPORARY IMMIGRANTS: SEGMENTED ASSIMILATION?

Recall that the theories of assimilation and pluralism presented to this point focus on European immigrants who arrived between the 1820s and 1920s and their descendants. Although their experiences were varied, all of the European groups eventually acculturated and integrated. Today, white ethnic groups are equal to national norms in terms of average income, education, unemployment, and other measures of economic success (see Chapter 12).

Are these experiences and the theoretical models based on them relevant for understanding more recent immigrants? How do the complex forces of American assimilation and pluralism shape the fate of these new arrivals (and their children)? Will contemporary immigrants simply duplicate the experiences of earlier groups? This may seem unlikely, given that present-day immigrants are much more diverse racially and culturally than immigrants from Europe and that they come (literally) from all over the globe. Also, consider that the United States today is a very different place from the society European immigrants confronted in the 19th and 20th centuries. Industrialization has advanced; relatively fewer of the blue-collar, manual labor jobs that sustained European immigrants are now available; economic inequality is greater; and social mobility is more difficult than in previous generations. (The changing context of U.S. society and its effects on dominant-minority relations will be discussed in detail in Chapters 5 and 6.)

Will these recent immigrant groups acculturate before they integrate? Will religion, social class, and race be important forces in their lives? Will they take as many as three (or more) generations to assimilate? What will their patterns of intermarriage look like? Will they achieve socioeconomic parity with the dominant group? When? How?

Sociologists and others are somewhat split in their answers to these questions. Some theorists believe that the "traditional" perspectives on assimilation do not apply and that the experiences of contemporary immigrant groups will differ greatly from those of European immigrants. They believe that assimilation today is fragmented or **segmented** and will have a number of different outcomes. Although some contemporary immigrant groups may integrate into the middle-class mainstream, others may find themselves permanently mired in the impoverished, alienated, and marginalized segments of racial minority groups. Still others may form close-knit enclaves based on their traditional cultures and become successful in the United States by resisting the forces of acculturation (Portes & Rumbaut, 2001, p. 45).

Other theorists believe that the traditional perspectives on assimilation are still relevant and that contemporary immigrant groups will follow the established pathways of mobility and assimilation. Of course, the process will be variable from group to group and place to place, but even the groups that are today the most impoverished and marginalized will, in time, move into mainstream society.

The debate over segmented assimilation is ongoing, and we will not resolve it in these pages. Rather, I will briefly summarize both points of view here, and we will return to the debate periodically in future chapters (especially in Chapters 9, 10, and 11).

**Segmented Assimilation.** This concept has been presented and developed in a series of research projects focused on a variety of new immigrant groups (Portes & Rumbaut, 2001; Portes & Zhou, 1993). According to these scholars, the key factors that shape the fate of the current immigrants—whether they will assimilate as groups have in the past or be stuck on the periphery of the larger society—include (a) the degree of racial discrimination and rejection directed at them, (b) the degree of cohesion and solidarity they maintain, (c) the resources or human capital they bring with them (e.g., wealth, education, business skills), and (d) the nature of the job market. For example, immigrants who are nonwhite, less educated, and unskilled (e.g., many Latino immigrants) will be forced by racial discrimination and by their relatively low levels of human capital into the lower class sectors of American society. On the other hand, immigrants who bring high levels of education (e.g., many Asians) will be able to penetrate the mainstream job market and achieve socioeconomic equality regardless of their race.

Exhibit 2.3 illustrates the impact of these forces for four new immigrant groups. The exhibit comes from a landmark study (Portes & Rumbaut, 2001) that focused on second-generation members of new immigrant groups in Florida and on the West Coast. The exhibit displays the profile of these groups in terms of the dimensions noted earlier: Data on education and poverty measure the human capital the groups bring with them, governmental and societal attitudes reflect the degree of discrimination and rejection that each group must face, and the nature of the "coethnic community" gives some information about the communities the groups have created in the United States. Using the concept of segmented assimilation, we would expect Mexicans and Laotians, who bring low levels of human capital, to find a generally hostile reception, and have poorer communities, to experience a less successful adjustment to the United States than Cubans and Filipinos, who bring higher levels of human capital and are received more favorably. In addition, Cuban Americans have formed an enclave based on small businesses ("entrepreneurial, concentrated"), and Filipinos are more residentially dispersed and tend to enter the job market in the upper middle class. Both of these patterns can speed the assimilation process.

Judging from these profiles, it might be reasonable to predict that Mexican and Laotian immigrants would have a more difficult adjustment and would be more likely to integrate into the urban poor and that Filipinos and Cubans would be more likely to follow the pathway of the European ethnic groups into the mainstream job market and middle class. If these predictions are borne out, they would support the idea that assimilation for immigrant groups today will be fragmented and variable.

**EXHIBIT 2.3**  Profiles of Foreign-Born Members of Four Groups

| Group | % College Graduates | % Living in Poverty | Governmental Attitude | Societal Attitude | Coethnic Community |
|-------|--------------------|--------------------|----------------------|-------------------|---------------------|
| Mexican | 3.5 | 29.7 | Hostile | Prejudiced | Working class, concentrated |
| Cuban | 15.6 | 14.7 | Favorable to hostile | Neutral to prejudiced | Entrepreneurial, concentrated |
| Filipino | 43.0 | 5.9 | Neutral | Neutral to prejudiced | Professional, dispersed |
| Laotian | 5.1 | 40.3 | Favorable | Prejudiced | Poor, concentrated |

SOURCE: Portes and Rumbaut (2001), pp. 50–51.

A further point made by the supporters of the segmented assimilation hypothesis is that U.S. society and American culture are more fragmented today. The traditional perspective on assimilation assumes a "two-group" model: immigrant groups, on one hand, and middle-class, white, mainstream society and culture, on the other. Today, new groups can assimilate with each other into one of the varieties of African American subcultures or into any number of other niches and spaces in American society (Alba & Nee, 1997, p. 828). Thus the notion of the triple melting pot (already expanded to four melting pots by Gordon in the 1960s) might have to be expanded many times over to accommodate the variety of ethnic and racial intermixing in contemporary society.

**Assimilation.** Other analysts argue that contemporary immigrant groups are following the familiar pathways carved out by the earlier wave of immigration. They are acculturating first and following generational patterns of adjustment. Class continues to play a key role in the fate of these groups, and there are sharp differences—today as there were 100 years ago—in the experiences of groups composed mostly of unskilled laborers and those that bring larger amounts of human capital.

These patterns can be illustrated by several recent studies. Exhibit 2.4, for example, illustrates some patterns of acculturation for Latino Americans today. By the third generation, Spanish disappears as the primary home language, and cultural values closely approximate those of the dominant group.

Exhibit 2.5 shows the pattern of language acculturation for children and grandchildren of immigrants. The subjects were 5 through 16 years old and classified as second generation if at least one of their parents was foreign born and third generation if both parents were born in the United States. The "mother-tongue" third-generation children were those who had at least one parent who spoke a language other than English at home, even though both parents were born in the United States. If the "traditional" patterns of language acculturation applied to contemporary immigrant groups, we would expect the percentage that speaks only English at home would increase sharply from the second to the third generation, with the "mother-tongue" third generation intermediate. Although there is some variability in the patterns displayed in Exhibit 2.5, the overall drift is unmistakably consistent with traditional assimilation theory.

How will the debate be resolved? We cannot say at the moment, but we can point out that this debate is reminiscent of the critique of Park's theory of assimilation. In both cases, the argument is partly about time: Even if assimilation seems to be segmented at present, the affected groups may find their way into the economic mainstream eventually, at some unspecified time in the future. There are also other levels of meaning in the debate, however, related to one's perception of the nature of modern U.S. society. Is U.S. society today growing more tolerant of diversity, more open and equal? If so, this would seem to favor the traditionalists. If not, this trend would clearly favor those who argue for the segmented assimilation hypothesis. Although we will not resolve this argument in this text, we will return to it on a number of occasions in future chapters.

## OTHER GROUP GOALS

Although this book concentrates on assimilation and pluralism, there are, of course, other possible group relationships and goals. Two commonly noted minority group goals

**EXHIBIT 2.4** Latino Acculturation (%)

LANGUAGE

| | What language do you usually speak at home? | | |
|---|---|---|---|
| | Only/More Spanish | Both Equally | Only/More English |
| First generation | 73 | 20 | 6 |
| Second generation | 17 | 43 | 40 |
| Third generation | 1 | 21 | 78 |

| | In what language are the TV programs you usually watch? | | |
|---|---|---|---|
| | Only/More Spanish | Both Equally | Only/More English |
| First generation | 31 | 42 | 27 |
| Second generation | 5 | 26 | 68 |
| Third generation | 1 | 11 | 88 |

FAMILY VALUES

| | Is it better for children to live in their parent's home until they get married? (Percentage of those answering yes) |
|---|---|
| First generation | 87 |
| Second generation | 62 |
| Third generation | 46 |
| Non-Latinos | 42 |

| | In general, the husband should have the final say in family matters. (Percentage of those who agreed) |
|---|---|
| First generation | 46 |
| Second generation | 27 |
| Third generation | 24 |
| Non-Latinos | 26 |

SOURCE: Godstein and Suro (2000), p. A1.

NOTE: These results are from a telephone survey of about 2400 Latinos and 2000 non-Latino adults conducted in the summer of 1999. Projections to the population are accurate to within ±2 percentage points.

are **separatism** and **revolution** (Wirth, 1945). The goal of separatism is for the group to sever all ties (political, cultural, and geographic) with the larger society. Thus separatism goes well beyond pluralism. Native Americans have expressed both separatist and pluralist goals, and separatism has also been pursued by some African American organizations, such as the Black Muslims.

A minority group promoting revolution seeks to switch places with the dominant group and become the ruling elite or create a new social order, perhaps in alliance with members of the dominant group. Although revolutionary activity can be found among some American minority groups (e.g., the Black Panthers), this goal has been relatively rare for minority groups in the United States. Revolutionary minority groups are more commonly found in situations

EXHIBIT 2.5   Percentage That Speaks Only English at Home, by Generation

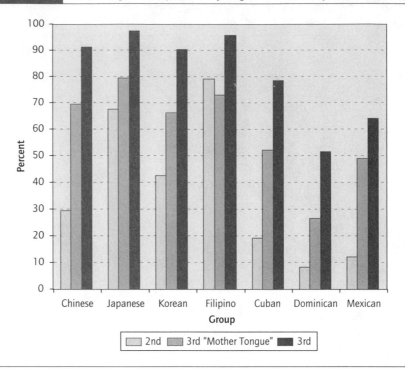

SOURCE: Alba, Logan, Lutz, and Stultz (2002), p. 472.

such as those in colonial Africa, in which one nation conquered and controlled another racially or culturally different nation.

The dominant group may also pursue goals other than assimilation and pluralism, including forced migration or expulsion, extermination or genocide, and continued subjugation of the minority group. Chinese immigrants were the victims of a policy of expulsion, beginning in the 1880s (see Chapter 10). Native Americans have also been the victims of expulsion. In 1830, all tribes living east of the Mississippi were forced to migrate to a new territory in the West. The most infamous example of genocide is the Holocaust in Nazi Germany, during which 6 million Jews were murdered. The dominant group pursues "continued subjugation" when, as with slavery in the antebellum South, it attempts to simply maintain the status quo. A dominant group may simultaneously pursue different policies with different minority groups and may, of course, change policies over time.

## IMPLICATIONS FOR EXAMINING DOMINANT-MINORITY RELATIONS

Chapters 1 and 2 have introduced many of the terms, concepts, and themes that form the core of the rest of this text. Although the connections between the concepts are not simple, some key points can be made to summarize these chapters and anticipate the material to come.

### Assimilation, Then and Now

*Mario Puzo and Luis Rodriguez are both sons of immigrants, but they grew up in two very different Americas. Puzo, best known as the author of* The Godfather, *grew up in the Italian American community, and his memoir of life in New York City in the 1930s illustrates some of the patterns that are at the root of Gordon's theory of assimilation. Writing in the 1970s, Puzo remembers the days of his boyhood and his certainty that he would escape the poverty that surrounded him. Note also his view of (and gratitude for) an America that gave people (or at least white people) the opportunity to rise above the circumstances of their birth.*

*Rodriguez paints a rather different picture of U.S society. He grew up in the Los Angeles area in the 1950s and 1960s and was a veteran of gang warfare by the time he reached high school. His memoir,* Always Running: La Vida Loca *(1993), illustrates the realities of segmented assimilation for contemporary immigrants. In this extract, he describes how his high school prepared Mexican American students for life. Contrast his despair with Puzo's gratitude. Which sector of American society is Rodriguez being prepared to enter? In Rodriguez's experience, is assimilation segmented?*

### CHOOSING A DREAM: ITALIANS IN HELL'S KITCHEN

**Mario Puzo**

In the summertime, I was one of the great Tenth Avenue athletes, but in the wintertime I became a sissy. I read books. At a very early age I discovered libraries. . . . My mother always looked at all this reading with a fishy Latin eye. She saw no profit in it, but since all her children were great readers, she was a good enough general to know she could not fight so pervasive an insubordination. And there may have been some envy. If she had been able to, she would have been the greatest reader of all.

My direct ancestors for a thousand years have most probably been illiterate. Italy, the golden land, . . . so majestic in its language and cultural treasures . . . has never cared for its poor people. My father and mother were both illiterates. Both grew up on rocky, hilly farms in the countryside adjoining Naples. . . . My mother was told that the family could not afford the traditional family gift of linens when she married, and it was this that decided her to emigrate to America. . . . My mother never heard of Michelangelo; the great deeds of the Caesars had not reached her ears. She never heard the great music of her native land. She could not sign her name.

And so it was hard for my mother to believe that her son could become an artist. After all, her one dream in coming to America had been to earn her daily bread, a wild dream in itself. And looking back, she was dead right. Her son an artist? To this day she shakes her head. I shake mine with her.

America may be a Fascistic, warmongering, racially prejudiced country today. It may deserve the hatred of its revolutionary young. But what a miracle it once was!

What has happened here has never happened in any other country in any other time. The poor, who have been poor for centuries . . . whose children had inherited their poverty, their illiteracy, their hopelessness, achieved some economic dignity and freedom. You didn't get it for nothing, you had to pay a price in tears, in suffering, but why not? And some even became artists.

SOURCE: Puzo, Mario. 1993. "Choosing a Dream: Italians in Hell's Kitchen." In W. Brown & A. Ling (Eds.), *Visions of America*. New York: Persea. Pp. 56-57.

## Always Running: La Vida Loca

**Luis Rodriguez**

Mark Keppel High School was a Depression-era structure with a brick and art deco facade and small, army-type bungalows in the back. Friction filled its hallways. The Anglo and Asian upper-class students from Monterey Park and Alhambra attended the school. They were tracked into the "A" classes; they were in the school clubs; they were the varsity team members and lettermen. They were the pep squad and cheerleaders.

But the school also took in the people from the Hills and surrounding community who somehow made it past junior high. They were mostly Mexican, in the "C" track (what were called the "stupid" classes). Only a few of these students participated in school government, in sports, or in the various clubs.

The school had two principal languages. Two skin tones and two cultures. It revolved around class differences. The white and Asian kids . . . were from professional, two-car households with watered lawns and trimmed trees. The laboring class, the sons and daughters of service workers, janitors, and factory hands lived in and around the Hills (or a section of Monterey Park called "Poor Side").

The school separated these two groups by levels of education: The professional-class kids were provided with college-preparatory classes; the blue-collar students were pushed into "industrial arts." . . .

If you came from the Hills, you were labeled from the start. I'd walk into the counselor's office and looks of disdain greeted me—one meant for a criminal, alien, to be feared. Already a thug. It was harder to defy this expectation than just accept it and fall into the trappings. It was a jacket I could try to take off, but they kept putting it back on. The first hint of trouble and the preconceptions proved true. So why not be an outlaw? Why not make it our own?

SOURCE: Rodriguez, Luis. 1993. *Always Running: La Vida Loca*. New York: Touchstone Books. Pp. 83-84.

First, minority group status has much more to do with power and the distribution of resources than with simple numbers or the percentage of the population in any particular category. We saw this notion expressed in chapter 1 in the definition of *minority group* and in our exploration of inequality. The themes of inequality and differentials in status were also covered in our discussion of prejudice, racism, and discrimination. To understand minority relations, we must examine some very basic realities of human society: inequalities in wealth, prestige, and the distribution of power. To discuss changes in minority group status, we must be prepared to discuss changes in the way society does business, makes decisions, and distributes income, jobs, health care, and opportunity.

A second area that we will focus on in the rest of the book is the question of how our society should develop. Assimilation and pluralism, with all their variations, define two broad directions. Each has been extensively examined and discussed by social scientists, by leaders and decision makers in American society, and by ordinary people from all groups and walks of life. The analysis and evaluation of these two broad directions is a thread running throughout this book.

## Immigration, Emigration, and Ireland

Immigrating and adjusting to a new society are among the most wrenching, exciting, disconcerting, exhilarating, and heartbreaking of human experiences. Immigrants have recorded these feelings, along with the adventures and experiences that sparked them, in every possible media, including letters, memoirs, poems, photos, stories, movies, jokes, and music. These immigrant tales recount the traumas of leaving home, dealing with a new language and customs, coping with rejection and discrimination, and thousands of other experiences. The most poignant of these stories express the sadness of parting from family and friends, perhaps forever.

Peter Jones captured some of these feelings in his song *Kilkelly,* based on letters written nearly 150 years earlier by an Irish father to his immigrant son—Jones's great-grandfather—in the United States. Each verse of the song paraphrases a letter and includes news of the family and community left behind and also expresses, in simple but powerful language, the deep sadness of separation and the longing for reunion:

Kilkelly, Ireland, 18 and 90, my dear and loving son John

I guess that I must be close on to eighty, it's thirty years since you're gone.

Because of all of the money you send me, I'm still living out on my own.

Michael has built himself a fine house and Brigid's daughters have grown.

Thank you for sending your family picture, they're lovely young women and men.

You say that you might even come for a visit, what joy to see you again.[2]

It is particularly appropriate to use an Irish song to illustrate the sorrows of immigration. Just as the United States has been a major receiver of immigrants for the last 200 years, Ireland has been

a major supplier. Mass immigration from Ireland began with the potato famines of the 1840s and continued through the end of the 20th century, motivated by continuing hard times, political unrest, and unemployment. The sadness of Peter Jones's ancestors was repeated over and over as the youth of Ireland left for jobs in Great Britain, the United States, and hundreds of other places, never expecting to return. This mass immigration cut the 1840 Irish population of 7 million in half, and today, the population is still less than 4 million.

History rarely runs in straight lines, however. Today, after nearly 200 years of supplying immigrants, Ireland (along with other nations of Northern and Western Europe) has become a consumer. As illustrated in Exhibit 2.6, the number of newcomers entering Ireland more than doubled between 1987 and 2002, to almost 50,000, and the number of people leaving decreased dramatically, to less than 20,000. These numbers are miniscule compared to the volume of immigrants received by the United States each year. Proportionally speaking, however, immigration to Ireland is actually greater than immigration to the United States. Ireland receives almost 5 immigrants per 1000 population; the United States receives only 3.4 immigrants per 1000 population (CIA, 2004).

What explains the switch from *out*migration to *in*migration? The answers are not hard to find. After decades of unemployment and depression, the Irish economy entered a boom phase in the early 1990s. Spurred by investments from multinational corporations and the benefits of joining the European Economic Union, the Irish economy and the job supply have grown rapidly. The unemployment rate was less than 5% in 2003 (CIA, 2004), and there is some concern that there actually may be more jobs than workers at some point in the future ("A Sorry Tale," 2000). Irish nationals who left Ireland to find work are now returning in large numbers, and people from Europe and other parts of the globe are also arriving. In addition, Ireland is receiving refugees and people seeking asylum. In 2002, for example, roughly 38% of immigrants were of Irish origin, 25% were from the United Kingdom or other nations of the European Union, and 35%

**EXHIBIT 2.6** Patterns of Immigration and Emigration: Ireland, 1987-2002

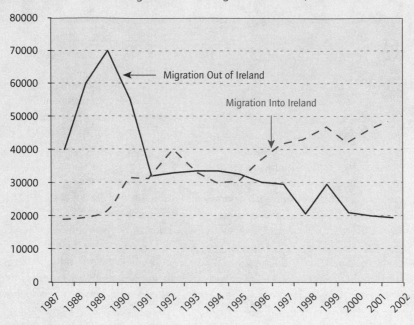

SOURCE: O'Sullivan (2003).

were from "the rest of the world," a category that includes the former Yugoslavia, the Middle East, Nigeria, and various "trouble spots" around the globe (O'Sullivan, 2003).

What awaits these newcomers when they arrive on the Emerald Isle? Will they be subjected to the Irish version of "Anglo-conformity"? Will Irish society become a melting pot? Will Gordon's ideas about assimilation be applicable to their experiences? Will their assimilation be segmented? Will the Irish, such immigrants themselves, be especially understanding and sympathetic to the traumas faced by the newcomers?

Although many Irish are very sympathetic to the immigrants and refugees, others have responded with racist sentiments and demands for exclusion, reactions that ironically echo the rejection Irish immigrants to the United States experienced in the 19th century (for example, job advertisements that included the stipulation "No Irish Need Apply"). Irish radio and TV talk shows commonly discuss issues of immigration and assimilation and frequently evoke prejudiced statements from the audience. There are also reports of rising racism and rejection: "The resentment at the browning of Ireland has manifested itself in increasing numbers of racist attacks, and . . . a poll conducted by the Dublin Sunday Independent in 1999 revealed that

78 per cent of the Irish public want quotas on immigration" (West, 2002, p. 21).

The rejection of non-Irish newcomers was also manifested in the passage of the "Citizenship Amendment" to the Irish constitution, which was overwhelmingly supported (80% in favor) by the Irish electorate in June 2004. Prior to the passage of the amendment, any baby born in Ireland had the right to claim Irish citizenship. The amendment denied the right of citizenship to any baby that did not have at least one Irish parent and was widely interpreted as a hostile rejection of immigrants (see Fanning, 2003).

Like the United States, Ireland finds itself dealing with diversity and debating what kind of society it should become. It is too early to tell whether the Irish experience will parallel the American or whether the sociological concepts presented in this chapter will prove useful in analyzing the Irish immigrant experience. We can be sure, however, that the experience of the immigrants in Ireland will be laced with plentiful doses of the loneliness and longing experienced by Peter Jones's ancestors. Times have changed, but today's immigrants will yearn for Abuja, Riga, or Baku with the same melancholy experienced by previous waves of immigrants yearning for Kilkelly, Dublin, or Galway. Who knows what songs and poems will come from this?

## English Only?

*What role should learning English take in the process of adjusting to the United States? Should English language proficiency be a prerequisite for full inclusion in the society? Should English be made the official language of the nation? Does the present multiplicity of languages represent a danger for social cohesion and unity? Following are two reactions to these questions.*

*The first excerpt is from Mauro Mujica, the chairman of U.S. English, Inc. (http://www.us-english.org/inc/), an immigrant himself and a passionate advocate for the unifying power of a single national language. His organization opposes efforts to recognize Spanish as an official second language (in part because of the expense and confusion that would ensue if all government documents, election ballots, street signs, etc. were published in both English and Spanish) and most forms of bilingual education. He is particularly concerned with stressing that the primary beneficiaries of learning English will be the immigrants.*

*An opposing point of view is presented by Hurtado and Vega, both professors of psychology. They argue that "English only" is a thinly disguised attack on Latinos and that there are multiple benefits to be gained, on a number of levels, from encouraging bilingualism.*

## English Only Will Speed the Assimilation of Immigrants

**MAURO MUJICA**

[During my 11 years as chairman] of U.S. ENGLISH . . . I have encountered many myths about official English legislation. . . . A few of these myths were recently repeated in an opinion piece in the Contra Costa Times. [The author] . . . writes,

" . . . the anti-bilingual education movement and the English-only movement could easily be labeled an anti-Spanish movement."

In that one sentence, [the author] repeats two of the most ridiculous myths about official English. There are other distortions as well. These will likely come up as Congress debates HR 997, the English Language Unity Act of 2003, which would make English the official language of the United States. . . .

Here are five of the most common myths about official English and the realities behind them.

*Myth No. 1: Official English Is Anti-Immigrant.* Declaring English the official language benefits all Americans, but it benefits immigrants most of all. Immigrants who speak English earn more money, do better in school and have more career options than those who do not.

As an immigrant from Chile, I can testify that English proficiency is the most important gift we can give to newcomers. In fact, polls show that 70% of Hispanics and 85% of all immigrants support making English the official language of the United States. Learning English is the key to assimilating into the mainstream of American society. That is why our organization, U.S. ENGLISH, Inc., advocates for English immersion classes for immigrant students and adults.

*Myth No. 2: Official English Is "English Only."* Many far-left opponents of official English, such as the ACLU, refer to our legislation as "English Only." Official English simply requires that government conduct its business in English. It does not dictate what language must be spoken in the home, during conversation, cultural celebrations or religious ceremonies. It does not prohibit the teaching of foreign languages. It does not affect private businesses or the services offered by them. In addition, HR 997 makes exceptions for emergency situations.

*Myth No. 3: Today's Immigrants Are Learning English Just Like the Immigrants of Old.*

The United States has a rapidly growing population of people—often native born—who are not proficient in English. The 2000 Census found that 21.3 million Americans (8% of the population) are classified as "limited English proficient," a 52% increase from 1990, and more than double the 1980 total. More than 5.6 million of these people were born in the United States. In states like California, 20% of the population is not proficient in English.

The Census also reports that 4.5 million American households are linguistically isolated, meaning that no one in the household older than age 14 can speak English. These numbers indicate that the American assimilation process is broken. If not fixed, we will see our own "American Quebec" in the Southwestern United States and perhaps other areas of the country.

*Myth No. 4: The Founding Fathers Rejected Making English the Official Language.* English has been the language of our nation from its earliest days. In 1789, 90% of our nation's non-slave inhabitants were of English descent. Any notion that they would have chosen another language or used precious resources on printing documents in multiple languages lacks common sense.

The issue of an official language was never discussed at the Constitutional Convention as the topic was not controversial enough to be debated. Even the Dutch colonies had been under English rule for more than a century. Contrary to popular belief, Congress never voted on a proposal to make German the official language. This myth is probably based on a 1794 bill to translate some documents into German (it was defeated).

*Myth No. 5: In a Global Culture, an Official Language Is Anachronistic.* Ninety-two percent of the world's countries (178 of 193) have at least one official language. English is the sole official language in 31 nations and has an official status in 20 other nations, including India, Singapore, the Philippines, Samoa and Nigeria.

There has never been a language so widely spread in so short a time as English. It is the lingua franca of the modern world as much as Latin was the common tongue of the Roman Empire. Roughly one quarter of the world's population is already fluent or competent in English and this number grows by the day.

English is the global language of business, communications, higher education, diplomacy, aviation, the Internet, science, popular music, entertainment and international travel. Immigrants who don't know English not only lose out in the American economy, but also in the global economy.

These are just some of the myths that must be corrected if we are to have a debate on a coherent language policy. This policy should be built on fact, not myth. Multilingual government is a disaster for American unity and results in billions of dollars in unnecessary government spending. We need only to look at Canada to see the problems that multilingualism can bring. HR 997 could be our last best chance to stop this process and we cannot let distortions about official English sidetrack this legislation.

SOURCE: Mujica, Mauro. 2003. "Official English Legislation: Myths and Realities." *Human Events*, 59: 24.

## Bilingualism Should Be Encouraged[3]

### AIDA HURTADO AND LUIS A. VEGA

Brown vs. the Board of Education of Topeka Kansas (1954) was the beginning of dismantling inequalities in education. As progress was made, . . . other indicators of group membership were examined to uncover their use in justifying blocked educational opportunity. Ethnicity, culture, language, and gender all began to be conceptualized as part of the social constellation used to justify certain groups not having the same educational access as others. For Latinos, . . . the Spanish language is a salient marker of their ethnic group membership. The use of Spanish, especially in an educational system that privileges the use of English . . . has been consistently used to justify repressive practices against its use, to assign Spanish-speaking children to special education regardless of intellectual abilities, and as an explanation for Latinos' lack of educational achievement and attainment.

The use of Spanish by Latinos in the United States has been identified as a social problem leading to increased economic and social isolation. Recent social policies, therefore, have focused on . . . limiting bilingual programs . . . efforts to make English the official language of the United States, and English-only local laws. Efforts to limit the use of Spanish in public life have impacted public translation services in courts and in voting ballots, further stigmatizing entire communities for the use of their ethnic groups' language. At the same time, multicultural diversity has increased in this country and economic and social globalization demands an increase in bilingual and multilingual citizens who can lead, work with, and manage a diverse workforce. . . . The Latino population is now the largest minority group . . . [and their] educational achievement continues to lag behind all other ethnic and racial groups. . . . The use of Spanish and transition into English become an important topic to achieve the goal of educational equity.

*Studies on Spanish to English Shift.* Spanish to English shift refers to the transition from Spanish monolingualism, to English monolingualism, with bilingualism defining this continuum. . . . Several researchers posit that situational pressures have the most important influence on the pace at which language shift occurs. For example, . . . a survey about language use among high school students of Mexican descent . . . found an equal level of Spanish proficiency in first-generation (immigrant) and second-generation (children born in the United States of Mexican parents) students. These findings are surprising considering that a rapid language shift occurs from Spanish to English in both first and second generations.

However, [an important reason for this is that] . . . Spanish serves an important social function for Spanish speakers—while English facilitates communication in most public settings, Spanish facilitates it in the intimate settings of home and community. Consequently, situational pressures come into play when most Latinos find occasions when Spanish is the preferred language . . .

An analysis of language maintenance [shows that] . . . as shift in language happens from Spanish to English and from one generation to the next, different levels of language use occur within the home, allowing exposure of Spanish to children, and exposure of English to parents. . . . These different levels or degrees of language use we have labeled "linguistic bands." . . .

It is the presence of linguistic bands that facilitate communication across different sociolinguistic domains. For example, parents . . . who speak predominantly Spanish represent one linguistic band within the family . . . their children who speak mostly English represent another. [The] different linguistic bands in the home environment . . . allow for learning to take place across bands, resulting in . . . varying degrees of English/Spanish bilingualism by all members of the household. . . . Bilingualism occurs when predominantly Spanish-speaking parents understand English, and when predominantly English-speaking children understand Spanish. [This will allow] Spanish to flourish in the future given an appropriate context. . . .

Shift happens, shift is inevitable. This study shows that language transition from Spanish to English among Mexican descendants is most pronounced inter-generationally. That is, succeeding generations of Mexicans continue the shift to English monolingualism, and while it might be expected that Spanish language loss is the price to pay, such is not the case, for the knowledge of the Spanish language remains viable through different degrees of bilingualism. This is made possible through linguistic bands, which allow for exposure of Spanish and English to speakers of only one language. . . . the use of Spanish or English at no time becomes mutually exclusive . . . Our findings suggest that Spanish will not disappear but instead, it will [survive] through different degrees of bilingualism. . . . Hence, given the appropriate contexts, Spanish will flourish and remain a viable language. . . .

*Policy Recommendations.* Cultural and linguistic assimilation consistently has been recommended . . . as the solution to Latinos' lack of full educational and economic integration. However, recent demographic changes and the globalization of the U. S. economy require that all citizens become adept at functioning in multiple cultural settings. Our results indicate that many Latinos begin life with an invaluable language resource that could be cultivated, rather than repressed or neglected, and that could blossom into full-scale bilingualism. In fact, . . . youth [from various groups] who are bilingual are less likely to drop out of school than those in English-dominant or English-limited households. [Various studies suggest that] it is not the most acculturated but rather those who have not abandoned their ethnic cultures that experience the greatest educational success. It is bicultural youths who can draw on resources from both the immigrant community and mainstream society who are best situated to enjoy educational success. Similarly, . . . second generation students who became fluent bilinguals report better relations with their families, greater self-esteem, and higher educational aspirations than those who became English monolinguals. . . .

Many states have dismantled long-term bilingual education and have opted for transitioning Limited Proficiency Students as quickly as possible into English by disregarding the cultivation of their ethnic language. A more sensible strategy would be . . . to cultivate the children's [bilingual] skills. . . . There is beginning to be evidence that this approach may facilitate the initial goals set forth by Brown vs. the Board of Education of Topeka Kansas (1954),

insuring the full educational and economic integration of all children regardless of race, ethnicity, language, and gender.

SOURCE: Hurtado, Aida, & Vega, Luis A. 2004. "Shift happens: Spanish and English Transmission Between Parents and Their Children." *Journal of Social Issues,* 60(1): 137-155.

## Debate Questions to Consider

1. What assumptions are these authors making about the role of language in the process of assimilation? Can a group adjust successfully to U.S. society without learning English? What stage of Gordon's model of assimilation are they discussing?

2. What reaction might other groups (recent immigrants, African Americans, Native Americans, white ethnics) have to making Spanish an official second language? What stake would they have in this policy issue?

3. As you think about the issue of bilingualism and multilingualism, see if you can identify some social class aspects. Which economic classes would benefit from an English-only policy? Which economic classes are hurt? How? Why?

4. Mujica argues that English is a global language and that non-English speakers are handicapped not only in the United States but in the global economy. Hurtado and Vega argue that bilingualism and biculturalism are important resources for success in the world and that the United States would greatly benefit from having more people who could truly function in multicultural settings. Who is right? Does the emerging global economy demand fluent English or fluency in multiple languages?

5. Should Spanish be made an official second language? Would this threaten societal unity (as Mujica argues), or would it empower currently excluded Spanish speakers (as Hurtado and Vega argue)?

# MAIN POINTS

- Assimilation and pluralism are two broad pathways of development for intergroup relations. Assimilation and pluralism are in some ways contrary processes but may appear together in a variety of combinations.

- Two types of assimilation are the melting pot and Anglo-conformity. The latter has historically been the dominant value in the United States.

- Gordon theorized that assimilation occurs through a series of stages, with integration being the crucial stage. In his view, it is common for American minority groups, especially racial minority groups, to be acculturated but not integrated. Once a group has begun to integrate, all other stages will follow in order.

- In the past few decades, there has been increased interest in pluralism. There are three types of pluralistic situations: cultural, or full, pluralism; structural pluralism; and enclave, or middleman, minority groups.

- According to many scholars, white ethnic groups survived decades of assimilation, albeit in altered forms. New ethnic (and racial) minority groups continue to appear, and old ones change form and function as society changes. At the dawn of the 21st century, however, white ethnicity may well be fading in salience for most people, except perhaps as a context for criticizing other groups.

- In the United States today, assimilation may be segmented and have outcomes other than equality with and acceptance into the middle class.

- Several opportunities for extending the concepts and issues discussed in this chapter are presented in the public sociology assignments included in the Introduction to Part I. If you choose to do research in your local schools, for example, you will find that the schools are grappling with issues of immigration, assimilation, language diversity, Americanization, and pluralism every day. If you choose to investigate one of your local soup kitchens, it is extremely likely that you will find recent immigrants among the clientele, people, and families wrestling, at a very personal level, with barriers created by language differences, low levels of human capital, discrimination, and racism, and a host of other problems discussed in this chapter.

## Study Site on the Web

Don't forget the interactive quizzes and other resources and learning aids at www.www.pineforge.com/healeystudy4.

## For Further Reading

Alba, Richard. 1990. *Ethnic Identity: The Transformation of White America*. New Haven, CT: Yale University Press. *(A useful analysis of the changing meanings of ethnic identity for the descendants of European immigrants.)*

Herberg, Will. 1960. *Protestant-Catholic-Jew: An Essay in American Religious Sociology*. New York: Anchor.

Gordon, Milton. 1964. *Assimilation in American Life*. New York: Oxford University Press. *(Two classic works of scholarship on assimilation, religion, and white ethnic groups.)*

Zhou, Min, & Bankston, Carl. 1998. *Growing Up American: How Vietnamese Children Adapt to Life in the United States*. New York: Russell Sage.

Portes, Alejandro, & Rumbaut, Richard. 2001. *Legacies: The Story of the Immigrant Second Generation.* Berkeley: University of California Press.

Portes, Alejandro, & Rumbaut, Richard. 2001. *Ethnicities: Children of Immigrants in America.* New York: Russell Sage Foundation. *(Three outstanding works analyzing the new immigrants and the concept of segmented assimilation.)*

Alba, Richard, and Nee, Victor. 2003. *Remaking the American Mainstream: Assimilation and Contemporary Immigration.* Cambridge, MA: Harvard University Press.

Bean, Frank, and Stevens, Gillian. 2003. *America's Newcomers and the Dynamics of Diversity*. New York: Russell Sage. *(Two outstanding recent works that argue that the "traditional" model of assimilation remains viable.)*

## Questions for Review and Study

1. Summarize Gordon's model of assimilation. Identify and explain each stage and how the stages are linked together. Explain Exhibits 2.2 and 2.4 in terms of Gordon's model.

2. "Human capital theory is not so much wrong as it is incomplete." Explain this statement. What does the theory leave out? What questionable assumptions does it make?

3. What are the major dimensions along which the experience of assimilation varies? Explain how and why the experience of assimilation can vary.

4. Define pluralism and explain the ways in which it differs from assimilation. Why has interest in pluralism increased? Explain the difference between and cite examples of structural and cultural pluralism. Describe enclave minority groups in terms of pluralism and in terms of Gordon's model of assimilation. How have contemporary theorists added to the concept of pluralism?

5. Define and explain *segmented assimilation* and explain how it differs from Gordon's model. What evidence is there that assimilation for recent immigrants is not segmented? What is the significance of this debate for the future of U.S. society? For other minority groups (e.g., African Americans)? For the immigrants themselves?

6. Do American theories and understandings of assimilation apply to the case of Ireland?

## Internet Research Project

Update and supplement the debate on language and assimilation presented at the end of the chapter. You might begin with the newspaper Web sites listed in the Appendix and search for relevant items within them or perhaps do a general search on the Internet itself, using key terms such as "English first" or "language diversity." Search for a variety of opinions and, to the extent that they are relevant, analyze the data you find in terms of Gordon's model of assimilation and the concepts of Americanization, the melting pot, acculturation, integration, pluralism, and human capital theory.

**Notes**

1. This phrase comes from Alba (1990).
2. Copyright © Green Linnet Music 1983. Used with permission.
3. To conserve space, references and footnotes have been omitted.

# PART II

## Understanding
## Prejudice and Discrimination

**Chapter 3**
Prejudice and
Discrimination in the Individual

**Chapter 4**
Societal Trends in
Prejudice and Discrimination

What causes prejudice? What are the relationships between prejudice and discrimination? Are there different types of prejudice? Who gains from prejudice? How? Can prejudice be reduced? Can it be eliminated?

These are some of the questions explored in Part II. Individual prejudice is a crucial component of dominant-minority relationships. It helps to sustain the disadvantage of minority groups over time, and shapes, or even controls, the way members of different groups think about one another. No exploration of dominant-minority relations would be complete without an understanding of the causes and functions of prejudice.

Part I was concerned primarily with introducing concepts and with the overall relationships between groups. In chapters 3 and 4, the level of our analysis shifts toward the individual or psychological level. Nonetheless, many of the sociological themes and ideas that will occupy our attention in the remainder of this text will continue to guide our inquiry. For example, we will see that social class, intergroup competition, and power all affect prejudice.

## ABOUT THE PUBLIC SOCIOLOGY ASSIGNMENTS

The public sociology assignments in this section connect students to both exponents and victims of prejudice and discrimination. The first assignment is focused on hate groups. Although they are largely on the fringes of mainstream society, these groups are vivid reminders of the persistence of racism in our society. An overview of these groups is presented at the end of Chapter 4. The second assignment focuses on one of the many targets of hate groups (and the casual rejection of everyday Americans throughout society): recent immigrants in general and Arab Americans in particular. Prejudice and discrimination against these groups is covered in a number of places in Chapters 3 and 4, including the sections on the scapegoat hypothesis and social distance scales in Chapter 3 and the section on hate crimes in Chapter 4.

# Public Sociology Assignments
*Marcus Griffin*

## Assignment 1
### Local Hate Groups

The United States is marred by a history of hate. Unfortunately, this hatred is not a thing of the past. In this assignment, you will work for the local chapter of the NAACP or Anti-Discrimination League or some other people's advocacy group by providing them with background research on hate groups within the area. These hate groups include those using such labels as Black Separatist, Neo-Nazi, Racist Skinhead, Ku Klux Klan, and Neo-Confederate. Research on these and other groups may benefit the organization by providing their personnel and clients with quick "hot sheets" that can be referred to when problems arise or when considering who might be disruptive during an advocacy event.

### Step 1

Contact the local chapter of the NAACP, Anti-Discrimination League, or other people's advocacy group. Discuss with their representative the assignment you would like to conduct and explore how it may serve their needs.

### Step 2

Review the organization's records of any hate groups they have previous experience with and write descriptive summaries of each, including political orientation, hate ideology, location, number of members, known hate crimes committed and alleged, and leadership's contact information.

### Step 3

Go online to the Southern Poverty Law Center's website at http://www.splcenter.org and use their data resources to locate hate groups in your area or region. As a courtesy, send them an e-mail to notify them of your project and ask them how they would prefer to be referenced in your research for having provided data. You may want to ask if they have suggestions for your project and other sources of data.

### Step 4

Write summaries of the information you have about each hate group in your area, including (if you have not already recorded this information in Step 2) political orientation, hate ideology, location, number of members, known hate crimes committed and alleged, and leadership's contact information. If any information is available on how the group has been successfully dealt with, be sure to include that and other pertinent information.

### Step 5

Share your summaries with your client group staff and solicit their help in making it even better. You will need to think of questions to ask the staff regarding how to create a custom fit between available information and information needs. These documents will ideally be dynamic, updated regularly to maintain currency and usefulness, and you will want their initial structure to reflect that potential.

### Step 6

Modify your "hot sheets" according to the feedback you get from your client and share the final results with staff. Ask them to let you know how the data are used and if particular hot sheets are instrumental in dealing with a hate group's activities.

### Step 7

Congratulate yourself for hard work well done!

# Assignment 2
## Cultural Brokerage and Arab Americans

The United States is home to more than a million new immigrants a year. Among these immigrants are Arabs from a variety of ethnic and religious backgrounds. Included in this group are doctors, lawyers, farmers, merchants, and laborers seeking a better life for their families, as well as refugees fleeing war-torn homelands and persecution. Many Arab Americans face strong discrimination in the United States because of ignorance and fear surrounding terrorism and the ongoing conflict in Iraq. This assignment is designed to facilitate better understanding between Arab Americans (immigrant or otherwise) and the communities they live and work within.

### Step 1

Contact a local mosque or Arab-American community center and meet with their staff. Discuss with them your interest in working for them as part of a school assignment on cultural brokerage. Assuming they agree that there is a need for such information and image management, proceed to Step 2. If they do not feel there is such a need, solicit their suggestions about which communities do, in fact, have such a need, and start over at one of these locations.

### Step 2

Develop a demographic description of the Arab American community using available records, such as census bureau records. With the help of the staff at the community center or mosque, develop a survey to augment the information available from public records. Be sure to include questions regarding the history of immigration and include such information as where community members emigrated from, how long they have been in the United States, and how long they have been in the local community. Count the number of men, women, and children and the ages of each. List occupations, general income brackets, and home ownership from which you can estimate income and property tax contributions. Place this data into a spreadsheet, using a program such as Microsoft Excel, and create a simple series of charts to visually represent this data. This data will help create a picture of what the Arab-American community contributes to the local economy and well-being of the town or city.

### Step 3

Using the community center staff as liaisons, solicit individual interviews to obtain a cultural collage of the Arab American community. This interview can be open ended and general. You could ask your interviewees about the values that are important to them as Arab Americans and to their community and how these values might conflict with U.S. culture. Your conversation might also cover other aspects of culture, including cuisine, popular culture and entertainment, religious practices, gender roles, or any other topic that arises during the course of the conversation. In these interviews, allow your informant some freedom to guide the session and provide information that he or she feels is important to convey. If you are not able to interview one of the genders due to cultural practice, solicit help from the center staff in getting an appropriate person to conduct the other interviews to ensure you do not end up with a collage that leaves out, for example, women's experiences and lives.

## Step 4

Using your creativity, combine the forms of data you collected and processed into a series of brochures and computer-based presentations that paint a portrait of the Arab community, using programs such as Microsoft PowerPoint or Apple Keynote. If you are proficient at creating Web pages, consider putting together the material you collected into Web site form.

## Step 5

With these files prepared, present the information to the community center staff and clientele to obtain vital feedback. Based on their suggestions, modify your material to best meet their concerns and interests.

## Step 6

Submit your final draft materials to the community center and congratulate yourself for hard work well done! Be sure to occasionally stop by the center and inquire about how members of the community are doing. You will probably have made several friends who not only contribute to the community but enrich your life as well!

# 3

# Prejudice and Discrimination in the Individual

WHAT CAUSES PREJUDICE? WHY DO SOME PEOPLE REGARD MEMBERS OF OTHER GROUPS WITH contempt, hostility, and even hatred? Why do people sometimes exclude, fear, and attack outsiders? What is the source of these negative attitudes and behaviors? American social scientists have been pursuing these issues for many decades, and we will explore their conclusions in this chapter.

*Prejudice* (as you learned in chapter 1) is the tendency of individuals to think and feel in negative ways about members of other groups, whereas *discrimination* is actual, overt, individual behavior. Although these concepts are obviously related, they do not always occur together or even necessarily have a causal relationship with each other. Exhibit 3.1 presents four possible combinations of prejudice and discrimination in individuals. In two cases, the relationship between prejudice and discrimination is consistent. The "all-weather liberal" is not prejudiced and does not discriminate, whereas the "all-weather bigot" is prejudiced and does discriminate. The other two combinations, however, are contradictory. The "fair-weather liberal" discriminates without prejudice, whereas the "timid bigot" is prejudiced but does not discriminate. These inconsistencies between attitudes and behavior are not uncommon and may be caused by a variety of social pressures, including the desire to conform to the expectations of others. These seemingly contradictory combinations illustrate the fact that prejudice and discrimination can be independent of each other. Most of the material in this chapter is focused more on prejudice than on discrimination, but we will address the relationship between the two concepts on several occasions.

Another point to keep in mind is that this chapter (and the next) will depart somewhat from the generally sociological focus of this book. Although we are generally concerned with ideological racism and institutional discrimination—the sociological manifestations of prejudice and discrimination (see Exhibit 1.3 in Chapter 1)—Chapters 3 and 4 include a psychological

| EXHIBIT 3.1 | Four Relationships Between Prejudice and Discrimination in Individuals | |
|---|---|---|
| | **Does Not Discriminate** | **Does Discriminate** |
| Unprejudiced | Unprejudiced nondiscriminator (all-weather liberal) | Unprejudiced discriminator (fair-weather liberal) |
| Prejudiced | Prejudiced nondiscriminator (timid bigot) | Prejudiced discriminator (all-weather bigot) |

SOURCE: Adapted from Merton (1968).

focus as well. As you will see, however, many "psychological" theories incorporate "sociological" concepts. Prejudice and discrimination are complex and multifaceted, and a broad perspective is required to explain them fully.

Conceptually, as you recall, prejudice has at least two dimensions: an affective, or emotional, dimension and a cognitive, or thinking, dimension. The affective dimension refers to the feelings we associate with other groups and may include fear, anger, strong dislike, hatred, and any number of other, generally negative emotions. The cognitive dimension of prejudice refers to the ways we think about other groups. In the sections that follow, we will first address the nature of stereotypes and then consider a number of theories that focus more on the emotional components of prejudice.

## STEREOTYPES

Stereotypes are generalizations about groups of people that are exaggerated, overly simplistic, and resistant to disproof (Pettigrew, 1980, p. 822; see also Jones, 1997, pp. 164-202). Stereotypes stress a few traits and assume that these characteristics apply to all members of the group, regardless of individual characteristics. Highly prejudiced people will maintain their stereotypical views even in the face of massive evidence that their views are wrong.

## Cognition and Categorization

**Cognition** is the thinking process by which people categorize and analyze information. We continually sort the impressions we receive from our environment into categories. The classification process is constant, natural, and necessary. Our world is complex, and we receive a huge volume of information and impressions every second. Because of the immensity of the task, we often make snap judgments and sort our impressions into superficial and, sometimes, incorrect categories. Our mental categorizations affect our actions. We respond differently to an object that we classify as a delicious cheeseburger than we do to an object we classify as a dangerous copperhead snake. Of course, we classify people and groups as well as things, and these categorizations also affect our behavior.

Sometimes we judge or categorize others based on nothing more than the most cursory appraisals of their most obvious characteristics—but what makes a characteristic "obvious"? When judging and classifying others, why do we tend to see certain traits (gender, skin color) and not others?

One answer is that our attention is drawn to the characteristics that have come to identify the dividing lines between groups. Racial characteristics such as skin color are not necessarily any more obvious than other traits (such as hair length or size of nose), but they are one of the first and, for many people, most important pieces of information we recognize about each other. The dividing lines between groups that were created in the past condition our perceptions and impressions in the present. Our "knowledge" that skin color can be used to judge others and our sensitivity to this characteristic reflect our **socialization** into a race-conscious society with a long history of racial stratification.

Beyond merely noting group membership, prejudiced individuals will attribute a wide range of traits to other people. They might assume that members of particular groups have certain personality characteristics ("Asians are clannish") or behavioral tendencies ("Italians are hot tempered"). They might make sweeping judgments about the worth of others and even commit acts of violence based solely on the group identity of another person. These assumptions we make about others based on their group memberships are stereotypes.

For the prejudiced individual, stereotypes are an important set of cognitive categories. Once a stereotype is learned, it can shape perceptions to the point that the individual pays attention only to information that confirms that stereotype. **Selective perception**, the tendency to see only what one expects to see, can reinforce and strengthen stereotypes to the point that the highly prejudiced individual simply does not accept evidence that challenges his or her views. Thus these overgeneralizations can become closed perceptual systems that screen out contrary information and absorb only the sensory impressions that ratify the original bias.

## Attribution Theory

**Attribution theory** was developed to describe how humans perceive and judge one another (Ashmore & DelBoca, 1976, p. 98). It is based on the premise that we try to understand and explain the behavior of others. Sometimes we explain behavior by attributing actions or behaviors to personality traits or *internal* dispositions ("She didn't offer to pay for lunch because she's stingy"). At other times, we may see behavior as a response to a particular situation or to *external* factors ("He was rude because of all the pressure he's under at work").

To illustrate further, consider the fact that high rates of poverty are common among minority groups in the United States. How do people account for this fact? Some might explain minority group poverty by attributing it to internal factors or individual personality characteristics: "Those people are lazy and irresponsible; they just don't want to work." Others might explain the poverty as being the result of external or environmental factors (such as discrimination, inferior health care, or inadequate schools) that work against the group.

Stereotypes provide one way of accounting for the behavior of others, especially members of groups against whom we are already prejudiced. Negative or threatening behaviors are seen as motivated by internal or personality characteristics ("That's just the way they are"), and positive behaviors are seen as caused by situational or external factors ("He's polite because he wants something"). This perceptual tendency helps maintain stereotypical thinking even in the face of contrary evidence (Pettigrew, 1980, p. 824). Any challenge to the stereotype—evidence of intelligence and good judgment from a member of a group that is regarded as inferior and undependable, for example—is dismissed as exceptional or situational. By "explaining" behavior in this way, the highly prejudiced individual receives only the information that confirms his or her stereotypes.

In contrast, in judging and explaining the behavior of people who are close to us or who are members of our own groups, we usually avoid stereotypical thinking and accord them the benefit of the doubt. We attribute their positive actions to internal factors ("He baked a cake for the new neighbors. That just shows that he has a good heart") and their negative actions to external or situational factors ("She yelled at her secretary this morning, but she's under a lot of pressure to meet the monthly sales quota") (Brown, 1995, pp. 99-102; Pettigrew, 1980, p. 824).

This pattern of attribution allows us to maintain positive thoughts about members of our groups even when their behavior is offensive to us. If their negative behavior can be attributed to their situation and not their nature, we can continue to think of "our" people in positive ways; they still can be seen as good people "inside." Members of other groups are not accorded this benefit of the doubt and their negative or offensive behaviors are seen as affirmations of their unworthiness.

## Cognitive and Emotional Dimensions of Stereotypes

Remember that individual prejudice has an *affective* dimension in addition to the cognitive. Robert Merton (1968), a prominent American sociologist, makes this distinction between dimensions dramatically. Merton analyzed stereotypical perceptions of Abraham Lincoln, Jews, and Japanese. In the following passage, he argues that the three "stereotypes" are identical in content but vastly different in emotional shading:

> The very same behavior undergoes a complete change of evaluation in its transition from the in-group Abe Lincoln to the out-group Abe Cohen or Abe Kurokawa. Did Lincoln work far into the night? This testifies that he was industrious, resolute, perseverant, and eager to realize his capacities to the full. Do the out-group Jews or Japanese keep these same hours? This only bears witness to their sweatshop mentality, their ruthless undercutting of American standards, their unfair competitive practices. Is the in-group hero frugal, thrifty, and sparing? Then the out-group villain is stingy, miserly, and penny-pinching. All honor is due to the in-group Abe for his having been smart, shrewd and intelligent, and, by the same token, all contempt is owing the out-group Abes for their being sharp, cunning, crafty, and too clever by far. (p. 482)

The stereotype of all three Abes is identical; what varies is the affect, or the emotional tone, reflected in the descriptive terms. Thus the same stereotype evokes different emotional responses for different groups or in different individuals.

## Types of Stereotypes

Stereotypes are, by definition, exaggerated overgeneralizations. At some level, though, even the most simplistic and derogatory stereotype can reflect some of the realities of dominant-minority group relationships. The content of a stereotype flows from the actual relationship between dominant and minority groups and is often one important way in which the dominant group tries to justify or rationalize that relationship.

For example, Pettigrew (1980) and others have pointed out that there are two general stereotypes of minority groups. The first attributes extreme inferiority (e.g., laziness, irresponsibility, or lack of intelligence) to minority group members and tends to be found in situations (such as slavery) in which a minority group is being heavily exploited and held in an impoverished and powerless status by the dominant group. This type of stereotype is a rationalization that helps to justify dominant group policies of control, discrimination, or exclusion.

The second type of stereotype is found when power and status differentials are less extreme, particularly when the minority group has succeeded in gaining some control over resources, has experienced some upward mobility, and has had some success in school and business. In this situation, credulity would be stretched too far to label the group inferior, so their relative success is viewed in negative terms: They are seen (like the "out-group Abes" mentioned earlier) as *too* smart, *too* materialistic, *too* crafty, *too* sly, or *too* ambitious (Pettigrew, 1980, p. 823; see also Simpson & Yinger, 1985, p. 101).

You should also realize that stereotypes and prejudice can exist apart from any need to rationalize or justify dominant-group advantage. Research shows that some individuals will readily stereotype groups about which they have little or no information. In fact, some individuals will express prejudice against groups that do not even exist! In one test of prejudice, respondents were asked how closely they would associate with "Daniereans, Pireneans, and Wallonians"—all fictitious groups. A number of white respondents apparently reacted to the "foreign" sound of the names, rejected these three groups, and indicated that they would treat them about the same as other minority groups (Hartley, 1946). Clearly, the negative judgments about these groups were not made on the basis of personal experience or a need to rationalize some system such as slavery. The subjects were exhibiting a generalized tendency to reject minority groups of all sorts.

## The Content of American Stereotypes

A series of studies with Princeton University undergraduates provides some interesting perspectives on the content of American stereotypes. Students were given a list of personality traits and asked to check those that applied to a number of different groups. The study was done first in 1933 and then repeated in 1951 and 1967 (Karlins, Coffman, & Walters, 1969). It is unusual to have comparable data covering such a long period of time, which makes these studies significant despite the fact that Princeton undergraduates are hardly a representative sample of American public opinion. Exhibit 3.2 lists the traits most commonly mentioned for four of the groups in the 1933 study and charts their changes over time.

Several elements of these data are worth noting. First, the two different types of stereotypes we previously discussed can be found in these results. Jews are seen as successful ("industrious," "intelligent") but pushy ("grasping," "mercenary"), whereas African Americans are seen as inferior ("lazy," "ignorant"). Second, the study shows that the willingness to stereotype seems to decline over the years. Princeton undergraduates in 1951 and 1967 were less willing to attach labels to entire groups than in 1933 (although there is not a particular decline between 1951 and 1967).

Third, although muted, the willingness to stereotype still existed in 1967. For example, about 30% still saw Jews as being "shrewd" and Italians as "impulsive" and "quick tempered." In fact, the attribution of some traits (the English as "conservative," African Americans as "musical") actually increased in the years between 1933 and 1967.

Similar studies of stereotypical thinking have been conducted on other campuses in more recent years. Clark and Person (1982) measured white stereotypes of African Americans among undergraduates at two southeastern universities in the early 1980s. They found some continuity in the content of the stereotypes from earlier studies but also found that their subjects were more likely to characterize African Americans as having seemingly positive traits such as "loyal

**EXHIBIT 3.2** Changes in Stereotypes Expressed by Princeton Undergraduates

| (Percentage Identifying Trait With Ethnic Group) | | | | | | | |
| --- | --- | --- | --- | --- | --- | --- | --- |
| **English** | | | | **Italians** | | | |
| | 1933 | 1951 | 1967 | | 1933 | 1951 | 1967 |
| Sportsmanlike | 53 | 21 | 22 | Artistic | 53 | 28 | 30 |
| Artistic | 46 | 29 | 23 | Impulsive | 44 | 19 | 28 |
| Conventional | 34 | 25 | 19 | Passionate | 37 | 25 | 44 |
| Tradition loving | 31 | 42 | 21 | Quick tempered | 35 | 15 | 28 |
| Conservative | 30 | 22 | 53 | Musical | 32 | 22 | 9 |
| **Jews** | | | | **African Americans** | | | |
| Shrewd | 79 | 47 | 30 | Superstitious | 84 | 41 | 13 |
| Mercenary | 49 | 28 | 15 | Lazy | 75 | 31 | 26 |
| Industrious | 48 | 29 | 33 | Happy-go-lucky | 38 | 17 | 27 |
| Grasping | 34 | 17 | 17 | Ignorant | 38 | 24 | 11 |
| Intelligent | 29 | 37 | 37 | Musical | 26 | 33 | 47 |

SOURCE: Karlins, Coffman, and Walters (1969).

to family" (Clark & Person, 1982). In contrast, a 1993 study conducted by Wood and Chesser found that white students at a large midwestern university had more negative stereotypes of African Americans. The top five most common traits selected by the sample were uniformly negative and included "loud," "aggressive," and "lazy" (Wood & Chesser, 1994). This finding was echoed in a 1995 study at the University of Wisconsin that replicated the three Princeton University tests. Three of the top five most commonly selected traits for African Americans were similar to those selected by Princeton undergraduates: "rhythmic" (vs. "musical"), "low in intelligence" (vs. "ignorant"), and "lazy," and two were new, "athletic" and "poor" (Devine & Elliot, 1995).

We should stress that these studies are very limited by time and place and are not necessarily consistent with the attitudes of Americans in general. Perhaps the most significant thing about this line of research is that when asked to characterize entire groups of people, the subjects—even highly educated college students—did so.

## Gender and Minority Group Stereotypes

Do stereotypes vary by gender? Are distinctions made between minority group males and females? How do stereotypes of minority group females compare with dominant-group females? Research on these questions is scanty, but Weitz and Gordon (1993) report some interesting results. They questioned several hundred undergraduate white students at Arizona State University about their perceptions of women and found sharp distinctions between "women in general" (a label that, to the students, apparently signified white women) and African American women in particular. When asked to select traits for "American women in general," the responses were overwhelmingly positive and included "intelligent," "sensitive" and "attractive." Of the 10 most commonly selected traits, only two ("materialistic" and "emotional") may have had some negative connotations.

The students selected very different terms to describe African American women. The single most commonly selected trait was "loud," and only 22% of the sample saw African American women as "intelligent." Of the 10 most commonly selected traits, five (e.g., "talkative," "stubborn") seemed to have at least some negative affect attached to them.

Another study used a sample of white college students to analyze how stereotypes about speech vary by race and gender. The researchers found that race generated a stronger stereotype than gender and that black speech was seen as more direct, emotional, profane, and grammatically incorrect than white speech. Although stereotypes based solely on gender may have softened over the years, perceptions of black women may be especially negative because of the combined disadvantages of race and gender (Popp, Donavan, Crawford, Marsh, & Peele, 2003).

As was true for the studies mentioned in the previous section, these studies cannot be easily generalized to the population as a whole. Nevertheless, they do suggest the presence of a gender dimension in stereotyping, and further research in this area would be worthwhile.

# THEORIES OF PREJUDICE

There have been many attempts to understand and explain prejudice, and this section has been limited to some of the more widely cited theories and concepts. These theories stress the origin or functions of the affective dimension of personal prejudice and have been organized around the type of explanation proposed:

- Theories that focus on personality needs as a cause of prejudice
- Theories that view prejudice as primarily a result of being raised in a racist society and interacting in many social situations in which discrimination is approved
- Theories that view prejudice as arising out of intergroup conflict

In the first two perspectives, levels of prejudice vary depending on socialization experiences, situational factors, and an array of other variables. The level of prejudice in the third perspective is seen as a function of the intensity of competition between groups. The causes of prejudice identified in each of these perspectives are conceptually independent. They can occur separately, or they can combine within the same individual and act to reinforce or negate each other.

## Personality-Centered Approaches to Prejudice

In this section, we consider attempts to locate the cause of prejudice within personality dynamics and early-childhood experiences. These explanations focus on individual personality and are thus psychological in nature.

One emotional function that prejudice can play is **projection**: seeing in others characteristics or feelings we cannot admit we have ourselves. People who are unable to deal with strong anger, fear, or sexual desire may deny these emotions in themselves and attribute them instead to out-groups. "If you have sexual problems, you may regard Latins as dangerously hypersexed. If you have problems with your conflict-ridden family, you may regard Jews as dangerously clannish" (Pettigrew, 1980, p. 825). Thus minority and other out-groups can serve as "living Rorschach inkblots" that take on the characteristics required by whatever psychodynamic issue is central for the individual. For certain people, the projection function of prejudice can be vital to mental health and stability. Projection may give them a way to avoid dealing with painful feelings or experiences.

Projection is a psychological process not necessarily related to group conflict, racial stratification, or any of the sociological forces we will discuss in coming chapters. Thus people who do not enjoy any objective political or economic benefits from systems of racial or ethnic inequality may still have a strong psychological stake in maintaining the unequal status of minority groups. They may need the minority group for psychological reasons, just as surely as plantation owners needed slaves for economic reasons (Levin & Levin, 1982, pp. 140-155).

**The Scapegoat Hypothesis.** The **scapegoat hypothesis** links prejudice to the individual's need to deal with frustration and express aggression. This hypothesis begins with the observation that failures, great and small, are common experiences for everyone. Frustration is a feeling of tension or unhappiness and is a natural response to the failure to achieve a goal or satisfy a need. Aggression, hostility, or violence can relieve the unpleasant sensation of frustration. If your goal of getting to work on time is blocked by a traffic jam, your resultant frustration might be expressed or released by the aggressive act of pounding your steering wheel.

What does frustration have to do with prejudice? Sometimes the cause of the frustration is not available as a target for your aggression. For example, what if you lost a job because of an economic recession? How could you vent your aggressions on something abstract and amorphous like a low level of economic performance? You have to be able to see or feel the target before you can attack it. In other situations, the source of the frustration might be too powerful to attack. If your boss unexpectedly orders you to work overtime or if your instructor announces a test on a day when you already had other plans, you might experience frustration but choose not to direct the resultant aggression against these more powerful individuals.

In circumstances in which targets are unavailable or inappropriate, a process called **displacement** might occur, in which the frustrated individual finds a substitute target—a scapegoat—on which to vent hostility and aggression. Thus, instead of yelling at your boss or your instructor, you might "take it out" on your spouse, child, or pet. It is not uncommon and is actually sensible, in a way, to choose substitute targets that are weak and unable to respond to your aggression. For members of the dominant group, minority groups are, by definition, less powerful, and they can make excellent substitute targets. Displacement to other groups is fundamentally irrational and is usually accompanied by an increase in individual prejudice. The role of prejudice in this process is rationalization: It makes displacement seem more reasonable (at least to the individual doing the displacement).

There is a long tradition of research on this hypothesis, and the process of scapegoating has been tested and documented a number of times. In an experimental situation, subjects are purposely frustrated by the experimenter and then offered the possibility of expressing their aggression against a minority group. In these situations, prejudice often increases measurably, indicating that hostility has been displaced onto the substitute target. To illustrate: Miller and Bugleski (1948) required white men in an isolated job training center to miss a recreational activity to complete a series of tedious and lengthy exams. Earlier, the men had completed a survey measuring their attitudes toward Mexicans and Japanese. After finishing the exams, the men were surveyed again, and as expected, the levels of anti-Japanese and anti-Mexican prejudice were significantly higher than before (Miller & Bugleski, 1948; see also Berkowitz, 1978; Dollard, Miller, Doob, Mowrer, & Sears, 1939).

One implication of this theory is that the level of prejudice in a society will reflect the level of individual frustration. The scapegoat theory has been used to explain the rise of the Nazi party in Germany in the 1930s. Germany not only lost World War I but experienced severe problems with economic recession, unemployment, and a horrific inflation during the 1920s. The success of the extremely racist, violently **anti-Semitic** Nazi party was in part a result of its ability to capture and express these intense frustrations (see Dollard et al., 1939). Along the same analytical lines, Hovland and Sears (1940) argued that the rate of lynching of African Americans in the South between 1882 and 1930 was correlated with fluctuations in cotton prices. Lynchings generally increased during hard times when the price of cotton was low and (presumably) frustrations were more widespread (for a different, more sociological view, see Beck & Tolnay, 1990, and Beck & Clark, 2002).

Scapegoating seems to have been implicated in violent attacks on Asians by American workers during economic hard times. In 1982, for example, two white automobile workers in Detroit murdered a Chinese American named Vincent Chin. The workers mistakenly identified Chin as Japanese and attacked him in retaliation for the loss of jobs in the American auto industry (U.S. Commission on Civil Rights, 1992, pp. 25-26). More recently, a number of Arab Americans and Middle Easterners (or those who appeared Middle Eastern) were attacked in the days following the September 11, 2001, attacks on the World Trade Center and the Pentagon. By one count, there were more than 700 violent attacks across the nation following 9-11, including several murders (Ibish, 2003).

Reasoning from the scapegoat hypothesis, we would expect that bad economic times, or national traumas such as the attacks on September 11, 2001, would cause an increase in displaced aggression, expressions of prejudice, and acts of discrimination (e.g., see Staub, 1996). Remember, however, that the scapegoat hypothesis is a psychological theory and that individuals may displace aggressions independent of economic or political conditions. By the same token, acts of violence and discrimination, such as the rise of the Nazi party, the lynching of African Americans in the South, or attacks on Arab Americans, are fueled by a complex array of economic, social, and political forces, not by individual frustration alone.

**The Authoritarian Personality.** A team of researchers, led by Professor T. W. Adorno, made one of the most important contributions in the study of individual prejudice. These researchers believed that there was a prejudiced personality type and that certain kinds of people require prejudice to function effectively. They presented their theory of prejudice in *The Authoritarian Personality* (Adorno, Frenkel-Brunswick, Levinson, & Sanford, 1950).

Adorno and his colleagues (1950) argued that prejudice is a component of an authoritarian personality syndrome developed in certain early childhood relationships with parents. Authoritarian personality tendencies develop in family situations in which discipline is harsh and parents are uncommunicative, emotionally cold, stern, and distant. A child raised in such an environment comes to see the parents, and eventually all authority figures, as dangerous and fearsome. The child may feel hostile and angry toward his or her parents, but the parents are too powerful to allow the direct expression of these feelings. Consequently, the child deals with these negative emotions by displacing the anger and hostility, more or less permanently, on out-groups. Projection also occurs, and the out-groups are seen as hostile and threatening.

This release of negative emotions permits the individual to fabricate and express conventional attitudes and emotion toward parental figures, feelings that are later generalized to include

EXHIBIT 3.3 The Authoritarian Personality

| Trait | Expression |
|---|---|
| 1. Pseudopatriotism | Unquestioning support for right-wing, conservative ideas and patriotic sentiments |
| 2. Conventionalism | Rigid adherence to conventional values |
| 3. Authoritarian submission | Uncritical acceptance of authority |
| 4. Authoritarian aggression | Aggression and hostility toward out-groups |
| 5. Projectivity | Attributes (or projects) to out-groups personality traits or feelings that cannot be consciously admitted (e.g., hostility toward parents) |
| 6. Anti-intraception | Unwillingness to examine self or explore the subjective world of feelings and imagination |
| 7. Stereotypical thinking | A rigid perception that all members of out-groups conform to his or her stereotypes |

SOURCE: Adapted from Farley (1988, p. 18) and Adorno et al. (1950).

all authority figures. The authoritarian individual is able to express "normal" family attitudes, but *only* by splitting off the negative emotions and attaching them to out-groups. For the highly authoritarian personality, prejudice is thus a fundamental and necessary personality component. Without prejudice, the authoritarian would have to confront his or her actual feelings about parents and family.

According to the original theory, prejudice is one of a constellation of related characteristics that together make up the authoritarian personality (see Exhibit 3.3). The combination of out-group rejection and in-group acceptance that is our focus is reflected in the first five traits in the exhibit.

Several of these traits should be explained in a little more detail. *Pseudopatriotism* goes far beyond simple love of country. This extreme, unthinking, and highly emotional attitude is a generalization of the conventionalized attachment to parental figures developed in early childhood and may be exemplified in such superpatriotic slogans as "My country, right or wrong." The highly authoritarian personality also rigidly supports conventional morality (*conventionalism*) and submits to authority without question (*authoritarian submission*).

More recent applications of this theory find that authoritarian tendencies are correlated with support for traditional gender roles and very negative attitudes toward alternative lifestyles and toward gays and lesbians. Researchers continue to find correlations between authoritarianism, right-wing conservatism, and prejudice. Some reject the psychodynamic approach of the original researchers, however, and argue that these attitudes and tendencies are the results of emulating parents who are extremely disciplinary and punitive in their child-rearing habits (Altemeyer, 2004; Jones, 2002; Rowatt & Franklin, 2004).

**Limitations of Personality-Centered Approaches.** After decades of research, it is now clear that the scapegoat hypothesis is overly simplistic. Aggression is not an automatic or invariable response to frustration, and the probability of displacement varies widely for different types of individuals. Many other variables can affect the scapegoating process. Personal threats, such as divorce or illness, are more likely to lead to scapegoating than are communal threats, such as floods or tornadoes (Feshbeck & Singer, 1957). People who are already highly prejudiced are more likely to scapegoat minority groups (Berkowitz, 1978). Also, people are more likely to scapegoat groups that they already dislike (Berkowitz & Green, 1962).

As for the theory of the authoritarian personality, it is now widely agreed that the original study suffered from a number of methodological flaws and weaknesses. For example, Adorno and his colleagues relied heavily on written surveys to measure authoritarianism. The items on the scales they used were phrased so that agreement always indicated a higher level of authoritarianism. This format can cause *response set*, or a tendency to agree with or endorse positive statements, regardless of one's actual feelings. To some extent, scores on the questionnaires measured this tendency to agree rather than measuring authoritarianism (Bass, 1955; Jackman, 1973). Furthermore, they relied on people's memories of their childhood—a potentially unreliable source—to provide evidence of authoritarian family structures.

Another common criticism is that the theory measures only right-wing authoritarianism. People who are politically conservative or extremely patriotic score higher on the authoritarianism scale than extreme liberals or people who are not patriotic. This is a problem, because liberals or left-wingers can also be dogmatic, closed minded, and narrow in their thinking. The theory may measure only half of the full syndrome (Shils, 1954).

It is worth noting in this regard that Adorno and most of his associates were Austrian Jews who fled the rise of Nazism in the 1930s. In fact, this experience and the rise of Italian and German fascism in general stimulated the research project. The influence of the researchers' concern with Nazism is reflected in the fact that they used the term *highly fascistic* as a synonym for *highly authoritarian*. Adorno and the others were affected in their thinking by the racism, submissiveness to authority, and superpatriotism of the extreme right-wing Nazi ideology (Christie & Yahoda, 1954). Thus, this theory, like all theories, must be seen in the context of its time and the life experiences of the theorists.

The more modern research conducted in this tradition avoids the theoretical and methodological weaknesses of the original theory. Nonetheless, all theories based solely on personality are limited in that they tend to focus on the individual in isolation and do not take sufficient account of the social setting or the context and history of group relations (Brown, 1995, pp. 31-36). Projection, scapegoating, and authoritarian tendencies are affected by social class, job security, education, and numerous individual characteristics other than childhood experience and personality traits. These processes must be understood in the social settings in which they occur, not as disembodied, stand-alone psychological phenomena (Simpson & Yinger, 1985, p. 74).

On the other hand, personality-centered approaches do help to explain some forms of prejudice. From the perspective of these theories, forces internal to the individual (emotional conflicts, unresolved problems with parents)—not a person's actual experiences with members of other groups—cause prejudice. Thus these theories may help to explain "irrational" forms of prejudice, cases in which people are highly prejudiced against groups they have no firsthand or "logical" reason to dislike.

## Culture-Based Approaches to Prejudice

In personality-centered approaches such as the authoritarian personality theory, prejudice is viewed as an indicator of an unhealthy personality. It permits otherwise seriously

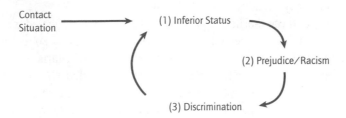

**EXHIBIT 3.4** Sexism and Prejudice (%)

Contact Situation → (1) Inferior Status → (2) Prejudice/Racism → (3) Discrimination →

SOURCE: Based on Myrdal (1962), pp. 25–28.

maladjusted people to deal with their problems and function from day to day. In contrast, culture-based approaches see individual prejudice as the predictable result of growing up in a society that incorporates racist ideology, extreme racial and ethnic inequalities, and systems of exploitation based on group membership. Rather than being an indicator of personality disorder or emotional maladjustment, prejudice is the "normal" result of conforming to racist environments.

**The Vicious Cycle.** Swedish economist Gunnar Myrdal explored the relationships between culture, racial or ethnic inequality, and the development of individual prejudice. In his classic analysis of American race relations, *An American Dilemma* (1962[1]), Myrdal proposed that these forces can powerfully reinforce each other over time. The process he described operates as a self-fulfilling prophecy or a **vicious cycle**: a certain condition is assumed to be true, and then forces are set in motion to create and perpetuate the original condition.

Exhibit 3.4 displays the vicious cycle as applied to prejudice and race relations. The dominant group uses its power to force the minority group into an inferior status, such as slavery (1). Partly to motivate the construction of a system of racial stratification and partly to justify its existence, individual prejudice and ideologies of racism are invented and accepted by the dominant group (2). Individual prejudices are reinforced by the everyday observation of the inferior status of the minority group. The fact that the minority group is in fact impoverished, enslaved, or otherwise exploited confirms and strengthens the attribution of inferiority. The belief in inferiority motivates further discrimination and unequal treatment (3), which reinforces the inferior status, which validates the prejudice and racism, which justifies further discrimination, and so on. Over not too many generations, a stable, internally reinforced system of racial inferiority becomes an integral, unremarkable, and (at least for the dominant group) accepted part of everyday life.

Culture is conservative, and the legacies of prejudice and racism can long outlive the situations in which they were created. Thus, for future generations, prejudice will be sustained and reproduced by socialization into a racist culture. Contrary to authoritarian personality theory, culture-based approaches see prejudice as an indication that a person is "normal" and well-adjusted to an environment that happens to be racist.

Furthermore, in a society with strong racist traditions, prejudice can be a way of expressing social solidarity and connectedness with others. People may express prejudice as a way of conforming to local expectations and expressing and affirming ties with emotionally significant others. When family, peers, and neighbors all subscribe to prejudice, the pressure to conform can be very strong, and people may join in the rejection of out-groups as a way of maintaining their standing in their in-groups.

We learn prejudice in the same way and for the same reasons that we learn any other aspect of our culture. Prejudice and racism come to us through our cultural heritage as a standardized package of attitudes, stereotypes, emotions, knowledge, and ideas. We learn which groups are "good" and which are "bad" in the same way we learn table manners and religious beliefs (Pettigrew, 1958, 1971, p. 137; Simpson & Yinger, 1985, pp. 107, 108).

**The Development of Prejudice in Children.** Evidence to support the idea that prejudice is at least partially an outcome of socialization in racist environments can be found in research on the development of intergroup attitudes in children. Children become aware of group differences (e.g., black vs. white) at a very early age. Between ages 3 and 5 years old, children begin to recognize the significance and the permanence of racial groups and can accurately classify people on the basis of skin color and other cues (Brown, 1995, pp. 121-136; Katz, 1976, p. 126). Once the racial categories are mentally established, the child begins the process of learning the "proper" attitudes and stereotypes to associate with the various groups.

Ashmore and DelBoca (1976) summarize the research in this area by making several points. First, even when parents make no overt racist statements, they can still shape prejudice in their children indirectly. For example, they might establish rules about whom the children can or cannot play with, or they may limit interracial interactions in other situations. Second, many parents find it difficult to deal directly and openly with children's questions regarding group differences. In these cases, the parent may change the subject and thus convey the idea that race is an anxiety-arousing topic, or resort to derogatory stereotypes. Third, children are permitted to overhear certain race-related conversations in which prejudice is expressed or minority groups are referred to in unfavorable terms, and subsequently they tend to imitate the attitudes and actions of their parents (Ashmore & DelBoca, 1976, p. 96). Children may not be directly instructed about presumed minority group characteristics; it is often said that racial attitudes are "caught and not taught."

Parents and other adult caregivers control the socialization process, at least in the early years. Parents control valuable resources (food, shelter, praise), and children are motivated to seek their approval and conform to their expectations. Thus there are strong pressures on the child to learn and internalize the prejudices of the older generation, even when the instruction is subtle and indirect. The power and subtlety of these cultural influences are illustrated in the following Narrative Portrait.

Much of the research on the development of prejudice is consistent with the idea that children are born without bias and have to be carefully taught who to like and dislike. A somewhat different view argues that children are actively engaged in their learning and that their levels of prejudice reflect their changing intellectual capabilities. Children as young as 5 to 6 months old can make some simple distinctions (e.g., by gender or race) between categories of people. The fact that this capability emerges so early in life suggests that it is not simply a response to adult teaching. "Adults use categories to simplify and make sense of their environment; apparently children do the same" (Brown, 1995, p. 126).

Gross, simplistic distinctions between people may help very young children organize and understand the world around them. The need for such primitive categorizations may decline as the child becomes more experienced in life and more sophisticated in his or her thinking.

# Narrative Portrait

## The Cultural Sources of Prejudice

Kaffir Boy, *Mark Mathabane's (1986) best-selling memoir of growing up in racist South Africa, provides abundant illustrations of the importance of culture and conformity in developing individual prejudice. Prior to recent social and political reforms, South Africa was the most rigidly race-conscious and segregated society on earth. Black South Africans were kept economically and politically powerless and were used as a source of cheap labor for the benefit of white South Africans. White South Africans of even modest economic means were able to afford domestic help (cooks, gardeners, maids, etc.) and other amenities because of this system of exploitation and discrimination.*

*This elaborate system of racial privilege was stabilized in part by a strong, government-sanctioned ideology of antiblack prejudice and racism. Black and white South Africans had little contact with each other except in situations in which the black person was clearly subordinate. What "knowledge" the white community had of blacks came from constrained, lopsided interactions or from the racist content of the culture. For example, the idea that blacks are inferior was taught in school as part of the official curriculum.*

*In the following passage, Mathabane recalls a day when he went to work with his grandmother, a gardener for an affluent white family named Smith. Clyde Smith was roughly the same age as Mark and clearly demonstrates the results of being socialized in a culture in which racism is both "normal" and government supported. Note that Mrs. Smith challenges her son's attitudes with antiracist values and beliefs—even blatantly racist cultures are not monolithic in their commitment to bias. How does she also reinforce racial inequality in her actions and words?*

### KAFFIR BOY

**Mark Mathabane**

"This is Mrs. Smith's house," Granny remarked as she led me up a long driveway of a beautiful villa-type house. . . . We went to a steel gate at the back of the yard, where Granny rang a bell.

"I'm here, madam," she shouted through the gate. . . . A door creaked open, and a high-pitched woman's voice called out, "I'm coming, Ellen." . . . Presently the gate clicked open, and there appeared a short, slender white woman. . . ."I'm just getting ready to leave for tennis," she said to Granny.

"Madam, guess who I have with me today," Granny said with the widest smile. . . ."

"My, what a big lad he is! . . . Is he really your grandson, Ellen?" The warmth in her voice somehow reduced my fears of her; her eyes shone with the same gentleness of the Catholic Sisters at the clinic.

"Yes, madam," Granny said proudly; "this is the one I've been telling you about. This is the one who'll some day go to university." . . .

"I believe you, Ellen," said Mrs. Smith. "He looks like a very smart pickaninny." . . .

Toward early afternoon Mrs. Smith returned. She called me to the car to remove several shopping bags from the backseat. . . . As we were talking, a busload of white schoolchildren stopped in front of the house and a young boy [Mrs. Smith's son, Clyde] alighted and ran up the driveway. . . .

"Who is he, Mother?"

"That's Ellen's grandson. . . . Now run along inside and change and . . . then maybe you can play with [the] pickaninny."

"I don't play with Kaffirs," the white boy declared. "At school they say we shouldn't."

"Watch your filthy mouth, Clyde," Mrs. Smith said, flushing crimson. "I thought I told you a million times to leave all that rubbish about Kaffirs in the classroom." . . . Turning to Granny, . . . Mrs. Smith said, in a voice of someone fighting a losing battle, "You know, Ellen, I simply don't understand why those damn uncivilized Boers from Pretoria teach children such things."

"I agree, madam," Granny said, "All children, black and white, are God's children." . . .

"I'm afraid you're right, Ellen," Mrs. Smith said, somewhat touched. . . .

Shortly, Clyde emerged. . . . He called to me. "Come here, pickanniny. My mother says I should show you around."

I went.

I followed him around as he showed me the things his parents regularly bought him. . . . I couldn't understand why his people had to have all the luxuries money could buy, while my people lived in abject poverty. . . . We finally came to Clyde's playroom. The room was roughly the size of our house, and was elaborately decorated. . . . What arrested my attention were the stacks of comic books on the floor and the shelves and shelves of books.

Never had I seen so many books. . . .

Sensing that I was in awe of his magnificent library, Clyde said, "Do you have this many books in your playroom?"

"I don't have a playroom."

"You don't have a playroom," he said bug-eyed. "Can you read? . . . My teachers tell us that Kaffirs can't read, speak, or write English like white people because they have smaller brains, which are already full of tribal things. My teachers say you're not people like us, because you belong to a jungle civilization. That's why you can't live or go to school with us, but can only be our servants."

"Stop saying that rubbish," Mrs. Smith said angrily as she entered the room. . . . "How many times have I told you that what your teachers say about black people is not true?"

"What do you know, Mama?" Clyde retorted impudently, "you're not a teacher. Besides, there are textbooks where it's so written."

SOURCE: Mathabane, Mark. 1986. *Kaffir Boy*. New York: Plume Books. Pp. 187-192.

NOTE: In South Africa, *Kaffir* is a derogatory term for blacks, roughly equivalent to nigger.

Doyle and Aboud (1995), for example, found that prejudice was highest for younger children and actually decreased between kindergarten and third grade. The decline was related to increased awareness of racial similarities (as well as differences) and diverse perspectives on race (see also Black-Gutman & Hickson, 1996; Brown, 1995, pp. 149-159; Powlishta, Serbin, Doyle, & White, 1994). Thus changing levels of prejudice in children may reflect an interaction between the child's changing mental capacities and his or her environment rather than a simple or straightforward learning of racist cultural beliefs or values.

**Social Distance.** Research on the concept of **social distance** provides further evidence that prejudice has a cultural component. Social distance is related to ethnocentrism and prejudice and has often been used as a measure of the latter. It is not quite the same thing, however. Social distance is defined as the degree of intimacy to which an individual is willing to admit persons of other groups. The most intimate relationship would be close kinship, and the most distant relationship would be exclusion from the country. The inventor of the social distance scale was

Emory Bogardus (1933), who specified a total of seven degrees of social distance:

1. To close kinship by marriage
2. To my club as personal chums
3. To my street as neighbors
4. To employment in my occupation
5. To citizenship in my country
6. As visitors only to my country
7. Would be excluded from my country

Research using social distance scales demonstrates that prejudice exists apart from individuals and that it is passed from generation to generation. These results show that Americans rank other groups in similar ways across time and space. The consistency indicates a common frame of reference or set of perceptions, a continuity of vision possible only if perceptions have been standardized by socialization in a common culture.

Exhibit 3.5 presents the results of seven administrations of the scale to samples of Americans from 1926 to 2001. The groups are listed by the rank order of their scores in 1926. In that year, the sample expressed the least social distance from the English and the most distance from Asian Indians. While the average social distance score for the English was 1.02, indicating virtually no sense of distance, the average score for Indians was 3.91, indicating a distance between "to employment in my occupation" and "to my street as neighbors."

Note, first of all, the stability in the rankings. The actual *scores* (not shown) generally decrease from decade to decade, indicating less social distance and presumably a decline in prejudice over the years (changes in prejudice over time will be discussed in chapter 4). The *rankings* of the various groups, however, tend to be the same year after year. This stability is clearly displayed in the bottom row of the exhibit, which shows correlations between the group rankings for each year and the 1926 ranking. If any of the lists of scores had been identical, this statistic would have shown its maximum value of 1.00. Although they weaken over time, the actual correlations approach that maximum value and indicate that the rank order of the groups from year to year has been substantially the same. Considering the changes that society has experienced between 1926 and 2001 (the Great Depression; World War II, the Korean War, and other wars; the Cold War with the U.S.S.R., the civil rights movement, the resumption of large-scale immigration, etc.), this overall continuity in group rankings is remarkable.

Second, note the nature of the ranking: Groups with origins in Northern and Western Europe are ranked highest, followed by groups from Southern and Eastern Europe, with racial minorities near the bottom. These preferences reflect the relative status of these groups in the U.S. hierarchy of racial and ethnic groups. The rankings also reflect the relative amount of exploitation and prejudice directed at each group over the course of U.S. history.

Although these patterns of social distance scores support the general point that prejudice is cultural, this body of research has some important limitations. The respondents were generally college students from a variety of campuses, not representative samples of the population, and the differences in scores from group to group are sometimes very small. Still, the stability of the patterns cannot be ignored: The top two or three groups are always European, Poles and Jews are always ranked in the middle third of the groups, and Koreans and Japanese

| Group | 1926 | 1946 | 1956 | 1966 | 1977 | 1993 | 2001 |
|---|---|---|---|---|---|---|---|
| **EXHIBIT 3.5** Rank on Social Distance for Selected Groups, 1926–2001[a] | | | | | | | |
| English | 1 | 3 | 3 | 2 | 2 | 2 | 4 |
| American Whites | 2 | 1 | 1 | 1 | 1 | — | 1 |
| Canadians | 3 | 2 | 2 | 3 | 3 | — | 3 |
| Scots | 4 | 5 | 7 | 9 | 9 | 6 | — |
| Irish | 5 | 4 | 5 | 5 | 7 | 1 | 5 |
| French | 6 | 6 | 4 | 4 | 4 | 4 | 6 |
| Germans | 7 | 10 | 8 | 10 | 11 | 10 | 8 |
| Swedes | 8 | 9 | 6 | 6 | 6 | 5 | — |
| Dutch | 9 | 8 | 9 | 11 | 8 | 9 | 10 |
| Norwegians | 10 | 7 | 10 | 7 | 12 | 8 | — |
| Spaniards | 11 | 15 | 14 | 14 | 13 | 11 | — |
| Finns | 12 | 11 | 11 | 12 | 14 | — | — |
| Russians | 13 | 13 | 24 | 24 | 29 | 13 | 20 |
| Italians | 14 | 16 | 12 | 8 | 5 | 3 | 2 |
| Poles | 15 | 14 | 13 | 16 | 18 | 12 | 14 |
| Armenians | 16 | 17 | 18 | 20 | 21 | — | — |
| Czechs | 17 | 12 | 17 | 17 | 22 | — | — |
| American Indians | 18 | 20 | 18 | 18 | 10 | 16 | 12 |
| Jews | 19 | 19 | 16 | 15 | 15 | 15 | 11 |
| Greeks | 20 | 18 | 15 | 13 | 16 | 14 | 7 |
| Mexicans | 21 | 24 | 28 | 28 | 26 | 18 | 25 |
| Japanese | 22 | 30 | 26 | 25 | 25 | 19 | 22 |
| Filipinos | 23 | 23 | 21 | 21 | 24 | — | 16 |
| African Americans | 24 | 29 | 27 | 29 | 17 | 17 | 9 |
| Turks | 25 | 25 | 23 | 26 | 28 | 22 | — |
| Chinese | 26 | 21 | 25 | 22 | 23 | 20 | 17 |
| Koreans | 27 | 27 | 30 | 27 | 30 | 21 | 24 |
| Asian Indians | 28 | 28 | 29 | 30 | 27 | — | 26 |
| Africans | — | — | — | — | — | — | 13 |
| Other Latinos | — | — | — | — | — | — | 15 |
| Puerto Ricans | — | — | — | — | — | — | 18 |
| Jamaicans | — | — | — | — | — | — | 19 |
| Dominicans | — | — | — | — | — | — | 20 |
| Cubans | — | — | — | — | — | — | 23 |
| Haitians | — | — | — | — | — | — | 27 |
| Vietnamese | — | — | — | — | — | — | 28 |
| Muslims | — | — | — | — | — | — | 29 |
| Arabs | — | — | — | — | — | — | 30 |
| Mean (all scores) | 2.14 | 2.12 | 2.08 | 1.92 | 1.93 | 1.43 | 1.44 |
| Range | 2.85 | 2.57 | 1.75 | 1.56 | 1.38 | 1.07 | 0.87 |
| Total number of groups included | 28 | 30 | 30 | 30 | 30 | 24 | 30 |
| Correlation with 1926 rankings | — | .95 | .93 | .90 | .84 | .92 | .76 |

SOURCES: 1926 through 1977, Smith and Dempsey (1983), p. 588; 1993, Kleg and Yamamoto (1998) and Parillo (2003).

a. Scores are the group's rank for the year in question. For example, the Irish were ranked fifth of 28 groups in 1926, rose to fourth of 30 in 1946, and so forth.

always fall in the bottom third. African Americans and American Indians were also ranked toward the bottom until the most recent rankings.

Finally, note how the relative positions of some groups change with international and domestic relations. For example, both Japanese and Germans fell in the rankings at the end of World War II (1946). Comparing 1966 with 1946, Russians fell and Japanese rose, reflecting changing patterns of alliance and enmity in the global system of societies. The dramatic rise of Native American and African Americans since the 1966 ranking may reflect declining levels of overt prejudice in American society. In 2001, the scale was administered in the weeks following the terrorist attacks on 9-11, and the low ranking of Arabs reflects the societal reaction toward those traumatic events.

How do we explain the fact that group rankings generally remain stable over the nearly eight decades from the 1920s to 2001? The stability across time, space, gender, and group strongly suggests that Americans view the various groups through the same culturally shaped lens. A sense of social distance, a perception of some groups as "higher" or "better" than others, is part of the cultural package of intergroup prejudices we acquire from socialization into American society. The social distance patterns illustrate the power of culture to shape individual perceptions and preferences and attest to the fundamentally racist nature of American culture.

**Situational Influences.** As a final point in our consideration of the cultural nature of prejudice, we should note the importance of the social situation in which attitudes are expressed and behavior occurs. What people think and what they do is not always the same. Even intense prejudice may not translate into discriminatory behavior, and discrimination is not always accompanied by prejudice (refer back to Exhibit 3.1).

One of the earliest demonstrations of the difference between what people think and feel (prejudice) and what they actually do (discrimination) was provided by sociologist Robert LaPiere (1934). In the 1930s, he escorted a Chinese couple on a tour of the United States. At that time, Chinese and other Asians were the victims of widespread discrimination and exclusion, and anti-Chinese prejudice was quite high, as demonstrated by the scores in Exhibit 3.5. However, LaPiere and his companions dined in restaurants and stayed in hotels without incident for the entire trip and experienced discrimination only once.

Six months later, LaPiere wrote to every establishment the group had patronized and inquired about reservations. He indicated that some of the party were Chinese and asked if that would be a problem. Of those establishments that replied (about half), 92% said that they would not serve Chinese and would be unable to accommodate the party.

Why the difference? Although not a definitive or particularly sophisticated method of data gathering (for example, there was no way to tell if the correspondents were the same persons they had dealt with in person), this episode exemplifies the difference between saying and doing and the importance of taking the situation into account. On LaPiere's original visit, anti-Asian prejudice may well have been present but was not expressed to avoid making a scene. In a different situation, the more distant interaction of letters and correspondence, the restaurant and hotel staffs may have allowed their prejudice to be expressed in open discrimination because the potential for embarrassment was much less.

The situation a person is in shapes the relationship between prejudice and discrimination. In highly prejudiced communities or groups, the pressure to conform may cause relatively unprejudiced individuals to discriminate. For example, if an ethnic or racial or gender joke is told in a group of friends or relatives, all might join in the laughter. Even a completely unprejudiced person might crack a smile or register a slight giggle to avoid embarrassing or offending the person who told the joke.

On the other hand, situations in which there are strong norms of equal and fair treatment may stifle the tendency of even the most bigoted individual to discriminate. For example, if a community vigorously enforces antidiscrimination laws, even the most prejudiced merchant might refrain from treating minority group customers unequally. Highly prejudiced individuals may not discriminate so they can "do business" (or at least avoid penalties or sanctions) in an environment in which discrimination is not tolerated or is too costly.

**Limitations of Culture-Based Approaches.** Although cultural causes of prejudice are obviously important, considering only cultural factors may lead us to the mistaken belief that all members of the same society have roughly similar levels of prejudice. On the contrary, no two people have the same socialization experiences or develop exactly the same prejudices (or any other attitude, for that matter). Differences in family structure, parenting style, school experiences, attitudes of peers, and a host of other factors affect the development of an individual's personality and attitude.

Furthermore, socialization is not a passive process; we are not neutral recipients of a culture that is simply forced down our throats. Our individuality, intelligence, and curiosity affect the nature and content of our socialization experiences. Even close siblings may have very different experiences and, consequently, different levels of prejudice. People raised in extremely prejudicial settings may moderate their attitudes as a result of experiences later in life, just as those raised in nonprejudiced settings may develop stronger biases as time passes.

The development of prejudice is further complicated by the fact that in the United States, we also learn egalitarian norms and values as we are socialized. Gunnar Myrdal was referring to this contrast when he titled his landmark study of race relations in the United States *An American Dilemma*. We learn norms of fairness and justice along with norms that condone or even demand unequal treatment based on group membership. Typically, people develop more than one attitude about other groups, and these multiple attitudes are not set in concrete. They can change from time to time and place to place, depending on the situation and a variety of other variables. The same point could be made about other attitudes besides prejudice; people have an array of attitudes, beliefs, and values about any particular subject, and some of them are mutually contradictory.

# Power-Conflict Theories

Personality-centered theories and culture-based approaches tell us something about how prejudice is passed on from generation to generation, how it persists through time, and why prejudice varies from person to person or from time to time within the same person. What these theories do not tell us is why and how prejudice begins in the first place. To deal with the origins of prejudice, we turn to power-conflict theories. These theories stress the idea that prejudice flows from competition between groups and then serves as a rationalization for exploitation and racial and ethnic stratification. Several different theories from the power-conflict tradition are introduced here, and this perspective is prominent in the chapters to come.

**The Robber's Cave Experiment.** A classic study that clearly shows the relationship between group conflict and prejudice (and also the situational nature of prejudice) was conducted in the 1950s by Muzafer Sherif at the Robber's Cave summer camp for 11- and 12-year-old boys (Sherif, Harvey, White, Hood, & Sherif, 1961). He divided the campers into two groups, the Rattlers and the Eagles. The groups lived in different cabins and were continually pitted against each other in a wide range of activities. Games, sports, and even housekeeping chores were set up on a competitive basis. The boys in each group began to express negative feelings (prejudice) against the other group. Competition and prejudicial feelings grew quite intense and were manifested in episodes of name calling and raids on the "enemy" group.

Sherif attempted to reduce the harsh feelings he had created by bringing the campers together in various pleasant situations featuring food, movies, and other treats. The rival groups used these opportunities only to express their enmity. Sherif then came up with some activities that required the members of the rival groups to work cooperatively. As a result of these cooperative activities, intergroup "prejudice" was observed to decline, and eventually, friendships were formed across groups.

In the Robber's Cave experiment, prejudice (negative feelings and stereotypes about other campers) was the result of a conflictual situation between groups. It helped to mobilize feelings and to justify rejection and attacks, both verbal and physical, against the out-group. When group competition was reduced, the levels of prejudice abated and eventually disappeared. Several theories, summarized next, make the same kinds of points regarding the causes of prejudice for society as a whole.

**Marxist Analysis.** In chapter 1, Marxism was discussed as a theory of social inequality. One of the tenets of Marxism is that the elites who control the means of production in a society also control the ideas and intellectual activity of the society. Ideologies and belief systems are shaped to support the dominance of the elites, and these ideologies and belief systems change when new elites come into control: "What else does the history of ideas prove, than that intellectual production changes in character in proportion as material production is changed? The ruling ideas of each age have been the ideas of its ruling class" (Marx & Engels, 1848/1967, p. 102).

Elite classes whose high status requires the subordination or exploitation of a minority group will develop and institutionalize ideologies to justify or "explain" the arrangement. The history of the United States (and many other nations) includes numerous situations in which prejudice was used to help sustain the control of elite classes. For example, slave owners in the South used antiblack prejudice to attempt to control perceptions and justify the exploitation of the slaves. If it were commonly believed that blacks were inferior and too irresponsible to care for themselves, the constraints of slavery would seem less oppressive and unjust. People who did not benefit directly from slavery might not oppose the institution if they accepted the idea of black inferiority.

The slave owners also attempted to use Christianity to "brainwash" the slaves into accepting their powerless status. The exposure of slaves to religion was carefully controlled and emphasized those aspects of Christianity that stress the virtues of meekness and humility and promise rewards—but only in heaven. Thus religion was used to stress obedience and to focus the attention of the slaves on the next life, not on the misery and injustice of this life.

In a more industrial example, the history of the United States for the past 150 years is replete with instances of struggle between the capitalists who control the means of production (factories, mills, mines, banks, etc.) and the workers. Earlier in this century, it was common for industrialists to try to weaken labor unions by splitting the working class along racial lines. The greater the extent to which black and white workers fought each other, the less likely there would be a unified uprising against the capitalist class. The capitalist class controlled the racially mixed working class by following a strategy of "divide and conquer" (Cox, 1948; Reich, 1986).

**Split Labor Market Theory.** This theory agrees with the Marxist idea that prejudice and racist ideologies serve the interest of a specific class, but it identifies a different beneficiary. In **split labor market theory**, there are three actors in the economic sector of an industrial society. First are the elites, the capitalists who own the means of production. The other two groups are segments of the working class. The labor market is divided (or split) into higher priced labor and cheaper labor. It is in the economic self-interest of the capitalist class to use cheaper labor whenever possible. Recent immigrants and minority groups often fill the role of cheaper labor.

Higher priced labor (usually consisting of members of the dominant group) will attempt to exclude cheaper labor from the marketplace whenever it can. Such efforts include barring minority groups from labor unions, violent attacks on minority group communities, support for discriminatory laws, and efforts to exclude groups from the United States entirely. Prejudice is used by higher priced labor to arouse and mobilize opposition to the cheaper labor pool represented by the minority group. The economic nature of the competition and the economic self-interest of higher priced labor are obscured by appeals to racial or cultural unity against the "threat" represented by the minority group. The major beneficiary of prejudice is not the capitalist class but the more powerful elements of the working class (Bonacich, 1972; Bonacich & Modell, 1980).

Power-conflict theories share the conclusion that prejudice begins as a side issue in a struggle to control or expand a group's share of scarce resources. The primary beneficiary of prejudice is sometimes the elite class (e.g., capitalists or plantation owners) and sometimes another segment of the dominant group (higher priced labor). In general, though, in the tradition of power-conflict theory, prejudice is not a matter of childhood experiences, social distance, or personal likes and dislikes; prejudice exists because someone or some group gains by it.

**Limitations of Power-Conflict Theory.** The limitations of power-conflict theories are mirror images of those of the other theories we have discussed. Individuals who have no material stake in minority group subordination can still be extremely prejudiced. The sources of prejudice can be found in culture, socialization, family structure, and personality development, as well as in politics and economics. Prejudice can have important psychological and social functions independent of group power relationships.

To illustrate these limitations, consider a recent analysis of attitudes toward immigrants. Burns and Gimpel (2000) found that, consistent with the power-conflict model, these attitudes are contingent on economic conditions: When times are hard and people fear for their jobs or feel economically threatened, they are more opposed to immigration. However, the researchers also found that anti-immigration prejudice cannot be explained by economics alone and persists even when economic conditions improve, a finding consistent with the idea that prejudice is shaped by cultural and personality factors in addition to conflict over scarce resources.

# TYPES OF PREJUDICE

Taken together, the diverse approaches we have discussed in this chapter illustrate the complex nature of prejudice. The various causes and manifestations of prejudice may appear in every possible combination. It seems that no single factor or theory can explain prejudice in all its forms.

Furthermore, even if we could explain prejudice, we would still have to account for its link with discrimination. Individuals with strong personality needs may maintain a high level of prejudice even in situations in which the attitude is disapproved. Some social situations may evoke prejudice or discrimination (or both) in otherwise unbigoted individuals. The changing fortunes and class standings of different groups and the changing threats of group competition may cause levels of prejudice to fluctuate—sometimes prejudice will be red-hot in intensity; at other times it will be nearly absent.

We also need to recognize that prejudice exists in society alongside norms and values that are either neutral or actively antiprejudicial. Racism is at the core of the American value system, but so are the values of equality, fairness, and justice, and these egalitarian beliefs can inhibit the expression of prejudice or reduce its intensity. Some conditions increase the levels of prejudice, whereas others lower them. Any combination of forces can be present in a given situation or within a certain person.

What do we know so far? We can summarize this chapter and make distinctions that will be useful in the next chapter by identifying three different types of prejudice based on their primary causes:

- Prejudice caused by personality needs
- Prejudice learned in response to socialization in a racist community
- Prejudice that arises during the heat of intergroup competition

These are ideal types, and any given manifestation of prejudice could involve any combination of the three.

These three forms of prejudice differ in ways other than in their causes. For example, some types are more subject to change than are others. The personality-based forms of prejudice are caused by tensions and problems internal to the individual and will be more constant and resistant to change. The objective or external situation of the individual will have less effect on personality-based prejudice. This type of prejudice may not increase during times of intense competition, but it may not go away during good times, either.

The second and third types of prejudice should be more responsive to the external situation of the individual, rising and falling in intensity as situations change and levels of threat and competition fluctuate. Because these forms of prejudice play no important psychological function for the individual, they should be easier to "unlearn." In Chapter 4, we refer to this typology as we continue to explore the nature of prejudice and assess efforts to reduce it.

## PREJUDICE VERSUS SEXISM: AN INTERNATIONAL PERSPECTIVE

If prejudice is the tendency to think and feel in negative ways about members of other groups, sexism can be defined as the tendency to have negative thoughts and feelings about a specific group: women. In this section, we raise three questions about the relationship between prejudice and sexism and about their varying levels around the globe.

Our first question: Are prejudice and sexism the same thing? Is sexism just a type of prejudice directed at a specific group? On one hand, prejudice and sexism share many similarities and many of the same kinds of causes. Highly prejudiced people tend to have very traditional ideas about gender roles, and just like prejudice, sexism can be acquired as part of a normal socialization in a biased community. Also, the willingness of people to express both prejudice and sexism can vary by the situation or social context in which a person is behaving, and scapegoating, projection, selective misperception, and attribution can be directed at women as well as at other minority groups.

On the other hand, research shows that there are some crucial differences between prejudice and sexism (Glick & Fiske, 1996; Glick et al., 2000). These differences reflect, in part, the unique status of women as a minority group and their intimate, domestic, and sexual relationships with men. Prejudice toward ethnic and racial minority groups tends to be uniformly negative, but attitudes toward women can have some seemingly positive dimensions, and there seem to be (at least) two kinds of sexism. Hostile sexism (HS) is more like a "typical" anti–minority group prejudice and incorporates negative attitudes and emotions about women. A person who ranks high on HS maintains negative stereotypes (for example, women might be seen as incompetent, inferior, or "flighty") and negative emotions (contempt and disdain, for example). Benevolent sexism (BS), in contrast, might be expressed as an apparently positive attitude of protection and affection. A person who ranks high on BS might see women as "wonderful, pure creatures" who are to be placed on pedestals and protected (Glick et al., 2000, p. 764). It is important to realize that, like racial and ethnic prejudice, both HS and BS promote stereotypical views of women and serve to justify and rationalize their lower status.

Given these differences, we would expect that prejudice and sexism would have a strong but not perfect relationship with each other. That is, although highly prejudiced people will tend to be highly sexist (and vice versa), the relationship will not be invariable or perfect. To illustrate, Exhibit 3.6 shows the relationship between a survey item that measures antiblack prejudice and one that measures support for traditional gender roles. The sample is representative of U.S. society, and results are shown only for white males (although the relationship between the variables stays roughly the same when white females are included in the sample).

Because the majority of prejudiced respondents (81%) have sexist views, whereas the majority of nonprejudiced respondents (63%) do not, we can say that sexism and prejudice are closely related. Note, however, that almost 20% of the prejudiced respondents did not choose the sexist response, and a similar inconsistency is found with the nonprejudiced respondents. This simple test supports the notion that sexism is not simply a type of prejudice and that these are overlapping but not synonymous attitudes.

**EXHIBIT 3.6**  Sexism and Prejudice (%)

| | | Prejudice[a] | |
|---|---|---|---|
| | | Prejudiced | Not prejudiced |
| Sexism[b] | Sexist | 81.1 | 36.6 |
| | Not sexist | 18.9 | 63.4 |
| | | 100.0 | 100.0 |

SOURCE: National Opinion Research Council (2002).

a. Prejudice is measured by agreement with the following item: "The reason blacks, on the average, have worse jobs, income and housing than white people is because they have less inborn ability to learn."

b. Sexism is measured by agreement with the following item: "It is much better for everyone involved if the man is the achiever outside the home and the women takes care of home and family."

Our second question: Is the United States more or less sexist and prejudiced than other societies? Comparing attitudes and emotions across nations is inherently difficult, but we do have some information on sexism and prejudice from surveys of representative samples drawn from nations at all levels of development and affluence. Exhibit 3.7 shows the level of support for traditional gender roles, and Exhibit 3.8 shows support for an item measuring prejudice. The United States ranks low on both variables: 29th out of the 37 nations on sexism and 24th on prejudice.

But remember that sexism consists of two different dimensions. How does the United States rank on HS and BS? Unfortunately, we do not have results from representative samples of different nations to answer this question. However, using samples of mostly college students, Glick and others compared levels of sexism in 19 nations and found, consistent with the results reported in Exhibit 3.7, that the United States ranks relatively low in both HS (16th) and BS (14th) (Glick et al., 2000, p. 770).

Our third question: Why do nations vary in their levels of prejudice and sexism? On the basis of the theories presented in this chapter, we might predict that prejudice would be highest in societies with the highest levels of minority group exploitation and in societies with the strongest traditions of overt racism (South Africa before the collapse of **apartheid** and Nazi

**EXHIBIT 3.7**    Sexism in a Sample of Nations[a]

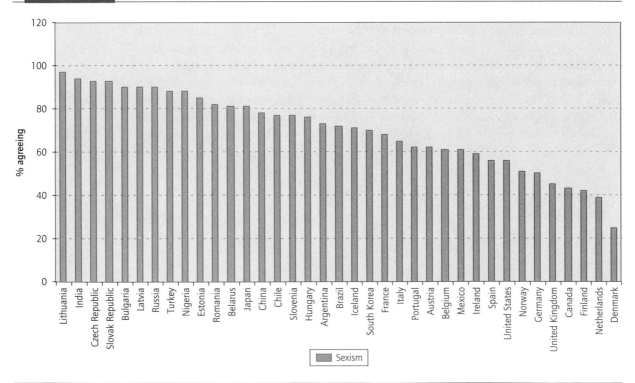

SOURCE: Institute for Social Research (1996).

a. Respondents were asked to agree or disagree with the statement, "What women really want is a home and children."

**EXHIBIT 3.8** Racism in a Sample of Nations[a]

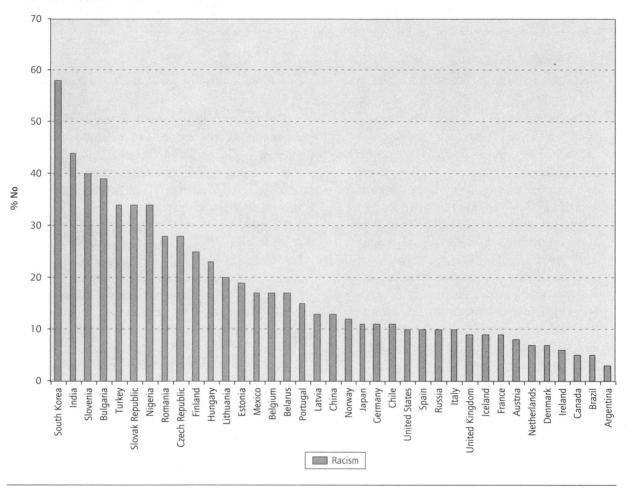

SOURCE: Institute for Social Research (1996).

a. Respondents were asked, "Would you want a member of another race as a neighbor?"

Germany, for example) or societies undergoing the most intense competition between groups (the Middle East, Northern Ireland, Rwanda, the former Yugoslavia). At present, and without denying our racist past, the levels of exploitation, racism, and competition in the United States are less than those in many other nations (see chapter 13), and we would expect that it would compare favorably. The same points can be made about comparative levels of sexism. HS is highest in societies with the greatest gender inequality (Glick et al., 2000, p. 771) and the strongest need to justify and rationalize the inferior status of women.

## Racial Profiling and Prejudice

Racial profiling is discrimination based on a stereotypical judgment of a person's group membership. The issue has been phrased most commonly in terms of relations between the police and African Americans (e.g., being stopped for "driving while black") but affects most minority groups (e.g., discriminatory treatment of Middle Eastern individuals by airport security personnel). Is racial profiling motivated by prejudice and stereotypical thinking, or is it a reasonable practice based on objective information about the relative threats presented by different groups in society? Under what conditions, if any, is it reasonable to treat people based on their group membership? To what extent is police behavior toward the black community a matter of taking sensible precautions and to what extent is it racist oppression?

The selections below present very different answers to these questions. Prosise and Johnson argue that racial profiling is racial discrimination motivated by stereotypes and reinforced by popular culture in general and by "reality" TV cop shows in particular. Taylor and Whitney, on the other hand, argue that racial profiling—specifically, police behavior toward African Americans—is justified by the relatively higher rate of crime in the African American community.

## Racial Profiling Is Motivated by Prejudice and Reinforced by Reality Cop Shows on Television

### THEODORE PROSISE AND ANN JOHNSON

For different reasons, "Reality TV" programming has captured the attention of television executives, public audiences, and media scholars. . . . The media's portrayal of law enforcement and crime tells public audiences about such things as "good and evil," heroes and villains, "morality," and it suggests appropriate societal responses to crime and social problems. . . . The reality TV [shows] that deal with . . . crime [blur the line between fact and fiction] . . . and . . . may influence how audiences view themselves and their society.

The focus of this study concerns two prominent crime-based reality programs: Cops and World's Wildest Police Videos (WWPV), both of which boast of representing the reality of police-suspect interaction. . . . The edited segments in Cops and WWPV, accompanied by narratives and interviews, present audiences with short dramatic engagements between law enforcement officials and citizen-suspects. These videotaped interactions intend . . . to present . . . the encounters between these characters as "real" rather than fictional.

Both programs are very popular, and . . . because the programs offer audiences the "reality" of police work, scholars . . . should consider what the programs present to viewers. Based upon our . . . analysis of these programs, . . . we argue that . . . they serve as justification for controversial police practices. Particularly troublesome, the [shows] . . . may serve as an implicit justification for the controversial practice of racial profiling. . . .

Most clearly, reality crime programming reinforces certain "myths" of crime and crime fighting in America. . . . Central elements of the media's dissemination of crime mythology involve characterizations of police and criminals. Specifically, a central myth of crime in American society concerns those types of citizens who are perceived to be criminals: . . . lower-class minority males . . . and in particular African Americans. [This can foster] a fear of crime associated with minority males . . . [and these] depictions further racism by bolstering audiences' conceptual link between minorities and crime.

Reality TV typically portrays crime as a threat to citizens that results from the pathology of individual criminals—not from the social and environmental conditions within which citizen-suspects are situated. . . . the suspected criminals [are] portrayed as "dangerous people who are beyond social control" . . . Thus, the solution to such a social problem is to apprehend and arrest the individual criminal. . . . By promoting a fear of crime and the image that minorities are responsible for most crime, these reality programs may serve as justification for harsher penalties and even police aggression toward citizen-suspects . . .

The vignettes [depicted on these shows] share key elements. To begin, a clear moral distinction exists between the heroic police and dangerous citizen-suspects. In Cops, for example, one officer comments that "we" are out here to "get the bad guy" and "fight crime." Officers describe their work as "doing our good deed." . . . criminals are "beyond insane," and the well-trained police must use many means, both standard and improvised, to combat them. . . . Whereas police are humanized through the use of actual names and portrayed as courageous defenders against the hordes of the criminally insane, the voice of the citizen-suspects is given little credibility. . . . Police work is also portrayed as exciting, a result of the menace of those who would antagonize the police. Officers in Cops explain that the street is "a madhouse, and that keeps you going." The life out here is much different than his memories of life on the street of his middle class upbringing, opines one officer. . . . Law enforcers are in total control and always in the right. . . .

In general, these programs work to legitimize police actions, even controversial police practices. For example, the celebration of police competence combined with their aggressive behaviors sends a message that . . . aggression by police [is] legitimate, given the intense danger suspects pose to the public. . . . Of significant concern, these programs justify the practice of racial profiling implicitly through the depiction of pretextual stops [where officers pull over motorists for a minor traffic violation or a "routine traffic stop" with the expectation that they will find evidence of a more serious crime.] Such profiling has recently become a major concern and public controversy. Studies drawing on victim testimony, police records, and court records reveal patterns of racial profiling from San Diego to New Jersey . . . Representative John Conyer, Jr. (Dem.-Michigan) maintains that "race-based traffic stops turn driving, one of our most ordinary and fundamental American activities, into an experience fraught with danger and risk for people of color" . . . Although African Americans comprise less than one-sixth of the population in the United States, they make up almost three-fourths of all routine traffic stops. . . .

Our argument . . . rests on the depiction of pretextual stops as an effective method of law enforcement. . . . Pretextual stops provide officers with a great deal of discretion, allowing them to act on a hunch or their intuition to determine who to tail, pursue, stop, and interrogate. Race and suspicion may be tangled in officers' minds . . .

Because the programs under study here show only successful stops, searches, seizures, and arrests, and many of these suspects are minority males, the programming sends a clear but disturbing message: stopping minority drivers or pedestrians when police notice minor traffic infractions or anomalies in behavior, such as possessing out of state plates, or because they are "acting squirrelly," or because they are "acting suspicious or something," is appropriate because it invariably leads to incarceration of serious criminals. . . . Racial profiling is legitimated through the celebration of the intuitive capacities of law enforcement officers.

SOURCE: Prosise, Theodore O, and Johnson, Ann. 2004. "Law Enforcement and Crime on *Cops* and *World's Wildest Police Videos:* Anecdotal Form and the Justification of Racial Profiling." *Western Journal of Communication,* 68(1): 72-92.

# Racial Profiling Is Rational and Justified by Differential Crime Rates

## JARED TAYLOR AND GLADE WHITNEY

One of the strangest phenomena in contemporary criminology is the treatment of race and ethnicity. On the one hand there is a long history of academic attention to differences among racial and ethnic groups in involvement in various sorts of criminality . . . On the other hand, there appears to be media and political pressure to avoid acknowledgement of the differences and possible consequences of the differences. . . . reports which criticize the practice of racial profiling and criticize the "belief" that there may be race differences in criminality get wide media coverage [but] other reports that deal with the actual incidence of crimes as related to race get short shrift. . . .

Different racial groups in the United States commit crimes at different rates. . . . The data show a consistent pattern: Blacks are arrested at dramatically higher rates than other racial groups. . . . The popular conception of crime in America is correct: rates are much higher among blacks than among whites or other groups.

[Do these data] . . . reflect police bias rather than genuine group differences in crime rates? Police actually have very little discretion in whom they arrest for violent crimes. Except for murder victims, most people can tell the police the race of an assailant. If a victim says she was mugged by a white man, the police cannot very well arrest a black man even if they want to. . . . if racist white police were unfairly arresting non-whites we would expect arrest rates for Asians to be higher than those for whites. Instead, they are lower for almost every kind of crime.

Many people resist the idea that different racial groups have substantially different rates of violent crime. However, there are several group differences in crime rates that virtually everyone accepts and, indeed, takes for granted. Men in their late teens and 20s, for example, are much more prone to violence than men beyond their 50s. . . . Likewise, virtually no one disputes the reason for higher arrest rates for men than for women: Men commit more violent crime than women. . . . This is the case for racial groups as well: Asians are arrested at lower rates than whites because they commit fewer crimes; blacks and Hispanics are arrested at higher rates because they commit more crimes. . . . The multiples of black v. white arrest rates are very close to the multiples of male v. female arrest rates, suggesting that blacks are as much more dangerous than whites as men are more dangerous than women.

What does this mean? Most people . . . have an intuitive understanding that men are more violent and dangerous than women. If someone in unfamiliar circumstances is approached by a group of strange men she feels more uneasy than if she is approached by an otherwise similar group of strange women. No one would suggest that this differential uneasiness is "prejudice." It is common sense, born out by the objective reality that men are more dangerous than women.

In fact, it is just as reasonable to feel more uneasy when approached by blacks than by otherwise similar whites; the difference in danger as reflected by arrest rates is virtually the same. It is rational to fear blacks more than whites, just as it is rational to fear men more than women. Whatever additional precautions a person would take [that] are justified because a potential assailant was male rather than female are, from a statistical point of view, equally justified if a potential assailant is black rather than white. . . .

There is now much controversy about so-called "racial profiling" by the police, that is, the practice of questioning blacks in disproportionate numbers in the expectation that they are more likely than people of other races to be criminals. . . . "Racial" profiling is just as rational and productive as "age" or "sex" profiling. Police would be wasting their time if they stopped and questioned as many little old ladies as they do young black men. It is the job of the police to catch criminals, and they know from experience who is likely to be an offender. Americans who do not question the wisdom of police officers who notice a possible suspect's age and sex should not be surprised to learn those officers also notice race.

SOURCE: Taylor, Jared, and Whitney, Glade. 2002. "Racial Profiling: Is There an Empirical Basis?" *Mankind Quarterly,* 42: 285-313.

## Debate Questions to Consider

1. This chapter presented three different types of prejudice. Which of these types is Prosise and Johnson discussing? How do you know? How serious is this form of prejudice? Can television really have much of an effect on level of prejudice? Are these TV shows isolated events, or are they part of a larger pattern in the U.S. culture of racial prejudice? How could you research this topic further?

2. Taylor and Whitney argue that racial profiling is justified—a point of view that might be regarded as evidence that the authors are prejudiced. Would such a charge be justified? Why or why not?

3. Are Taylor and Whitney including all types of crime when they say that blacks have higher crime rates? What types of crime might be higher in the white community? How would inclusion of such crimes change their argument, if at all?

4. If you were the police chief of your town, what specific guidelines could you use to differentiate between prejudiced racial profiling and legitimate policing? What would you tell your officers to not do when they are on patrol?

- Prejudice is the tendency to think and feel negatively about the members of other groups. Discrimination refers to negative acts of behavior motivated by a person's group membership. Prejudice has at least two dimensions: the cognitive and the affective.

- Attribution theory suggests how stereotypes can be used to help people maintain positive views of their in-groups and negative views of their out-groups. Stereotypes come in two main types: One alleges inferiority in the group, and the other exaggerates the positive group traits and gives them a negative twist.

- Theories of prejudice vary by the type of explanation they propose. Theories may seek the causes of prejudice in personality characteristics, in cultural and situational variables, or in intergroup conflicts.

- Personality-based theories of prejudice include the scapegoating hypothesis and the theory of the authoritarian personality.

- Culture-based approaches see prejudice as a "normal" result of socialization into a racist society. The likelihood that prejudice or discrimination will be expressed depends heavily on the situation the individual is in.

- Power-conflict theories help explain the origins of prejudice. Prejudice is seen as the result of intergroup conflict over scarce resources.

- Prejudice is a complex phenomenon with diverse manifestations and, therefore, many possible causes. Prejudice may be caused by (a) personality needs, (b) socialization into racist cultures, or (c) intergroup competition—or any combination of these three forces.

- Prejudice and sexism are similar but distinct attitude systems. Compared to other nations, the U.S. ranks relatively low on both prejudice and sexism.

- The concepts and theories developed in this chapter can be applied in the public sociology assignments presented in the Introduction to Part II in a variety of ways. If you explore the dynamics of local hate groups, for example, what theories of prejudice might be most applicable? You will probably find that all theories have some application, but some might seem more relevant.

- If you do the second public sociology assignment, you will probably find an opportunity to apply the material in this chapter on stereotypes. For example, do anti-Arab stereotypes stress inferiority? are these stereotypes more comparable to traditional American stereotypes of African Americans or Jews?

## Study Site on the Web

Don't forget the interactive quizzes and other resources and learning aids at www.www.pineforge.com/healeystudy4.

## For Further Reading

Allport, Gordon. (1954). *The Nature of Prejudice.* Reading, MA: Addison-Wesley.
   *(A classic work in the field. A comprehensive summary of theory and research.)*

Brown, Rupert. (1995). *Prejudice: Its Social Psychology.* Cambridge, MA: Blackwell.
   *(A comprehensive review of the literature.)*

Bonacich, Edna, & Modell, John. (1980). *The Economic Basis of Ethnic Solidarity: Small Business in the Japanese American Community.* Berkeley: University of California Press. *(Split labor market theory applied to the Japanese American community.)*

Levin, Jack, & Levin, William. (1982). *The Functions of Discrimination and Prejudice.* New York: Harper & Row. *(Good summaries of theories. Examines the benefits of prejudice and discrimination for dominant and minority group members.)*

Simpson, George, & Yinger, Milton. (1985). *Racial and Cultural Minorities: An Analysis of Prejudice and Discrimination.* New York: Plenum. *(An indispensable source on theories of prejudice. Encyclopedic.)*

## Questions for Review and Study

1. Distinguish between prejudice and discrimination and explain clear examples of both. Explain the different dimensions of prejudice and differentiate between them. What are stereotypes? What forms do stereotypes take? How are stereotypes formed and maintained?

2. Explain the three levels of theories of prejudice. State and summarize examples of theories from each level. Explain and evaluate the evidence that has been developed to support each theory. Which theories seem most credible in terms of evidence? Why? Try to think of an incident—from your own experience, the news, or popular culture—that illustrates each theory.

3. Explain the limitations of each of the types of theories. Do some theories have strengths in areas where other theories are weak? Can you identify ways in which the theories can complement each other in a more comprehensive understanding of prejudice?

4. Which type of prejudice is hardest to change? Why? Which is easiest to change? Why?

5. Explain the similarities and differences between sexism and prejudice.

## Internet Research Project

Additional information and a list of relevant Web sites are included in the Appendix (Internet Resources).

Test your individual level of racial prejudice at https://implicit.harvard.edu/implicit/demo/. Follow the links to the Race Implicit Attitude test and try some of the other tests as well. Be sure to explore the site and learn more about the test before signing off. What type of prejudice (personality based, culture based, or prejudice based on group competition) does the Implicit Attitude Test measure? Do you feel that the test produced valid results in your case?

**Note**

1. Originally published in 1944.

# Societal Trends in Prejudice and Discrimination

IF YOU WERE TO TRAVEL BACK IN TIME TO THE MID-20TH CENTURY, YOU WOULD UNDOUBTEDLY BE struck by the differences in dominant-minority relations between then and now. Among other changes, you would probably be impressed by the absence of racial and ethnic minorities from public life (except, in a limited way, in sports and entertainment) and by the strength of the systems of repression that limited the lives of African Americans in the South, Mexican Americans in the Southwest, and Native Americans on their reservations. Today, people of color are visible in nearly all walks of life and at the very top of the social structure. Also, the formal systems of oppression (such as segregated school systems) have been dismantled and minority groups have the same formal legal rights as the dominant group.

Although the changes are striking, some would argue that they are more cosmetic than real and that the actual nature and scope of the difference between then and now is a matter of debate. Consider these two statements:

Over the past 50 years, prejudice has steadily diminished, and the United States is more tolerant now than ever before. Public opinion polls, social distance scales, and studies of stereotyping all lead to the same conclusion: At the start of the 21st century, Americans are much less prejudiced than they were at the mid-20th century.

Over the past 50 years, the most extreme forms of prejudice may have become less visible, but tolerance has not really increased. These days, people disguise their prejudices and express them indirectly. Public opinion polls, social distance scales, and studies of stereotyping only measure what people say, not what they truly believe. Prejudice and intolerance are alive and well but have taken on new, subtler forms. In fact, there is reason to believe that prejudice today is just as vicious and violent as in the past.

Which is the more accurate statement? Can both be true? This chapter begins by exploring the reduction in overt, personal prejudice since World War II and then analyzes some possible causes for this decline. We also examine the possibility that the decline is more apparent than

**EXHIBIT 4.1** Declining Prejudice in the United States

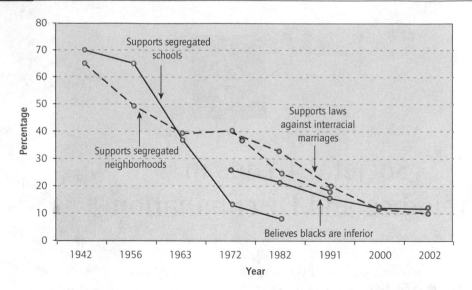

| Item | Survey Question |
|------|-----------------|
| Supports segregated schools | "Do you think that white and (Negro/black) children should go to the same or separate schools?" The figure shows the percentage choosing "separate." This item was not asked after 1982. |
| Supports segregated neighborhoods | "White people have the right to keep (Negroes/blacks) out of their neighborhoods and (Negroes/blacks) should respect that right." The figure shows the percent choosing "agree slightly" and "agree strongly." This item was not asked after 1996. |
| Supports laws against interracial marriages | "Do you think there should be laws against marriages between (Negroes/blacks) and whites?" The figure shows the percent choosing "Yes." This item was not asked before 1972. |
| Believes blacks are inferior | "On the average, blacks have worse jobs, income, and housing than white people. Do you think these differences are because blacks have less inborn ability to learn?" Figure shows the percent choosing "Yes." The first two responses are for 1977 and 1985. This item was not asked before 1977. |

SOURCE: 1942, 1956, 1963, Hyman and Sheatsley (1964); 1972-2000: National Opinion Research Council (1972-2002).

NOTE: Results are accurate to within 3 or 4 percentage points.

real and that prejudice is only changing in form. We conclude with an analysis of a recurrent and sometimes deadly form of prejudice and discrimination: hate crime.

# THE DECLINE OF PREJUDICE

In chapter 3, we examined several studies supporting the idea that prejudice in the United States has been declining. For instance, research conducted at Princeton University demonstrated that the willingness to stereotype minority groups had declined over a 35-year period, and Exhibit 3.5 displayed a decline in social distance scale scores since the 1920s, indicating less perceived social distance between groups and (presumably) less prejudice.

Further evidence of declining prejudice comes from public opinion polls. Surveys measuring prejudice have been administered to representative samples of U.S. citizens since the early 1940s, and these polls document a consistent decrease in support for prejudicial statements, as the data in Exhibit 4.1 indicate.

In 1942, the huge majority—a little more than 70%—of white Americans thought that black and white children should attend different schools. Forty years later, in 1982, support for separate schools had dropped to less than 10%. Similarly, support for the right of white people to maintain separate neighborhoods declined from 65% in 1942 to 18% in the early 1990s. In more recent decades, the percentage of white respondents who support laws against interracial marriage decreased from almost 40% in the early 1970s to about 10% in 2002, and the percentage that believe that blacks are inferior fell from 26% to 12% in the same time period.

The overall trend is unmistakable: There has been a dramatic decline in support for prejudiced statements since World War II. In the early 1940s, most white Americans supported prejudiced views. In recent years, only a small minority expresses such views.

Of course, these polls also show that prejudice has not vanished. A percentage of the white population continues to endorse highly prejudicial sentiments and opinions. Remember also that the polls show only what people *say* they feel and think, which might be different from what they truly believe. Consistent with the second statement that opened this chapter, it may be that prejudice remains strong but has become disguised or more subtle and indirect.

Putting aside cautions and qualifications for the moment, what forces could have caused a reduction in overt prejudice? In the next section, several possibilities are considered.

# EFFORTS TO REDUCE PREJUDICE AND DISCRIMINATION

Under what conditions will people alter their stereotypes and feelings about other groups? What changes in U.S. society over the past half century might account for declining prejudice? These are complex questions, and it will take much of the remainder of this textbook to answer them fully. In this section, we will begin to develop some answers by considering three possible causes for recent changes in intergroup attitudes.

## Persuasion and the Mass Media

**Persuasion** is a form of communication that is deliberately intended to change opinions and attitudes; it advocates a particular point of view and attempts to create agreement. The persuasive communication may be highly emotional or dry and factual, delivered face to face or through the mass media. The latter, particularly television, have become major forms of communication and socialization since World War II and are an important focus in the material that follows.

In our consumer-oriented, politicized society, persuasion is a familiar feature of our daily lives. We are constantly exposed to commercials, paid political advertisements, and partisan arguments for a wide array of different causes, products, and points of view. The media convey cultural values and themes and thus play an important role in socialization and the development of attitudes and feelings about other groups. The media have been used to convey both prejudicial and antiprejudice messages. How much impact have those messages had? What role has television and other media played in the reduction of prejudice documented in Exhibit 4.1?

The body of research in this area is somewhat mixed. Earlier research suggests that the impact of the mass media is minimal and reinforces existing attitudes rather than changing them. More recent evidence seems to show an appreciable relationship between certain types of exposure to the media and a reduction in prejudice. We will consider each point of view separately.

One early study was conducted by Vidmar and Rokeach (1974), who investigated the impact of the popular 1970s TV program *All in the Family* on the prejudices of viewers. This situation comedy featured an extremely bigoted central character, Archie Bunker, whose prejudice and knee-jerk racism were the bases for the program's satire. The producers and writers of the show intentionally used the Archie Bunker character to satirize racist thinking and, they hoped, reduce it. The impact of the show was limited, however, partly because people avoid communications that are unpleasant or disturbing to them. Thus extremely prejudiced people simply did not watch the show. For actual viewers, Vidmar and Rokeach (1974) found that the show basically reinforced the attitudes people already had: The viewers took from the show what they needed to sustain their attitudes and opinions (see also Ball-Rokeach, Grube, & Rokeach, 1981; Hur & Robinson, 1978; Vrij, van Schie, & Cherryman, 1996).

More recent research finds that television shows may be more effective in reducing prejudice. Several studies of American TV in the 1990s suggest that positive representations of blacks on television can reduce prejudice, at least under certain conditions and for certain people (for a review, see Coover, 2001). Repeated exposures to positive portrayals of blacks in the media could "gradually chip away at . . . negative stereotypes," especially for whites who have had limited experience with blacks in their daily lives (Coover, 2001, p. 414). Furthermore, there is some evidence that programs such as "Sesame Street"—aimed at children and consistently exemplifying themes of tolerance and respect—can improve intergroup attitudes among young children (Graves, 1999).

As for the larger issue: It seems unlikely that persuasion and the mass media could account for much of the decrease in prejudice in American society since World War II. On one hand, the mass media today are more positive and balanced in their portrayal of minority groups than they were in the 1930s and 1940s. On the other hand, given the racist, negative portraits that were common 60 years ago, that is not saying much. Whenever the mass media *did* portray minority groups in earlier times, they were highly stereotyped characters such as Amos 'n' Andy or monosyllabic Indians whose only role was to serve as targets for the cavalry.

The media today, although more sensitive to minority concerns and issues (in large part because of pressure from minority groups and their allies), are hardly bastions of enlightenment. Any number of studies document the relative absence of minority characters and the frequency with which those characters continue to be portrayed in negative or unrealistic ways. For example, Asian Americans still tend to be presented in stereotypical roles (e.g., laundry owner, kung fu warrior, "nerdy" computer science major) to the extent that they are portrayed at all. Racial, ethnic, and gender stereotypes—some subtle, some blatant—continue to abound (Bird, 1999; Coltrane & Messineo, 2000; Graves, 1999; Shim, 1998). As recently as 1999, the major TV networks announced a fall prime-time schedule that was virtually devoid of nonwhite characters, an omission that suggests the continuing strength of prejudice and racism in the media (Starling, 1999).

Although the contemporary media may play a role in sustaining and reinforcing tolerance, it is also true that people are quite adept at evading messages that challenge their beliefs or values. *Selective perception* (see Chapter 3), the tendency to filter out unpleasant or disconcerting

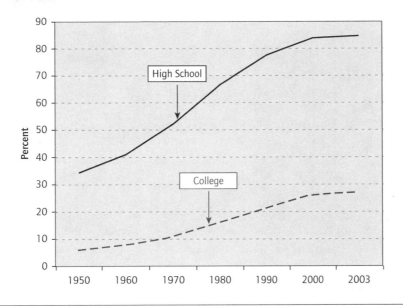

SOURCE: 1950, U.S. Bureau of the Census (1996); 1960-2003, U.S. Bureau of the Census (2005), p. 141.

information, permits people to maintain their views even in the face of massive persuasion to the contrary. Highly prejudiced people tend to be unmoved by arguments for tolerance presented by the media, and unprejudiced people are not easily persuaded by racist messages. All in all, it may be that the mass media reflect more than create public tastes. The media today reflect a society that is more tolerant and accepting but not a society in which all intergroup issues have been resolved and in which prejudice and racial inequality are things of the past.

## Education

*Education* differs from persuasion in both goals and methods. Persuasion aims to change opinions and attitudes, whereas education is more neutral and objective. The goal of education is to inform and enlighten. Arguments and interpretations are more grounded in "the facts," which are (at least ideally) examined from multiple viewpoints. Education involves a more critical and open-minded learning process, whereas persuasion is narrower and closed to multiple points of view.

Education has frequently been singled out as the most effective cure for prejudice and discrimination. Education, like travel, is said to "broaden one's perspective" and encourage a more sophisticated view of human affairs. People with higher levels of education are more likely to view other people in terms of their competence and abilities and not in terms of physical or ethnic characteristics. In some theories of assimilation (see chapter 2), education is one of the modernizing forces that will lead to a more rational, competency-based social system.

Much of the evidence that education can reduce prejudice centers on the relationship between declining levels of prejudice over the past 50 years and the dramatic increase in average level of education during the same time period. From 1950 to 2002, the percentage of

**EXHIBIT 4.3** Prejudice and Level of Education, 2002

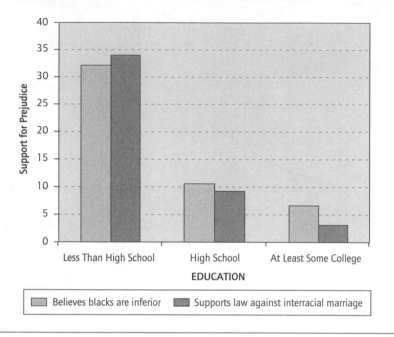

SOURCE: National Opinion Research Council (1972-2002).

the U.S. population with high school degrees increased almost 2½ times, from 34% to 84% (see Exhibit 4.2). In the same period, the percentage of the population with college degrees rose at an even faster rate (more than 4 times), from about 6% to more than 26%. Is it merely coincidental that prejudice declined so dramatically during the same time period?

Many studies have also found statistical correlations between an individual's level of prejudice and level of education. Exhibit 4.3 shows the relationships between two of the measures of prejudice used in Exhibit 4.1 and level of education for a representative sample of white Americans in the year 2002. These graphs show that support for prejudiced responses declines as education increases. White respondents with less education express greater support for the belief that blacks are inferior and for laws banning racial intermarriage.

The correlation between increased education and decreased prejudice supports the common wisdom that education is the enemy of (and antidote to) prejudice, but we need to consider some caveats and qualifications before we come to any conclusions. Correlation is not the same thing as causation, and just because education and prejudice change together over time and are statistically associated does not prove that one is causing the change in the other. Besides education, there are at least two other plausible explanations for the decline in overt, blatant prejudice. First of all, it is possible that prejudice lives on but has assumed a more subtle and indirect form. We consider this possibility when we discuss modern racism later in this chapter.

A second possibility, considered here, is that prejudice has not changed at all and that people (especially the more educated) are hiding their true feelings from the public opinion pollsters. There is an obvious social stigma associated with prejudice, and even very prejudiced people may observe the canons of political correctness when responding to survey items such as "Black and white children should attend separate schools." Also, the limited set of possible responses offered to respondents (for example, "agree" or "disagree") might not record the full range, subtlety, or complexity of people's feelings. As was pointed out in chapter 3, people typically have many attitudes about a subject, especially one as emotionally charged as prejudice. Different situations may activate different sets of attitudes, and public opinion surveys may evoke more tolerant responses. The more educated are particularly likely to be aware of the "correct" responses and more likely to express socially acceptable opinions. The bottom line is that it is hard to determine how much of the apparent reduction in prejudice has been genuine and how much of it is due to conformity to the prevailing and fashionable attitudes of the day (see Jackman, 1978, 1981; Jackman & Muha, 1984; Smith & Seelbach, 1987; Weil, 1985).

As we have suggested, part of the problem here may lie in the way questions are asked in surveys. Open-ended interviews, in which people are able to express themselves in more detail and in their own words, result in a somewhat different picture of American prejudice. In this format, a general topic is presented to respondents, who are then encouraged to speak their mind and not simply select "agree" or "disagree." For example, Gallagher (2001), whose study was mentioned in chapter 3, conducted in-depth, open-ended interviews. Although respondents were not asked directly about their prejudices, their true feelings for other groups often emerged in the conversation. Consider the responses of Shannon, a white female, when she was asked why she believed that blacks see racial inequality in situations in which she does not:

> I think that the black people have a very hard time accepting that they are not succeeding because they don't want to work, when they could work and they could succeed just like—I mean look at all the black people who have succeeded in this world—even in this country—how can they say that we're like, suppressing them in any way. I mean look at all the ways you can succeed. I think that they are blaming the wrong people and I think that the Korean and the Chinese, I don't think they do that. . . . I mean when we came to this country no one had anything—I mean they [Asians] had less than the blacks when they came over to this country, way less. And look at where this country has come. They [blacks] can work just as hard and succeed way above their expectations if they just stopped and looked at themselves. (Gallagher, 2001)

Someone like Shannon might sincerely oppose segregated schools and neighborhoods and reject the notion that blacks are biologically inferior. Yet her attitudes mix negative views and stereotypes (e.g., she sees blacks as lazy and solely responsible for their own poverty) with selective misinformation (e.g., her assertion that Asians had less than blacks when they came to this country). Someone like Shannon could choose all the "right" answers to a survey measuring prejudice but still be highly prejudiced in her views and attitudes.

Finally, research shows that the impact of education on prejudice is subject to many of the same kinds of limitations persuasion is. People evade unpleasant or disconcerting information in the classroom just as they deflect persuasive messages in the media. Selective perception can limit or even nullify arguments contrary to one's point of view, and even highly educated people can sustain a racist view of the world. For example, David Duke, a former leader of the Ku Klux Klan and a politician, holds a master's degree in history (see also Selznik & Steinberg, 1969; Stember, 1961; Williams, 1964).

## Contact Between Groups

Like education, *contact* and *increased communication* between groups have often been suggested as remedies for prejudice, misunderstandings, and hostile race and ethnic relations. A generic statement of this point of view might read something like this: "If only people would get together and really *talk* to one another, they would see that we're all the same, all human beings with hopes and dreams," and so on, and so forth. Such sentiments are common, and a number of organizations at all levels of society are devoted to opening and sustaining a dialogue between groups. How effective are such efforts? Does increased contact reduce prejudice? If so, under what conditions?

First of all, contact between groups is not, in and of itself, an immediate or automatic antidote for prejudice and negative feelings. Contact can have a variety of outcomes, and depending on the nature of the situation, it can either reduce or increase prejudice. When contact occurs under conditions of structured inequality in which people have unequal status because of the structure of society (such as the interaction between Mrs. Smith and Mark Mathabane's grandmother described in the Narrative Portrait in chapter 3), prejudice is likely to be reinforced, not reduced.

**The Equal Status Contact Hypothesis.** The conditions under which intergroup contact does seem to reduce prejudice are described in the **equal status contact hypothesis**: Prejudice will tend to decline when members of different groups (a) with equal status and (b) common goals are brought together (c) to interact intensively in noncompetitive, cooperative tasks (d) with the active endorsement of authority figures (Pettigrew, 1998, pp. 66-67).

Each of the four conditions is crucial to the reduction of prejudice.

*1. Equal Status.* When the people involved in intergroup contacts are unequal in status, they are likely to sustain or even reinforce and intensify prejudice. Not only do the two groups mirror the power differentials and inequalities of the larger society, their members will continue to view each other through the perceptual filters of their customary stereotypes. During slavery, for example, there was a high volume of contact across racial lines because of the nature of agricultural work. These interactions between blacks and whites were conducted in a context of massive inequality, however, and the contact did not encourage (to say the least) an honest and open sharing of views. Under the system of segregation that followed slavery, the frequency of interracial contact actually declined as blacks and whites were separated into unequal communities. By World War II, segregation was so complete that whites and blacks hardly saw each other except in situations in which blacks were clearly lower in status (Woodward, 1974, p. 118). Only in situations in which all groups have equal resources and prestige are people likely to view one another as individuals, not as representatives of their respective groups.

*2. Common Goals.* The most effective contact situations for reducing prejudice are those in which members of different groups come together in a single group with a common goal. Examples of such settings include athletic teams working for victories; study groups of students helping each other prepare for tests; community groups organized to build a playground, combat crime, raise money for cancer research; and so forth.

*3. Intergroup Cooperation and Intensive Interaction.* If contact is to reduce prejudice, it must occur in an atmosphere free from threat or competition between groups. When intergroup contact is motivated by competition for scarce resources, prejudice tends to increase and may even be accompanied by hatred and violence. Recall the Robbers Cave experiment summarized in chapter 3 and the levels of prejudice that were manufactured in that situation. If contact is to have a moderating effect on attitudes, it must occur in a setting where there is nothing at stake, no real (or imagined) resource that might be allocated differently as a result of the contact. If people are bound together by cooperative behavior across group lines aimed at achieving some common goal, they are much more likely to come to regard one another as individuals, not as caricatures or stereotypical representatives of their groups. Furthermore, the contact has to be more than superficial. The situation must last for a significant length of time, and the participants must be fully involved. Standing next to each other at a bus stop or eating at adjoining tables in a restaurant does not meet this criterion; people of different groups must deal with each other face to face and on a personal level.

4. *Support of Authority, Law, or Custom.* The greater the extent to which contact takes place with strong support from authority figures (politicians, teachers, ministers, etc.) and is supported by moral codes and values, the more likely it is to have a positive impact on intergroup attitudes.

**Evidence Regarding the Contact Hypothesis.** One of the most persuasive and interesting illustrations of the contact hypothesis is the Robbers Cave experiment, the study discussed in chapter 3 in connection with the power-conflict model of prejudice and discrimination (Sherif et al., 1961). As you recall, rival groups of campers were placed in competitive situations and became prejudiced as a result. It was not until the researchers created some situations in which the rival groups had to actively cooperate to achieve some common goals that prejudice began to decline. The teams were brought together to raise money to finance some social occasions and to repair the water supply line for the camp (the plumbing had deliberately been sabotaged to create an "emergency," requiring all to respond). After several such cooperative activities, the rivalries and name-calling faded away, and friendships were formed across group lines. Contact, in and of itself, did not affect inter-group attitudes. Only contact that required the goal-oriented cooperation of equals in status reduced, and eventually eliminated, prejudice.

The Robbers Cave experiment provides dramatic support for the contact hypothesis, but we must be cautious in evaluating this evidence. One important limitation of this study is that Sherif produced and then erased feelings of prejudice in a "pristine" environment. The campers had no prior acquaintance with one another, and they were all white, middle-class boys. Thus they brought no backlog of grievances and no traditions of prejudice to the contact situation. The study illustrates and supports (but cannot prove) the contact hypothesis. For additional evidence, we turn to everyday life and more realistic intergroup contact situations.

In another classic study, Deutsch and Collins studied the antiblack prejudices of white residents of public housing projects (1951). This study is significant because Deutsch and Collins were able to eliminate the problem of self-selection. In other studies, participation in the contact situation is typically voluntary. The people who volunteer for experiments in interracial contacts are usually not very prejudiced in the first place or at least are more open to change. Thus any change in prejudice might be due to the characteristics of the people involved, not to the contact situation itself. By contrast, in the Deutsch and Collins study, some of the white participants were *randomly* assigned to live close to black families. The participants had no control over their living arrangement and thus were not self-selected for lower prejudice or openness to change.

A total of four public housing projects were studied. In two of the projects, black and white families were assigned to separate buildings or areas. In the remaining two, dwelling units were assigned regardless of race, and black and white families lived next to one another. As a result of proximity, the white subjects in these two housing projects had higher rates of contact with their black neighbors than did the white families assigned to "segregated" units.

The researchers interviewed the mothers of the white families and found that those living in the integrated projects were less racially prejudiced and much more likely to interact with their African American neighbors than those living in the segregated setting. Deutsch and Collins (1951) concluded that the higher volume of interracial contact had led to lower prejudice.

More recent studies have been based on surveys administered to large, representative samples of black and white Americans and have generally supported the contact hypothesis. Sigelman and Welch (1993), for example, report that although results are sometimes inconsistent and contact has sometimes had a very modest relationship with reduced prejudice, the professional research literature is generally consistent with the predictions of the contact hypothesis (Sigelman & Welch, 1993, p. 793). Also, several international studies with Western European nations found substantial support for the contact hypothesis (Pettigrew, 1997; McLaren, 2003) (For more on the contact hypothesis, see Aberson, Shoemaker, & Tomolillo, 2004; Damico & Sparks, 1986; Ellison & Powers, 1994; Forbes, 1997; Katz & Taylor, 1988; Miller & Brewer, 1984; Pettigrew, 1998; Powers & Ellison, 1995; Smith, 1994; Wittig & Grant-Thompson, 1998; Yancey, 1999.)

**Recent Trends in Intergroup Contact.** Since the 1950s, concerted attempts have been made to reduce discrimination against minority groups in virtually every American social institution. In Gordon's (1964) terms, these efforts increased structural assimilation or integration (see chapter 2) and provided opportunities for dominant and minority group members to associate with one another. Compared to the days of slavery and segregation, there is considerably more contact across group lines today in schools and colleges, workplaces, neighborhoods, and social gatherings.

Some of this increased contact has reduced prejudice. In other instances, contact situations that seem on paper to be highly conducive to the reduction of prejudice have had no effect or have actually made matters worse. For example, schools and universities across the country have been officially integrated for decades, but these situations do not always lead to increased acceptance and the growth of friendships across group boundaries. The groups involved—whites, African Americans, Latinos, Asians, or Native Americans—sometimes organize themselves in a way that minimizes face-to-face interaction and contact across the social dividing lines.

Consider the observations of a 16-year-old white high school student from St. Louis. The patterns he describes are common on college and high school campuses across the country.

> I always notice one thing when I walk through the commons at my high school: The whites are on one side and the blacks are on the other. When I enter the room, I think I'm at an African nationalist meeting. The atmosphere is lively, the clothes are colorful, . . . and there's not a white face to be seen. But the moment I cross the invisible line to the other side, I feel that I've moved to another country. There are three times as many people, the voices are softer, the clothes more subdued . . . and one has as much chance of seeing a black student as a Martian.
>
> The commons is a gathering spot. . . . It's a place where all sorts of things happen. But you'll never find a black student and a white student talking to each other. . . . After three years, I still feel uncomfortable when I have to walk through the "black" side. . . . It's not that the black students threaten or harass me. They just quietly ignore me and look in the other direction and I do the same. (Jarvis, 1993, p. 14)

In this student's environment, the school buildings are integrated, but actual contact across groups is rare and is not leading toward more acceptance or reductions in prejudice.

The contact hypothesis offers a possible explanation for this pattern of separation within integration. The student body in many schools and colleges is organized along lines that meet some, but not all, of the conditions specified earlier for a contact situation to result in lower prejudice. Even when students from the various racial and ethnic groups are roughly equal in status, they do not engage in many cooperative activities that cross group lines. Classrooms themselves are typically competitive and individualistic; students compete for grades and recognition on a one-by-one basis. Cooperation among students (either within or across groups) is not required and is not, in fact, particularly encouraged. The group separation and the lack of opportunities for cooperation often extend beyond the classroom into clubs, sports, and other activities (for an application of the contact hypothesis to high school sports teams, see Brown, Brown, Jackson, Sellers & Manuel, 2003).

The separation might be reduced and positive contacts increased by encouraging cooperative activities between members of different groups—for example, by imitating the plumbing "emergency" fabricated during the Robbers Cave experiment. One successful attempt to increase cooperation and positive contact was made using a cooperative learning technique called the **jigsaw method** (Aronson & Gonzalez, 1988).

In this experiment, the students in a fifth-grade class were divided into groups. A certain learning task was divided into separate parts, like a jigsaw puzzle. Researchers ensured that each jigsaw group included both dominant and minority group children. Each student in the jigsaw group was responsible for learning one part of the lesson and then teaching his or her piece to the other students. Everyone was tested on *all* of the pieces, not just his or her own. Each study group needed to make sure that everyone had all of the information necessary to pass the test. This goal could be achieved only through the cooperation of all members of the group.

Unlike typical classroom activities, the jigsaw method satisfies all the characteristics for a positive contact experience: Students of equal status are engaged in a cooperative project in which mutual interdependence is essential for the success of all. As Aronson and Gonzalez point out, the students do not need to be idealistic, altruistic, or motivated by a commitment to racial justice for this method to work. Rather, the students are motivated by pure self-interest; without the help of every member of their group, they cannot pass the test (Aronson & Gonzalez, 1988, p. 307).

As we would expect under true equal status contact, the results of the jigsaw method included reductions in prejudice. Interestingly, Anglo children as well as ethnic minorities also showed an increase in self-esteem (Aronson & Gonzales, 1988, p. 307; see also Aronson and Patnoe, 1997).

**Limitations of the Contact Hypothesis.** The contact hypothesis is supported by evidence from a variety of sources. However, it would be a mistake to conclude that all that is necessary to further reduce prejudice is to contrive more equal-status contact situations. In many cases, the reduction in prejudice resulting from contact is situation specific; that is, the changed attitudes in one situation (e.g., the workplace) do not necessarily generalize to other situations (e.g., neighborhoods). Both prejudice and discrimination are situational, and stereotypes can be astonishingly resilient perceptual categories. Nonetheless, although this strategy is not a panacea, equal-status cooperative contact does seem to have an effect in reducing prejudice and discrimination.

# Prospects for Reducing Prejudice Further

Three possible causes for the recent reduction in overt prejudice have been examined so far in this chapter: persuasion and the mass media, education, and contact between groups. Before

| Model | Assumes | Proposes |
|-------|---------|----------|
| Persuasion and education | Prejudice causes discrimination | New information reduces prejudice, which in turn reduces discrimination |
| Equal status contact hypothesis | Discrimination causes prejudice | Contact situation reduces discrimination, which in turn reduces prejudice |

examining the prospects for continued reductions in prejudice and discrimination, let us step back for a moment and examine the assumptions underlying these three models for change.

First, note that for us to accept any of the three models as a way to reduce hostile feelings and attitudes, we must assume that prejudice fluctuates and tends to vary from situation to situation. Some approaches to prejudice, such as the authoritarian personality theory discussed in chapter 3, assume that prejudice is a fixed and stable condition that can be altered only by individual therapy.

For us to accept that persuasion and education can reduce prejudice, two more key assumptions are required: (a) Prejudice is the result of misinformation or inadequate information about other groups, and (b) prejudice causes discrimination, or, more generally, attitudes cause behaviors. If people acquire new or better information about other groups, their prejudice will decrease and their rates of discrimination will decrease. In contrast, the equal-status contact hypothesis assumes that discrimination causes prejudice (or behavior causes attitudes). If people behave in nondiscriminatory ways, their levels of prejudice will decline. These contrasting causal models are depicted in Exhibit 4.4.

Both of these causal models are partially correct. To put it another way, neither model is complete by itself. To create a more comprehensive synthesis, we need to recognize that prejudice and discrimination (a) have multiple causes, (b) are not necessarily causes of each other (either may occur in the absence of the other), and (c) can change as situations change.

In Chapter 3, three different types of prejudice were suggested: prejudice arising from personality needs, prejudice learned as a result of socialization in a racist culture ("traditional" prejudice), and prejudice arising in response to intergroup competition. Different strategies are appropriate for reducing these different types of prejudice, and no strategy will work all of the time.

1. Personality-based prejudice will be relatively unaffected by persuasion, education, or intergroup contact. If prejudice is deeply embedded or is an important emotional crutch, it will not respond to changes in information or experience. Counseling and therapy may be required. It may be difficult to reduce this type of prejudice and impossible to eliminate it altogether. A more realistic goal might be to discourage the open expression of personality-based prejudice. This goal is achievable where public opinion is solidly and clearly against prejudice and where there is a penalty of some kind attached to discriminatory behavior (e.g., a fine or jail term for merchants convicted of refusing service to members of a particular group). The greater the extent to which social situations discourage prejudice, the more likely that even people with strong personality needs for prejudice can be turned into prejudiced nondiscriminators or "timid bigots" (see Exhibit 3.1). Limiting the tendency for prejudice to be expressed in actual behavior could minimize the social harm done by discrimination.

2. Culture-based or "traditional" prejudice can be just as vicious and extreme as personality-based prejudice. This type of prejudice differs not in intensity but in the extent to which it is resistant to change. A person who has learned to be prejudiced should be more open to change than the authoritarian personality and more responsive to persuasion, education, and contact with members of other groups. To create more "all-weather liberals," situations that encourage or reward prejudice and discrimination must be minimized, and public opinion, the views of community and societal leaders, and the legal code must all promote tolerance. The reduction in overt prejudice over the past five or six decades probably reflects a decline in culture-based or traditional prejudice sparked in large part by antidiscrimination laws and the protests of minority groups.

3. Intergroup conflict also produces vicious, even lethal, prejudice and discrimination. The key to reducing this form of prejudice is to reduce the likelihood of clashes between groups. The problems here are conflict and inequality, not prejudice. Intergroup rivalries are more likely to be provoked by inequities in the distribution of resources and opportunities than by stereotypes or negative attitudes. Even the most concerted attacks on individual prejudice—powerful persuasion or extensive education—cannot by themselves eliminate this type of prejudice. Group conflicts and the prejudices they stimulate will continue as long as society is stratified along the lines of race and ethnicity. Efforts to decrease hostile attitudes without also reducing inequality and exploitative relationships treat the symptoms rather than the disease.

A major limitation of all three strategies for reducing prejudice is that none of them speaks directly to the situation of minority groups, the fundamental problems of inequality, or the system of privilege that sustains the advantages of the dominant group. Dominant group prejudice is a problem, but it is not *the* problem. Reducing prejudice will not eliminate minority group poverty or unemployment or end institutional discrimination in schools or in the criminal justice system. Remember that individual prejudice and discrimination are not the same as racism and institutional discrimination (see Chapter 1) and that any one of these variables can change independently of the others. Thus we should not confuse the recent reductions in overt individual prejudice with the resolution of American minority group problems. Prejudice is only part of the problem and, in many ways, not the most important part.

Unless there is a reduction in the level of racial and ethnic stratification in American society, individual prejudice will persist at some level despite persistent efforts at persuasion, rising levels of education, and increased contact and association across group lines. The system of dominant group privilege requires rationalization and justification and thus a continuing need for prejudice. Furthermore, the vicious cycles created in previous generations will continue to turn, and minority group inequality will continue to be taken as proof of the allegations of inferiority included in traditional stereotypes. Until there is an end to racial and ethnic stratification, prejudice may weaken, but it will not entirely disappear.

These points are reflected in key trends of the past several decades: Ethnic and racial inequalities persist despite the declining overt prejudice documented in public opinion polls and social distance scales. The verbal rejection of extreme or overt prejudice has been combined with an unwillingness to examine the social, political, and economic forces that sustain minority group inequality and institutional discrimination. Unless there are significant changes in the structure of the economy and the distribution of opportunities, prejudice will most likely decline no further. Under the status quo, we may have reached the limits of tolerance in America.

## Understanding Discrimination

Prejudice is the tendency of individuals to think and feel negatively towards other groups, and the consequences of this tendency can be shocking, horrible, and deadly. As hard as it may be to accept, prejudice has long been a part of American culture. This image of American Nazis was not taken recently as documentation of the current rise of Neo-Nazism and white separatism, it was taken in 1936, on the eve of our entry into World War II. Although we collectively fought on the side of the Allies in Europe against fascism, it still remained with us at home.

With the war overseas won, prejudice, and the desire to overcome it, came to the forefront of hometown American politics and social relations in the form of the Watts and Detroit race riots of the 1960s. In Alabama, individuals who protested prejudicial treatment against blacks were jailed, hosed, tear gassed, beaten, and killed.

The civil rights and black power movements challenged both individual prejudice and institutional discrimination on a battery of fronts: from bus seats to schools to sports. After winning Olympic medals in 1968, Tommie Smith and John Carlos raised their fists in protest of racial discrimination while the United States' national anthem was played (photo, left). For this act of rebellion they were severely sanctioned.

In a great many ways, these social movements persevered over prejudice and much institutional discrimination was banned through the passage of the 1964 Civil Rights Act. But unfortunately,

prejudice has not disappeared. Lynchings have not been relegated to the Civil War past: The above photograph of a cross burning in 1997 indicates that the ideas of racial superiority may not be slowly fading into history, as we would like to believe. Other forms of violence against African Americans remain prevalent today, as illustrated by the image, right, of a black church burned out in 1996.

Although their legacy of discrimination may be the most enduring and brutal, African Americans are not the only minority group to suffer from hate crimes within recent history. More recently, anti-Semitic graffiti defaced the House of Israel in San Diego and in a small Iowa town, a Swastika was painted on a synagogue (middle right). As the tensions in Israel rise, anti-Semitism has grown world wide.

While religion is usually considered a way to bring peace both to individuals and between groups, it sometimes is used to propagate hate. In the photo to the bottom right racism is inextricably bound to Christian ideals, much to the disgust of many Christians. Such bigoted thoughts masquerading as religion fuels antiblack and anti-Semitic sentiment.

A day after its unveiling, a Holocaust monument was defaced with Nazi symbols and slogans questioning the veracity of the Holocaust in which 6 million Jews were exterminated. The questioning of the Holocaust works by putting Jews, the victims of Nazi hatred, on the defensive.

With anti-immigrant rhetoric and legislation growing, Hispanics have also found themselves the target of hate groups, as a vandalized billboard in Texas (below) demonstrates.

While the results of prejudice are horrifying and frightening, the acts of violence are often conducted in the dark by people unwilling to claim responsibility in the light of day. With this facelessness, our American imagination has set up the perpetrators of hate crimes as horrible monsters. This chapter discusses several theories on the origin and continuation of prejudice, but still it is hard for us to visualize prejudiced people accurately. What face does hate wear? It is important for us to remember that members of supremacist and hate groups are not unlike ourselves and may, in fact, be our neighbors. The people pictured below are all very proud to be American. They have, however, chosen to link their sense of patriotism and Christianity to the Aryan movement.

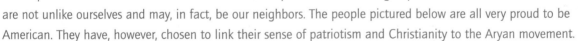

Prejudice may have a familiar face, and an ugly disposition, but does it have a future? Thirty years ago, Martin Luther King expressed his dream of a future without bigotry. How much closer are we to realizing his dream?

# MODERN RACISM AND MODERN SEXISM

A number of scholars reject the idea that prejudice in the United States has declined and argue that it is simply changing forms. They have been investigating **symbolic** or **modern racism**, a more subtle, complex, and indirect way of expressing negative feelings toward minority groups and opposition to change in dominant-minority relations (see Bobo, 1988, 2001; Kinder & Sears, 1981; Kluegel & Smith, 1982; McConahy, 1986; Sears, 1988).

People affected by modern racism have negative feelings (the affective aspect of prejudice) toward minority groups but reject the idea of genetic or biological inferiority and do not think in terms of the traditional stereotypes. Instead, their prejudicial feelings are expressed indirectly and subtly. The attitudes that define modern racism tend to be consistent with some tenets of the traditional assimilation perspective discussed in chapter 2, especially human capital theory and the "Protestant Ethic": the traditional American value system that stresses individual responsibility and the importance of hard work. Specifically, modern racism assumes that

- There is no longer any serious or important racial, ethnic, or religious discrimination in American society
- Any remaining racial or ethnic inequality is the fault of members of the minority group, who simply are not working hard enough
- Demands for preferential treatment or affirmative action for minorities are unjustified
- Minority groups (especially African Americans) have already gotten more than they deserve (Sears & Henry, 2003)

Modern racism tends to "blame the victim" and place the responsibility for change and improvements on the minority groups, not on the larger society.

To illustrate the difference between traditional and modern racism, consider the results of a recent public opinion survey administered to a representative sample of Americans (National Opinion Research Council, 2002). Respondents were asked to choose from among four explanations of why black people, on the average, have "worse jobs, income, and housing than white people." Respondents could choose as many explanations as they wanted.

One explanation, consistent with traditional antiblack prejudice, attributed racial inequality to the genetic or biological inferiority of African Americans ("The differences are mainly because blacks have less in-born ability to learn"). About 12% of the white respondents chose this explanation. A second explanation attributed continuing racial inequality to discrimination and a third to the lack of opportunity for an education. Of white respondents, 31% chose the former, and 43% chose the latter.

A fourth explanation, consistent with modern racism (and with the views of Shannon, whose interview was quoted earlier), attributes racial inequality to a lack of effort by African Americans ("The differences are because most blacks just don't have the motivation or willpower to pull themselves up out of poverty"). Of the white respondents, 50% chose this explanation, the most popular of the four.

Thus the survey found support for the idea that racial inequality was the result of discrimination and lack of educational opportunities, views that are consistent with the analysis presented in this book, and relatively little support for traditional antiblack prejudice based on genetic or biological stereotypes. However, the single most widely endorsed explanation was that the root of the problem of continuing racial inequality lies in the African American

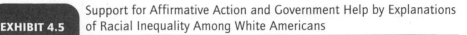

**EXHIBIT 4.5** Support for Affirmative Action and Government Help by Explanations of Racial Inequality Among White Americans

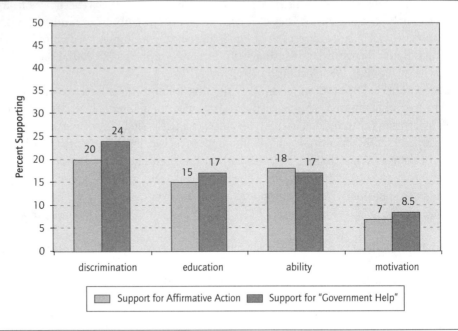

SOURCE: National Opinion Research Council (2002).

community, not the society as a whole. Modern racism asserts that African Americans could solve their problems themselves but are not willing to do so.

What makes this view an expression of prejudice? Besides blaming the victim, it deflects attention away from centuries of oppression and continuing inequality and discrimination in modern society. It stereotypes African Americans and encourages the expression of negative attitudes against them (but without invoking the traditional image of innate inferiority).

Researchers have consistently found that modern racism is correlated with opposition to policies and programs intended to reduce racial inequality (Bobo, 2001, p. 292). In the survey summarized earlier, for example, respondents who blamed continuing racial inequality on the lack of motivation or willpower of blacks—the "modern racists"—were the least likely to support government help for African Americans and affirmative action programs. In fact, as Exhibit 4.5 shows, the modern racists were less supportive of these programs than the traditional racists (those who chose the "inborn ability" explanation)!

In the view of many researchers, modern racism has taken the place of traditional or overt prejudice. If this view is correct, the "report card" on progress in the reduction of racial hostility in the United States must be rather mixed. On one hand, we should not understate the importance of the fading of blatant, overt prejudice. On the other hand, we cannot ignore the evidence that antiblack prejudice has changed in form rather than declined in degree. Subtle and diffuse prejudice is probably preferable to the blunt and vicious variety, but it should not be mistaken for its demise. In fact, there is considerable reason to believe that "old-fashioned," blatant racism lives on and in some ways is thriving. This possibility is considered in the last section of this chapter.

# Has Sexism Been Modernized?

Has sexism, like racism, evolved into more "modern" (more subtle and indirect) forms? A number of researchers have been investigating this possibility and have found substantial similarities between modern racism and sexism. Also, they have compiled evidence that modern sexism is related to lack of support for (or interest in) women's rights, gender equality, and "women's issues" (e.g., sexual harassment). We review these findings in this section.

Modern sexism, in parallel to modern racism, asserts that  (make this a bulleted list like the list describing modern racism)

(a)  there is no longer any serious discrimination against women,

(b)  women (specifically, feminists) are pushing their agenda too hard, and

(c)  programs such as affirmative action are unwarranted and give women unfair advantages over men (Swim & Cohen, 1997, p. 105; Swim, Mallet, & Stangor, 2004; Tougas, Rupert, & Joly, 1995, p. 843).

As with the modern racist, the modern sexist has negative feelings but expresses them indirectly and symbolically. The old-fashioned sexist believes that gender inequality is natural and even desirable; the modern sexist denies the existence of sexual discrimination and inequality and trivializes or dismisses the concerns of women. Modern sexism is harder to detect and measure, in part because it is often expressed in the language of equality and fairness. For example, the modern sexist might express opposition to affirmative action programs for women by arguing that such programs are unfair to men rather than by invoking notions of female inferiority or incompetence (Beaton, Tougas, & Joly, 1996).

Before considering modern sexism further, we should pause to address the assertion that gender inequality is a thing of the past in U.S. society. In the chapters to come, we will present evidence that documents the lower (often, much lower) status of female minority group members. Here, we will compare the overall status of all men and women in the U.S., but because of space considerations, we will consider only inequalities of income. Exhibit 4.6 shows median income for full-time workers and documents a persistent, though shrinking, gender gap. In 1966, women earned about 58% of what men earned. In the years following, men's earnings flattened out while women's earnings continued to rise. By the year 2003, the gender gap in income had shrunk, but women were still earning only about 76% of what men earned. Contrary to the assertion that the United States has achieved gender equality, these results document the persistence of a substantial (though declining) gender gap in income.

Why do women continue to earn less than men do? This is a complex question that would require the analysis of many factors (e.g., the changing American economy and the career choices made by men and women) to answer fully. However, research findings suggest that modern sexism is one important factor in the continued maintenance of gender inequality. The studies indicate that modern sexists are less likely to perceive instances of sexist discrimination and more likely to dismiss complaints of sexism as trivial (for example, see Swim, Mallett, & Stangor, 2004, and Cameron, 2001). Also, modern sexists were less likely to identify instances of sexist discrimination and more likely to use sexist language. Another study (Swim & Cohen, 1997) examined reactions to several situations involving charges of sexual harassment (e.g., an offer to trade career assistance for sexual favors and a work situation in which male employees displayed sexually explicit photos or made sexual comments to female employees). The subjects in the study, all male, were asked to judge the seriousness of these various scenarios. Subjects

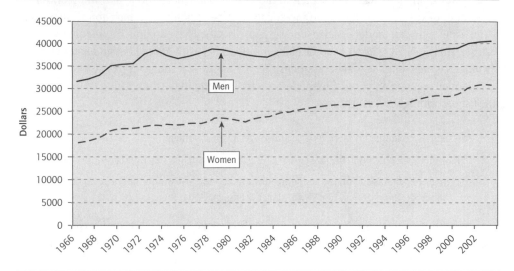

**EXHIBIT 4.6** Median Earnings for Full-Time, Year-Round Workers Over Age 15 by Gender, 1966-2003

SOURCE: DeNavas, Proctor, and Mills (2004)

who scored higher on modern sexism were less likely to classify the incidents as sexual harassment, had less sympathy for victims, were more likely to see the female victims as overreacting, and were less likely to recommend harsh punishments for perpetrators.

Finally, Tougas et al. (1995) tested a sample of employees of a Canadian company that had a long-term, well-publicized, and successful affirmative action program for women and minorities. In addition to being tested for modern sexism, subjects in the study were asked about their support for affirmative action programs, their attitudes about the specific program in place at their company, and their evaluation of the competence of women in general. Respondents who scored higher on modern sexism were more opposed to affirmative action in general, had negative opinions about their company's program, and were more likely to agree that women were not competent and had lesser qualifications for the workplace.

These research projects indicate that modern sexism shapes perceptions and attitudes, desensitizes people to the damage that can be caused by sexually hostile work environments, and predisposes them to be unsympathetic to programs designed to reduce gender inequality. Thus gender attitudes appear to be becoming "modernized" along with racial prejudice. Gender inequality remains a pervasive reality in modern American society and is perpetuated in part by attitudes of modern sexism that allow people to express opposition to the changing role of women without appearing to be blatantly or overtly sexist.

## HATE CRIME: A RESURGENCE OF PREJUDICE?

On a spring day in 1998 in Jasper, Texas, James Byrd, Jr., an African American, accepted a ride from Shawn Berry, one of three young white men driving around in Berry's pickup truck. According to Berry, one of the other white men, John William King, became outraged at Berry's friendly gesture, took over the wheel and drove to a secluded clearing. King and the third white man, Lawrence Brewer, dragged Byrd out of the truck and beat him unmercifully. They then tied Byrd feet first to the back of the truck and began to drag him down a dirt road. After half a mile, they had to stop to change a flat tire, and at that point, Byrd was still alive. They completed the repair, climbed back into the truck, and dragged Byrd for another 2½ miles. Byrd died sometime during that second episode, his body flying apart from the pounding. When the police investigated the murder scene, they found body parts scattered in dozens of different locations. All three of Byrd's assailants were convicted of this horrific crime, and two—King and Brewer—were sentenced to death.

Contrary to the idea that prejudice is declining or becoming subtler, vicious attacks and hate crimes motivated by the group membership of the victims have been prominently featured in the media and, although the available data are not very trustworthy, may have increased in the past quarter century. Assaults and murders, arson against black churches, vandalism of Jewish synagogues, cross burnings, and other acts of intimidation and harassment have all been featured in newspaper headlines and on national television news broadcasts. Furthermore, a number of violent, openly racist extremist groups—skinheads, the Ku Klux Klan, White Aryan Resistance (WAR), and Aryan Nations—have achieved widespread notoriety.

Do these attacks and these groups contradict the public opinion polls? Do they balance the shift to modern racism with an opposite shift to blatant, violent racism? What has caused this upsurge? What are the implications?

As we will see in chapters to come, racial violence, hate crimes, and extremist racist groups are hardly new to the United States. Violence between whites and nonwhites began in the earliest days of this society (e.g., conflicts with Native Americans, the kidnapping and enslavement of Africans) and has continued, in one form or another, to the present. Contemporary racist attacks and hate crimes, in all their manifestations, have deep roots in the American past.

Also, racist and extremist groups are no strangers to American history. The Klan, for example, was founded almost 150 years ago, shortly after the Civil War, and has since played a significant role in local and state politics and in everyday life at various times and places—and not just in the South. During the turbulent 1920s, the Klan reached what was probably the height of its popularity. It had a membership in the millions and was said to openly control many U.S. senators, governors, and local politicians.

Modern day hate crimes and extremist groups do have some new aspects. First, targets now include the gay community in addition to racial, ethnic, and religious minorities. In 2002, about 17% of the 7462 hate crimes reported to law enforcement agencies were motivated by the sexual orientation of the victim.[1] In that same year, racially motivated hate crimes were most common (49%, with most incidents involving white attackers and black victims), but 19% of the attacks were religious (most against Jews), and 15% were ethnic (most directed against Hispanics) (Federal Bureau of Investigation, 2004).

Second, hate groups are not limited to any one region or group. The Southern Poverty Law Center (SPLC), which tracks hate groups and hate crimes around the nation, estimates that there were 751 hate groups (defined as groups that "have beliefs or practices that attack or malign an entire class of people, typically for their immutable characteristics") active in the United States in 2003 (SPLC, 2005). These groups include the KKK, various skinhead and white power groups, and black groups such as the Nation of Islam. The SPLC maintains a map showing the location of the known hate groups at its Web site. The map shows that although the greatest concentration is in the Southeast, Texas, and California, hate groups are spread across the nation and can be found in all but two states.

Third, contemporary white supremacist groups commonly use modern, sophisticated communications technology, including computer bulletin boards, the Internet, and fax machines. Thus the message is more broadly available than ever before.

What causes hate crimes and extremist groups? One possible explanation for at least some hate crimes is that they are fueled by perceived threats, frustration and fear, anger and scapegoating. Some white Americans believe that minority groups are threatening their position in the society and making unfair progress at their expense. They feel threatened by what they perceive to be an undeserved rise in the status of minority groups and fear that they may lose their jobs, incomes, neighborhoods, and schools to what they see as "inferior" groups.

Given the nature of American history, it is logical to suppose that the white Americans who feel most threatened and angriest would be those toward the bottom of the stratification system: lower class and working-class whites. It seems significant, for example, that the three murderers of James Byrd were unemployed exconvicts with low levels of education and few prospects for economic success (at least in the conventional economy). On a broader scale, there is evidence that males from these classes commit the bulk of the hate crimes and are the primary sources of membership for the extremist racist groups (Schafer & Navarro, 2004). In the eyes of the perpetrators, attacks on minorities may represent attempts to preserve status and privilege. These ideas are illustrated in the following Narrative Portrait.

The connection between social class and hate crimes might also reflect some broad structural changes in the economy. The United States has been shifting from an industrial, manufacturing economy to a postindustrial, information-processing economy since the mid-20th century. We will examine this transition in depth in later chapters, but here, we will note that this economic change has meant a decline in the supply of stable, well-paying, blue-collar jobs. Many manufacturing jobs have been lost to other nations with cheaper work forces; others have been lost to automation and mechanization. The tensions resulting from the decline in desirable employment opportunities for people with lower levels of education have been exacerbated by industry downsizing, increasing inequality in the class structure, and rising costs of living. These economic forces have squeezed the middle and lower ranges of the dominant group's class system, creating considerable pressure and frustration, some of which may be expressed by scapegoating directed at African Americans, Hispanics, and other minority groups.

The idea that many hate crimes involve scapegoating is also supported by the spontaneous, unplanned, and highly emotional nature of these crimes. Consider how these themes of economic dislocation and scapegoating are illustrated in the murder of Vincent Chin, the Chinese American who was mentioned in Chapter 3. While enjoying a final bachelor fling in a bar in a working-class Detroit neighborhood in June 1982, Chin was confronted by two drunken autoworkers who blamed Japanese auto companies for their unemployment. Making no distinction between Chinese and Japanese (or American and Japanese), the autoworkers attacked and murdered Chin with a baseball bat. Apparently, any Asian would have served as a scapegoat for their resentment and anger (Levin & McDevitt, 1993, p. 58).

Several studies also support the idea that hate crimes are motivated at least in part by scapegoating. One study found that, at the level of states, the rate of hate crimes was found to increase as unemployment rose and as the percentage of the population between 15 and 19 years old increased. Also, the rate fell as average wages rose (Medoff, 1999, p. 970; see also Jacobs & Wood, 1999). Another study, based on county-level data gathered in South Carolina, found a correlation between white-on-black hate crimes and economic competition (D'Alessio, Stolzenberg, & Eitle, 2002) Finally, Arab Americans were victimized by a rash of violent attacks after the events

## The Dynamics of Racial Hatred

*C. P. Ellis was born in North Carolina in the 1930s to a poor white family. When his father passed away, he had to drop out of the eighth grade and take the first in a long line of hard, poorly paid jobs. The frustration of trying to support himself and his family finally motivated him to join the KKK. During the 1950s and 1960s, he became deeply involved in Klan activity and participated in many confrontations with the Civil Rights movement, some of them verging on violence. Eventually, however, his involvement led him to an unexpected metamorphosis. How many different theories of prejudice from chapters 3 and 4 can be applied to Ellis's memoir (as transcribed by Studs Terkel, 1992)?*

### THE MAKING (AND UNMAKING) OF A KLANSMAN

**C. P. Ellis**

All my life, I had work, never a day without work, worked all the overtime I could get and still could not survive financially. I began to say there's somethin' wrong with this country. . . . They say to abide by the law, go to church, do right and live for the Lord, and everything will work out. But it didn't work out. It just kept gettin' worse and worse.

I really began to get bitter. I didn't know who to blame. I tried to find somebody. I began to blame it on black people. I had to hate somebody. Hatin' America is hard to do because you can't see it to hate it. You gotta have something to look at. The natural person for me to hate would be black people, because my father before me was a member of the Klan.

[A group of men I knew] said they were with the Klan. . . . Would I be interested? Boy, that was an opportunity I really looked forward to! To be part of somethin'! I joined the Klan, went from member to chaplain, from chaplain to vice-president, from vice-president to president. The title is exalted cyclops. . . .

It disturbs me when people . . . are so critical of individual Klansmen. The majority of 'em are low-income whites. People who really don't have a part in something. They have been shut out as well as blacks. Some are not very well educated either. Just like myself. . . .

Maybe they've had a bitter experience in this life and they had to hate somebody. So the natural person to hate would be the black person. He's beginnin' to come up, he's beginnin' to learn to read and start votin' and run for political office. Here are white people who are supposed to be superior to them, and we're shut out. . . .

This was the time when the civil rights movement was really beginnin' to peak. The blacks were beginnin' to demonstrate and picket downtown stores. I never will forget some black lady I hated with a purple passion. Ann Atwater. Every time I'd go downtown, she'd be leadin' a boycott. How I hated—pardon the expression, I don't use it much now—how I just hated that black nigger. . . . Her and I had some pretty close confrontations. . . .

[A series of meetings was organized to attempt to reconcile blacks and whites and focus on problems in the schools. Ellis, as a representative of the Klan, was invited to attend. He went reluctantly but gradually became committed to the peacemaking efforts.] The third night, after they elected all the committees, they went to elect [cochairpersons. Ellis was nominated] . . . and, of all things, they nominated Ann Atwater, the big old fat black gal that I just hated with a purple passion, as co-chairman. . . .

Finally, I agreed to accept it, 'cause at that point, I was tired of fightin', either for survival or against black people or against Jews or against Catholics. . . . A Klansman and a militant black woman, co-chairmen of a school committee. It was impossible. . . .

[Both Ellis and Atwater experienced intense pressure from their respective constituencies to dissolve their relationship.] One day, Ann and I went back to school and we sat down. We began to talk and just reflect. . . . I began to see, here we are, two people from the far ends of the fence, havin' identical problems, except her bein' black and me bein' white. From that moment on, I tell ya, that gal and I worked together good. I began to love that girl, really.

SOURCE: Terkel, Studs. 1992. *Race.* New York: New Press. Pp. 271-276.

of 9-11 (Ibish, 2003). Although not definitive, these patterns are exactly what one would expect if the perpetrators of hate crimes tended to be young men motivated by a sense of threat and economic distress.

Hate crimes can be horrific, and white supremacist groups might seem bizarre, but just how far out of the mainstream of American life are they? It is important to remember that extreme racism and antiminority violence were open, mainstream, and ordinary not so long ago. Even now, they may be seen as exaggerations or distortions of everyday values rather than completely disconnected from the rest of U.S. society. For example, about 12% of the sample that completed the 2002 General Social Survey (National Opinion Research Council, 2002) supported the idea that black Americans "have worse jobs" because they are innately inferior. The most blatant edges of traditional prejudice may now be hidden in polite company, but the ancient attitudes, feelings, and stereotypes that rationalize and support intergroup violence are not so far from view (see Feagin & Vera, 1995).

To be sure, the publicity accorded to hate crimes and groups may exaggerate their importance; they may be less significant than they sometimes seem. The hate groups are small in membership and on the fringe of society, and compared to other crimes, hate crimes are rare. If it is true, however, that these phenomena are motivated by feelings of insecurity, what will happen as the U.S. economy continues to downsize and automate? Extreme manifestations of prejudice and racism are not uncommon in our past and, if conditions are right, may not be so rare in the future.

## Is Modern Racism Real?

*Modern or symbolic racism is a key concept in contemporary social science. A great deal of energy has been invested in developing, exploring, and measuring this attitude, and a number of important studies link it to resistance to racial change and opposition to programs (e.g., affirmative action) designed to ameliorate the plight of minority groups. Although subtle and hard to measure, modern racism has been at the core of the claim of social scientists that the battle for racial (and gender) equality is far from won.*

*However, the very subtlety of modern racism raises some questions: Does it really exist? If it's so subtle and hard to measure, can it really be such an important force in maintaining racial inequality?*

*In the selections below, Dr. Larry Bobo, one of the leading researchers in this area of sociology, makes the case for modern racism. Bobo sees modern racism as part of a continuing effort by the white community to defend its privilege and resist racial change.*

*Taking an opposite point of view is Dr. G. E. Zuriff, a professor of psychology. In fact, after a brief history of the concept, Zuriff argues that modern racism may not exist. His concerns are partly methodological, and his argument raises fundamental questions about the definition and measurement of concepts such as prejudice and racism. How do we really know when someone is prejudiced? Measuring a subtle attitude such as modern racism is certainly difficult, but Zuriff believes that the concept may dilute the meaning of racism and be used politically, as a way of stigmatizing opposition to programs such as affirmative action.*

## Modern Racism is a Major Obstacle to Further Racial Equality

### LAWRENCE BOBO

Symbolic [or modern] racism is a theory of modern prejudice . . . [that] maintains that a new form of politically potent anti-Black prejudice emerged after the Civil Rights era [which ended in the 1960s]. The waning of "old-fashioned racism" . . . which involved overt derogation of Blacks as inferior to Whites and explicit insistence on racial segregation, opened the door to newer, more subtle anti-Black sentiments. These new sentiments fused deeply rooted anti-Black feelings, typically learned early in life, with other long-standing American values such as the Protestant work ethic. Thus, when Blacks demanded integration or such policies as affirmative action, according to this theory, many Whites reacted with opposition based on this attitude. The symbolic racist resents Black's demands and views them as unfair impositions on a just and good society. . . . [This] new type of racial resentment crystallized during the mid- to late 1960s as Whites watched social protest and rising Black militancy pose an increasing challenge to their social order. Although the theory of symbolic racism began as an effort to understand the dynamics of Black-White relations . . . it has been extended to include how whites respond to Hispanics and such issues as bilingual education and immigration policies. . . .

Empirically, research on symbolic racism has sought to establish that narrow, objective self-interest has little bearing on why Black candidates for political office become controversial . . . or why Whites mobilize against school busing . . . or may oppose affirmative action. . . . Thus, for example, having children in the public schools or living in an area where busing is used for desegregation does not affect attitudes on school busing.

In addition, symbolic racism research has set out to establish that measures of traditional, old-fashioned racism do not predict issue position or candidate preference as strongly as do measures of symbolic racism. Symbolic racism has been measured in a variety of ways, with some recent consensus that it involves resentment of minority demands, resentment of special treatment or consideration of minorities, and a tendency to deny the potency of racial discrimination. . . . Symbolic racism researchers have effectively substantiated [that] racial attitudes have changed in important ways; yet, negative views of blacks remain all too common and all too often of tangible political consequence.

[We] have witnessed the virtual disappearance of overt bigotry, demands for strict segregation, advocacy of governmentally enforced discrimination, and adherence to the beliefs that Blacks are categorically the intellectual inferiors of Whites. Yet, overt racism has evidently not been supplanted by an embracing and democratic vision of the common humanity, worth, dignity, and equal membership in the polity for Blacks. Instead, the tenacious institutionalized disadvantages and inequalities created by the long slavery and Jim Crow eras are now popularly accepted and condoned under a modern free-market or laissez-faire racist ideology. The new ideology incorporates negative stereotypes of Blacks: a preference for individualistic, and rejection of structural, accounts of racial inequality; and an unwillingness to see government activity work to dismantle inequality. The new pattern of belief is more subtle and covert than its predecessor, making it more difficult to directly confront.

SOURCE: Bobo, Lawrence. 2001. "Racial Attitudes and Relations at the Close of the Twentieth Century." In N. Smelser, W. Wilson, & F. Mitchell (Eds). 2001. *America Becoming: Racial Trends and Their Consequences* (Vol. 1). Washington, DC: National Academy Press. Pp. 291-292.

## Modern Racism Dilutes the Meaning of Racism

**G. E. ZURIFF**

Despite lingering traces of racial prejudice, America has become, in principle at least, racially egalitarian. This is a momentous change. . . . Nevertheless, charges of systematic racism continue to fill the media. . . . This paradox of a constant appeal to racism in the context of a precipitous decline in racism is in part a consequence of a dilution of the meaning of racism for which social scientists are largely responsible. Historically, racism has been viewed as a set of negative feelings, beliefs, and actions directed against minority races, especially African Americans. Racism was understood as feelings of contempt, disgust, hostility, and hatred toward blacks and a belief that blacks were inherently inferior to whites. . . .

Over the past two decades, . . . problems arose for researchers as fewer and fewer people expressed racist attitudes in surveys. . . . [Some] scholars . . . argued that because of changing social morals, racists were simply too embarrassed to reveal their true sentiments when responding to questionnaires. This group theorized that racism had not died but had simply gone underground and evolved into new forms. As a result, they have devoted themselves to devising innovative methods for uncovering . . . a new breed of racists whose racism is buried deep in their unconscious. . . .

In the early 1970s, [some scholars] . . . defined [modern racism] as "a blend of anti-black affect and the kind of traditional American moral values embodied in the Protestant Ethic. . ." . For many whites, these negative feelings are unconscious, and they would firmly deny possessing racist sentiments. Modern racists rationalize their anti-black feelings in terms of traditional values, and can thereby express them without fear of social embarrassment. . . .

In support of their theory, [these scholars] . . . have shown that voting patterns in elections . . . [are correlated] with scores on the modern-racism scale. . . . In fact, the modern-racism scale has emerged as the principal method of measuring racism used by experimental social scientists today. . . .

At first blush, the modern-racism thesis appears revolutionary. . . . Not only are the motives of those who oppose [programs such as affirmative action] . . . impugned as racist, but the prevalence of racism is discovered to exceed all previous estimates. However, a close scrutiny of the research behind modern-racism theory reveals that what is astounding is not these researchers' findings but rather the manner in which they arrived at their conclusions.

[Modern racism is measured by a survey, and] . . . an unbiased look at the questionnaire statements quickly reveals the underlying assumptions of modern-racism theory. Some of the statements are like this one: "Over the past few years, the government and news media have shown more respect for blacks than they deserve." Although this item does not demonstrate the animosity of "old-fashioned racism," it still suggests a certain dislike for blacks. However, an examination of many of the other items is disconcerting: "blacks have it better than they ever had it before"; "blacks are getting too demanding in their push for equal rights"; "blacks who receive money from welfare programs could get along without if they tried." If you strongly agree with the (doubtless true) statement that the economic and social status of blacks is better today than it was in the past, or if you oppose programs such as school busing or affirmative action and as a result believe that advocates of these programs are demanding too much, or if you think that many people on welfare could find jobs if welfare were cut off, . . . then you will score high in modern racism. . . .

The reconceptualization of racism at the heart of modern racism theory has profound implications. It has significantly lowered the bar for racism, and as a result, the proportion of people thought to be racist has dramatically increased. . . . Modern-racism theory works to discredit opposition to race-based government programs, as objections to school busing, racial preference in hiring, or welfare can now be dismissed as mere camouflage for underlying racism. Even though the theory acknowledges that the "modern racist" is different from the "old-fashioned racist," the use of the inflammatory term "racist" inevitably leads the public to believe that modern racists share the bigoted feelings, beliefs, and behaviors of old-fashioned racists.

In addition, modern-racism theory seems designed to ensure racism's longevity. . . . Its existence cannot be refuted despite its apparent invisibility because it resides in the unconscious mind. And it is guaranteed to exist as long as there is any dissent from programs said to promote racial equality.

SOURCE: Zuriff, G. E. 2002. "Inventing Racism." *Public Interest*, 146: 114–130.

## Debate Questions to Consider

1. In Bobo's view, is American society open and fair? How does symbolic or modern racism incorporate the Protestant Ethic and other traditional American values related to individualism and the importance of hard work? How do white Americans use this new form of racism to support their privilege and resist change?

2. What are Zuriff's objections to the use of modern racism? Is he saying that it simply does not exist or that it has been poorly measured? What arguments could supporters of the concept develop to refute Zuriff? If Zuriff is correct, how could the relationships in Exhibit 4.5 be explained?

3. Could modern racism be measured in ways that address Zuriff's concerns? How? Zuriff seems to be suggesting that modern racism was invented, in part, to maintain the pressure for racial change even after the decline of overt prejudice documented in Exhibit 4.1. Could this charge be true? How would Bobo respond?

4. Is all opposition to busing or affirmative action motivated by racism, as the concept of modern racism would suggest? If not, what might motivate it?

5. What type or types of prejudice are these authors discussing? Personality-based prejudice? Traditional prejudice based on genetic or biological assumptions? Competition-based prejudice?

# MAIN POINTS

- Traditional, overt prejudice has been declining in the United States since World War II.

- Persuasion is generally not an effective way of reducing prejudice, nor do antiracist messages in the mass media seem to account for the decline in prejudice.

- People with more education tend to be less prejudiced, and part of the reduction in prejudice in recent decades may be explained by the rising average level of education in U.S. society. However, the reduction in prejudice may be more apparent than real, and people simply may be less willing to admit their prejudices openly.

- The equal-status contact hypothesis, which suggests that certain kinds of contact across group lines may be the most effective method for reducing prejudice, is supported by a large volume of social science research.

- Prejudice and discrimination have multiple causes and are situational. No strategy for the reduction of prejudice will work on all types of prejudice, and none speaks directly to the fundamental problems of racial and ethnic inequality. Individual prejudice will persist at some level as long as U.S. society continues to be racially and ethnically stratified.

- Modern racism may be rising even as traditional prejudice declines, a phenomenon that may mark the limit of the trend toward decreased prejudice in U.S. society.

- Hate crimes signal the persistence of discrimination and extreme forms of traditional prejudice.

- The public sociology assignment on hate groups has obvious relevance to the material presented at the end of this chapter. If you complete this assignment, you might want to test some of the ideas about the possible causes of hate crimes presented in this chapter.

- The public sociology assignment on Anti-Arab prejudice can be related to this chapter in a variety of ways. For example, you might pursue questions such as: How has persuasion been used to shape American attitudes towards Arabs? How common has equal status contact been?

### Study Site on the Web

Don't forget the interactive quizzes and other resources and learning aids at www.www.pineforge.com/healeystudy4.

## For Further Reading

Pettigrew, Thomas. 1998. "Inter-group Contact Theory." *Annual Review of Psychology*, 49: 65-85. *(An overview of theory and research on the contact hypothesis.)*

Kinder, Donald R., & Sears, David O. 1981. "Prejudice and Politics: Symbolic Racism Versus Racial Threats to the Good Life." *Journal of Personality and Social Psychology*, 40: 414-431.

Kluegel, James R., & Smith, Eliot R. 1982. "Whites' Beliefs About Blacks' Opportunities." *American Sociological Review,* 47: 518-532.

Schumann, Howard, Steeh, Charlotte, & Bobo, Lawrence. 1997. *Racial Attitudes in America: Trends and Interpretations.* Cambridge, MA: Harvard University Press.

Bobo, Lawrence D. 2001. "Racial Attitudes and Relations at the Close of the Twentieth Century." In N. Smelser, W. Wilson, & F. Mitchell (Eds.), *America Becoming: Racial Trends and Their Consequences.* (Vol. 1, pp. 264-301). Washington, DC: National Academy Press.

Sears, David, & Henry, P. J. 2003. "The Origins of Modern Racism." *Journal of Personality and Social Psychology,* 85(2): 259-275. *(Five pioneering and recent sources on theory and research in American prejudice and modern racism.)*

## Questions for Review and Study

1. After considering the material presented in this chapter, which of the two statements presented in the introduction seem more reasonable? Is prejudice truly decreasing, or is it merely changing shape? What evidence seems most convincing to you in support of your position? Why?

2. Evaluate the three possible causes for the reduction of prejudice mentioned in this chapter: persuasion, education, and equal status contact. Which seems the most powerful? What evidence seems the most convincing? Why?

3. Relate the three possible causes for the decline in prejudice (persuasion, education, and equal status contact) to the three general types of theories of prejudice covered in chapter 3 (personality based, cultural, and group competition). Which cause would effectively lower each type of prejudice? For example, would persuasion work on an authoritarian personality? Can traditional or culture-based prejudice be reduced by education?

4. Evaluate the effect of education on your own views and feelings about other groups over the course of your life. Has your education had any impact on your views (negative or positive)? What about equal status contacts, such as those described in the chapter? Have these situations affected your views? How?

5. Interpret the information presented in Exhibit 4.5. How do these relationships support the notion that modern racism is an important cause of resistance to racial change?

6. Define and differentiate between modern racism and modern sexism. How are they alike and how do they differ?

7. What type of prejudice (see chapter 3) is involved in hate crimes? Are these acts motivated by scapegoating? Group competition? Authoritarian tendencies? Develop an explanation for hate crime from each of these perspectives. Which approach seems most convincing? Why?

## Internet Research Project

Additional information and a list of relevant Web sites are included in the Appendix (Internet Resources).

### A. Is American Prejudice Continuing to Decline?

Go to the home page for the Gallup polls (http://www.gallup.com) and search for poll results measuring prejudice. You might search using the key words "prejudice" or "African American." Compare your results with those presented in Exhibit 4.1. Can you determine whether your results support the idea that racial intolerance in the U.S. is declining? How?

As an alternative, do an Internet search for relevant survey results using key words such as "prejudice," "race relations," and "survey." Make sure that the information you find is from a reputable source before placing any trust in the results.

### B. Hate Groups in the United States

(CAUTION: The contents of these sites may be offensive to you or to others. Please use discretion in completing this assignment.)

Search the Internet for Web sites of white extremist or racist groups. Two addresses with links to other sites are http://www.stormfront.org and http://www.kkk.com. Describe and analyze the content of the Web sites you visit and link the material to chapters 3 and 4. What type of prejudice (personality based, culture based, or prejudice that results from group competition) is displayed on these sites? Do these Web sites contradict the idea that U.S. prejudice is declining? As an alternative, visit the Web site of the Southern Poverty Law Center (http://www.splcenter.org). They track hate group activity around the nation, and the Web site offers a variety of valuable information.

### Note

1. These statistics must be regarded with caution. They underestimate the actual volume of hate crimes by some unknown but possibly large margin. The undercounting occurs because (a) not all incidents are reported to the authorities, (b) not all jurisdictions classify incidents as hate crimes in the same way, and (c) not all jurisdictions keep track of the hate crimes that are reported to them. These figures were collected from an area that included about 85% of the total U.S. population. The actual volume of hate crime, although higher than the official statistics, is impossible to estimate with any certainty.

# PART III

## The Evolution of Dominant-Minority Relations in the United States

**Chapter 5**

The Development of Dominant-Minority Group Relations in Preindustrial America: The Origins of Slavery

**Chapter 6**

Industrialization and Dominant-Minority Relations: From Slavery to Segregation and the Coming of Postindustrial Society

The chapters in Part III explore several questions: Why do some groups become minorities? How and why do dominant-minority relations change over time? These questions are more than casual or merely academic. Understanding the dynamics that created and sustained prejudice, racism, discrimination, and inequality in the past will build understanding about group relations in the present and future, and such understanding is crucial if we are ever to deal effectively with these problems.

Both chapters in Part III use African Americans as the primary case study. Chapter 5 focuses on the preindustrial United States and the creation of slavery but also considers the fate of American Indians and Mexican Americans during the same time period. Chapter 6 analyzes the changes in group relations that were caused by the industrial revolution and focuses on the shift from slavery to segregation for African Americans and their migration out of the South. Throughout the 20th century, industrial technology continued to evolve and shape American society and group relationships. We begin to explore the consequences of these changes in Chapter 6, and we continue the investigation in the case studies of contemporary minority groups in Part IV.

The concepts introduced in Parts I and II are used throughout chapters 5 and 6, and some very important new concepts and theories are introduced as well. By the end of Part III, you will be familiar with virtually the entire conceptual framework that will guide us through the remainder of this text.

## A NOTE ON THE MORALITY AND THE HISTORY OF MINORITY RELATIONS IN AMERICA: GUILT, BLAME, UNDERSTANDING, AND COMMUNICATION

Very often, when people confront the kind of material presented in the next few chapters, they react on a personal level. Some might feel a sense of guilt for America's less-than-wholesome history of group relations. Others might respond with anger about the injustice and unfairness that remains in American society. Still others might respond with denial or indifference and might argue that the events discussed in chapters 5 and 6 are so distant in time that they have no importance or meaning today.

These reactions—guilt, anger, denial, and indifference—are common, and I ask you to consider them. First, the awful things I will discuss did happen, and they were done largely by members of a particular racial and ethnic group: white Europeans and their descendants in America. No amount of denial, distancing, or disassociation can make these facts go away. African Americans, American Indians, Mexican Americans, and other groups were victims, and they paid a terrible price for the early growth and success of white American society.

Second, the successful domination and exploitation of these groups were made easier by the cooperation of members of each of the minority groups. The slave trade relied on agents and slavers that were black Africans, some American Indians aided and abetted the cause of white society, and some Mexicans helped to cheat other Mexicans. There is plenty of guilt to go around, and Euro-Americans do not have a monopoly on greed, bigotry, or viciousness. Indeed, some white Southerners opposed slavery and fought for the abolition of the "peculiar institution." Many of the ideas and values on which the United States was founded (justice, equality, liberty) had their origins in European intellectual traditions, and minority group protest has often involved little more than insisting that the nation live up to these ideals. Segments of the white community were appalled at the treatment of American Indians and Mexicans. Some members of the dominant group devoted (and sometimes gave) their lives to end oppression, bigotry, and racial stratification.

My point is to urge you to avoid, insofar as is possible, a "good-guy/bad-guy" approach to this subject matter. Guilt, anger, denial, and indifference are common reactions to this material, but these emotions do little to advance understanding, and often they impede communication between members of different groups. I believe that an understanding of America's racial past is vitally important for understanding the present. Historical background provides a perspective for viewing the present and allows us to identify important concepts and principles that we can use to disentangle the intergroup complexities surrounding us.

The goal of the chapters to come is not to make you feel any particular emotion. I will try to present the often ugly facts neutrally and without extraneous editorializing. As scholars, your goal should be to absorb the material, understand the principles, and apply them to your own life and the society around you—not to indulge yourself in elaborate moral denunciations of American society, develop apologies for the past, or deny the realities of what happened.

By dealing objectively with this material, we can begin to liberate our perspectives and build an understanding of the realities of American society and American minority groups.

## ABOUT THE PUBLIC SOCIOLOGY ASSIGNMENTS

The public sociology assignments in Part III are focused on two controversial issues. Affirmative action, as a tool for combating modern institutional discrimination and increasing diversity on campus and in the workplace, is covered at the end of Chapter 6. How exactly has affirmative action worked on your campus? Has it increased diversity? This assignment will provide you with answers to these questions.

The second assignment takes up a topic of "self-segregation" of racial and ethnic groups on campus. How prevalent is this phenomenon on your campus? What social processes lead students to sort themselves out by group? This assignment connects to a number of ideas presented in this part, including the Noel and Blauner hypotheses (chapter 5) and the equal status contact hypothesis (Chapter 6).

# Assignment 1

## Employment and Achieving the American Dream

Much of U.S. immigration history is characterized by people coming to the United States in the hope of achieving economic and social success. This story of immigrant rags to riches is often referred to as the "American Dream" and the United States itself as the "Land of Opportunity." Is this dream really possible for the average person (immigrant or otherwise), or is it only for white males generally? This assignment is designed to answer this question by exploring affirmative action at your school or a large corporation.

### Step 1

Review the suggested resource at the end of this assignment or conduct a literature review on equal employment opportunity and affirmative action (EEO/AA) issues prior to meeting with the company or school program director so that you are best able to articulate your project and be an informed listener. Your school is required to remain in compliance with a variety of federal and state laws, plus any directions the board of regents or visitors mandate. A passing familiarity with these compliance issues will enable you to productively discuss the project with the director.

### Step 2

Meet with your university or college's EEO/AA director to discuss your interest in studying the school's staff diversity over the past 20 years. The basic question you will propose to answer is whether or not historical inequalities among ethnic groups and genders have declined during the past 20 years at your institution. If you are at a very large university (which as a whole would require a scope of work beyond this assignment), you may want to limit your study to a particular college or school, such as the College of Engineering, Arts and Letters, or School of Business. The college that oversees your major course of study is a good place to start, in this case, and you will probably want to speak initially with the Dean. You may alternatively choose to conduct this research in a relatively large corporation instead of your college or university and follow the same steps.

### Step 3

Using data your institution provides, chart the number of staff in each racial or ethnic group for the past 20 years. Chart the number of male and female staff in each racial ethnic category. As you go through each year's data, group individuals according to professional status (e.g., professor, secretary, janitor, and so on).

### Step 4

Compare your institution to other entities. A good source of professorial staffing data is the American Association of University Professors at http://www.aaup.org. Your institution may have their *Annual Report on the Economic Status of the Profession*. This report can be mined for excellent data. Another source of general income data according to ethnic or racial grouping and according to gender is the U.S. Census Bureau at http://www.census.gov. You will want to obtain data from both the 2000 and 1990 decennial censuses. A good place to start is the Census Bureau's Historical Census Reports, whose most current URL may be obtained by entering the name on the Census Home Page search field.

### Step 5

Compare the data trends you obtained for your institution, universities nationwide, and the U.S. population as a whole. Your object is to try to decide whether affirmative action and equal employment opportunity laws are creating a trend toward reduced inequalities among historically advantaged and disadvantaged populations.

### Step 6

Present your data in spreadsheet and chart form with accompanying summary descriptions and analyses of the data to the EEO/AA director and his or her chief academic officer (this may be a dean, provost, or chancellor). Ask them to inform you of any initiatives implemented to improve the recruitment, retention, and promotion of historically disadvantaged populations as a result of your study.

### Step 7

Congratulate yourself for hard work well done!

### Suggested Resource

Vander Waerdt, Lois. 1997. Affirmative Action in Higher Education: A Source Book (3rd ed.). St. Louis, MO: Employment Partnership.

# Assignment 2
## Ethnic Self-Segregation in College

Many schools are characterized by the tendency for ethnic groups, like other groups, to self-segregate. This can be observed in dining halls, the student center, residence halls, and classrooms. The social risk of this phenomenon is that people are not given the opportunity to discover the rich diversity their classmates bring to campus. Individuals who do not experience much contact with minority groups will fail to learn the common ground they share. The end result is often the perpetuation of ethnocentrism, increased competition, and eventual differentials in power among students. Following the Noel hypothesis outlined in Part III, these conditions lead to some form of ethnic or racial stratification (social inequality), not just in society at large but within the college or university itself.

This assignment is designed as a group research project for approximately five students, who will gauge the degree of self-segregation in the college or university and determine its social implications. The research design is primarily unobtrusive.

### Step 1

Form your research team and divide the labor according to individual interest and ability. The basis of your group's research design is unobtrusive observation of group clustering in a variety of social environments. These environments are likely to include dining facilities, the student center or union, residence halls, classrooms, and the library. You may, of course, choose other places to observe people based on your own experience. One member of the team should request student demographic data from the admissions office or dean of students' office to construct a series of numbers-based diversity profiles of the student body.

### Step 2

Over a 2-week period, go to your chosen or assigned location(s) and observe how people congregate. Take notes on your observations, including ethnic similarity or difference, gender, age, behavior and mannerisms of individuals and groups, and other characteristics you determine are noteworthy. Be sure to go to your locations at different times of the day and to continuously observe for at least 1 hour at a time. You should have approximately 10 hours of observation recorded for each location.

### Step 3

As a group, review your notes and look for patterns in the way people group themselves, separate themselves from others, and behave. The student who compiles the demographic data should present her or his charts and insight to the group regarding what is institutionally known about the student body.

### Step 4

Brainstorm questions that might be asked of individuals in a personal interview. The following are a few questions that might be asked, but your group should collectively decide the final questions to ask based on the unique insight derived from the observations and demographic data.

- How do you define your ethnic identity?
- How do you define other students' ethnic identities?
- Are there school clubs or activities that promote ethnic segregation or blending?
- In your experience, do students use their ethnic consciousness to self-segregate?

### Step 5

Conduct three or four interviews per researcher. Be sure to take note of material your informants provide you with, and raise questions not initially considered that may present themselves.

### Step 6

Gather as a group and share the results of your interviews with each other. Explore the patterns in the responses and particularly cogent responses to get a better understanding of how the informants perceive ethnic stratification, consciousness, and segregation.

**Step 7**

Collaboratively write the results of your group research. The paper should contain an executive summary; discussion of methods; discussion of observation, demographic, and interview data; and conclusion regarding the prevalence and character of self-segregation at your college or university.

**Step 8**

Present a copy of your paper and data to the dean of students and ask that he or she share with each researcher any policy changes that might result from the research.

**Step 9**

Do not forget to congratulate yourself for socially sensitive work well done, and the next time you are at the dining facility, consider eating with someone or some group you have not joined before. It's likely that you will no longer be surprised at how much you have in common now that you have conducted this research.

# The Development of Dominant-Minority Group Relations in Preindustrial America

## The Origins of Slavery

FROM THE FIRST SETTLEMENTS IN THE 1600S UNTIL THE 19TH CENTURY, MOST PEOPLE living in what was to become the United States relied directly on farming for food, shelter, and other necessities of life. In an agricultural society, land and labor are central concerns, and the struggle to control these resources led directly to the creation of minority group status for three groups: African Americans, American Indians, and Mexican Americans. Why did the colonists create slavery? Why were Africans enslaved but not American Indians or Europeans? Why did American Indians lose their land and most of their population by the 1890s? How did the Mexican population in the Southwest become "Mexican Americans"? How did the experience of becoming a subordinated minority group vary by gender?

In this chapter, the concepts introduced in Parts I and II will be used to answer these questions. Some new ideas and theories will also be introduced, and by the end of the chapter, we will have developed a theoretical model of the process that leads to the creation of a minority group. The creation of black slavery in colonial America, arguably the single most significant event in the early years of this nation, will be used to illustrate the process of minority group creation. We will also consider the subordination of American Indians and Mexican Americans—two more historical events of great significance—as additional case studies. We will follow the experiences of African Americans through the days of segregation (Chapter 6) and into the contemporary era (Chapter 7). The story of the development of minority group status for American Indians and Mexican Americans will be picked up again in Chapters 8 and 9, respectively.

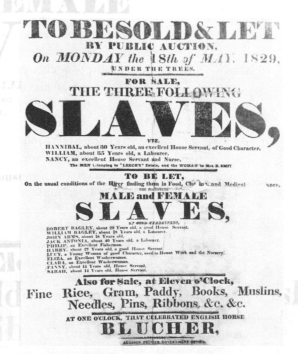

TO BE SOLD & LET
BY PUBLIC AUCTION,
On MONDAY the 18th of MAY, 1829,
UNDER THE TREES.

FOR SALE,
THE THREE FOLLOWING

# SLAVES,
VIZ.

HANNIBAL, about 30 Years old, an excellent House Servant, of Good Character.
WILLIAM, about 35 Years old, a Labourer.
NANCY, an excellent House Servant and Nurse.

The MEN belonging to "LEECH'S" Estate, and the WOMAN to Mrs. D. SMIT

TO BE LET,
On the usual conditions of the Hirer finding them in Food, Clothing and Medical attendance, THE FOLLOWING

MALE and FEMALE

# SLAVES,

ROBERT BAGLEY, about 20 Years old, a good House Servant.
WILLIAM BAGLEY, about 18 Years old, a Labourer.
JOHN ARMS, about 18 Years old.
JACK ANTONIA, about 40 Years old, a Labourer.
PHILIP, an Excellent Fisherman.
HARRY, about 27 Years old, a good House Servant.
LUCY, a Young Woman of good Character, used to House Work and the Nursery.
ELIZA, an Excellent Washerwoman.
CLARA, an Excellent House Servant.
FANNY, about 14 Years old, House Servant.
SARAH, about 14 Years old, House Servant.

Also for Sale, at Eleven o'Clock,
Fine Rice, Gram, Paddy, Books, Muslins, Needles, Pins, Ribbons, &c. &c.

AT ONE OCLOCK, THAT CELEBRATED ENGLISH HORSE

BLUCHER,

ADDISON PRINTER GOVERNMENT OFFICE.

Two broad themes underlie this chapter and, indeed, the remainder of the text:

1. The nature of dominant-minority group relations at any point in time is largely a function of the characteristics of the society as a whole. The situation of a minority group will reflect the realities of everyday social life and particularly the subsistence technology (the means by which the society satisfies basic needs such as food and shelter). As explained by Gerhard Lenski (see chapter 1), the subsistence technology of a society acts as a foundation, shaping and affecting every other aspect of the social structure, including minority group relations.

2. The contact situation—the conditions under which groups first come together—is the single most significant factor in the creation of minority group status. The nature of the contact situation has long-lasting consequences for the minority group and the extent of racial or ethnic stratification, the levels of racism and prejudice, the possibilities for assimilation and pluralism, and virtually every other aspect of the dominant-minority relationship.

## THE ORIGINS OF SLAVERY IN AMERICA

By the beginning of the 1600s, Spanish explorers had conquered much of Central and South America, and the influx of gold, silver, and other riches from the New World had made Spain a powerful nation. Following Spain's lead, England proceeded to establish its presence in the Western Hemisphere, but its efforts at colonization were more modest than those of Spain. By the early 1600s, only two small colonies had been established: Plymouth, settled by pious Protestant families, and Jamestown, populated primarily by males seeking their fortunes.

By 1619, the British colony at Jamestown, Virginia, had survived for more than a decade. The residents of the settlement had fought with the local natives and struggled continuously to eke out a living from the land. Starvation, disease, and death were frequent visitors, and the future of the enterprise continued to be in doubt.

In August of that year, a Dutch ship arrived in colonial Virginia. The master of the ship needed provisions and offered to trade his only cargo: about 20 black Africans. Many of the details of this transaction have been lost and we probably will never know exactly how these people came to be chained in the hold of a ship. Regardless, this brief episode was a landmark event in the formation of what would become the United States. In combination with the strained relations between the English settlers and American Indians, the presence of these first few Africans raised an issue that has never been fully resolved: How should different groups in this society relate to each other?

The colonists at Jamestown had no ready answer. In 1619, England and its colonies did not practice slavery, so these first Africans were probably incorporated into colonial society as **indentured servants**, contract laborers who are obligated to serve a master for a specific number of years. At the end of the indenture, or contract, the servant became a free citizen. The colonies depended heavily on indentured servants from the British Isles for labor, and this status apparently provided a convenient way of defining the newcomers from Africa, who were, after all, treated as commodities and exchanged for food and water.

The position of African indentured servants in the colonies remained ambiguous for several decades. American slavery evolved gradually and in small steps; in fact, there was little demand for African labor during the years following 1619. By 1625, there still were only 23 blacks in Virginia, and that number had increased to perhaps 300 by midcentury (Franklin & Moss,

1994, p. 57). In the decades before the dawn of slavery, we know that some African indentured servants did become free citizens. Some became successful farmers and landowners and, like their white neighbors, purchased African and white indentured servants themselves (Smedley, 1999, p. 97). By the 1650s, however, many African Americans (and their offspring) were being treated as the property of others, or in other words, as slaves (Morgan, 1975, p. 154).

It was not until the 1660s that the first laws defining slavery were enacted. In the century that followed, hundreds of additional laws were passed to clarify and formalize the status of Africans in colonial America. By the 1750s, slavery had been clearly defined in law and in custom, and the idea that a person could own another person—not just the labor or the energy or the work of a person, but the actual person—had been thoroughly institutionalized.

What caused slavery? The gradual evolution and low demand for indentured servants from Africa suggest that slavery was not somehow inevitable or preordained. Why did the colonists deliberately create this repressive system? Why did they reach out all the way to Africa for their slaves? If they wanted to create a slave system, why didn't they enslave the American Indians nearby or the white indentured servants already present in the colonies?

## The Labor Supply Problem

American colonists of the 1600s saw slavery as a solution to several problems they faced. The business of the colonies was agriculture, and farm work at this time was **labor intensive**, performed almost entirely by hand. The industrial revolution was two centuries in the future, and there were few machines or labor-saving devices available to ease the everyday burden of work. A successful harvest depended largely on human effort.

As colonial society grew and developed, a specific form of agricultural production began to emerge. The **plantation system** was based on cultivating and exporting crops such as sugar, tobacco, and rice on large tracts of land using a large, cheap labor force. Profit margins tended to be small, so planters sought to stabilize their incomes by farming in volume and keeping the costs of production as low as possible. Profits in the labor-intensive plantation system could be maximized if a large, disciplined, and cheap workforce could be maintained by the landowners (Curtin, 1990; Morgan, 1975).

At about the same time the plantation system began to emerge, the supply of white indentured servants from the British Isles began to dwindle. Furthermore, the white indentured servants who did come to the colonies had to be released from their indenture every few years. Land was available, and these newly freed citizens tended to strike out on their own. Thus landowners who relied on white indentured servants had to deal with high turnover rates in their workforces and faced a continually uncertain supply of labor.

Attempts to solve the labor supply problem by using American Indians failed. The tribes closest to the colonies were sometimes exploited for manpower. However, by the time the plantation system had evolved, the local tribes had dwindled in numbers as a result of warfare and disease. Other Indian nations across the continent retained enough power to resist enslavement, and it was relatively easy for American Indians to escape back to their kinfolk.

This left black Africans as a potential source of manpower. The slave trade from Africa to the Spanish and Portuguese colonies of South America was firmly established by the mid-1600s and could be expanded to fill the needs of the British colonies as well. The colonists came to see slaves imported from Africa as the most logical, cost-effective way to solve their vexing shortage of labor. The colonists created slavery to cultivate their lands and generate profits, status, and success. The paradox at the core of U.S. society had been established: The construction of a social system devoted to freedom and individual liberty "in the New World was made possible only by the revival of an institution of naked tyranny foresworn for centuries in the Old" (Lacy, 1972, p. 22).

## The Contact Situation

The conditions under which groups first come into contact determine the immediate fate of the minority group and shape intergroup relations for years to come. Two theories serve as analytical guides in understanding this crucial phase of group relationships.

**The Noel Hypothesis.** Sociologist Donald Noel (1968) identifies three features of the contact situation that in combination lead to some form of inequality between groups. The **Noel hypothesis** states: *If two or more groups come together in a contact situation characterized by ethnocentrism, competition, and a differential in power, then some form of racial or ethnic stratification will result* (p. 163). If the contact situation has all three characteristics, some dominant-minority group structure will be created.

Noel's first characteristic, **ethnocentrism**, is the tendency to judge other groups, societies, or lifestyles by the standards of one's own culture. Ethnocentrism is probably a universal component of human society, and some degree of ethnocentrism is essential to the maintenance of social solidarity and cohesion. Without some minimal level of pride in and loyalty to one's own society and cultural traditions, there would be no particular reason to observe the norms and laws, honor the sacred symbols, or cooperate with others in doing the daily work of society.

Regardless of its importance, ethnocentrism can have negative consequences. At its worst, it can lead to the view that other cultures and peoples are not just different but inferior. At the very least, ethnocentrism creates a social boundary line that members of the groups involved will recognize and observe. When ethnocentrism exists in any degree, people will tend to sort themselves out along group lines and identify characteristics that differentiate "us" from "them."

**Competition** is a struggle over a scarce commodity. As we saw in chapters 3 and 4, competition between groups often leads to harsh negative feelings (prejudice) and hostile actions (discrimination). In competitive contact situations, the victorious group becomes the dominant group, and the losers become the minority group. The competition may center on land, labor, jobs, housing, educational opportunities, political office, or anything else that is mutually desired by both groups or that one group has and the other group wants. Competition provides the eventual dominant group with the motivation to establish superiority. The dominant group serves its own interests by ending the competition and exploiting, controlling, eliminating, or otherwise dominating the minority group.

The third feature of the contact situation is a **differential in power** between the groups. Power, as you recall from Chapter 1, is the ability of a group to achieve its goals even in the face of opposition from other groups. The amount of power commanded by a group is a function of three factors. First, the size of the group can make a difference, and all other things being equal, larger groups are more powerful. Second, in addition to raw numbers, the degree of organization, discipline, and the quality of group leadership can make a difference in the ability of a group to pursue its goals. A third component of power is resources: anything that

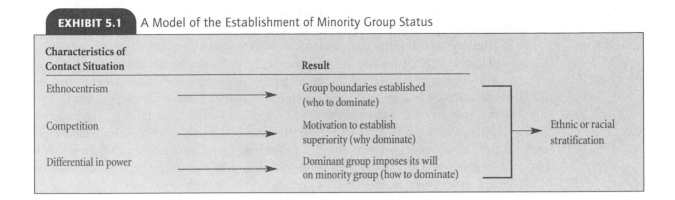

**EXHIBIT 5.1** A Model of the Establishment of Minority Group Status

| Characteristics of Contact Situation | | Result | |
|---|---|---|---|
| Ethnocentrism | → | Group boundaries established (who to dominate) | |
| Competition | → | Motivation to establish superiority (why dominate) | → Ethnic or racial stratification |
| Differential in power | → | Dominant group imposes its will on minority group (how to dominate) | |

can be used to help the group achieve its goals. Depending on the context, resources might include anything from land to information to money. The greater the number and variety of resources at the disposal of a group, the greater that group's potential ability to dominate other groups. Thus a larger, better organized group with more resources at its disposal will generally be able to impose its will on smaller, less well-organized groups with fewer resources. The Noel hypothesis is diagrammed in Exhibit 5.1.

Note the respective functions of each of the three factors in shaping the contact situation and the emergence of inequality. If ethnocentrism is present, the groups will recognize their differences and maintain their boundaries. If competition is also present, the group that eventually dominates will attempt to maximize its share of scarce commodities by controlling or subordinating the group that eventually becomes the "minority" group. The differential in power allows the dominant group to succeed in establishing a superior position. Ethnocentrism tells the dominant group *who* to dominate, competition tells the dominant group *why* it should establish a structure of dominance, and power is *how* the dominant group's will is imposed on the minority group.

The Noel hypothesis can be applied to the creation of minority groups in a variety of situations. We will also use the model to analyze changes in dominant-minority structures over time.

**The Blauner Hypothesis.** The contact situation has also been analyzed by sociologist Robert Blauner, in his book *Racial Oppression in America* (1972). Blauner identifies two different initial relationships—colonization and immigration—and hypothesizes that *minority groups created by colonization will experience more intense prejudice, racism, and discrimination than those created by immigration. Furthermore, the disadvantaged status of colonized groups will persist longer and be more difficult to overcome than the disadvantaged status faced by groups created by immigration.*

**Colonized minority groups,** such as African Americans, are forced into minority status by the superior military and political power of the dominant group. At the time of contact with the dominant group, colonized groups are subjected to massive inequalities and attacks on their cultures. They are assigned to positions, such as slave status, from which any form of assimilation is extremely difficult and perhaps even forbidden by the dominant group. Frequently, members of the minority group are identified by highly visible racial or physical characteristics that maintain and reinforce the oppressive system. Thus minority groups created by colonization experience harsher and more persistent rejection and oppression than groups created by immigration.

**Immigrant minority groups** are at least in part voluntary participants in the host society. That is, although the decision to immigrate may be motivated by extreme pressures, such as famine or political persecution, immigrant groups have at least some control over their destination and their position in the host society. As a result, they do not occupy positions that are as markedly inferior as those of colonized groups. They retain enough internal organization and resources to pursue their own self-interests, and they commonly experience more rapid acceptance and easier movement to equality. The boundaries between groups are not so rigidly maintained, especially when the groups are racially similar. In discussing European immigrant groups, for example, Blauner (1972) states that entering into American society

> involved a degree of choice and self-direction that was for the most part denied to people of color. Voluntary immigration made it more likely that . . . European . . . ethnic groups would identify with America and see the host culture as a positive opportunity. (p. 56)

Acculturation and, particularly, integration were significantly more possible for European immigrant groups than for the groups formed under conquest or colonization.

Blauner stresses that these initial differences have consequences that persist long after the original contact. For example, based on measures of equality or integration into the secondary sector (see chapter 2), such as average income, years of education, and unemployment rate, the descendants of the European immigrants are equal with national norms today (see chapter 12 for specific data). In contrast, the descendants of colonized and conquered groups (e.g., African Americans) are, on the average, below the national norms on virtually all measures of equality and integration (see chapters 7-11 for specific data).

Blauner's two types of minority groups lie at opposite ends of a continuum, but there are intermediate positions between the extremes. Enclave and middleman minorities (see chapter 2) often originate as immigrant groups who bring some resources and thus have more opportunities than colonized minority groups to carve out places for themselves in the host society. Unlike European groups, however, many of these minorities are also racially distinguishable, and certain kinds of opportunities may be closed to them. For instance, U.S. citizenship was expressly forbidden to immigrants from China for most of the last 100 years. Federal laws restricted the entrance of Chinese immigrants, and state and local laws restricted their opportunities for education, jobs, and housing. For this and other reasons, the Asian immigrant experience cannot be equated with European immigrant patterns (Blauner, 1972, p. 55). Because they combine characteristics of both the colonized and the immigrant minority group experience, we can predict that in terms of equality, enclave and middleman minority groups will occupy an intermediate status between the more assimilated white ethnic groups and the colonized racial minorities.

Blauner's typology has proven to be an extremely useful conceptual tool for the analysis of U.S. dominant-minority relations, and it is used extensively throughout this text. In fact, the case studies that comprise Part IV of this text are arranged in approximate order from groups created by colonization to those created by immigration. Of course, it is difficult to measure such things as the extent of colonization objectively or precisely, and the exact order of the groups is somewhat arbitrary.

# The Creation of American Slavery

The Noel hypothesis helps explain why colonists enslaved black Africans instead of white indentured servants or American Indians. First, all three groups were the objects of ethnocentric feelings on the part of the elite groups that dominated colonial society. Black Africans and American Indians were perceived as being different on religious as well as racial grounds. Many white indentured servants were Irish Catholics, criminals, or paupers. They not only occupied a lowly status in society, they were perceived as different from the British Protestants who dominated colonial society.

Second, competition of some sort existed between the colonists and all three groups. The competition with American Indians was direct and focused on control of land. Competition with indentured servants, white and black, was more indirect; these groups were the labor force that the landowners needed to work their plantations and become successful in the New World.

Noel's third variable, differential in power, is the key variable that explains why Africans were enslaved instead of the other groups. During the first several decades of colonial history, the balance of power between the colonists and American Indians was relatively even, and in fact, often favored American Indians (Lurie, 1982, pp. 131-133). The colonists were outnumbered, and their muskets and cannons were only marginally more effective than bows and spears. The American Indian tribes were well-organized social units capable of sustaining resistance to and mounting reprisals against the colonists, and it took centuries for the nascent United States to finally defeat American Indians militarily.

White indentured servants, on the one hand, had the advantage of being preferred over black indentured servants (Noel, 1968, p. 168). Their greater desirability gave them bargaining power and the ability to negotiate better treatment and more lenient terms than black indentured servants. If the planters had attempted to enslave white indentured servants, this source of labor would have dwindled even more rapidly.

Africans, on the other hand, had become indentured servants by force and coercion. In Blauner's terms, they were a colonized group that did not freely choose to enter the British colonies. Thus they had no bargaining power. Unlike American Indians, they had no nearby relatives, no knowledge of the countryside, and no safe havens to which to escape. Exhibit 5.2 summarizes the impact of these three factors on the three potential sources of labor in colonial America.

**EXHIBIT 5.2**  The Noel Hypothesis Applied to the Origins of Slavery

| Potential Sources of Labor | Three Causal Factors | | |
|---|---|---|---|
| | Ethnocentrism | Competition | Differential in Power |
| White indentured servants | Yes | Yes | No |
| American Indians | Yes | Yes | No |
| Black indentured servants | Yes | Yes | Yes |

# Paternalistic Relations

Recall the first theme stated at the beginning of this chapter: The nature of intergroup relationships will reflect the characteristics of the larger society. The most important and profitable unit of economic production in the colonial South was the plantation, and the region was dominated by a small group of wealthy landowners. A society with a small elite class and a plantation-based economy will often develop a form of minority relations called **paternalism** (van den Berghe, 1967; Wilson, 1973). The key features of paternalism are vast power differentials and huge inequalities between dominant and minority groups, elaborate and repressive systems of control over the minority group, caste-like barriers between groups, elaborate and highly stylized codes of behavior and communication between groups, and low rates of overt conflict. Each of these characteristics will be considered in turn.

As slavery evolved in the colonies, the dominant group shaped the system to fit its needs. To solidify control of the labor of their slaves, the plantation elite designed and enacted an elaborate system of laws and customs that gave masters nearly total legal power over slaves. In these laws, slaves were defined as *chattel*, or personal property, rather than as persons, and they were accorded no civil or political rights. Slaves could not own property, sign contracts, bring lawsuits, or even testify in court (except against another slave). The masters were given the legal authority to determine almost every aspect of a slave's life, including work schedules, living arrangements, diets, and even names (Elkins, 1959; Franklin & Moss, 1994; Genovese, 1974; Jordan, 1968; Stampp, 1956).

The law permitted the master to determine the type and severity of punishment for misbehavior. Slaves were forbidden by law to read or write, and marriages between slaves were not legally recognized. Masters could separate husbands from wives and parents from children if it suited them. Slaves had little formal decision-making ability or control over their lives or the lives of their loved ones.

In colonial America, slavery became synonymous with race. Race, slavery, inferiority, and powerlessness became intertwined in ways that, according to many analysts, still affect the ways black and white Americans think about one another (Hacker, 1992). Slavery was a **caste system**, or closed stratification system. In a caste system, there is no mobility between social positions, and the social class you are born into (your ascribed status) is permanent. Slave status was for life and was passed on to any children a slave might have. Whites, no matter what they did, could not become slaves.

Interaction between members of the dominant and minority groups in a paternalistic system is governed by a rigid, strictly enforced code of etiquette. Slaves were expected to show deference and humility and visibly display their lower status when interacting with whites. These rigid behavioral codes made it possible for blacks and whites to work together, sometimes intimately, sometimes for their entire lives, without threatening the power and status differentials inherent in the system. Plantation and farm work required close and frequent contact between blacks and whites, and status differentials were maintained socially rather than physically.

The frequent but unequal interactions allowed the elites to maintain a pseudotolerance, an attitude of benevolent despotism, toward their slaves. Their prejudice and racism were often expressed as positive emotions of affection for their black slaves. The attitude of the planters toward their slaves was often paternalistic and even genteel (Wilson, 1973, pp. 52-55).

For their part, black slaves often could not hate their owners as much as they hated the system that constrained them. The system defined slaves as pieces of property owned by their masters—yet they were, undeniably, human beings. Thus slavery was based on a contradiction.

> The master learned to treat his slaves both as property and as men and women, the slaves learned to express and affirm their humanity even while they were constrained in much of their lives to accept their status as chattel. (Parish, 1989, p. 1)

The powerlessness of slaves made it difficult for them to openly reject or resist the system. Slaves had few ways in which they could directly challenge the institution of slavery or their position in it. Open defiance was ineffective and could result in punishment or even death. In general, masters would not be prosecuted for physically abusing their slaves.

One of the few slave revolts that occurred in the United States illustrates both the futility of overt challenge and the degree of repression built into the system. In 1831, in Southhampton County, Virginia, a slave named Nat Turner led an uprising during which 57 whites were killed. The revolt was starting to spread when the state militia met and routed the growing slave army. More than 100 slaves died in the armed encounter, and Nat Turner and 13 others were later executed. Slave owners and white southerners in general were greatly alarmed by the uprising and consequently tightened the system of control over slaves, making it even more repressive (Franklin & Moss, 1994, p. 147). Ironically, the result of Nat Turner's attempt to lead slaves to freedom was greater oppression and control by the dominant group.

Others were more successful in resisting the system. Runaway slaves were a constant problem for slave owners, especially in the states bordering the free states of the North. The difficulty of escape and the low likelihood of successfully reaching the North did not deter thousands from attempting the feat, some of them repeatedly. Many runaway slaves received help from the Underground Railroad, an informal network of safe houses supported by African Americans and whites involved in **abolitionism**, the movement to abolish slavery. These escapes created colorful legends and heroic figures, including Frederick Douglass, Sojourner Truth, and Harriet Tubman. The following Narrative Portrait presents the experiences of two exslaves who eventually escaped to the North.

Besides running away and open rebellion, slaves used the forms of resistance most readily available to them: sabotage, intentional carelessness, dragging their feet, and work slowdowns. As historian Peter Parish (1989) points out, it is difficult to separate "a natural desire to avoid hard work [from a] conscious decision to protest or resist" (p. 73), and much of this behavior may fall more into the category of noncooperation than deliberate political rebellion. Nonetheless, these behaviors were widespread and document the rejection of the system by its victims.

On an everyday basis, the slaves managed their lives and families as best they could. Most slaves were neither docile victims nor unyielding rebels. As the institution of slavery developed, a distinct African American experience accumulated, and traditions of resistance and accommodation developed side by side. Most slaves worked to create a world for themselves within the confines and restraints of the plantation system, avoiding the more vicious repression as much as possible while attending to their own needs and those of their families. An African American culture was forged in response to the realities of slavery and was manifested in folklore, music, religion, family and kinship structures, and other aspects of everyday life (Blassingame, 1972; Genovese, 1974; Gutman, 1976).

## Early Images of African Americans by *Eric Margolis*

The representation of African Americans in paintings, drawings, and photography has been extremely problematic. You might think of visual images of black Americans as a struggle, as a sort of contested terrain, in which a variety of imagemakers have sought to use visual representations to impose an identity on African Americans. In this brief essay I can only sketch some of the issues. If you are interested in this I suggest going to the Library of Congress Web site at http://www.loc .gov/rr/print/catalog.html. Search the catalog for "African Americans." When I did this in March 2005 I changed the display

to return up to 5,000 records and discovered 4,041 images with the exact phrase "African Americans." More photos are added on a regular basis. Browsing through these images is a remarkable tour of American history. All of our founding fathers owned slaves. African Americans have been part of the American family from the earliest days; this painting (above) of the Washington family depicts George and Martha with their two grandchildren. In the background stands William Lee, one of their African American slaves. It is well known that in his will Washington ordered that his slaves be set free upon his death. Thomas Jefferson, on the other hand, fathered a child with Sally Hemmings, a young black woman that he owned, and his slaves were sold upon his death to pay his debts.

African Americans were brought to America as slaves, and for centuries even after the Civil War were seen in the popular imagination as servants. This daguerreotype shows a child named Georgina Holmes and her "nurse" (perhaps meaning wet nurse) who has no name. According to the notes accompanying the photo: "There is limited historical documentation to accompany this image: The family, originally from Louisiana, moved their household to New York City whereupon the slaves were released. The nurse depicted in this daguerreotype chose not to leave the household."

In 1817 The American Colonization Society was formed to repatriate African Americans to Liberia. The society certainly made the point that politics makes strange bedfellows; it included abolitionists, free blacks

in an early "back to Africa" movement, and a number of whites who wanted to "ethnically cleanse" the new Republic by eliminating the black population. Portraits of some of those who moved to Liberia were made by an African American

FARMERS    NOONING.

daguerreotypist named Augustus Washington. The above daguerreotype shows Chancy Brown, who is identified as the Sergeant at Arms of the Liberian Senate.

At right is a remarkable painting from 1843 titled "Farmers Nooning," remarkable because it depicts whites and blacks in a "normal" scene, resting during their lunch break. The workers rest in the shade of a tree, one sharpens a scythe, an African American man reclines on a hay stack, a young white boy leans next to him. It is a bucolic scene with no indication of the racial turmoil racking the country in these pre-Civil War years.

In the years before the Civil War a propaganda struggle was waged between Abolitionists and defenders of slavery. This lithograph represents an anti-abolitionist view. The description reads: "A diverse group of abolitionists try to drag an unwilling black man toward the left with a large gaff hook. Holding the hook are (left to right) an old hag, a Quaker

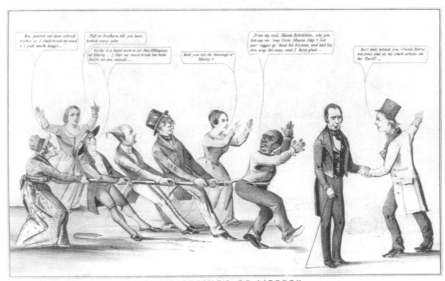

THE BLESSINGS OF LIBERTY.
OR HOW TO HOOK A "GENTLEMAN OB COLOR"

man, and two other homely men. The hag declares, 'How perverse our dear colored brother is, I shall break my wind if I pull much longer.' The Quaker says, 'Verily it is hard work to set this Ethiopian at liberty. I fear we must break his back before we can succeed.' A woman behind him enjoins 'Pull on brethren till you have broken every yoke.' Another young woman (center) asks the black, 'Don't you feel the blessings of liberty?' The black protests, 'Bress my soul, Massa Robolition, why you kidnap me 'way from Massa Clay? Let poor nigger go 'bout his bizness, and hab his own way dis once, and I berry glad.' The black struggles to join Henry Clay and Horace Greeley, on the right, who stand with hands joined."

In the 1850s, Louis Agassiz, a Harvard professor who opposed Darwin's theory of evolution, commissioned a set of daguerreotypes made of African-born slaves. In these images (see right), the people are literally stripped naked, pictured like specimens, identified by first name, region or tribe of origin, and plantation. These images were

meant as photographic evidence of the difference between the races and to support Agassiz's view that Africans were distinctly inferior to whites, perhaps not even of the same species, and thus their enslavement and servitude was justified.

Needless to say the abolitionists published their own image of African Americans and the horrors of slavery. The photo far left is termed a "Propaganda portrait" of Fannie Virginia

Redeemed in Virginia

By Catherine S. Lawrence. Baptized in Brooklyn, at Plymouth Church, by Henry Ward Beecher, May, 1863. Fannie Virginia Casseopia Lawrence, a Redeemed SLAVE CHILD, 5 years of age. Entered according to Act of Congress, in the year 1863, by C. S. Lawrence, in the Clerk's Office of the district Court of the United States, for the Southern District of New-York.

Photograph by Renowden, 65 Fulton Av. Brooklyn.

No. 12.

Casseopia Lawrence, a Redeemed Slave child, 5 years of age. It was made in 1863 as a Carte-de-Visite. The original caption reads: "Redeemed in Virginia by Catherine S. Lawrence. Baptized in Brooklyn. . . . by Henry Ward Beecher, May, 1863. Fannie Virginia Casseopia Lawrence, a Redeemed Slave Child, 5 years of age."

This lithograph titled "He Died for Me," also from 1863, shows a woman symbolizing America holding a wreath over a dying black man, perhaps in military uniform and holding a sword. Many African Americans fought in the Civil War, as this image suggests, to preserve the Union.

After the Civil War, Americans produced huge numbers of images of African Americans, portrayed as drunks, gamblers, layabouts; chicken-stealing, watermelon-eating fools. These offensive visual representations that one scholar has termed "contemptible collectibles" were circulated as postcards, stereo views, in magazines, and as dolls and trinkets (Turner, Patricia [1994] *Ceramic Uncles & Celluloid Mammies*). Believe it or not, these racist representations are still in circulation in antique shops and on E-Bay. Black stereotypes were also the subject of the kind of theater called minstrel shows, where white performers in "black face" often played the parts of African Americans. These images persisted for more than a century, through the Civil Rights movement of the 1960s when African Americans and others found ways to counter and protest this propaganda. Nevertheless, stereotypes are difficult to extinguish, and these images contributed to a widespread social belief by white people that black people in fact had these characteristics. Shown here are a few examples.

THE TABLEAUX AT COON CORNERS.

DARKIES' DAY AT THE FAIR.

A FULL HAND!

961—"Ise de Happiest Little Coon in de Cotton Field."

A Free Lunch.

There were also many images made apparently to make white America feel that all that had been done to African Americans was not that serious. These "happy darkies" photographs were also in wide circulation.

## A Slave's Life

*The memoirs of two escaped slaves, Henry Bibb and Harriet Jacobs, illustrate some of the features of Southern slavery. Bibb was married and had a child when he escaped to the North, where he spent the rest of his life working for the abolition of slavery. The passage printed here gives an overview of his early life and expresses his commitment to freedom and his family. He also describes some of the abuses he and his family suffered under the reign of a particularly cruel master. Bibb was unable to rescue his daughter from slavery and agonizes over leaving her in bondage.*

*Harriet Jacobs grew up as a slave in Edenton, North Carolina, and, in this excerpt, she recounts some of her experiences, especially the sexual harassment she suffered at the hand of her master. Her narrative illustrates the dynamics of power and sex in the "peculiar institution" and the very limited options she had for defending herself from the advances of her master. She eventually escaped from slavery by hiding in her grandmother's house for nearly 17 years and then making her way to the North.*

### NARRATIVE OF THE LIFE AND ADVENTURES OF HENRY BIBB

**Henry Bibb**

I was born May 1815, of a slave mother, in Shelby County, Kentucky, and was claimed as the property of David White. I was brought up . . . or, more correctly speaking, I was flogged up; for where I should have received moral, mental, and religious instruction, I received stripes without number, the object of which was to degrade and keep me in subordination. . . . The first time I was separated from my mother, I was young and small . . . I was . . . hired out to labor for various persons and all my wages were expended for the education of [my master's daughter]. It was then I first commenced seeing and feeling that I was a wretched slave, compelled to work under the lash without wages, and often without clothes to hide my nakedness. . . .

All that I heard about liberty and freedom . . . I never forgot. Among other good trades I learned the art of running away to perfection. I made a regular business of it, and never gave it up, until I had broken the bands of slavery, and landed myself safely in Canada, where I was regarded as a man, and not a thing.

[Bibb describes his childhood and adolescence, his early attempts to escape to the North, and his marriage to Malinda.] Not many months [later] Malinda made me a father. The dear little daughter was called Mary Frances. She was nurtured and caressed by her mother and father. . . . Malinda's business was to labor out in the field the greater part of her time, and there was no one to take care of poor little Frances. . . . She was left at the house to creep under the feet of an unmerciful old mistress, Mrs. Gatewood (the owner's wife). I recollect that [we] came in from the field one day and poor little Frances came creeping to her mother smiling, but with large tear drops standing in her dear little eyes. . . . Her little face was bruised black with the whole print of Mrs. Gatewood's hand. . . . Who can imagine the feelings of a mother and father, when looking upon their infant child whipped and tortured with impunity, and they placed in a situation where they could afford it no protection? But we were all claimed and held as property; the father and mother were slaves!

On this same plantation, I was compelled to stand and see my wife shamefully scourged and abused by her master; and the manner in which this was done was so violent and inhuman that I despair in finding decent language to describe the bloody act of cruelty. My happiness or pleasure was all blasted; for it was sometimes a pleasure to be with my little family even in slavery. I loved them as my wife and child. Little

Frances was a pretty child; she was quiet, playful, bright, and interesting. . . . But I could never look upon the dear child without being filled with sorrow and fearful apprehensions, of being separated by slaveholders, because she was a slave, regarded as property. . . . But Oh! When I remember that my daughter, my only child, is still there, . . . it is too much to bear. If ever there was any one act of my life as a slave, that I have to lament over, it is that of being a father and a husband to slaves. I have the satisfaction of knowing that I am the father of only one slave. She is bone of my bone, and flesh of my flesh; poor unfortunate child. She was the first and shall be the last slave that ever I will father, for chains and slavery on this earth.

SOURCE: Osofsky, Gilbert. 1969. Puttin' on Ole Massa. New York: Harper & Row. Pp. 54-65, 80-81.

## LIFE AS A SLAVE GIRL

**Harriet Jacobs**

During the first years of my service in Dr. Flint's family, I was accustomed to share some indulgences with the children of my mistress. Though this seemed to me no more than right, I was grateful for it, and tried to merit the kindness by the faithful discharge of my duties. But I now entered on my fifteenth year—a sad epoch in the life of a slave girl. My master began to whisper foul words in my ear. Young as I was, I could not remain ignorant of their import. I tried to treat them with indifference or contempt. The master's age, my extreme youth, and the fear that misconduct would be reported to my grandmother made me bear this treatment for many months.

He was a crafty man, and resorted to many means to accomplish his purposes. Sometimes he had stormy, terrific ways, that made his victims tremble; sometimes he assumed a gentleness that he thought must surely subdue. Of the two, I preferred his stormy moods, although they left me trembling. He tried his utmost to corrupt the pure principles my grandmother had instilled. He peopled my young mind with unclean images, such as only a vile monster could think of. I turned from him with

disgust and hatred. But he was my master. I was compelled to live under the same roof with him, where I saw a man forty years my senior daily violating the most sacred commandments of nature. He told me I was his property; that I must be subject to his will in all things. My soul revolted against the mean tyranny. But where could I turn for protection? No matter whether the slave girl be as black as ebony or as fair as her mistress. In either case, there is no shadow of law to protect her from insult, from violence, or even from death; all these are inflicted by fiends who bear the shape of men. The mistress, who ought to protect the helpless victim, has no other feelings towards her but those of jealousy and rage. The degradation, the wrongs, the vices that grow out of slavery, are more than I can describe. They are greater than you would willingly believe. Surely, if you credited on half the truths that are told you concerning the helpless millions suffering in this cruel bondage, you at the north would not help tighten the yoke. You surely would refuse to do for the master, on your own soil, the mean and cruel work which trained bloodhounds and the lowest class of whites do for him at the south.

SOURCE: Jacobs, Harriet. 1987. *Incidents in the Life of a Slave Girl, Written by Herself* (Jean Yellin, Ed.). Cambridge, MA: Harvard University Press. Pp. 27-31.

# The Dimensions of Minority Group Status

The situation of African Americans under slavery can be more completely described by applying some of the concepts developed in Parts I and II.

**Power, Inequality, and Institutional Discrimination.** The key concepts for understanding the creation of slavery are power, inequality, and institutional discrimination. The plantation elite used its greater power resources to consign black Africans to an inferior status. The system of racial inequality was implemented and reinforced by institutionalized discrimination and became a central aspect of everyday life in the antebellum South. The legal and political institutions of colonial society were shaped to benefit the landowners and give them almost total control over their slaves.

**Prejudice and Racism.** What about the attitudes and feelings of the people involved? What was the role of personal prejudice? How and why did the ideology of antiblack racism start? Most scholars agree that individual prejudices and ideological racism are not so important as *causes* of the creation of minority group status but are more the *results* of systems of racial inequality (Jordan, 1968, p. 80; Smedley, 1999, pp. 94-111). The colonists did not enslave black indentured servants because they were prejudiced or because they disliked blacks or thought them inferior. As we have seen, the decision to enslave black Africans was an attempt to resolve a labor supply problem. The primary roles of prejudice and racism in the creation of minority group status are to rationalize and "explain" the emerging system of racial and ethnic advantage (Wilson, 1973, pp. 76-78).

Prejudice and racism help to mobilize support for the creation of minority group status and to stabilize the system as it emerges. Prejudice and racism can provide convenient and convincing justifications for exploitation. They can help insulate a system like slavery from questioning and criticism and make it appear reasonable and even desirable. Thus the intensity, strength, and popularity of antiblack Southern racism actually reached its height almost 200 years after slavery began to emerge. During the early 1800s, the American abolitionist movement brought slavery under heavy attack, and in response, the ideology of antiblack racism was strengthened (Wilson, 1973, p. 79). The greater the opposition to a system of racial stratification or the greater the magnitude of the exploitation, the greater the need of the beneficiaries and their apologists to justify, rationalize, and explain.

Once created, dominant group prejudice and racism become widespread and common ways of thinking about the minority group. In the case of colonial slavery, antiblack beliefs and feelings became part of the standard package of knowledge, understanding, and truths shared by members of the dominant group. As the decades wore on and the institution of slavery solidified, prejudice and racism were passed on from generation to generation. For succeeding generations, antiblack prejudice became just another piece of information and perspective on the world learned during socialization. Antiblack prejudice and racism began as part of an attempt to control the labor of black indentured servants, became embedded in early American culture, and were established as integral parts of the socialization process for succeeding generations.

These conceptual relationships are presented in Exhibit 5.3. Racial inequality arises from the contact situation, as specified in the Noel hypothesis. As the dominant-minority relationship begins to take shape, prejudice and racism develop as rationalizations. Over time, a vicious cycle develops as prejudice and racism reinforce the pattern of inequality between groups, which was the cause of prejudice and racism in the first place. Thus, the Blauner hypothesis states, the subordination of colonized minority groups is perpetuated through time.

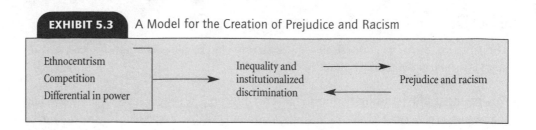

**EXHIBIT 5.3**  A Model for the Creation of Prejudice and Racism

Ethnocentrism
Competition
Differential in power

→

Inequality and
institutionalized
discrimination

→
←

Prejudice and racism

**Assimilation.** There is an enormous literature on American slavery, and research on the nature and meaning of the system continues to this day. Many issues remain unsettled, however, and one of the more controversial, consequential, and interesting of these concerns the effect of slavery on the slaves.

Apologists for the system of slavery and some historians of the South writing early in the 20th century accepted the rationalizations inherent in antiblack prejudice and argued that slavery was actually beneficial for black Africans. According to this view, British-American slavery operated as a "school for civilization" (Phillips, 1918) that rescued savages from the jungles of Africa and exposed them to Christianity and Western civilization. Some argued that slavery was benevolent because it protected slaves from the evils and exploitation of the factory system of the industrial North. These racist views were most popular a century ago, early in the development of the social sciences. Since that time, scholars have established a number of facts (e.g., Western Africa, the area from which most slaves came, had been the site of a number of powerful, advanced civilizations) that make this view untenable by anyone but the most dedicated racist thinkers.

At the opposite extreme, slavery has been compared with Nazi concentration camps and likened to a "perverted patriarchy" that brainwashed, emasculated, and dehumanized slaves, stripping them of their heritage and culture. Historian Stanley Elkins provocatively argued this interpretation, now widely regarded as overstated, in his book *Slavery: A Problem in American Institutional and Intellectual Life* (1959). Although his conclusions might be overdrawn, Elkins's argument and evidence are important for any exploration of the nature of American slavery. In fact, much of the scholarship on slavery since the publication of Elkins's book has been an attempt to refute or at least modify the points he made.

Still a third view of the impact of slavery maintains that through all the horror and abuse of enslavement, slaves retained a sense of self and a firm anchor in their African traditions. This point of view stresses the importance of kinship, religion, and culture in helping African Americans cope and has been presented most poignantly in Alex Haley's semifictional family history *Roots*, but it is also represented in the scholarly literature on slavery since Elkins (see Blassingame, 1972; Genovese, 1974).

The debate over the impact of slavery continues (see the Current Debates section at the end of this chapter), and we cannot hope to resolve the issues here. However, it is clear that African Americans, in Blauner's terms, were a "colonized" minority group who were extensively—and coercively—acculturated. Language acculturation began on the slave ships, where different tribal and language groups were mixed together to inhibit communication and lower the potential for resistance and revolt (Mannix, 1962).

The plantation elite and their agents needed to communicate with their workforce and insisted on using English. Within a generation or two, African language use died out. Some scholars argue that some African words and language patterns persist to the present day, but even if this is true, the significance of this survival is trivial compared with the coerced adoption of English. To the extent that culture depends on language, Africans under slavery experienced massive acculturation.

Acculturation through slavery was clearly a process that was forced on African Americans. Because they were a colonized minority group and unwilling participants in the system, they had little choice but to adjust to the conditions established by the plantation elite as best they could. Their traditional culture was suppressed, and their choices for adjustment to the system were sharply constrained. Black slaves developed new cultural forms and social relationships, but they did so in a situation with few options or choices (Blauner, 1972, p. 66). The extent to which any African cultural elements survived the institution of slavery is a matter of some controversy, but given the power differentials inherent in the system, African Americans had few choices regarding their manner of adjustment.

**Gender Relations.** Southern agrarian society developed into a complex social system stratified by race and gender as well as by class. The plantation elite, small in number but wealthy and politically powerful, was at the top of the structure. Most whites in the South were small farmers, and relatively few of them owned slaves. In 1860, for example, only 25% of all Southern whites owned slaves (Franklin & Moss, 1994, p. 123).

The principal line of differentiation in the antebellum South was, of course, race, which was largely synonymous with slave versus nonslave status. Each of the racial groups was in turn stratified by gender. White women were subordinate to the males of the plantation elite, and the slave community echoed the patriarchal pattern of Southern society, except that the degree of gender inequality among blacks was sharply truncated by the fact that slaves had little autonomy and few resources. At the bottom of the system were African American female slaves. Minority women are generally in double jeopardy, oppressed through their gender as well as their race. For black female slaves, the constraints were triple: "Black in a white society, slave in a free society, women in a society ruled by men, female slaves had the least formal power and were perhaps the most vulnerable group of antebellum America" (White, 1985, p. 15).

The race and gender roles of the day idealized Southern white women and placed them on a pedestal. A romanticized conception of femininity was quite inconsistent with the roles women slaves were required to play. Besides domestic roles, female slaves also worked in the fields and did their share of the hardest, most physically demanding, least "feminine" farm work. Southern ideas about feminine fragility and daintiness were quickly abandoned when they interfered with work and the profit to be made from slave labor (Amott & Matthaei, 1991, p. 146).

Reflecting their vulnerability and powerlessness, women slaves were sometimes used to breed more slaves to sell. They were raped and otherwise abused by the males of the dominant group. John Blassingame (1972) expresses their vulnerability to sexual victimization:

> Many white men considered every slave cabin a house of ill-fame. Often through "gifts" but usually by force, white overseers and planters obtained the sexual favors of black women. Generally speaking, the women were literally forced to offer themselves "willingly" and receive a trinket for their compliance rather than a flogging for their refusal. (p. 83)

Note the power relationships implicit in this passage: Female slaves had little choice but to feign willing submission to their white owners.

The routines of work and everyday life differed for male and female slaves. Although they sometimes worked with the men, especially during harvest time, women more often worked in sex-segregated groups organized around domestic as well as farm chores. In addition to working in the fields, they attended the births and cared for the children of both races, cooked and cleaned, wove cloth and sewed clothes, and did the laundry. The women often worked longer hours than the men, doing housework and other chores long after the men retired (Robertson, 1996, p. 21; White, 1985, p. 122).

The group-oriented nature of their tasks gave female slaves an opportunity to develop same-sex bonds and relationships. Women cooperated in their chores, in caring for their children, in the maintenance of their quarters, and in myriad other domestic and family chores. These networks and interpersonal bonds could be used to resist the system. For example, slave women sometimes induced abortions rather than bring more children into bondage. They often controlled the role of midwife and were able to effectively deceive slave owners and disguise the abortions as miscarriages (White, 1985, pp. 125-126). The networks of relationships among the female slaves provided mutual aid and support for everyday problems, solace and companionship during the travails of a vulnerable and exploited existence, and some ability to buffer and resist the influence and power of the slave owners (Andersen, 1993, pp. 164-165).

Slaves in the American system were brutally repressed and exploited, but females were even more subordinated than males. Also, their oppression and exclusion sharply differentiated female slaves from white females. The white "Southern belle," chaste, untouchable, and unremittingly virtuous, had little in common with African American women under slavery.

## THE CREATION OF MINORITY STATUS FOR AMERICAN INDIANS AND MEXICAN AMERICANS

Two other groups became minorities during the preindustrial period. In this section, we will review the dynamics of these processes and make some comparisons with African Americans. As you will see, both the Noel and Blauner hypotheses provide some extremely useful insights into these experiences.

### American Indians

As Europeans began to penetrate the New World, they encountered hundreds of societies that had lived on this land for thousands of years. American Indian societies were highly variable in culture, language, size, and subsistence technology. Some were small, nomadic, hunter-gatherer bands, whereas others were more developed societies in which people lived in settled villages and tended large gardens. Regardless of their exact nature, the inexorable advance of white society eventually devastated them all. Contact began in the East and established a pattern of conflict and defeat for American Indians that continued until the last of the tribes were finally defeated in the late 1800s. The continual expansion of white society into the West allowed many settlers to fulfill their dreams of economic self-sufficiency, but American Indians, who lost not only their lives and their land but also much of their traditional way of life, paid an incalculable price.

An important and widely unrecognized point about American Indians is that there is no such thing as *the* American Indian. Rather, there were—and are—hundreds of different tribes or nations, each with its own language, culture, home territory, and unique history. There are, of course, similarities from tribe to tribe, but there are also vast differences between, for example, the forest-dwelling tribes of Virginia, who lived in longhouses and cultivated gardens, and the nomadic Plains tribes, who relied on hunting to satisfy their needs. Each tribe was and remains a unique blend of language, values, and social structure. Because of space constraints, we will not always be able to take all these differences into account. Nonetheless, it is important to be aware of the diversity and sensitive to the variety of peoples and histories subsumed within the general category of *American Indian*.

A second important point is that many American Indian tribes no longer exist or are vastly diminished in size. When Jamestown was established in 1607, it is estimated that there were anywhere from 1 million to more than 10 million American Indians living in what became the United States. By 1890, when the Indian Wars finally ended, the number of American Indians had fallen to fewer than 250,000. By the end of the nearly 300-year-long "contact situation," American Indian populations had declined by 75% or more (Wax, 1971, p. 17; see also McNickle, 1973).

Very little of this population loss was due directly to warfare and battle casualties. The greatest part was caused by European diseases brought over by the colonists and by the destruction of the food supplies on which American Indian societies relied. American Indians died by the thousands from measles, influenza, smallpox, cholera, tuberculosis, and a variety of other infectious diseases (Wax, 1971, p. 17; see also Oswalt & Neely, 1996; Snipp, 1989). Traditional hunting grounds and garden plots were taken over by the expanding American society, and game such as the buffalo was slaughtered to the point of extinction. The result of the contact situation for American Indians very nearly approached genocide.

**American Indians and the Noel and Blauner Hypotheses.** We have already used the Noel hypothesis to analyze why American Indians were not enslaved during the colonial era. Their competition with whites centered on land, not labor, and the Indian nations were often successful in resisting domination (at least temporarily). As American society spread to the West, competition over land continued, and the growing power, superior technology, and greater resource base of the dominant group gradually pushed American Indians to near extinction.

Various attempts were made to control the persistent warfare, the most important of which occurred before independence from Great Britain. In 1763, the British Crown ruled that the various tribes were to be considered "sovereign nations with inalienable rights to their land" (see Lurie, 1982; McNickle, 1973; Wax, 1971). In other words, each tribe was to be treated as a nation-state, like France or Russia, and the colonists could not simply expropriate tribal lands. Rather, negotiations had to take place, and treaties of agreement had to be signed by all affected parties. The tribes had to be compensated for any loss of land.

This policy was often ignored but was continued by the newborn federal government after the American Revolution. The principle of sovereignty is important because it established a unique relationship between the federal government and American Indians. The fact that the policy was ignored in practice and that treaties were regularly broken or unilaterally renegotiated by white society gives American Indians legal claims against the federal government that are also unique.

East of the Mississippi River, the period of open conflict was brought to a close by the Indian Removal Act of 1830, which dictated a policy of forced emigration to the tribes. The law required all eastern tribes to move to new lands west of the Mississippi. Some of the affected tribes went without resistance, others fought, and still others fled to Canada rather than move to the new territory. Regardless, the Indian Removal Act "solved" the Indian problem in the East. The relative scarcity of American Indians in the eastern United States continues to the present, and the majority of American Indians live in the western two thirds of the nation.

In the West, the grim story of competition for land accompanied by rising hostility and aggression repeated itself. Wars were fought, buffalo were killed, territory was expropriated, atrocities were committed on both sides, and the fate of the tribes became more and more certain. By 1890, the greater power and resources of white society had defeated the Indian nations. All of the great warrior chiefs were dead or in prison, and almost all American Indians were living on reservations controlled by agencies of the federal government. The reservations consisted of land set aside for the tribes by the government during treaty negotiations. Often, these lands were not the traditional homelands and were hundreds or even thousands of miles away from what the tribe considered to be "home." It is not surprising that the reservations were usually on undesirable, often worthless land.

The 1890s mark a low point in American Indian history, a time of great demoralization and sadness. The tribes had to find a way to adapt to reservation life and new forms of subordination to the federal government. Although elements of the tribal way of life have survived, the tribes were impoverished and without resources and had little ability to pursue their own interests.

American Indians, in Blauner's terms, were a colonized minority group who faced high levels of prejudice, racism, and discrimination. Like African Americans, they were controlled by paternalistic systems (the reservations) and in a variety of ways were coercively acculturated. Furthermore, according to Blauner, the negative consequences of colonized minority groups status will persist long after the contact situation has been resolved. As we will see in chapter 8, there is a great deal of evidence to support this prediction.

**Gender Relations.** In the centuries before contact with Europeans, American Indian societies distributed resources and power in a wide variety of ways. At one extreme, some American Indian societies were highly stratified, and many practiced various forms of slavery. Others stressed equality, sharing of resources, and respect for the autonomy and dignity of each individual, including women and children (Amott & Matthaei, 1991, p. 33). American Indian societies were generally patriarchal and followed a strict gender-based division of labor, but this did not necessarily mean that women were subordinate. In many tribes, women held positions of great responsibility and controlled the wealth. For example, among the Iroquois (a large and powerful federation of tribes located in the Northeast), women controlled the land and the harvest, arranged marriages, supervised the children, and were responsible for the appointment of tribal leaders and decisions about peace and war (Oswalt & Neely, 1996, pp. 404-405). It was not unusual for women in many tribes to play key roles in religion, politics, warfare, and the economy. Some women even became highly respected warriors and chiefs (Amott & Matthaei, 1991, p. 36).

Gender relations were affected in a variety of ways during the prolonged contact period. In some cases, the relative status and power of women rose. For example, the women of the Navajo tribe (located mainly in what is now Arizona and New Mexico) were traditionally responsible for the care of herd animals and livestock. When the Spanish introduced sheep and goats into the region, the importance of this sector of the subsistence economy increased, and the power and status of women grew along with it.

In other cases, women were affected adversely. The women of the tribes of the Great Plains, for example, suffered a dramatic loss as a result of contact. The sexual division of labor in these tribes was that women were responsible for gardening, whereas men handled the hunting. When horses were introduced from Europe, the productivity of the male hunters was greatly increased. As their economic importance increased, males became more dominant, and women lost status and power. Women in the Cherokee nation—a large tribe whose original homelands were in the Southeast—similarly lost considerable status and power under the pressure to assimilate. Traditionally, Cherokee land was cultivated, controlled, and passed down from generation to generation by the women. This matrilineal pattern was abandoned in favor of the European pattern of male ownership when the Cherokee attempted (futilely, as it turned out) to acculturate and avoid relocation under the Indian Relocation act of 1830 (Evans, 1989, pp. 12-18).

By the end of the contact period, the surviving American Indian tribes were impoverished, powerless, and clearly subordinate to white society and the federal government. Like African Americans, they were sharply differentiated from the dominant group by race and, in many cases, internally stratified by gender. As was the case with African American slaves, the degree of gender inequality within the tribes was limited by their overall lack of autonomy and resources.

## Mexican Americans

As the population of the United States increased and spread across the continent, contact with Mexicans inevitably occurred. Spanish explorers and settlers had lived in what is now the Southwestern United States long before the wave of American settlers broke across this region. For example, Santa Fe, New Mexico, was founded in 1598, nearly a decade before Jamestown. As late as the 1820s, Mexicans and American Indians were almost the sole residents of the region.

In the early 1800s, four areas of Mexican settlement had developed, roughly corresponding to what was to become Texas, California, New Mexico, and Arizona. These areas were sparsely settled, and most Mexicans lived in what was to become New Mexico (Cortes, 1980, p. 701). The economy of the regions was based on farming and herding. Most people lived in villages and small towns or on ranches and farms. Social and political life was organized around family and the Catholic Church and tended to be dominated by an elite class of wealthy landowners.

**Texas.** Some of the first effects of U.S. expansion to the West were felt in Texas early in the 1800s. Mexico was no military match for its neighbor to the north, and the farmland of East Texas was a tempting resource for the cotton-growing interests in the American South. Anglo-Americans began to immigrate to Texas in sizable numbers in the 1820s, and by 1835, they outnumbered Mexicans 6 to 1. The attempts by the Mexican government to control these immigrants were clumsy and ineffective and eventually precipitated a successful revolution by the Anglo-Americans, with some Mexicans also joining the rebels. At this point in time, competition between Anglos and Texans of Mexican descent (called Tejanos) was muted by the abundance of land and opportunity in the area. Population density was low, fertile land was readily available for all, and the "general tone of the time was that of inter-cultural cooperation" (Alvarez, 1973, p. 922).

Competition between Anglo-Texans and Tejanos became increasingly intense. When the United States annexed Texas in the 1840s, full-scale war broke out, and Mexico was defeated. Under the Treaty of Guadalupe Hidalgo in 1848, Mexico ceded much of the Southwest to the United States. In the Gadsden Purchase of 1853, the United States acquired the remainder of the territory that now composes the Southwestern United States. As a result of these treaties, the Mexican population of this region had become, without moving an inch from their traditional villages and farms, both a conquered people and a minority group.

Following the war, intergroup relations continued to sour, and the political and legal rights of the Tejano community were often ignored in the hunger for land. Increasingly impoverished and powerless, the Tejanos had few resources with which to resist the growth of Anglo-American domination. They were badly outnumbered and stigmatized by the recent Mexican military defeat. Land that had once been Mexican increasingly came under Anglo control, and widespread violence and lynching reinforced the growth of Anglo dominance (Moquin & Van Doren, 1971, p. 253).

**California.** In California, the Gold Rush of 1849 spurred a massive population movement from the East. Early relations between Anglos and Californios (native Mexicans in the state) had been relatively cordial, forming the basis for a multiethnic, bilingual state. The rapid growth of an Anglo majority after statehood in 1850 doomed these efforts, however, and the Californios, like the Tejanos, lost their land and political power.

Laws were passed encouraging Anglos to settle on land traditionally held by Californios. In such situations, the burden was placed on the Mexican American landowners to show that their deeds were valid. The Californios protested the seizure of their land but found it difficult to argue their cases in the English-speaking, Anglo-controlled court system. By the mid-1850s, a massive transfer of land to Anglo-American hands had taken place in California (Mirandé, 1985, pp. 20-21; see also Pitt, 1970).

Other laws passed in the 1850s made it increasingly difficult for Californios to retain their property and power as Anglo-Americans became the dominant group as well as the majority of the population. The Mexican heritage was suppressed and eliminated from public life and institutions such as schools and local government. For example, in 1855, California repealed a requirement in the state constitution that all laws be published in Spanish as well as English (Cortes, 1980, p. 706). Anglo-Americans used violence, biased laws, discrimination, and other means to exploit and repress Californios, and the new wealth generated by gold mining flowed into Anglo hands.

**Arizona and New Mexico.** The Anglo immigration into Arizona and New Mexico was less voluminous than that into Texas and California, and both states retained Mexican numerical majorities for a number of decades. In Arizona, most of the Mexican population were immigrants themselves, seeking work on farms, ranches, and in the mines and railroads. The economic and political structures of the state quickly came under the control of the Anglo population.

Only in New Mexico did Mexican Americans retain some political power and economic clout, mostly because of the relatively large size of the group and their skill in mobilizing for political activity. New Mexico did not become a state until 1912, and Mexican Americans continued to play a prominent role in governmental affairs even after statehood (Cortes, 1980, p. 706).

Thus the contact situation for Mexican Americans was highly variable by region. Although some areas were affected more rapidly and more completely than others, the ultimate result was the creation of minority group status for Mexican Americans (Acuna, 1999; Alvarez, 1973; McLemore, 1973; McWilliams, 1961; Moore, 1970; Stoddard, 1973).

**Mexican Americans and the Noel and Blauner Hypotheses.** The causal model we have applied to the origins of slavery and the domination of American Indians also provides a way of explaining the development of minority group status for Mexican Americans. Ethnocentrism was clearly present from the very first contact between Anglo immigrants and Mexicans. Many American migrants to the Southwest brought with them the prejudices and racism they had acquired with regard to African Americans and American Indians. In fact, many of the settlers who moved into Texas came directly from the South in search of new lands for the cultivation of cotton. They readily transferred their prejudiced views to at least the poorer Mexicans, who were stereotyped as lazy and shiftless (McLemore, 1973, p. 664). The visibility of group boundaries was heightened and reinforced by physical and religious differences.

Mexicans were "racially" a mixture of Spaniards and American Indians, and the differences in skin color and other physical characteristics provided a convenient marker of group membership. In addition, the vast majority of Mexicans were Roman Catholic, whereas the vast majority of Anglo-Americans were Protestant.

Competition for land began with the first contact between the groups. However, for many years, population density was low in the Southwest, and the competition did not immediately or always erupt into violent domination and expropriation. Nonetheless, the loss of land and power for Mexican Americans was inexorable, although variable in speed.

The size of the power differential between the groups was variable and partly explains why domination was established faster in some places than others. In both Texas and California, the subordination of the Mexican American population followed quickly after a rapid influx of Anglos and the military defeat of Mexico. Anglo-Americans used their superior numbers and military power to acquire control of the political and economic structures and expropriate the resources of the Mexican American community. In New Mexico, the groups were more evenly matched in size, and Mexican Americans were able to retain a measure of power for decades.

Unlike the case of American Indians, however, the labor as well as the land of the Mexicans was coveted. On cotton plantations, ranches, farms, and in mining and railroad construction, Mexican Americans became a vital source of inexpensive labor. During times of high demand, this labor force was supplemented by workers who were encouraged to emigrate from Mexico. When demand for workers decreased, these laborers were forced back to Mexico. Thus began a pattern of labor flow that continues to the present.

As in the case of African Americans and American Indians, the contact period clearly established a colonized status for Mexican Americans in all areas of the Southwest. Their culture and language were suppressed even as their property rights were abrogated and their status lowered. In countless ways, they, too, were subjected to coercive acculturation. For example, California banned the use of Spanish in public schools, and bullfighting and other Mexican sports and recreational activities were severely restricted (Moore, 1970, p. 19; Pitt, 1970). In contrast to African Americans, however, Mexican Americans were in close proximity to their homeland and maintained close ties with villages and families. Constant movement across the border with Mexico kept the Spanish language and much of the Mexican heritage alive in the Southwest. Nonetheless, 19th-century Mexican Americans fit Blauner's category of a colonized minority group, and the suppression of their culture was part of the process by which the dominant culture was established.

Anglo-American economic interests benefited enormously from the conquest of the Southwest and the colonization of the Mexican people. Growers and other businessmen came to rely on the cheap labor pool formed by Mexican Americans and immigrant and day laborers from Mexico. The region grew in affluence and productivity, but Mexican Americans were now outsiders in their own land and did not share in the prosperity. In the land grab of the 1800s and the conquest of the indigenous Mexican population lies one of the roots of Mexican American relations with the dominant U.S. society today.

**Gender Relations.** Prior to the arrival of Anglo-Americans, Mexican society in the Southwest was patriarchal and maintained a clear gender-based division of labor. These characteristics tended to persist after the conquest and the creation of minority group status.

Most Mexican Americans lived in small villages or on large ranches and farms. The women devoted their energies to the family, child rearing, and household tasks. As Mexican

Americans were reduced to a landless labor force, women along with men suffered the economic devastation that accompanied military conquest by a foreign power. The kinds of jobs available to the men (mining, seasonal farm work, railroad construction) often required them to be away from home for extended periods of time, and women, by default, began to take over the economic and other tasks traditionally performed by males.

Poverty and economic insecurity placed the family structures under considerable strain. Traditional cultural understandings about male dominance and patriarchy became moot when the men were absent for long periods of time and the decision-making power of Mexican-American women increased. Also, women were often forced to work outside the household for the family to survive economically. The economics of conquest led to increased matriarchy and more working mothers (Becerra, 1988, p. 149).

For Mexican American women, the consequences of contact were variable even though the ultimate result was a loss of status within the context of the conquest and colonization of the group as a whole. Like black female slaves, Mexican American women became the most vulnerable part of the social system.

## COMPARING MINORITY GROUPS

American Indians and black slaves were the victims of the explosive growth of European power in the Western Hemisphere that began with Columbus's voyage in 1492. Europeans needed labor to fuel the plantations of the mid-17th-century American colonies and settled on slaves from Africa as the most logical, cost-effective means of resolving their labor supply problems. Black Africans had a commodity the colonists coveted (labor), and the colonists subsequently constructed a system to control and exploit this commodity.

To satisfy the demand for land created by the stream of European immigrants to North America, the threat represented by American Indians had to be eliminated. Once their land was expropriated, American Indians ceased to be of much concern. The only valuable resource they possessed—their land—was under the control of white society by 1890, and American Indians were thought to be unsuitable as a source of labor.

Mexico, like the United States, had been colonized by a European power; in this case, Spain. In the early 1800s, the Mexican communities in the Southwest were a series of outpost settlements, remote and difficult to defend. Through warfare and a variety of other aggressive means, Mexican citizens living in this area were conquered and became an exploited minority group.

Each of these three groups, in their separate ways, became involuntary players in the growth and development of European and, later, American economic and political power. None of these groups had much choice in their respective fates; all three were overpowered and relegated to an inferior, subordinate status. Many views of assimilation (such as the "melting pot" metaphor discussed in Chapter 2) have little relevance to these situations. These minority groups had little control over their destinies, their degree of acculturation, or even their survival as groups. African Americans, American Indians, and Mexican Americans were coercively acculturated in the context of paternalistic relations in an agrarian economy. Meaningful integration (structural assimilation) was not a real possibility, especially for African Americans and American Indians. In Milton Gordon's (1964) terms (see Chapter 2), we might characterize these situations as "acculturation without integration" or structural pluralism. Given the grim realities described in this chapter, Gordon's terms seem a little antiseptic, and Blauner's concept of colonized minority groups seems far more descriptive.

## Mexico, Canada, and the United States

In this chapter, we argued that dominant-minority relations are profoundly shaped by the contact situation and by the characteristics of the groups involved (especially their subsistence technologies). We saw how these factors shaped relations with Native American and Mexican Americans and how they led British colonists to create a system of slavery to control the labor of African Americans. How do the experiences of the Spanish and the French in the Western Hemisphere compare with those of the British in what became the United States? What roles did the contact situation and subsistence technology play in the development of group relations in these two neighbors of the United States?[2]

The Spanish were the first of the three European nations to invade the Western Hemisphere, and they conquered much of what is now Central and South America about a century before Jamestown was founded. Their first encounter with an American Indian society occurred in 1521, when they defeated the Aztec Empire, located in what is now central Mexico. Aztec society was large, highly organized, and complex. It was ruled by an emperor and included scores of different societies, each with their own language and identity, which had been conquered by the fiercely warlike Aztecs. The bulk of the population of the empire consisted of peasants or agricultural laborers who farmed small plots of land owned by members of the elite classes, to whom they paid rents. Peasants are a fundamental part of any labor-intensive, preindustrial agrarian societies and were just as common in Spain as they were among the Aztecs.

When the Spanish defeated the Aztecs, they destroyed their cities, their temples, and their leadership (the emperor, the nobility, priests, etc.). They did not destroy the Aztec social structure; rather, they absorbed it and used it for their own benefit. For example, the Aztec Empire had financed its central government by collecting taxes and rents from citizens and tribute from conquered tribes. The Spanish simply grafted their own tax collection system onto this structure and diverted the flow from the Aztec elite classes (which they had, at any rate, destroyed) to themselves (Russell, 1994, pp. 29-30).

The Spanish tendency to absorb rather than destroy operated at many levels. For example, Aztec peasants became Spanish (and then Mexican) peasants, occupying roughly the same role in the new society that they had in the old, save for paying their rents to different landlords. There was also extensive interbreeding between the Spanish and the conquered tribes of Mexico, but again, unlike the situation in the English colonies, the Spanish recognized the resultant racial diversity and developed an elaborate system for classifying people by race. They recognized as many as 56 racial groups, including whites, **mestizos** (mixed European-Indian), and mulattos (mixed European-African) (Russell, 1994, p. 35). The society that emerged was highly race conscious, and race was highly correlated with social class: The elite classes were white, and the lower classes were nonwhite. However, the large-scale intermarriage and the official recognition of mixed-race peoples did establish the foundation for a racially mixed society. Today, the huge majority of the Mexican population is mestizo, although there remains a very strong correlation between race and class, and the elite positions in the society tend to be monopolized by people of "purer" European ancestry.

The French began to colonize Canada at about the same time the English established their colonies further south. The dominant economic enterprise in the early days was not farming, but trapping and the fur trade. The French developed a lucrative trade in this area by allying themselves with some American Indian tribes. The Indians produced the furs and traded them to the French, who in turn sold them on the world market. Like the Spanish in Mexico, the French in Canada tended to link to and absorb Native American social structures. There was also a significant amount of intermarriage between the French and Native Americans, resulting in a mixed-race group, called Métis, who had their own identities and, indeed, their own settlements along the Canadian frontier (Russell, 1994, p. 39).

Note the profound differences in these three contact situations between Europeans and Native Americans. The Spanish confronted a large, well-organized social system and found it expeditious to adapt Aztec practices to their own benefit. The French developed an economy that required cooperation with at least some of the Native American tribes they encountered, and they, too, found benefits in adaptation. The tribes encountered by the English were much smaller and much less developed than the Aztecs, and there was no particular reason for the English to adapt to or absorb these social structures. Furthermore, because the business of the English colonies was agriculture (not trapping), the competition at the heart of the contact situation was for land, and American Indians were seen as rivals for control of that most valuable resource. Thus the English tended to confront and exclude American Indians, keeping them on the outside of their emerging society and building strong boundaries between their own "civilized" world and the "savages" that surrounded them. The Spanish and French colonists had to adapt their societies to fit with American Indians, but the English faced no such restraints. They could create their institutions and design their social structure to suit themselves (Russell, 1994, p. 30).

As we have seen, one of the institutions created in the English colonies was slavery based on African labor. Slavery was also practiced in New Spain (Mexico) and New France (Canada), but the institution evolved in very different ways in those colonies and never assumed the importance that it did in the United States. Why? As you might suspect, the answer has a lot to do with the nature of the contact situation. Like the English colonists, both the Spanish and French attempted large-scale agricultural enterprises that might have created a demand for imported slave labor. In the case of New Spain, however, there was a ready supply of Native American peasants available to fill the role played by blacks in the English colonies. Although Africans became a part of the admixture that shaped modern Mexico racially and socially, demand for black slaves never matched that of the English colonies. Similarly, in Canada, slaves from Africa were sometimes used, but farmers there tended to rely on the flow of labor from France to fill their agricultural needs. The British opted for slave labor from Africa over indentured labor from Europe, and the French made the opposite decision.

Another difference between the three European nations that helps to explain the divergent development of group relations is their relative level of modernization. Compared to England, Spain and France were more traditional and feudalistic in their cultures and social structures. Among other things, this meant that they had to shape their agricultural enterprises in the New World around the ancient social relations between peasants and landlords they brought from the Old World. Thus the Spanish and French colonists were limited in their actions by these ancient customs, traditions, and understandings. Such old-fashioned institutions were much weaker in England, and thus the English colonists were much freer to design their social structure to suit their own needs. Whereas the Spanish and French had to shape their colonial societies to fit both American Indian social patterns and European traditions, the English could improvise and attend only to their own needs and desires. The closed, complex, and repressive institution of American slavery—designed and crafted from scratch in the New World—was one result.

Finally, we should note that many of the modern racial characteristics of these three neighboring societies were foreshadowed in their colonial origins (for example, the greater concentration of African Americans in the United States and the more racially intermixed population of Mexico). The differences run much deeper than race alone, of course, and include differences in class structure and relative levels of industrialization and affluence. For our purposes, however, this brief comparison of the origins of dominant-minority relations underscores the importance of the contact situation in shaping group relations for centuries to come.

## How Did Slavery Affect the Origins of African American Culture?

A debate over the impact of slavery on African American culture began in the 1960s and continues to the present day. Stanley Elkins, in his 1959 book Slavery: A Problem in American Institutional and Intellectual Life, laid down the terms of the debate. Elkins concluded that African American culture in the United States was created in response to the repressive plantation system and in the context of brutalization, total control of the slaves by their owners, and dehumanization. He argued that black culture was "made in America," but in an abnormal, even pathological social setting. The plantation was a sick society that dominated and infantilized black slaves. The dominant reality for slaves—and the only significant other person in their lives—was the master. Elkins described the system as a "perverted patriarchy" that psychologically forced the slaves to identify with their oppressors and to absorb the racist values at the core of the structure.

Elkins's book has been called "a work of great intellectual audacity, based on a methodology which has little connection with conventional historical research and arriving at conclusions which were challenging or outrageous, according to one's point of view" (Parish, 1989, p. 7). The book stimulated an enormous amount of controversy and research on the impact of slavery and the origins of African American culture. This body of research developed new sources of evidence and new perspectives and generally concluded that African American culture is a combination of elements, some from the traditional cultures of Africa and others fabricated on the plantation. The selection that follows, from the work of historian William Piersen, illustrates this argument and focuses on West African and African American family customs.

A third view is presented in an excerpt from the writings of Deborah Gray White. She argues that most scholarly work in slavery is written from the perspective of the male slave only, to the point of excluding the female experience. In the passage from her 1985 book Ar'n't I a Woman? Female Slaves in the Plantation South, she also addresses the problems of research in the area of minority group females and summarizes some of what has been learned from recent scholarship on the impact of slavery.

All three of these views are consistent with Blauner's idea that the cultures of colonized minority groups are attacked and that the groups are forcibly acculturated. Elkins's argument is the most extreme in that it sees African American culture as fabricated entirely in response to the demands of enslavement and the fearful, all-powerful figure of the master.

## Slavery Created African American Culture

### STANLEY ELKINS

Both [the Nazi concentration camps and the American slave plantations] were closed systems from which all standards based on prior connections had been effectively detached. A working adjustment to either system required a childlike conformity, a limited choice of "significant other." Cruelty per se cannot be considered the primary key to this; of far greater importance was the simple "closedness" of the system, in which all lines of authority descended from the master and in which alternative social bases that might have supported alternative standards were systematically suppressed. The individual, consequently, for his very psychic security, had to picture his master in some way as the "good father," even when, as in the concentration camp, it made no sense at all.

For the Negro child, in particular, the plantation offered no really satisfactory father image other than the master. The "real" father was virtually without authority over his child, since discipline, parental responsibility, and control of rewards and punishments all rested in other hands; the slave father could not even protect the mother of his children.

From the master's viewpoint, slaves had been defined in law as property, and the master's power over his property must be absolute. . . . Absolute power for him meant absolute dependency for the slave—the dependency not of the developing child but of the perpetual child. For the master, the role most aptly fitting such a relationship would naturally be that of father.

SOURCE: Elkins, Stanley. 1959. *Slavery: A Problem in American Institutional and Intellectual Life*. New York: Universal Library. Pp. 130-131.

## African American Culture Was Created by an Interplay of Elements From Africa and America

WILLIAM D. PIERSEN

In the colonial environment, . . . [African and European] traditions were fused. . . . The result was an unprecedented and unintended new multicultural American way of life. . . .

[Africans] had little choice [but this] adjustment was not as difficult . . . as we might suppose: the cultures of Africa and Europe were both dominated by the rhythms and sensibilities of a premodern, agricultural way of life shaped more by folk religion than by science, and domestic responsibilities were relatively similar on both continents. . . .

One of the greatest sacrifices that faced the new African Americans was the loss of the extended families that had structured most social relationships in Africa. . . . [African marriage customs were usually polygynous (permitting more than one wife) and patrilineal (tracing ancestry

through the male side).] With marriage, most African Americans seem . . . to have settled quickly into Euro-American–style monogamous nuclear families that trace inheritance bilaterally through the lines of both parents. Nonetheless, colonial naming choices show the continuing importance of African ideas of kinship among African Americans, for black children were more commonly . . . named after recently deceased relatives, a practice rooted in the African belief of rebirth across generations. . . .

African Americans . . . tried to rebuild as best they could the social cohesion once provided by the now missing extended families of Africa. [They] tried to duplicate some of the kinship . . . functions . . . by forging close relationships with their countrymen and shipmates from the Middle Passage. . . . [Many] treated both the blacks and whites that lived with them . . . as a kind of artificial kin. . . .

In North America many white colonials soon gave up traditional European village residence patterns to move out individually on the land, but African Americans, when they had the choice, generally preferred to stay together. . . . Such communalism [was] a reflection of the value that Africans and African Americans put on collective living.

In West Africa kin groups gathered in their housing together in large compounds that featured centralized open spaces devoted to social functions and collective recreation. Husbands and wives within the compounds usually had their own separate family quarters. . . . In colonial African American housing the old ways were maintained. . . . [In early 18th century Virginia,] most slaves lived in clusterings of more than 10 people. In these quarters, black social life was centered not on the interior of the small dark sleeping structures but outside on the common space devoted to social functions.

SOURCE: Piersen, William D. 1996. *From Africa to America: African American History From the Colonial Era to the Early Republic, 1526-1790*. New York: Twayne.

## The Experiences of Female Slaves Have Been Under-Researched and Under-Reported

**DEBORAH GRAY WHITE**

Stanley Elkins began [the debate] by alleging that the American slave master had such absolute power and authority over the bondsman that the slave was reduced to childlike dependency. "Sambo," Elkins argued, was more than a product of Southern fantasy. He could not be dismissed as a "stereotype." . . .

Elkins' thesis had a profound effect upon the research and writing of the history of slavery. The direction that the research took, however, was in large part predetermined because Elkins' slavery defined the parameters of the debate. In a very subtle way these parameters had more to do with the nature of male slavery than with female slavery. . . .

John Blassingame's The Slave Community is a classic but much of it deals with male status. For instance, Blassingame stressed the fact that many masters recognized the male as the head of the family. He observed that during courtship, men flattered women and exaggerated their prowess. There was, however, little discussion of the reciprocal activities of slave women. Blassingame also described how slave men gained status in the family and slave community, but did not do the same for women. . . .

The reality of slave life gives us reason to suspect that we do black women a disservice when we rob them of a history that placed them at the side of their men in their race's struggle for freedom. The present study takes a look at slave women and argues that they were not submissive, subordinate, or prudish and they were not expected to be so. Women had different roles from those of men and they also had a great deal in common with their African foremothers, who held positions not inferior but complementary to those of men. . . .

Source material on the general nature of slavery exists in abundance, but it is very difficult to find source material about slave women in particular. Slave women are everywhere, yet nowhere. . . .

The source problem is directly related to what was and still is the black woman's condition. Every economic and political index demonstrated the black woman's virtual powerlessness in American society. A consequence of the double jeopardy and powerlessness is the black woman's invisibility. . . .

The history of slavery has come a long way. We have learned that race relations were never so clear-cut as to be solely a matter of white over black, but that in the assimilation of culture, in the interaction of blacks and whites, there were gray areas and relationships more aptly described in terms of black over white. We have also begun to understand that despite the brutality and inhumanity, or perhaps because of it, a distinct African American culture based on close-knit kinship relationships grew and thrived, and that it was this culture that sustained black people through many trials before and after emancipation.

SOURCE: White, Deborah Gray. 1985. *Ar'n't I a Woman? Female Slaves in the Plantation South*. New York: Norton. Pp. 17-18.

## Debate Questions to Consider

1. Why is the origin of African American culture an important issue? What difference does it make today? If you believe Elkins is correct, what are the implications for dealing with racial inequality in the present? Could a culture that was created under a pathological system and a sick society be an adequate basis for the pursuit of equality and justice today? Is Elkins's thesis a form of blaming the victim? Is it a way of blaming the present inequality of the black community on an "inadequate" culture, thus absolving the rest of society from blame?

2. If you agree with Piersen's or White's viewpoints, what are the implications for how African Americans think about their history and about themselves? What difference does it make if your roots are in Africa or in colonial Virginia or, as White and Piersen argue, in both?

3. What does White add to the debate? What are some of the challenges in researching the experiences of female slaves? How did the experiences of female slaves differ from those of male slaves?

# MAIN POINTS

- Dominant-minority relations are shaped by the characteristics of society as a whole, particularly by subsistence technology. The contact situation is the single most important factor in the development of dominant-minority relations.

- The Noel hypothesis states that when a contact situation is characterized by ethnocentrism, competition, and a differential in power, ethnic or racial stratification will result. In colonial America, Africans were enslaved instead of white indentured servants or American Indians because only they fit all three conditions. American slavery was a paternalistic system.

- Prejudice and racism are more the results of systems of racial and ethnic inequality than they are the causes. They serve to rationalize, "explain," and stabilize these systems.

- The competition with American Indians centered on control of the land. American Indian tribes were conquered and pressed into a paternalistic relationship with white society. American Indians became a colonized minority group and were subjected to forced acculturation.

- Mexican Americans were the third minority group created during the preindustrial era. Mexican Americans competed with white settlers over both land and labor. Like Africans and American Indians, Mexican Americans were a colonized minority group subjected to forced acculturation.

- Conquest and colonization affected men and women differently. Women's roles changed, and they sometimes were less constrained by patriarchal traditions. These changes were always in the context of increasing powerlessness and poverty for the group as a whole, however, and minority women have been doubly oppressed by their gender roles as well as their minority group status.

- How long do patterns of ethnic and racial stratification persist? The two public sociology assignments presented in the Introduction to Part III give you an opportunity to research this question on your own campus in terms of the diversity and equality of the work force and in terms of "self-segregation" in the student body.

## Study Site on the Web

Don't forget the interactive quizzes and other resources and learning aids at www.www.pineforge.com/healeystudy4.

## For Further Reading

Genovese, Eugene D. 1974. *Roll, Jordan, Roll.* New York: Pantheon.

Gutman, Herbert G. 1976. *The Black Family in Slavery and Freedom.* New York: Vintage.

Levine, Lawrence. 1977. *Black Culture and Black Consciousness.* New York: Oxford University Press.

Rawick, George P. 1972. *From Sundown to Sunup: The Making of the Black Community.* Westport, CT: Greenwood Press.

Stuckey, Sterling. 1987. *Slave Culture: Nationalist Theory and the Foundations of Black America.* New York: Harper & Row. *(A short list of five vital sources on the origins and psychological and cultural impact of slavery in America.)*

Brown, Dee. 1970. *Bury My Heart at Wounded Knee.* New York: Holt, Rinehart & Winston. *(An eloquent and moving account of the conquest of American Indians.)*

Nabakov, Peter. (Ed.). 1999. *Native American Testimony* (Rev. ed.). New York: Penguin. *(A collection of valuable and insightful American Indian accounts of the last 500 years.)*

Wax, Murray. 1971. *Indian Americans: Unity and Diversity.* Englewood Cliffs, NJ: Prentice Hall. *(A compact and informative analysis of the history and present situation of American Indians.)*

McWilliams, Carey. 1961. *North from Mexico: The Spanish Speaking People of the United States.* New York: Monthly Review Press.*( A classic overview of the historical development of Mexican Americans.)*

Acuna, Rodolfo. 1999. *Occupied America* (4th ed.). New York: Harper & Row. *(Acuna examines a broad sweep of Mexican American experiences and argues that their status is comparable to that of other colonized groups.)*

Mirandé, Alfredo. 1985. *The Chicano Experience: An Alternative Perspective.* Notre Dame, IN: University of Notre Dame Press.*( A passionate argument for a new sociological approach to the study of Mexican Americans. Many useful insights into Mexican American family structures, the problem of crime, and other areas.)*

## Questions for Review and Study

1. State and explain the two themes presented at the beginning of the chapter. Apply each to the contact situations between white European colonists, African Americans, American Indians, and Mexican Americans. Identify and explain the key differences and similarities between the three situations.

2. Explain what a plantation system is and why this system of production is important for understanding the origins of slavery in colonial America. Why are plantation systems usually characterized by (a) paternalism, (b) huge inequalities between groups, (c) repressive systems of control, (d) rigid codes of behavior, and (e) low rates of overt conflict?

3. Explain the Noel and Blauner hypotheses and explain how they apply to the contact situations covered in this chapter. Explain each of the following key terms: ethnocentrism, competition, power, colonized minority group, immigrant minority group. How did group conflict vary when competition was over land versus when it was over labor?

4. Explain the role of prejudice and racism in the creation of minority group status. Do prejudice and racism help cause minority group status or are they caused by minority group status? Explain.

5. Compare and contrast gender relations in regard to each of the contact situations discussed in this chapter. Why do the relationships vary?

6. What does it mean to say that, under slavery, acculturation for African Americans was coerced? What are the implications for assimilation, inequality, and African American culture?

7. Compare and contrast the contact situations in colonial America, Canada, and Mexico. What groups were involved in each situation? What was the nature of the competition and what were the consequences?

## Internet Research Project

Additional information and a list of relevant Web sites are included in the Appendix (Internet Resources).

The "slave narratives" are one interesting source of information about the nature of everyday life under slavery. The narratives were compiled during the 1930s in interviews with exslaves, and although they are limited in many ways, the interviews do provide a close-up, personal view of the system of slavery from the perspective of its victims. To use this resource, go to http://newdeal.feri.org/asn/index.htm and read the home page carefully, especially the cautions. Select several of the narratives and analyze them in terms of the concepts introduced in this chapter (e.g., paternalism, labor-intensive systems of work, the Noel and Blauner hypotheses)

# 6

# Industrialization and Dominant-Minority Relations

### From Slavery to Segregation and the Coming of Postindustrial Society

ONE THEME STATED AT THE BEGINNING OF CHAPTER 5 WAS THAT A SOCIETY'S SUBSISTENCE technology profoundly affects the nature of dominant-minority group relations. A corollary of this theme, explored in this chapter, is that *dominant-minority group relations change as the subsistence technology changes.* As we saw in chapter 5, agrarian technology and the concern for control of land and labor profoundly shaped dominant-minority relations in the formative years of the United States. The agrarian era ended in the 1800s, and since that time, the United States has experienced two major transformations in subsistence technology, each of which has, in turn, transformed dominant-minority relations.

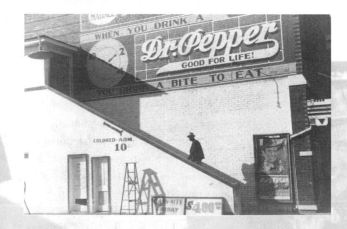

The first transformation began in the early 1800s as American society began to experience the effects of the *industrial revolution,* or the shift from agrarian technology to machine-based, manufacturing technology. In the agrarian era, as we saw in chapter 5, work was labor intensive, done by hand or with the aid of draft animals. As industrialization proceeded, work became *capital intensive* as machines replaced people and animals.

The new industrial technology rapidly increased productivity and efficiency and quickly began to change every aspect of U.S. society, including the nature of work, politics, communication, transportation, family life, birth rates and death rates, the system of education, and, of course, dominant-minority relations. The groups that had become minorities during the agrarian era (African Americans, American Indians, and Mexican Americans) faced new possibilities and new dangers. Industrialization also created new minority groups, new forms of exploitation and oppression and, for some, new opportunities to rise in the social structure and succeed in America. In this chapter, we will explore this transformation and illustrate its effects by analyzing the changing status of African Americans after the abolition of slavery. The impact of industrialization on other minority groups will be considered in the case studies presented in Part IV.

The second transformation in subsistence technology brings us to more recent times. Industrialization is a continuous process, and beginning in the mid-20th century, the United States entered a stage of late industrialization (also called **deindustrialization,** or the *postindustrial* era). This shift in subsistence technology was marked by a decline in the manufacturing sector of the economy and a decrease in the supply of secure, well-paying, blue-collar, manual labor jobs. At the same time, there was an expansion in the service and information-based sectors of the economy and an increase in the proportion of white-collar and "high-tech" jobs. Like the 19th-century industrial revolution, these 20th-century changes have profound implications not just for dominant-minority relations but for every aspect of modern society. Work, family, politics, popular culture, and thousands of other characteristics of American society are being transformed as the subsistence technology continues to develop and modernize. In the latter part of this chapter, we examine this latest transformation in general terms and point out some of its implications for minority groups. We also present some new concepts and establish some important groundwork for the case studies in Part IV, in which the effects of late industrialization on America's minority groups will be considered in detail.

## INDUSTRIALIZATION AND THE SHIFT FROM PATERNALISTIC TO RIGID COMPETITIVE GROUP RELATIONS

The industrial revolution began in England in the mid-1700s and spread from there to the rest of Europe, to the United States, and eventually to the rest of the world. The key innovations associated with the industrial revolution were the application of machine power to production and the harnessing of inanimate sources of energy, such as steam and coal, to fuel the machines. As machines replaced humans and animals, work became many times more productive, the economy grew, and the volume and variety of goods produced increased dramatically.

As the industrial economy grew, the close, paternalistic control of minority groups found in agrarian societies gradually became irrelevant. Paternalistic relationships such as slavery are found in societies with labor-intensive technologies and are designed to organize and control a large, involuntary, geographically immobile labor force. An industrial economy, in contrast, requires a workforce that is geographically and socially mobile, skilled, and literate. Furthermore, with industrialization comes urbanization, and close, paternalistic controls are difficult to maintain in a city.

Thus as industrialization progresses, agrarian paternalism tends to give way to **rigid competitive** group relations. Under this system, minority group members are freer to compete for jobs and other valued commodities with dominant group members, especially the lower class segments of the dominant group. As competition increases, the threatened members of the dominant group become more hostile, and attacks on the minority groups tend to increase. Whereas paternalistic systems seek to directly dominate and control the minority group (and its labor), rigid competitive systems are more defensive in nature. The threatened segments of the dominant group seek to minimize or eliminate minority group encroachment on jobs, housing, or other valuable goods or services (van den Berghe, 1967; Wilson, 1973).

Paternalistic systems such as slavery required members of the minority group to be active, if involuntary, participants. In rigid competitive systems, the dominant group seeks to preserve its advantage by handicapping the minority group's ability to compete effectively or, in some cases, by eliminating competition from the minority group altogether. For example, in a rigid competitive system, the dominant group might make the minority group politically powerless by depriving them of (or never granting them) the right to vote. The lower the power of the minority group, the lower the threat to the interests of the dominant group.

## THE IMPACT OF INDUSTRIALIZATION ON AFRICAN AMERICANS: FROM SLAVERY TO SEGREGATION

Industrial technology began to transform American society in the early 1800s, but its effects were not felt equally in all regions. The Northern states industrialized first, while the South remained primarily agrarian. This economic diversity was one of the underlying causes of the regional conflict that led to the Civil War. Because of its more productive technology, the North had more resources and, in a bloody war of attrition, was able to defeat the Confederacy. Slavery was abolished, and black-white relations in the South entered a new era when the Civil War ended in April 1865.

The Southern system of race relations that ultimately emerged after the Civil War was designed in part to continue the control of African American labor institutionalized under slavery. It was also intended to eliminate any political or economic threat from the African American community. This rigid competitive system grew to be highly elaborate and inflexible, partly because of the high racial visibility and long history of inferior status and powerlessness of African Americans in the South and partly because of the particular needs of Southern agriculture. In this section, we look at black-white relations from the end of the Civil War through the ascendance of segregation in the South and the mass migration of African Americans to the cities of the industrializing North.

## Reconstruction

The period of **Reconstruction**, from 1865 to the 1880s, was a brief respite in the long history of oppression and exploitation of African Americans. The Union army and other agencies of the federal government, such as the Freedman's Bureau, were used to enforce racial freedom in the defeated Confederacy. Black Southerners took advantage of the 15th Amendment to the Constitution, passed in 1870, which states that the right to vote cannot be denied on the grounds of "race, color, or previous condition of servitude." They registered to vote in large numbers and turned out on Election Day, and some were elected to high political office. Schools for the former slaves were opened, and African Americans purchased land and houses and founded businesses.

The era of freedom was short, however, and Reconstruction began to end when the federal government demobilized its armies of occupation and turned its attention to other matters. By the 1880s, the federal government had withdrawn from the South, Reconstruction was over, and black Southerners began to fall rapidly into a new system of exploitation and inequality.

## Images of African Americans:
## Post Civil War to World War II by *Eric Margolis*

Popular bigotry and prejudice was bolstered by eugenics and a "scientific" version of racism. At right is a page from a high school science textbook published in 1886 which purports to offer visual proof of the superiority of the white race, arguing that the students (assumed to be white) "must know that white men, being more intelligent, more industrious, and more courageous than the others, have spread over the whole world, so that the inferior races disappear as they are crowded out by the whites."

To counter some of the stereotyped images of black people in wide circulation in white America, W.E.B. DuBois, one of the founding fathers of American sociology, collected a large number of photographs of African Americans. Many were exhibited in albums of photographs at the Paris Exposition Universelle in 1900. There were hundreds of photographs in albums titled "Types of American Negroes" and "African Americans in Georgia." Most of the portraits were quite formal, conforming to the general standards of studio portraiture common in the Victorian era. For example, below is a lovely half-length portrait of a young girl standing at a table looking at an illustrated book.

less easily defined. We will for the time being take notice only of the *white* race of Europe, the *yellow* race of Asia,

FIG. 21.—White race (Europe).

FIG. 22.—Yellow race (Asia).

the *black* race of Africa, and the *red* race of America. Only you must know that white men, being more intelligent, more

FIG. 23.—Negro race (Africa).

FIG. 24.—Red race (America).

industrious, and more courageous than the others, have spread over the whole world, so that the inferior races disappear as they are crowded out by the whites.

There were also images on everyday life in Georgia in which African Americans were portrayed going about their lives.

The dehumanization of African Americans in the popular imagination was accomplished partly by the use of visual images. People were reduced to stereotypes and tagged as poor, criminal, and immoral. Between 1880 and 1930 more than 4,000 blacks were lynched. Many of these hangings and burnings of black men were photographed. The photos often included crowds of unabashed whites enjoying the murderous spectacle (see below). Of the tens of thousands of lynchers and watchers, only 49 people were indicted and 4 convicted. In a remarkable book called *Without Sanctuary*, the sociologist James Allen (2000) accumulated and published many photographs of lynchings that had been made into postcards and were widely bought and mailed. The photo reproduced here shows Thomas Shipp and Abram Smith, who were dragged from their cell and lynched on August 7, 1930 in Marion, Indiana.

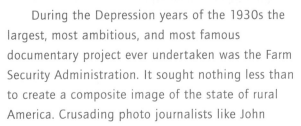

During the Depression years of the 1930s the largest, most ambitious, and most famous documentary project ever undertaken was the Farm Security Administration. It sought nothing less than to create a composite image of the state of rural America. Crusading photo journalists like John

Vachon, Ben Shahn, and Marion Post Wolcott documented the situation of African Americans in the rural south. They showed the realities of segregation and Jim Crow laws, as well as working conditions in which entire families labored in the cotton fields.

As the depression came to an end and World War II began, the Farm Security Administration (FSA) photographic project was taken over by the Office of War Information. Images of rural poverty began to disappear and were replaced by images of recovery and strength. For example, Jack Delano presented this image of a young girl with a jar of beans that her mother had canned. It is a metaphor of plenty that starkly contrasted with some of the earlier FSA images.

African Americans fought in each of America's wars. Crispus Atticus was one of the twelve patriots killed in the "Boston Massacre" of 1770 that helped set the stage for our revolution. The famous "Buffalo Soldiers" of the Tenth Calvary fought in the Indian Wars and the Spanish American War; and blacks fought in segregated units in both the First and Second World Wars.

Many blacks had high hopes that World War II would free them from segregation. Despite the revisionist histories of Hollywood war movies, however, more African Americans served in service positions than ever saw combat. After the war President Truman integrated the Armed Forces, over objections that white soldiers would never serve with blacks, and that integration would destroy unit cohesion. Forty years later the same arguments were used against allowing women in combat positions, and currently similar objections are raised to allowing gays and lesbians in the military.

Reconstruction was too brief to change two of the most important legacies of slavery. First, the centuries of bondage left black Southerners impoverished, largely illiterate and uneducated, and with few power resources. When new threats of racial oppression appeared, African Americans found it difficult to defend their group interests. These developments are, of course, highly consistent with the Blauner hypothesis: Because colonized minority groups confront greater inequalities and have fewer resources at their disposal, they will face greater difficulties in improving their disadvantaged status.

Second, slavery left a strong tradition of racism in the white community. Antiblack prejudice and racism originated as rationalizations for slavery but had taken on lives of their own over the generations. After two centuries of slavery, the heritage of prejudice and racism was thoroughly ingrained in Southern culture. White Southerners were predisposed by this cultural legacy to see racial inequality and exploitation of African Americans as normal and desirable, and after Reconstruction ended and the federal government withdrew, they were able to construct a social system based on the assumption of racial inferiority.

## De Jure Segregation

The system of race relations that replaced slavery in the South was **de jure segregation**, sometimes referred to as the Jim Crow system. Under segregation, the minority group is physically and socially separated from the dominant group and consigned to an inferior position in virtually every area of social life. The phrase *de jure* ("by law") means that the system is sanctioned and reinforced by the legal code; the inferior status of African Americans was actually mandated or required by state and local laws. For example, Southern cities during this era had laws requiring African Americans to ride at the back of the bus. If an African American refused to comply with this seating arrangement, he or she could be arrested.

De jure segregation came to encompass all aspects of Southern life. Neighborhoods, jobs, stores, restaurants, and parks were segregated. When new social forms, such as movie theaters, sports stadiums, and interstate buses appeared in the South, they, too, were quickly segregated.

The logic of segregation created a vicious cycle. The more African Americans were excluded from the mainstream of society, the greater their objective poverty and powerlessness became. The more inferior their status, the easier it was to mandate more inequality. High levels of inequality reinforced racial prejudice and made it easy to use racism to justify further separation. The system kept turning on itself, finding new social niches to segregate and reinforcing the inequality that was its starting point. For example, at the height of the Jim Crow era, the system had evolved to the point that some courtrooms maintained separate Bibles for African American witnesses to swear on. Also, in Birmingham, Alabama, it was against the law for blacks and whites to play checkers and dominoes together (Woodward, 1974, p. 118).

What were the causes of this massive separation of the races? Once again, the concepts of the Noel hypothesis prove useful. Because strong antiblack prejudice was already in existence when segregation began, we do not need to account for ethnocentrism. The post-Reconstruction competition between the racial groups was reminiscent of the origins of slavery in that black Southerners had something that white Southerners wanted: labor. In addition, a free black electorate threatened the political and economic dominance of the elite segments of the white community. Finally, after the withdrawal of federal troops and the end of Reconstruction, white southerners had sufficient power resources to end the competition on their own terms and construct repressive systems of control for black Southerners.

**The Origins of De Jure Segregation.** Although the South lost the Civil War, its basic class structure and agrarian economy remained intact. The plantation elite, with their huge tracts of land, remained the dominant class, and cotton remained the primary cash crop. As was the case before the Civil War, the landowners needed a workforce to farm the land. Because of the depredations and economic disruptions of the war, the old plantation elite was short on cash and liquid capital. Hiring workers on a wage system was not feasible for them. In fact, almost as soon as the war ended, Southern legislatures attempted to force African Americans back into involuntary servitude by passing a series of laws known as the Black Codes. Only the beginning of Reconstruction and the active intervention of the federal government halted the implementation of this legislation (Geschwender, 1978, p. 158; Wilson, 1973, p. 99).

The plantation elite solved their manpower problem this time by developing a system of **sharecropping**, or tenant farming. The sharecroppers worked the land, which was actually owned by the planters, in return for payment in shares of the profit when the crop was taken to market. The landowner would supply a place to live and food and clothing on credit. After the harvest, tenant and landowner would split the profits (sometimes very unequally), and the tenant's debts would be deducted from his share. The accounts were kept by the landowner. Black sharecroppers lacked political and civil rights and found it difficult to keep unscrupulous white landowners honest. The landowner could inflate the indebtedness of the sharecropper and claim that he was still owed money even after profits had been split. Under this system, sharecroppers had few opportunities to improve their situations and could be bound to the land until their "debts" were paid off (Geschwender, 1978, p. 163).

By 1910, more than half of all employed African Americans worked in agriculture, and more than half of the remainder (25% of the total) worked in domestic occupations such as maid or janitor (Geschwender, 1978, p. 169). The manpower shortage in Southern agriculture was solved, and the African American community once again found itself in a subservient status. At the same time, the white Southern working class was protected from direct job competition with African Americans. As the South began to industrialize, white workers were able to monopolize the better paying jobs. With a combination of direct discrimination by whites-only labor unions and strong antiblack laws and customs, white workers erected barriers that excluded black workers and reserved the better industrial jobs in cities and mill towns for themselves. White workers took advantage of the new jobs brought by industrialization, while black Southerners remained a rural peasantry, excluded from participation in this process of modernization.

In some sectors of the changing Southern economy, the status of African Americans actually fell lower than it had been during slavery. For example, in 1865, 83% of the artisans in the South were African Americans; by 1900, this percentage had fallen to 5% (Geschwender, 1978, p. 170). The Jim Crow system confined African Americans to the agrarian and domestic sectors of the labor force, denied them the opportunity for a decent education, and excluded them from politics. The system was reinforced by still more laws and customs that drastically limited the options and life courses available to black Southerners.

A final force behind the creation of de jure segregation was more political than economic. As the 19th century drew to a close, a wave of agrarian radicalism known as *populism* spread across the country. This antielitist movement was a reaction to changes in agriculture caused by industrialization. The movement attempted to unite poor whites and blacks in the rural South against the traditional elite classes. The economic elite was frightened by the possibility of a loss of power and split the incipient coalition between whites and blacks by fanning the flames of racial hatred. The strategy of "divide and conquer" proved to be effective (as it often has both before and since this time), and states throughout the South eliminated the possibility of future threats by depriving African Americans of the right to vote (Woodward, 1974).

The disenfranchisement of the black community was accomplished by measures such as literacy tests, poll taxes, and property requirements. The literacy tests were officially justified as promoting a better-informed electorate but were shamelessly rigged to favor white voters. The requirement that voters pay a tax or prove ownership of a certain amount of property could also disenfranchise poor whites, but again, the implementation of these policies was racially biased.

The policies were extremely effective, and by the early 20th century, the political power of the Southern black community was virtually nonexistent. For example, as late as 1896 in Louisiana, there had been more than 100,000 registered African American voters, and African American voters were a majority in 26 parishes (counties). In 1898, the state adopted a new constitution containing stiff educational and property requirements for voting unless the voter's father or grandfather had been eligible to vote as of January 1, 1867. At that time, the 14th and 15th Amendments, which guaranteed suffrage for black males, had not yet been passed. Such "grandfather clauses" made it easy for white males to register while disenfranchising blacks. By 1900, only about 5000 African Americans were registered to vote in Louisiana, and African American voters were not a majority in any parish. A similar decline occurred in Alabama, where an electorate of more than 180,000 African American males was reduced to 3000 by provision of a new state constitution. This story repeated itself throughout the South, and African American political powerlessness had become a reality by 1905 (Franklin & Moss, 1994, p. 261).

This system of legally mandated racial privilege was approved by the U.S. Supreme Court, which ruled in the case of *Plessy v. Ferguson* (1896) that it was constitutional for states to require separate facilities (schools, parks, etc.) for African Americans as long as the separate facilities were fully equal. The Southern states paid close attention to *separate* but ignored *equal*.

**Reinforcing the System.** Under de jure segregation, as under slavery, the subordination of the African American community was reinforced and supplemented by an elaborate system of racial etiquette. Everyday interactions between blacks and whites proceeded according to highly stylized and rigidly followed codes of conduct intended to underscore the inferior status of the African American community. Whites were addressed as "Mister" or "Ma'am," whereas African Americans were called by their first names or perhaps by an honorific title such as Aunt, Uncle, or Professor. Blacks were expected to assume a humble and deferential manner, remove their hats, cast their eyes downward, and enact the role of the subordinate in all interactions with whites. If an African American had reason to call on anyone in the white community, he or she was expected to go to the back door.

These expectations and "good manners" for black Southerners were systematically enforced. Anyone who ignored them ran the risk of reprisal, physical attacks, and even death by lynching. During the decades in which the Jim Crow system was being imposed, there were thousands of lynchings in the South. From 1884 until the end of the century, lynchings averaged almost one every other day (Franklin & Moss, 1994, p. 312). The bulk of this violent terrorism was racial and intended to reinforce the system of racial advantage or punish real or imagined transgressors. Also, various secret organizations, such as the Ku Klux Klan, engaged in terrorist attacks against the African American community and anyone else who failed to conform to the dictates of the system.

**Increases in Prejudice and Racism.** As the system of racial advantage formed and solidified, levels of prejudice and racism increased (Wilson, 1973, p. 101). The new system needed justification and rationalization, just as slavery did, and antiblack sentiment, stereotypes, and ideologies of racial inferiority grew stronger. At the start of the 20th century, the United States in general—not just the South—was a very racist and intolerant society. This spirit of rejection and scorn for all out-groups coalesced with the need for justification of the Jim Crow system and created an especially negative brand of racism in the South.

## THE "GREAT MIGRATION"

Although African Americans lacked the power resources to withstand the resurrection of Southern racism and oppression, they did have one option that had not been available under slavery: freedom of movement. African Americans were no longer legally tied to a specific master or to a certain plot of land. In the early 20th century, a massive population movement out of the South began. Slowly at first, African Americans began to move to other regions of the nation and from the countryside to the city. The movement increased when hard times hit Southern agriculture and slowed down during better times. It has been said that African Americans voted against Southern segregation with their feet.

As Exhibits 6.1 and 6.2 show, an urban black population living outside the South is a late 20th-century phenomenon. A majority of African Americans continue to live in the South, but the group is more evenly distributed across the nation and much more urbanized than a century ago. The significance of this population redistribution is manifold. Most important, perhaps, was the fact that by moving out of the South and from rural to urban areas, African Americans moved from areas of great resistance to racial change to areas of lower resistance. In the Northern cities, for example, it was far easier to register and to vote. Black political power began to grow and eventually provided many of the crucial resources that fueled the civil rights movement of the 1950s and 1960s.

## Life in the North

What did African American migrants find when they got to the industrializing cities of the North? There is no doubt that life in the North was better for the vast majority of African American migrants. The growing Northern African American communities relished the absence of Jim Crow laws and oppressive racial etiquette, the relative freedom to pursue jobs, and the greater opportunities to educate their children. Inevitably, however, life in the North fell short of utopia. Many aspects of African American culture—literature, poetry, music—flourished in the heady new atmosphere of freedom, but on other fronts, Northern African American communities faced discrimination in housing, schools, and the job market. Along with freedom and such cultural flowerings as the Harlem Renaissance came black ghettoes and new forms of oppression and exploitation.

## Competition With White Ethnic Groups

It is useful to see the movement of African Americans out of the South in terms of the resultant relationship with other groups. Southern blacks began to migrate to the North at about the same time that a huge wave of immigration from Europe that had begun in the 1820s came to an end. By the time substantial numbers of black Southerners began arriving in the North, European

**EXHIBIT 6.1** Regional Distribution of the African American Population

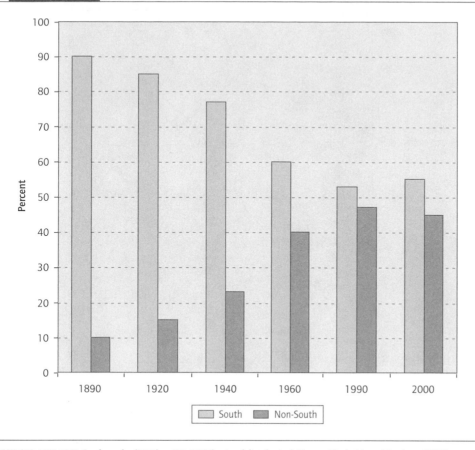

SOURCES: 1890-1960, Geschwender (1978), p. 173; 1990 (regional distribution), Heaton, Chadwick, and Jacobson (2000), p. 26; 2000 (regional distribution), U.S. Bureau of the Census (2005), p. 25.

immigrants and their descendants had had years, decades, and even generations to establish themselves in the job markets, political systems, labor unions, and neighborhoods of the North. Many of the European ethnic groups had also been the victims of discrimination and rejection, and their hold on economic security and status was tenuous for much of the 20th century. They saw the newly arriving black migrants as a threat to their status, a perception that was reinforced by the fact that industrialists and factory owners often used African Americans as strikebreakers and scabs during strikes. The white ethnic groups responded by developing defensive strategies to limit the dangers presented by these migrants from the South. They tried to exclude African Americans from their labor unions and other associations and limit their impact on the political system. They also attempted, often successfully, to maintain segregated neighborhoods and schools (although the legal system outside the South did not sanction de jure segregation).

This competition led to hostile relations between black Southern migrants and white ethnic groups, especially the lower and working-class segments of those groups. Ironically, however, the newly arriving African Americans actually helped white ethnic groups become upwardly mobile.

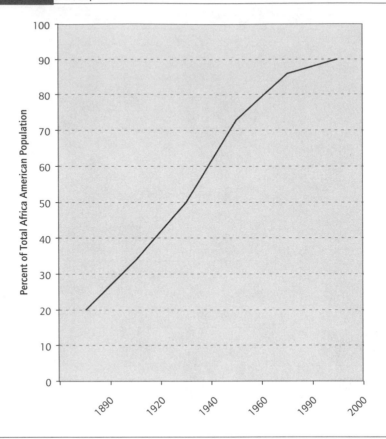

SOURCE: 1950, U.S. Bureau of the Census (1996); 1960-2003, U.S. Bureau of the Census (2005), p. 141.

Dominant group whites became less vocal about their contempt for the white ethnic groups as their alarm over the presence of African Americans increased. The greater antipathy of the white community toward African Americans made the immigrants less undesirable and thus hastened their admittance to the institutions of the larger society. For many white ethnic groups, the increased tolerance of the larger society coincided happily with the coming of age of the more educated and skilled descendants of the original immigrants, further abetting the rise of these groups in the U.S. social class structure (Lieberson, 1980).

For more than a century, each new European immigrant group had helped to push previous groups up the ladder of socioeconomic success and out of the old, ghettoized neighborhoods. The Irish, for example, pushed the Germans up and were in turn pushed up by Italians and Poles. Black Southerners got to the cities after immigration from Europe had been curtailed and no newly arrived immigrants appeared to continue the pattern of succession for Northern African Americans. Instead, American cities developed concentrations of low-income blacks who were economically vulnerable and politically weak and whose position was further solidified by antiblack prejudice and discrimination (Wilson, 1987, p. 34).

## The Kitchenette

*Richard Wright (1908-1960), one of the most powerful writers of the 20th century, lived through and wrote about many of the social changes discussed in this chapter. He grew up in the South during the height of the Jim Crow system, and his passionate hatred for segregation and bigotry is expressed in his major works* Native Son *(1940) and the autobiographical* Black Boy *(1945). In 1941, Wright helped to produce* Twelve Million Black Voices, *a folk history of African Americans. A combination of photos and brief essays, the work is a powerful commentary on three centuries of oppression.*

*The following selection is adapted from "Death on the City Pavement," which expresses Wright's view of the African American [black] migration out of the South, a journey he himself experienced. This bittersweet migration often traded the harsh, rural repression of the South for the overcrowded, anonymous ghettoes of the North. Housing discrimination, both overt and covert, confined African American migrants to the least desirable, most overcrowded areas of the city—in many cases, the neighborhoods that had first housed immigrants from Europe. Unscrupulous landlords subdivided buildings into the tiniest possible apartments ("kitchenettes"), and as impoverished newcomers who could afford no better, African American migrants were forced to cope with overpriced, substandard housing as best they could. Much of the passage, incidentally, could have been written about any 20th-century minority group.*

### DEATH ON THE CITY PAVEMENT

**Richard Wright**

A war sets up in our emotions: one part of our feelings tells us it is good to be in the city, that we have a chance at life here, that we need but turn a corner to become a stranger, that we need no longer bow and dodge at the sight of the Lords of the Land. Another part of our feelings tells us that, in terms of worry and strain, the cost of living in the kitchenettes is too high, that the city heaps too much responsibility on us and gives too little security in return. . . .

The kitchenette, with its filth and foul air, with its one toilet for thirty or more tenants, kills our black babies so fast that in many cities twice as many of them die as white babies. . . .

The kitchenette scatters death so widely among us that our death rate exceeds our birth rate, and if it were not for the trains and autos bringing us daily into the city from the plantations, we black folk who dwell in northern cities would die out entirely over the course of a few years. . . .

The kitchenette throws desperate and unhappy people into an unbearable closeness of association, thereby increasing latent friction, giving birth to never-ending quarrels of recrimination, accusation, and vindictiveness, producing warped personalities.

The kitchenette injects pressure and tension into our individual personalities, making many of us give up the struggle, walk off and leave wives, husbands, and even children behind to shift for themselves. . . .

The kitchenette reaches out with fingers of golden bribes to the officials of the city, persuading them to allow old firetraps to remain standing and occupied long after they should have been torn down.

The kitchenette is the funnel through which our pulverized lives flow to ruin and death on the city pavement, at a profit.

SOURCE: Wright, Richard. 1988. *12 Million Black Voices.* New York: Thunder's Mouth Press. Pp. 105-111.

# THE ORIGINS OF BLACK PROTEST

As I pointed out in chapter 5, African Americans have always resisted their oppression and protested their situation. Under slavery, however, the inequalities they faced were so great and their resources so meager that the protest was ineffective. With the increased freedom that followed slavery, a national African American leadership developed and spoke out against oppression and founded organizations that eventually helped to lead the fight for freedom and equality. Even at its birth, the black protest movement was diverse and incorporated a variety of viewpoints and leaders.

Booker T. Washington was the most prominent African American leader prior to World War I. Washington had been born in slavery and was the founder and president of Tuskegee Institute, a college in Alabama dedicated to educating African Americans. His public advice to African Americans in the South was to be patient, to accommodate to the Jim Crow system for now, to raise their levels of education and job skills, and to take full advantage of whatever opportunities became available. This nonconfrontational stance earned Washington praise and support from the white community and widespread popularity in the nation. Privately, he worked behind the scenes to end discrimination and implement full racial integration and equality (Franklin & Moss, 1994, pp. 272-274; Hawkins, 1962; Washington, 1965).

Washington's most vocal opponent was W.E.B. Du Bois, an intellectual and activist who was born in the North and educated at some of the leading universities of the day. Among his many other accomplishments, Du Bois was part of a coalition of blacks and white liberals who founded the National Association for the Advancement of Colored People (NAACP) in 1909. Du Bois rejected Washington's accommodationist stance and advocated immediate pursuit of racial equality and a direct assault on de jure segregation. Almost from the beginning of its existence, the NAACP filed lawsuits that challenged the legal foundations of Jim Crow segregation (Du Bois, 1961). As we shall see in Chapter 7, this legal strategy was eventually successful and led to the demise of the Jim Crow system.

Washington and Du Bois may have differed on matters of strategy and tactics, but they agreed that the only acceptable goal for African Americans was an integrated, racially equal United States. A third leader who emerged early in the 20th century called for a very different approach to the problems of U.S. race relations. Marcus Garvey was born in Jamaica and immigrated to the United States during World War I. He argued that the white-dominated U.S. society was hopelessly racist and would never truly support integration and racial equality. He advocated separatist goals, including a return to Africa. Garvey founded the Universal Negro Improvement Association in 1914 in his native Jamaica and founded the first U.S. branch in 1916. Garvey's organization was very popular for a time in African American communities outside the South, and he helped to establish some of the themes and ideas of black nationalism and pride in African heritage that would become prominent again in the pluralistic 1960s (Essien-Udom, 1962; Garvey, 1969, 1977; Vincent, 1976).

These early leaders and organizations established some of the foundation for later protest movements, but prior to the mid-20th century, they made few actual improvements in the situation of African Americans in the North or South. Jim Crow was a formidable opponent, and the African American community lacked the resources to successfully challenge the status quo until the century was well along and some basic structural features of American society had changed.

# APPLYING CONCEPTS
## Acculturation and Integration

During this era of Southern segregation and migration to the North, assimilation was not a major factor in the African American experience. Rather, black-white relations are better described as a system of structural pluralism combined with great inequality. Excluded from the mainstream but freed from the limitations of slavery, African Americans constructed a separate subsociety and subculture. In all regions of the nation, African Americans developed their own institutions and organizations, including separate neighborhoods, churches, businesses, and schools. Like immigrants from Europe in the same era, they organized their communities to cater to their own needs and problems and pursue their agenda as a group.

During the era of segregation, a small, African American middle class emerged based on leadership roles in the church, education, and business. A network of black colleges and universities was constructed to educate the children of the growing middle class, as well as other classes. Through this infrastructure, African Americans began to develop the resources and leadership that in the decades ahead would attack, head-on, the structures of racial inequality.

# Gender and Race

For African American men and women, the changes wrought by industrialization and the population movement to the North created new possibilities and new roles. However, as African Americans continued to be the victims of exploitation and exclusion in both the North and the South, African American women continued to be among the most vulnerable groups in society.

Following Emancipation, there was a flurry of marriages and weddings among African Americans, as they were finally able to legitimate their family relationships (Staples, 1988, p. 306). African American women continued to have primary responsibility for home and children. Historian Herbert Gutman (1976) reports that it was common for married women to drop out of the labor force and attend solely to household and family duties, because a working wife was too reminiscent of a slave role. This pattern became so widespread that it created serious labor shortages in many areas (Gutman, 1976; see also Staples, 1988, p. 307).

The former slaves were hardly affluent, however, and as sharecropping and segregation began to shape race relations in the South, women often had to return to the fields or to domestic work for the family to survive. One former slave woman noted that women "do double duty, a man's share in the field and a woman's part at home" (Evans, 1989, p. 121). During the bleak decades following the end of Reconstruction, Southern black families and black women in particular lived "close to the bone" (Evans, 1989, p. 121).

In the cities and in the growing African American neighborhoods in the North, African American women played a role that in some ways paralleled the role of immigrant women from Europe. The men often moved north first and sent for the women after they had attained some level of financial stability or after the pain of separation became too great (Almquist, 1979, p. 434). In other cases, African American women by the thousands left the South to work as domestic servants; they often replaced European immigrant women, who had moved up in the job structure (Amott & Matthaei, 1991, p. 168).

In the North, discrimination and racism created constant problems of unemployment for the men, and families often relied on the income supplied by the women to make ends meet. It was comparatively easy for women to find employment, but only in the low-paying, less desirable areas, such as domestic work. In both the South and the North, African American women worked outside the home in larger proportions than did white women. For example, in 1900, 41% of African American women were employed, compared with only 16% of white women (Staples, 1988, p. 307).

In 1890, more than a generation after the end of slavery, 85% of all African American men and 96% of African American women were employed in just two occupational categories: agriculture and domestic or personal service. By 1930, 90% of employed African American women were still in these same two categories, whereas the corresponding percentage for employed African American males had dropped to 54% (although nearly all of the remaining 46% were unskilled workers) (Steinberg, 1981, pp. 206-207). Since the inception of segregation, African American women have had consistently higher unemployment rates and lower incomes than African American men and white women (Almquist, 1979, p. 437). These gaps, as we shall see in chapter 7, persist to the present day.

During the years following Emancipation, some issues did split men and women, within both the African American community and the larger society. Prominent among these was suffrage, or the right to vote, which was still limited to men only. The abolitionist movement, which had been so instrumental in ending slavery, also supported universal suffrage. Efforts to enfranchise women, though, were abandoned by the Republican Party and large parts of the abolitionist movement to concentrate on efforts to secure the vote for African American males in the South. Ratification of the 15th Amendment in 1870 extended the vote, in principle, to African American men, but the 19th Amendment enfranchising women would not be passed for another 50 years (Almquist, 1979, pp. 433-434; Evans, 1989, pp. 121-124).

## INDUSTRIALIZATION, THE SHIFT TO POSTINDUSTRIAL SOCIETY, AND DOMINANT-MINORITY GROUP RELATIONS: GENERAL TRENDS

The process of industrialization that began in the 19th century continued to shape the larger society and dominant-minority relations throughout the 20th century. At the start of the 21st century, the United States bears little resemblance to the society it was a century ago. The population has more than tripled in size and has urbanized even more rapidly than it has grown. New organizational forms (bureaucracies, corporations, multinational businesses) and new technologies (nuclear power, computers) dominate everyday life. Levels of education have risen, and the public schools have produced one of the most literate populations and best-trained workforces in the history of the world.

Minority groups also grew in size during this period, and most became even more urbanized than the general population. Minority group members have come to participate in an increasing array of occupations, and their average levels of education have also risen. Despite these real improvements, however, virtually all U.S. minority groups continue to face racism, poverty, discrimination, and exclusion. In this section, we outline the ways in which industrialization has changed American society and examine some of the implications for minority groups in general. We also note some of the ways in which industrialization has aided minority groups and address some of the barriers to full participation in the larger society that continue to operate in the present era. The impact of industrialization and the coming of postindustrial society will be considered in detail in the case studies that comprise Part IV of this text.

# Urbanization

We have already noted that urbanization made close, paternalistic controls of minority groups irrelevant. For example, the racial etiquette required by Southern de jure segregation, such as African Americans deferring to whites on crowded sidewalks, tended to disappear in the chaos of an urban rush hour. Besides weakening dominant group controls, urbanization also created the potential for minority groups to mobilize and organize large numbers of people. As stated in chapters 1 and 5, the sheer size of a group is a source of power. Without the freedom to organize, however, size means little, and urbanization increased both the concentration of populations and the freedom to organize.

# Occupational Specialization

One of the first and most important results of industrialization, even in its earliest days, was an increase in occupational specialization and the variety of jobs available in the workforce. The growing needs of an urbanizing population increased the number of jobs available in the production, transport, and sale of goods and services. Occupational specialization was also stimulated by the very nature of industrial production. Complex manufacturing processes could be performed more efficiently if they were broken down into the narrower component tasks. It was easier and more efficient to train the workforce in the simpler, specialized jobs. Assembly lines were invented, the work was subdivided, the division of labor became increasingly complex, and the number of different occupations continued to grow.

The sheer complexity of the industrial job structure made it difficult to maintain rigid, caste-like divisions of labor between dominant and minority groups. Rigid competitive forms of group relations, such as Jim Crow segregation, became less viable as the job market became more diversified and changeable. Simple, clear rules about which groups could do which jobs disappeared. As the more repressive systems of control weakened, job opportunities for minority group members sometimes increased. However, as the relationships between group memberships and positions in the job market became more blurred, conflict between groups also increased. For example, as we have noted, African Americans moving from the South often found themselves in competition for jobs with white ethnic groups, labor unions, and other elements of the dominant group.

# Bureaucracy and Rationality

As industrialization continued, privately owned corporations and businesses came to have workforces numbering in the hundreds of thousands. Gigantic factories employing thousands of workers became common. To coordinate the efforts of these huge workforces, bureaucracy became the dominant form of organization in the economy and, indeed, throughout the society. Bureaucracies are large-scale, impersonal, formal organizations that run "by the book." They are governed by rules and regulations (i.e., "red tape") and are "rational" in that they attempt to find the most efficient ways to accomplish their tasks. Although they typically fail to attain the ideal of fully rational efficiency, bureaucracies tend to recruit, reward, and promote employees on the basis of competence and performance (Gerth & Mills, 1946).

The stress on rationality and objectivity can counteract the more blatant forms of racism and increase the array of opportunities available to members of minority groups. Although they are often nullified by other forces (see Blumer, 1965), these antiprejudicial tendencies do not exist at all or are much weaker in preindustrial economies.

The history of the concept of race illustrates the effect of rationality and scientific ways of thinking. Today, virtually the entire scientific community regards race as a biological triviality, a conclusion based on decades of research. This scientific finding undermined and contributed to the destruction of the formal systems of privilege based solely on race (e.g., segregated school systems) and individual perceptual systems (e.g., traditional prejudice) based on the assumption that race is a crucial personal characteristic.

## Growth of White-Collar Jobs and the Service Sector

Industrialization changed the composition of the labor force. As work became more complex and specialized, the need to coordinate and regulate the production process increased, and as a result, bureaucracies and other organizations grew larger still. Within these organizations, white-collar occupations, those that coordinate, manage, and deal with the flow of paperwork, continued to expand. As industrialization progressed, mechanization and automation reduced the number of manual or blue-collar workers, and white-collar occupations became the dominant sector of the job market in the United States.

The changing nature of the workforce can be illustrated by looking at the proportional representation of three different types of jobs:

1.  **Extractive (or primary) occupations** are those that produce raw materials, such as food and agricultural products, minerals, and lumber. The jobs in this sector often involve unskilled manual labor, require little formal education, and are generally low paying.

2.  **Manufacturing (or secondary) occupations** transform raw materials into finished products ready for sale in the marketplace. Like jobs in the extractive sector, these blue-collar jobs involve manual labor, but they tend to require higher levels of skill and are more highly rewarded. Examples of occupations in this sector include the assembly line jobs that transform steel, rubber, plastic, and other materials into finished automobiles.

3.  **Service (or tertiary) occupations** are those in which the people in them do not produce "things"; rather, they provide services. As urbanization increased and self-sufficiency decreased, opportunities for work in this sector grew. Examples of tertiary occupations include police officer, clerk, waiter, teacher, nurse, doctor, and cab driver.

The course of industrialization is traced in the changing structure of the labor market depicted in Exhibit 6.3. In 1840, when industrialization was just beginning in the United States, most of the workforce was in the extractive sector, with agriculture being the dominant occupation. As industrialization progressed, the manufacturing, or secondary, sector grew, reaching a peak after World War II. Today, the large majority of jobs are in the service, or tertiary, sector. This shift away from blue-collar jobs and manufacturing is sometimes referred to as *deindustrialization* or discussed in terms of the emergence of postindustrial society. The U.S. economy has lost millions of unionized, high-paying factory jobs over the past several decades, and the downward trend will continue. The industrial jobs that sustained so many generations of American workers have moved to other nations where wages are considerably lower than in the United States or have been eliminated by robots or other automated manufacturing processes (see Rifkin, 1996).

The changing structure of the job market helps to clarify the nature of intergroup competition and the sources of wealth and power in society. Job growth in the United States today is

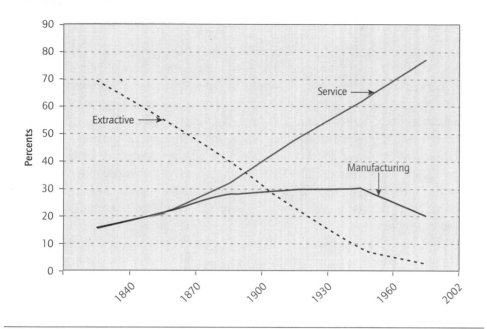

SOURCE: 1840-1990 adapted from Lenski, Nolan, and Lenski (1995); 2002 calculated from U.S. Bureau of the Census (2005), pp. 385-388.

largely in the service sector, and these occupations are highly variable. At one end are low-paying jobs with few, if any, benefits or chances for advancement (e.g., washing dishes in a restaurant). At the upper end are high-prestige, lucrative positions, such as Supreme Court justice, scientist, and financial analyst. The new service sector jobs are either highly desirable technical, professional, or administrative jobs with demanding entry requirements (e.g., physician or nurse) or low-paying, low-skilled jobs with few benefits and little security (e.g., receptionist, nurse's aide). For the last half century, job growth in the United States has been either in areas in which educationally deprived minority group members find it difficult to compete or in areas that offer little compensation, upward mobility, or security. As we will see in Part IV, the economic situation of contemporary minority groups reflects these fundamental trends.

## The Growing Importance of Education

Education has been an increasingly important prerequisite for employability. A high school or, increasingly, a college degree has become the minimum entry-level requirement for employment. However, opportunities for high-quality education are not distributed equally across the population. Some minority groups, especially those created by colonization, have been systematically excluded from the schools of the dominant society, and today, they are less likely to have the educational backgrounds needed to compete for better jobs. Access to education is a key issue for almost all U.S. minority groups, and the average educational levels of these groups have been rising since

World War II. Still, minority children continue to be much more likely to attend segregated, underfunded, deteriorated schools and to receive inferior educations (see Orfield, 2001).

## A Dual Labor Market

The changing composition of the labor force and increasing importance of educational credentials has split the U.S. labor market into two segments or types of jobs. The **primary labor market** includes jobs usually located in large, bureaucratic organizations. These positions offer higher pay, more security, better opportunities for advancement, health and retirement benefits, and other amenities. Entry requirements often include college degrees, even when people with fewer years of schooling could competently perform the work.

The **secondary labor market**, sometimes called the competitive market, includes low-paying, low-skilled, insecure jobs. Many of these jobs are in the service sector. They do not represent a career and offer little opportunity for promotion or upward mobility. Very often, they do not offer health or retirement benefits, have high rates of turnover, and are part-time, seasonal, or temporary.

Many American minority groups are concentrated in the secondary job market. Their exclusion from better jobs is perpetuated not so much by direct or obvious discrimination as by educational and other credentials required to enter the primary sector. The differential distribution of educational opportunities, in the past as well as in the present, effectively protects workers in the primary sector from competition from minority groups.

## Globalization

Over the past century, the United States became an economic, political, and military world power with interests around the globe. These worldwide ties have created new minority groups through population movement and have changed the status of others. Immigration to this country has been considerable for the past three decades. The American economy is one of the most productive in the world, and jobs, even those in the low-paying secondary sector, are the primary goals for millions of newcomers. For other immigrants, this country continues to play its historic role as a refuge from political and religious persecution.

Many of the wars, conflicts, and other disputes in which the United States has been involved have had consequences for American minority groups. For example, both Puerto Ricans and Cuban Americans became U.S. minority groups as the result of processes set in motion during the Spanish-American War of 1898. Both World War I and World War II created new job opportunities for many minority groups, including African Americans and Mexican Americans. After the Korean War, international ties were forged between the United States and South Korea, and this led to an increase in immigration from that nation. In the 1960s and 1970s, the military involvement of the United States in Southeast Asia led to the arrival of Vietnamese, Cambodians, and other Asian immigrants.

Dominant-minority relations in the United States have been increasingly played out on an international stage as the world has effectively "shrunk" in size and become more interconnected by international organizations, such as the United Nations; by ties of trade and commerce; and by modern means of transportation and communication. In a world in which two thirds of the population is nonwhite and many important nations (such as China, India, and Nigeria) represent peoples of color, the treatment of racial minorities by the U.S. dominant group has come under increased scrutiny. It is difficult to preach principles of fairness, equality, and justice—which the United States claims as its own—when domestic realities suggest an embarrassing failure to fully implement these standards. Part of the pressure for the United States to end blatant systems of discrimination such as de jure segregation came from the desire to maintain a leading position in the world.

# THE SHIFT FROM RIGID TO FLUID COMPETITIVE RELATIONSHIPS

The recent changes in the structure of American society are so fundamental and profound that they are often described in terms of a revolution in subsistence technology: from an industrial society, based on manufacturing, to a postindustrial society, based on information processing and computer-related or other new technologies.

As the subsistence technology has evolved and changed, so have American dominant-minority relations. The rigid competitive systems (such as Jim Crow) associated with earlier phases of industrialization have given way to **fluid competitive systems** of group relations. In fluid competitive relations, there are no formal or legal barriers to competition such as Jim Crow laws. Both geographic and social mobility are greater, and the limitations imposed by minority group status are less restrictive and burdensome. Rigid caste systems of stratification, in which group membership determines opportunities, adult statuses, and jobs, are replaced by more open class systems, in which there are weaker relationships between group membership and wealth, prestige, and power. Because fluid competitive systems are more open and the position of the minority group is less fixed, the fear of competition from minority groups becomes more widespread for the dominant group, and intergroup conflict increases. Exhibit 6.4 compares the characteristics of the three systems of group relations.

| **EXHIBIT 6.4** | Characteristics of Three Systems of Group Relationships |

|  | Paternalistic | Competitive | |
|  |  | Rigid | Fluid |
|---|---|---|---|
| **Subsistence technology** | Agrarian | Early industrial | Advanced industrial |
| **Stratification** | *Caste.* Group determines status. | *Mixed.* Elements of caste and class. Status largely determined by group. | *Variable.* Status strongly affected by group. Inequality varies within groups. |
| **Division of labor** | *Simple.* Determined by group. | *More complex.* Job largely determined by group but some sharing of jobs by different groups. | *Most complex.* Group and job less related. Complex specialization and great variation within groups. |
| **Contact between groups** | *Common.* but statuses unequal | *Less common* and mostly unequal | *More common;* highest rates of equal status contact |
| **Overt intergroup conflict** | Rare | More common | Common |
| **Power differential** | *Maximum.* Minority groups have little ability to pursue self-interests. | *Less.* Minority groups have some ability to pursue self-interests. | *Least.* Minority groups have more ability to pursue self-interests. |

**Source:** Based on Farley (2000), p. 109.

Compared with previous systems, the fluid competitive system is closer to the American ideal of an open, fair system of stratification in which effort and competence are rewarded and race, ethnicity, gender, religion, and other "birthmarks" are irrelevant. However, as we will see in chapters to come, race and ethnicity continue to affect life chances and limit opportunities for minority group members even in fluid competitive systems. As suggested by the Noel hypothesis, people continue to identify themselves with particular groups (ethnocentrism), and competition for resources continues to play out along group lines. Consistent with the Blauner hypothesis, the minority groups that were formed by colonization remain at a disadvantage in the pursuit of opportunities, education, prestige, and other resources.

## GENDER INEQUALITY IN A GLOBALIZING, POSTINDUSTRIAL WORLD

Deindustrialization and globalization are transforming gender relations along with dominant-minority relations. Everywhere, even in the most traditional and sexist societies, women are moving away from their traditional wife and mother roles, taking on new responsibilities, and facing new challenges. Some women are also encountering new dangers and new forms of exploitation that perpetuate their lower status and extend it into new areas.

In the United States, the transition to a postindustrial society has changed gender relations and the status of women on a number of levels. Women and men are now nearly equal in terms of levels of education (U.S. Bureau of the Census, 2003c, p.154), and the shift to fluid competitive group relations has weakened the barriers to gender equality along with the barriers to racial equality. The changing role of women is also shaped by other characteristics of a modern society: smaller families, high divorce rates, and rising numbers of single mothers who must work to support their children as well as themselves.

Many of these trends have coalesced to motivate women to enter the paid labor force in unprecedented numbers over the past half century. Women are now employed at almost the same levels as men. In the year 2003, for example, 66% of single women (vs. about 70% of single men) and about 61% of married women (vs. about 77% of married men) had jobs outside the home (U.S. Bureau of the Census, 2005, p. 376). Furthermore, between 1970 and 2003, the participation of married women with children in the workforce increased from a little less than 40% to almost 70% (U.S. Bureau of the Census, 2005, p. 377).

Many women workers enter the paid labor force to compensate for the declining earning power of men. Before deindustrialization began to transform U.S. society, men monopolized the more desirable, higher paid, unionized jobs in the manufacturing sector. For much of the 20th century, these blue-collar jobs paid well enough to subsidize a comfortable lifestyle, a house in the suburbs, and vacations, with enough money left over to save for a rainy day or for college for the kids. However, when deindustrialization began, many of these desirable jobs were lost to automation and to cheaper labor forces outside the United States and were replaced, if at all, by low-paying jobs in the service sector. Thus deindustrialization tended to drive men's wages down, and many women were forced to take jobs to supplement the family income. This trend was reflected in Exhibit 4.6 in Chapter 4, which shows that average wages for men have been stagnant or actually declining since the early 1970s.

A large number of the "new" women workers have taken jobs in a limited number of female-dominated occupations, most of which are in the less-well-paid service sector, and this

**EXHIBIT 6.5** Selected Occupations, 1983 and 2002

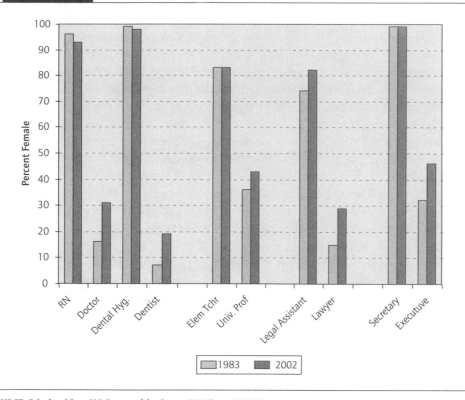

1983    2002

SOURCE: Calculated from U.S. Bureau of the Census (2005), pp. 385-388.

pattern of occupational segregation is one important reason for the continuing gender gap in income. For example, Exhibit 6.5 lists some of the occupations that were dominated by females in 1983 and 2002. Where possible, the percentages of females in comparable but higher status occupations are also included in the chart. For example, in 2002, 93% of nurses and nearly 100% of dental hygienists were female. The comparable figures for physicians and dentists were 31% and 19%, respectively.

In part, this occupational segregation is a result of the choices women make to balance the demands of their jobs with their family obligations. Whereas men are expected to make a total commitment to their jobs and careers, women are expected to find ways to continue to fulfill their domestic roles even while working full-time, and many "female jobs" offer some flexibility in this area (Shelton & John, 1996). For example, many women become elementary educators despite the lower salaries because the job offers predictable hours and long summer breaks, both of which can help women meet their child-care and other family responsibilities. This pattern of gender occupational segregation testifies to the lingering effects of minority status for women and the choices they make to reconcile the demands of career and family.

Exhibit 6.5 also shows that gender segregation in the world of work is declining, at least in some areas. Women are moving into traditionally male (and higher paid) occupations, as reflected by the rising percentages of female physicians, dentists, college professors, and lawyers. Also, some of the occupational areas that have traditionally had high concentrations of women—for example, finance, insurance, and real estate—actually benefited from deindustrialization and the shift to a service economy. Job opportunities in the finance, insurance, and real estate sector have expanded rapidly since the 1960s and have provided opportunities for women to rise in the social structure, and this has, in turn, tended to elevate average salaries for women in general (Farley, 1996, pp. 95-101). The movement of females into these more lucrative occupations is one reason why the gender gap in income is decreasing, as reflected in Exhibit 4.6 in Chapter 4.

How have deindustrialization and globalization affected women internationally? In part, the trends worldwide parallel those in the United States. According to a United Nations (2000) report, indicators such as rising education levels for women and lower rates of early marriage and childbirth show that women around the world are moving out of their traditional (and often highly controlled and repressed) status. They are entering the labor force in unprecedented numbers virtually everywhere, and women now comprise at least a third of the global workforce.

Although the status of women is generally rising, the movement away from traditional gender roles also brings exposure to new forms of exploitation. Around the globe, women have become a source of cheap labor, often in jobs that have recently been exported from the U.S. economy. For example, many manufacturing jobs formerly held by men in the United States have migrated just south of the border to Mexico, where they are held by women. *Maquiladoras* are assembly plants built by corporations (often headquartered in the United States) to take advantage of the plentiful supply of working-class females who will work for low wages and in conditions that would not be tolerated in the United States (for a recent analysis of the Mexican female labor force and the maquiladora phenomenon, see Parrado & Zenteno, 2001).

The weakening of traditional gender roles has increased women's vulnerability in other areas as well. A global sex trade in prostitution and pornography is flourishing and accounts for a significant portion of the economy of Thailand, the Philippines, and other nations. This international industry depends on impoverished women (and children) pushed out of the subsistence rural economy by industrialization and globalization and made vulnerable for exploitation by their lack of resources and power (Poulan, 2003).

Across all these changes and around the globe, women commonly face the challenge of reconciling their new work demands with their traditional family responsibilities. Also, women face challenges and issues, such as sexual harassment and domestic violence, which clearly differentiate their status from that of men. In this context, minority group women face a double disadvantage because the issues they face as women are complicated by the barriers created by racial and ethnic prejudice and discrimination. As we shall see in Chapters 7 to 10, minority group women are often the poorest, most vulnerable, and exploited groups in U.S. society and around the globe.

## Modern Institutional Discrimination

Virtually all American minority groups continue to lag behind national averages in income, employment, and other measures of equality, despite the greater fluidity of group relations, the greater openness in the U.S. stratification system, the dramatic declines in overt prejudice (see Chapter 4), and the introduction of numerous laws designed to ensure that all people are treated without regard to race, gender, or ethnicity. After all this change, shouldn't there be less minority group inequality?

As we saw in chapter 4, many Americans attribute the persisting patterns of inequality to the minority groups' lack of willpower or motivation to get ahead. In the remaining chapters of this text, however, I argue that the major barrier facing minority groups in late industrial, post–Jim Crow America is a more subtle but still powerful form of discrimination: **modern institutional discrimination**.

As you recall from chapter 1, institutional discrimination is built into the everyday operation of the social structure of society. The routine procedures and policies of institutions and organizations are arranged so that minority group members are automatically put at a disadvantage. In the Jim Crow era in the South, for example, African Americans were deprived of the right to vote by overt institutional discrimination and could acquire little in the way of political power.

The forms of institutional discrimination that persist in the present are more subtle and less overt than those that defined the Jim Crow system. In fact, they are often unintentional or unconscious and are manifested more in the results for minority groups than in the intentions or prejudices of dominant group members. Modern institutional discrimination is not necessarily linked to prejudice, and the decision makers who implement it may sincerely think of themselves as behaving rationally and in the best interests of their organizations.

When employers make hiring decisions based solely on educational criteria, they may be putting minority group members at a disadvantage. When banks use strictly economic criteria to deny money for home mortgages or home improvement loans in certain run-down neighborhoods, they may be handicapping the efforts of minority groups to cope with the results of the blatant, legal housing segregation of the past. When businesspeople decide to lower their overhead by moving their operations away from center cities, they may be reducing the ability of America's highly urbanized minority groups to earn a living and educate their children. When educators rely solely on standardized tests of ability that have been developed from white, middle-class experiences to decide who will be placed in college preparatory courses, they may be limiting the ability of minority group children to compete for jobs in the primary sector.

Any and all of these decisions can and do have devastating consequences for minority individuals, even though decision makers may be entirely unaware of the discriminatory effects. Employers, bankers, and educators do not have to be personally prejudiced for their actions to have negative consequences for minority groups. Modern institutional discrimination helps to perpetuate systems of inequality that can be just as pervasive and stifling as those of the past.

To illustrate, consider the effects of **past-in-present institutional discrimination**, which involves practices in the present that have discriminatory consequences because of some pattern of discrimination or exclusion in the past (Feagin & Feagin, 1986, p. 32). One form of this discrimination is found in workforces organized around the principle of seniority. In these systems, which are quite common, workers who have been on the job longer have higher incomes; more privileges; and other benefits, such as longer vacations. The "old-timers" often have more job security and are designated in official, written policy as the last to be fired or laid off in the event of hard times. Workers and employers alike may think of the privileges of seniority as just rewards for long years of service, familiarity with the job, and so forth.

Personnel policies based on seniority may seem perfectly reasonable, neutral, and fair. However, they can have discriminatory results in the present because in the past, members of minority groups and women were excluded from specific occupations by racist or sexist labor unions, discriminatory employers, or both. As a result, minority group workers and women may have fewer years of experience than dominant group workers and may be the first to go when layoffs are necessary. The adage "last hired, first fired" describes the situation of minority group and female employees who are more vulnerable not because of some overtly racist or sexist policy but because of the routine operation of the seemingly neutral principle of seniority.

It is much more difficult to identify, measure, and eliminate this more subtle form of institutional discrimination, and some of the most heated disputes in recent group relations have concerned public policy and law in this area. Among the most controversial issues are affirmative action programs that attempt to ameliorate the legacy of past discrimination or increase diversity in the workplace or in schools. In many cases, the Supreme Court has found that programs designed to favor minority employees as a strategy for overcoming overt discrimination in the past are constitutional (e.g., *Firefighters Local Union No. 1784 v. Stotts*, 1984; *Sheet Metal Workers v. EEOC*, 1986; *United Steelworkers of America, AFL-CIO-CLC v. Weber*, 1979). Virtually all these decisions, however, were based on narrow margins (votes of 5 to 4) and featured acrimonious and bitter debates. More recently, the Supreme Court narrowed the grounds on which such past grievances could be redressed, and in the eyes of many observers, dealt serious blows to affirmative action programs (e.g., *Adarand Constructors Inc. v. Pena, 1995*).

One of the more prominent battlegrounds for affirmative action programs has been in higher education. Since the 1960s, it has been common for colleges and universities to implement programs to increase the number of minority students on campus at both the undergraduate and graduate levels, sometimes admitting minority students who had lower grade point averages or test scores than dominant group students, who were turned away. In general, these programs have been justified in terms of redressing the discriminatory practices of the past or increasing diversity on campus and making the student body a more faithful representation of the surrounding society.

To say the least, these programs have been highly controversial and the targets of frequent lawsuits, some of which have found their way to the highest courts in the land. The future of these programs remains unclear. At present, a number of states have banned affirmative action programs in their universities and colleges, but the legality of these outright bans remains in some doubt. For example, in 1996, the voters in California passed an amendment to the state constitution that banned all use of racial, ethnic, or sexual preferences in education, hiring, and in the conduct of state business. In the spring of 2001, after years of protest and pressure by a variety of groups, the governing body of the California system of higher education ended the ban on affirmative action. This decision seems mainly symbolic, however, because the university system cannot exempt itself from the state constitution.

Recent lawsuits have upheld some affirmative action programs in higher education but only under very limited conditions. In the spring of 2003, the U.S. Supreme Court ruled in two cases against the University of Michigan (*Grutter v. Bollinger* and *Gratz v. Bollinger*) that the U.M. Law School *could* use race as one criterion in deciding admissions but that undergraduate admissions could *not* award an automatic advantage to minority applicants. Both rulings were split, and these decisions were widely interpreted as, at best, weak endorsements of very limited affirmative action programs. The administration of President Bush took the side of the plaintiffs in both cases (i.e., in opposition to affirmative action) and made it clear that, while respecting the law, it was opposed to affirmative action in general and would not place a high priority on these programs.

Although the Supreme Court did not end affirmative action with these decisions, the program appears to be very much in danger. Furthermore, there is very little support for affirmative action in the society as a whole. According to a public opinion survey conducted in 2002, affirmative action is supported by only 10% of white respondents. More surprising, perhaps, is that it is supported by less than a majority of black respondents (44%) and only 16% of female respondents (National Opinion Research Council, 2002). It would not be surprising to see all affirmative action programs end in the next 5 to 10 years, and if they do, one of the few tools available to combat modern institutional discrimination will be eliminated. (See the Current Debates section at the end of this chapter for more.)

## SOCIAL CHANGE AND MINORITY GROUP ACTIVISM

This chapter has focused on the continuing industrial revolution and its impact on minority groups in general and black-white relations in particular. For the most part, changes in group relations have been presented as the results of the fundamental transformation of the U.S. economic institution from agrarian to industrial to late industrial (or postindustrial). However, the changes in the situation of African Americans and other minority groups did not "just happen" as society modernized. Although the opportunity to pursue favorable change was the result of broad structural changes in American society, the realization of these opportunities came from the efforts of the many who gave their time, their voices, their resources, and sometimes their lives in pursuit of racial justice in America. Since World War II, African Americans have often been in the vanguard of protest activity, and we focus on the contemporary situation of this group in the next chapter.

## Affirmative Action

Should minorities be favored in the job market? Should colleges and graduate schools judge minority candidates differently than members of the dominant group? Programs that confer advantages on minorities at work and at school—attempts to take affirmative action in the struggle to achieve racial integration and equality—have been controversial since their inception nearly four decades ago. The arguments in favor of affirmative action usually cite the intractability of institutional discrimination, the pervasiveness of racism, and the continuing importance of race in American life. Without a strong program to force employers to balance their workforces and to require college admission programs to seek out qualified minority candidates, the racial status quo will be perpetuated indefinitely.

Opponents argue that affirmative action actually hurts the groups it is intended to help and that the "reverse discrimination" used by these programs is simply wrong. A familiar argument against affirmative action is that if racial discrimination was wrong when used to perpetuate the privileges of whites under slavery and Jim Crow, then it is just as wrong as a technique to combat racial inequality. Discrimination is discrimination, and the United States should strive to be "color-blind," not color conscious. A third view shifts the terms of the debate and argues that the real barriers to equality are based on class, not race, and that affirmative action programs need to be reformulated on this basis. These arguments are reprised in the selections below.

I made the point earlier that the black community today is not particularly supportive of affirmative action. This split is reflected in the writings below. Thomas Sowell, an economist, and Orlando Patterson, a sociologist, are both African Americans; Richard Kahlenberg, a lawyer and scholar, is white.

## Affirmative Action Casts Suspicions on Legitimate Black Achievement and Depicts African Americans as Incapable

THOMAS SOWELL

The Hippocratic Oath says: "First, do no harm." By that standard, affirmative action would have been gotten rid of years ago. There are many ways in which it hurts the very people it claims to help, as well as polarizing the society at large.

A couple of years ago, I met with the editorial staff of one of the leading publications in America. Among them was a black man who was by no means stupid—but he said many stupid things at that meeting. . . . Why? He was mismatched, out of his league, among people who were at the pinnacle of their profession. If he played it straight, he would have been nobody in this setting, though there are probably hundreds of other reputable publications on which he would have been a valuable and respected writer. Saying off-the-wall things was his only way of even seeming to be significant among the cream of the crop of his profession. . . . Nor was this man unique. There is a whole class of such people teaching in the leading law schools, many of them promoting a convoluted set of doctrines known as critical race theory. Their counterparts can also be found in literature, among other fields. . . .

Affirmative action also amounts to a virtual moratorium on recognition of black achievement. Consider the case of [Supreme Court] Justice Clarence Thomas. His critics have repeatedly accused him of benefiting from affirmative action, when he went to college or to law school, and then wanting to deny its benefits to other blacks. In all the endless reiterations of this theme, no one has ever found it necessary to demonstrate that it was true. It so happens that affirmative action had not yet begun when Clarence Thomas entered Holy Cross College. Nor has anyone even considered it necessary to try to show that Thomas was admitted under the Yale law school's affirmative action program, rather than by the regular admissions process. . . . Justice Thomas' credentials are questioned precisely because of affirmative action. . . .

In short, blacks fall under a cloud of suspicion of being substandard, even when they match or surpass the performances of their white counterparts. Who gains from creating such awkward situations and the unnecessary problems that flow from them?

Guilty whites gain by salving their guilt through affirmative action. Black hustlers gain by either getting things for themselves or by leading movements which are able to dispense largess that they have talked or pressured guilty whites into providing.

Institutions, such as universities, that receive millions of federal dollars gain by having enough black body count around to avoid having the flow of that money jeopardized by claims of discrimination based on statistics.

Liberals who secretly believe that blacks are innately inferior . . . feel like they have done the best they can do by giving blacks or other minorities something that those minorities would otherwise be incapable of getting.

Do any of the people who claim to want to see blacks advance ever ask: Under what conditions have blacks in fact been most successful? Where have they advanced most? Blacks have done best in situations radically different from those of affirmative action. Blacks are overrepresented in sports and entertainment, especially among the highest-paid performers. In both fields, competition is merciless. You can be the top performer this year and yet they will drop you like a hot potato if your performance slacks off next year.

Nobody has given blacks anything in sports or entertainment. Blacks have had to shape up or ship out. Most shape up. It is where blacks are given double standards and coddled that they end up tarnished in their own eyes or in the eyes of others.

SOURCE: Sowell, Thomas. October 6, 1997. "How 'Affirmative Action' Hurts Blacks." *Forbes*, 160: 64.

## Why We Still Need Affirmative Action

ORLANDO PATTERSON

The most important way in which affirmative action helps those on the outside is to provide them access to circles and networks that they would otherwise never penetrate.

For Afro-Americans, one of the most egregious effects of past . . . exclusion has been their isolation from cultural capital and personal networks that are essential for success. . . . This important sociological fact is usually simply neglected by those who imagine capitalist America to be a perfectly competitive, meritocratic system in which people rise to their positions based solely on their training and motivation. There is some truth to this but it is at best a half-truth. . . .

Let us assume that there is a firm with one hundred entry level employees, exactly 13 of whom are Afro-Americans, and that all these employees have . . . equal . . . ability, educational attainment, and motivation. Let us assume further an . . . unbiased . . . organization [and staff]. . . . Even under these circumstances . . . it is almost certain that the Afro-American . . . employees will never make it to the top echelons of the organization if there is no account taken of ethnicity in promotion; indeed, they will hardly move beyond their entry-level jobs.

These claims seem counterintuitive because we assume that, in the normal course of events, each equally qualified entry-level Afro-American will have a 13% chance of being promoted, resulting eventually in a similar ratio of Afro-Americans moving up the firm's opportunity ladder. This is what misguided liberal and neo-conservatives have in mind when they speak naively about a "color-blind" system. The problem . . . [is] that when firms promote workers they consider not simply the characteristics of the employees but organizational criteria, among the most important of which is the degree to which a candidate . . . will fit into the upper echelon for which he or she is being considered. And it is precisely here that Afro-Americans lose out because of their small numbers, their ethnic differences, and the tendency of personnel officers to follow one well-established law of microsociology, first formally propounded by the sociologist George Casper Homans.

The very simple principle of human behavior—call it the principle of homophyly—is that people who share common attitudes tend to marry each other, . . . play more together, and in general tend to get along better and to form more effective work teams. Thus, a non-racist personnel officer, under no pressure to consider ethnic attributes—indeed, under strong . . . pressure to follow a "color-blind" policy—would always find it organizationally rational to choose a Euro-American . . . in spite of the technical equality of the Afro-American candidates. The Euro-American person's organizational fit—which comes simply from being Euro-American—will so significantly reduce the cost . . . of incorporation and training that it would be irresponsible of our ethnically unbiased personnel officer, under orders to select in a color-blind manner, ever to promote an Afro-American person.

Of course, when one introduces one well-known real-world feature of American society to this model of "color-blind" organizational behavior, the cards are even more heavily stacked against our thirteen entry-level Afro-American employees: This is the fact that Euro-Americans have a hard time taking orders from Afro-American supervisors. . . . This being so, the cost to our non-racist . . . personnel officer becomes even greater; and it gets worse the more real-world attitudes and behaviors we introduce.

SOURCE: Patterson, Orlando. 1997. *The Ordeal of Integration.* Washington, DC: Civitas. Pp. 160-162.

## Affirmative Action Should Be Based on Class Rather Than Race

### RICHARD KAHLENBERG

Class-based affirmative action, a system of preferences for the economically disadvantaged . . . will achieve the legitimate goals of affirmative action while avoiding the major pitfalls associated with race and gender preferences. . . . The central and overriding argument for class-based affirmative action is that it will help move us from today's inadequate system of formal equal opportunity toward a more genuine system . . . under which individuals born into very different circumstances can flourish to their natural potential. . . . Equal opportunity exists when individuals have equal life chances to develop their natural talents to the fullest, should they choose to take the time and effort to do so.

[Equal opportunity] stresses equality to the extent that social factors should not be allowed to inhibit the chance to develop one's natural talents. It stresses liberty to the extent that it does not guarantee equal results: The naturally talented are allowed to do better than the untalented to the extent, and only to the extent, that individuals work hard to achieve what they are capable of achieving. . . . Equal opportunity is, as Gary Wills (the conservative newspaper columnist) notes, "The great agreed-on undebated premise of our politics. Left and right, liberal and conservative, Democrat and Republican, all work from this basis."

As long as antidiscrimination laws work, race and gender are not impediments per se, but class differences . . . remain and civil rights legislation does nothing to address that inequality. Some are born poor and underprivileged, others wealthy and advantaged. In this sense, antidiscrimination laws may be seen as necessary but not sufficient for achieving equal opportunity. . . .

If we are trying to place the most talented in the most important positions, formal equal opportunity is not enough. Failing to correct for the social positions into which people are born runs the great risk of missing most of the latent talent of the poor. . . .

[If] we want to reward hard work, failing to provide an equal start is morally indefensible. To reward individuals born with advantages arising from their parents' effort makes no moral sense. Indeed, Theodore Roosevelt, in pushing for a heavily progressive income tax in 1906, argued that a commitment to rugged individualism required each generation to run its own race.

SOURCE: Kahlenberg, Richard. 1997. The Remedy: Class, Race, and Affirmative Action. New York: Basic Books. Pp. 83-86.

## Debate Questions to Consider

1. What assumptions does Sowell make about the overall fairness of the American workplace? Are there any similarities between his position and human capital theory (see chapter 2)? What are the implications of his argument that blacks have been most successful precisely in the areas in which affirmative action has been irrelevant: entertainment and sports? In contrast, what assumptions does Patterson make about the ability of employers to make unbiased decisions about promotions? Is Kahlenberg's position consistent with human capital theory?

2. Which author(s) directly addresses "past-in-present" discrimination? How? What are the limitations of a "color-blind" approach? Why does Patterson call it "naive"? How strong is his argument compared with Sowell's? Which would you choose? Why?

3. Based on Patterson's position, design a simple affirmative action program for your workplace or school. How would your program change if you incorporated Kahlenberg's ideas?

4. Which of these three positions is most appealing to you? If you agree with Sowell, how would you combat modern institutional discrimination? If you agree with Patterson, how would you respond to the charge of "reverse discrimination?" If you choose Kahlenberg, how would you answer the criticism that class-based remedies ignore the realities of racism and prejudice?

# MAIN POINTS

- Group relations change as the subsistence technology and the level of development of the larger society change. As nations industrialize and urbanize, dominant-minority relations change from paternalistic to rigid competitive forms.

- In the South, slavery was replaced by de jure segregation, a system that combined racial separation with great inequality. The Jim Crow system was motivated by a need to control labor and was reinforced by coercion and intense racism and prejudice.

- Black Southerners responded to segregation in part by moving to Northern urban areas. The Northern African American population enjoyed greater freedom and developed some political and economic resources, but a large concentration of low-income, relatively powerless African Americans developed in the ghetto neighborhoods.

- In response to segregation, the African American community developed a separate institutional life centered on family, church, and community. An African American middle class emerged, as well as a protest movement.

- African American women remain one of the most exploited groups. Combining work with family roles, African American females were employed mostly in agriculture and domestic service during the era of segregation.

- Industrialization continued throughout the 20th century and has profoundly affected dominant-minority relations. Urbanization, specialization, bureaucratization, and other trends have changed the shape of race relations, as have the changing structure of the occupational sector and the growing importance of education. Group relations have shifted from rigid to fluid competitive. Modern institutional discrimination is one of the major challenges facing minority groups.

- What efforts have been made on your campus to combat modern institutional discrimination? How effective have these programs been? The public sociology assignment on affirmative action gives you a chance to research these questions.

### Study Site on the Web

Don't forget the interactive quizzes and other resources and learning aids at www.www.pineforge.com/healeystudy4.

## For Further Reading

Bluestone, Barry, & Harrison, Bennet. 1982. *The Deindustrialization of America.* New York: Basic Books. *(An important analysis of the shift from a manufacturing to a service-based, information society.)*

Feagin, Joe R., & Feagin, Clairece Booher. 1986. *Discrimination American Style: Institutional Racism and Sexism.* Malabar, FL: Robert E. Krieger. *(A comprehensive and provocative look at modern institutional discrimination.)*

Geschwender, James A. 1978. *Racial Stratification in America.* Dubuque, IA: W. C. Brown.

Wilson, William J. 1973. *Power, Racism, and Privilege: Race Relations in Theoretical and Sociohistorical Perspectives.* New York: Free Press.

Woodward, C. Vann. 1974. *The Strange Career of Jim Crow* (3rd ed., Rev.). New York: Oxford University Press. *(Three outstanding analyses of black-white relations in the United States, with a major focus on the historical periods covered in this chapter.)*

## Questions for Review and Study

1. A corollary to two themes from chapter 5 is presented at the beginning of chapter 6. How exactly does the material in the chapter illustrate the usefulness of this corollary?

2. Explain paternalistic and rigid competitive relations and link them to industrialization. How does the shift from slavery to de jure segregation illustrate the dynamics of these two systems?

3. What was the "Great Migration" to the North? How did it change American race relations?

4. Explain the transition from rigid competitive to fluid competitive relations and explain how this transition is related to the coming of postindustrial society. Explain the roles of urbanization, bureaucracy, the service sector of the job market, and education in this transition.

5. What is modern institutional discrimination? How does it differ from "traditional" institutional discrimination? Explain the role of affirmative action in combating each.

6. Explain the impact of industrialization and globalization on gender relations. Compare and contrast these changes with the changes that occurred for racial and ethnic minority groups.

## Internet Research Project

### A. Everyday Life Under Jim Crow

The daily workings of the Jim Crow system of segregation are analyzed and described in a collection of interviews, photos, and memories archived at http://www.american-radioworks.org/features/remembering/. Explore the site, look at the photos, listen to the clips, and analyze them in terms of the concepts introduced in this chapter.

### B. The Debate Over Affirmative Action

Update and supplement the debate on affirmative action presented at the end of the chapter. Start with the newspaper home pages listed in the Appendix and search for recent news items or opinion pieces on the issue. Search the Internet for other viewpoints and perspectives from other groups and positions on the political spectrum. One place you might start is http://aad.english.ucsb.edu/, a Web site that presents diverse opinions on the topic and brings many different voices to the debates. Analyze events and opinions in terms of the concepts introduced in this chapter, especially *modern institutional discrimination*.

# PART IV

## Understanding Dominant-Minority Relations in the United States Today

I n Part IV, we turn to contemporary intergroup relations. The emphasis is on the present
situation of American minority groups, but the recent past is also investigated to see how
present situations developed. We explore the ways minority and dominant groups respond
to a changing American society and to each other and how minority groups define and pursue
their own self-interest in interaction with other groups, American culture and values, and the
institutions of the larger society.

The themes and ideas developed in the first three parts of this text will continue to be
central to the analysis. For example, these case studies are presented in an order that roughly
follows the Blauner hypothesis: Colonized groups are presented first, and we end with groups
created by immigration. Also, we will continue to rely on the concepts of the Noel hypothesis
to analyze and explain contemporary dominant-minority patterns.

The history and present conditions of each minority group are unique, and no two groups
have had the same experiences. To help identify and understand these differences, the concepts
developed in the first three parts of this text and a common comparative frame of reference
are used throughout Part IV. We stress assimilation and pluralism; inequality and power; and
prejudice, racism, and discrimination. For ease of comparison, the final sections of the first four
case study chapters (7-10) all use the same titles and subtitles in the same order. The final two
case study chapters depart from this format but still use the same concepts and types of data.

Much of the conceptual frame of reference employed in these case studies can be summarized in seven themes. The first six themes are based on material from previous chapters;
the last is covered in the forthcoming chapters.

1.  Consistent with the Noel hypothesis, the present conditions of America's minority groups reflect
    their contact situations, especially the nature of their competition with the dominant group (e.g.,
    competition over land vs. competition over labor) and the size of the power differential between
    groups at the time of contact.

2.  Consistent with the Blauner hypothesis, minority groups created by colonization experience
    economic and political inequalities that have lasted longer and been more severe than those
    experienced by minority groups created by immigration.

3.  Power and economic differentials and barriers to upward mobility are especially pronounced
    for groups identified by racial or physical characteristics, as opposed to cultural or linguistic
    traits.

4.  Consistent with the themes stated in chapters 5 and 6, dominant-minority relations reflect the
    economic and political characteristics of the larger society and change as those characteristics
    change. Changes in the subsistence technology of the larger society are particularly conse-
    quential for dominant-minority relations. The shift from a manufacturing to a service economy
    (deindustrialization) is one of the key factors shaping dominant-minority relations in the United
    States today.

5.  As we saw in chapter 4, the "mood" of the dominant group over the past four decades combines
    a rejection of blatant racism with the belief that the modern United States is nondiscrimina-
    tory and that success is attainable for all who are willing to work hard enough. It is also common
    for dominant group Americans to believe that further reforms of the larger society or special
    programs or treatment for minorities are unnecessary and unjustified. Efforts to address

contemporary minority group problems must deal with the pervasive "modern racism" of the dominant group.

6. The development of group relations, both in the past and for the future, can be analyzed in terms of assimilation (more unity) and pluralism (more diversity). Group relations in the past (e.g., the degree of assimilation permitted or required of the minority group) reflected mainly dominant group needs and wishes. Although the pressure for Americanization remains considerable, there is more flexibility and variety in group relations today.

7. Since World War II, minority groups have gained significantly more control over the direction of group relationships. This trend reflects the decline of traditional prejudice in the larger society and the successful efforts of minority groups to protest, resist, and change patterns of exclusion and domination. These successes have been possible, in large part, because American minority groups have increased their share of political and economic resources.

## ABOUT THE PUBLIC SOCIOLOGY ASSIGNMENTS

The first assignment in this installment of public sociology connects you to the American Indian tribes that may once have lived in your area. As we discussed in Chapter 5 and in Chapter 8, one of the most devastating consequences of the colonization of this group was the loss of their traditional homelands. In this exercise, you will explore one of the present-day aspects of that loss.

The second exercise can be done with any (or all) of the groups covered in Chapters 7 through 12. The focus is on health and health care, one of the many aspects of inequality not covered in the text. It is likely that you will find patterns reminiscent of those documented in the chapter sections titled "secondary structural assimilation."

# Assignment 1
## American Indian Cultural Affiliation

American Indians have very little control or ownership of land and resources once entirely theirs. Many tribes were forced by the federal and state governments to resettle far from their ancestral domains so that immigrant Europeans could benefit from tribal loss. Today, there are a variety of federal and state laws that protect archeological deposits and require the repatriation of certain kinds of materials to their rightful owners: American Indians. One particular law, the Native American Graves Protection and Repatriation Act of 1990 (NAGPRA) requires that Native American human remains, funerary objects, objects of cultural patrimony, and sacred objects be returned to the tribal descendants with which they are associated.

Like many laws, there are complications to NAGPRA that present difficulties both for American Indians and federal and state agencies. The first complication is that given forced resettlement and migration of American Indian groups, which uncovered materials belong to which tribe (in a cultural sense) is not always clear—usually it is not. The second complication is that agencies are required to consult with federally recognized tribes first and foremost—namely, those that acquired recognized tribal status from the Bureau of Indian Affairs. State-recognized tribes without federal recognition, as well as other self-identified American Indian groups, do not have much legal standing insofar as repatriation is concerned.

Your assignment is to work on an American Indian cultural affiliation overview of your home region. This document can be provided to federally recognized tribes and Native American communities that once lived in the area. It may also be provided to federal and state agencies in an effort to reduce uncertainty regarding who must be consulted and who should be secondarily consulted and thereby speed up the process of repatriation when human remains or sacred items are inadvertently discovered.

### Step 1

You must first familiarize yourself with legislation and policy involving American Indian archeological deposits. Perhaps the best place to start is the National Park Service Web site devoted to NAGPRA at http://www.cr.nps.gov/nagpra/. The next government Web site you should search for background information is that of the Advisory Council on Historic Preservation, which has pages on federal, state, and tribal historic preservation programs at http://www.achp.gov/programs.html. You may conduct an Internet search for related documentation, but be careful of what you read, because the issue is quite sensitive and prone to passionate loss of objectivity. If you are not certain of the reasoned nature of material you encounter, ask your university librarians, who are experts at information literacy and may help you discern the worth of your sources.

### Step 2

Using the Web-based databases of the National Park Service and Advisory Council on Historic Preservation, determine who are the federal, state, and tribal historic preservation contacts for your region. Contact them and explain the cultural affiliation overview project you would like to conduct on their behalf. In your conversations, explore what has already been done and what remains to be completed. Your area may well already have an affiliation overview, but even so, there are likely to be areas that you could add to. Use your agency personnel as advisors on how best to proceed.

### Step 3

Once you have sufficiently narrowed the focus of your cultural affiliation overview through your conversations (and, hopefully, face-to-face visits) with tribal, state, and federal historic preservation officers, begin your research. Your method will be primarily historical and literature-based, and much of your time will be spent in the library or at agency offices reviewing archeological reports and historical documents. To assist your systematic review, you may want to keep a dialogic notebook of your readings. To create this, use three-ring binder paper and draw a straight line vertically midway through each sheet, essentially creating a two-columned sheet of paper. On the left-side column of the page, write quotes and references from your readings. On the right side of the page, write your own observations, connections you make to other material you encountered, and notes to yourself. This will aid you in your final analysis and write-up, because you will have a systematic overview of all the material read and reviewed.

### Step 4

Return to your agency contacts once you are well into your review of the literature and historical documentation. Discuss with them what you are finding and obtain feedback. They are experts in their field and can provide guidance, alternatives, and insight should you feel stuck or confused in one area of the research.

### Step 5

Using your dialogic notebook, begin drafting an outline of your cultural affiliation overview. Look for gaps in the research and decide whether they can be fixed or whether they should be highlighted in the executive summary and conclusion for future research effort. Using your outline, begin crafting the narrative of your report, keeping in mind that you want to make the prose readable yet not unduly passionate or lacking in objectivity. This is where your creativity as a writer may shine, but in the end, simply try to write to the best of your ability.

### Step 6

Share the draft report with your agency contacts and seek their comments and suggestions for improvement. All writing requires outside review to make it better than it is. Keep in mind that editorial comments are never about you as a writer; they are simply about communicating effectively.

### Step 7

Revise your report based on the comments and suggestions you received and submit your final draft to the agency contacts you worked with from the beginning. Ask them to keep you informed of any repatriations or newly discovered materials and how repatriation consultations used and benefited from your research.

Congratulate yourself for hard work well done and be sure to stay in touch with your agency contacts! You may be surprised at an offer of summer employment or an internship to continue your scholarship for a good cause.

# Assignment 2
## Race and Class—Epidemiology and Surveillance

Social inequality often results in inadequate health care and unhealthy lifestyle choices. To understand the impact today of racism, sexism, and class-based discrimination, you can study the health and vital statistics of your county's population. This data, presented by you in an easily understood format, may assist local social service and welfare agencies in targeting their services efficiently and communicating the magnitude of health problems effectively. Included at the end of the assignment is an Internet link to a presentation on epidemiology in Ventura, California, that will help you envision your own end product.

### Step 1

Locate your local county's department of health online and search for their health and vital statistics page. This is where you will get some of your data. There may also be data already tabulated or charted in your state's annual databook. This may be found by using an Internet search engine such as Google, using keywords such as "[your state] annual databook." A third source of data is the U.S. Census Bureau at http://www.census.gov/, especially their FactFinder feature, as well as their dynamic maps (which you may capture for inclusion in your report using the Shift+PrtSc keys). Be sure to keep track of all your data sources and cite them properly. If you come across material already compiled by someone else that is just what you were looking for, an e-mail for permission to use the data is the proper professional courtesy.

### Step 2

Take your time wading through the data and various sources. You want to get a good understanding of current and historical patterns in the data. Variables you may want to include in your initial survey are

- Population and ethnic makeup characteristics, by zip code
- Poverty level by zip code
- Percentage of low and very low birth weight babies, by ethnicity
- First trimester prenatal care, by ethnicity
- Childhood obesity, by ethnicity
- Asthma, by ethnicity
- Homicide, by ethnicity.

### Step 3

Contact a local community development organization or nongovernmental social service agency. This could be the YMCA; the Women, Infants, and Children (WIC) center; or some other entity. Make an appointment to meet with one of their personnel to discuss your research project. When you meet with her or him, share what patterns and numbers you came up with and seek to discover how this data might help the organization or agency. Listen carefully to their response to your data and their needs so that in the end you are providing them with material they can actually use rather than data that is simply interesting in and of itself.

## Step 4

Make an appointment with your county department of health, perhaps asking to speak with the coroner. He or she will probably encourage you to further discuss your research with other personnel, perhaps even a statistician. Share with them your research project, which agency you are working with, what data you have obtained, and the patterns you have discerned thus far. Seek their input and guidance. They are likely to have additional data that will greatly help you in creating a fuller picture, such as data going back several years that will enable you to create a time series comparing past with present.

## Step 5

Revise your compiled data and include new data provided by department of health personnel. Write a paragraph or two for each chart of data you create that explains what is implied by the chart. Do the same for any table of data you include in your report. When you have completed these, write an executive summary of the project data.

## Step 6

Meet with the social service organization you are working with and share with its personnel your completed draft materials. Discuss any gaps in data that they are concerned about and revise your draft into a final form they can use.

## Step 7

Submit your final draft to the social service agency. You may also want to provide a copy to the personnel who assisted you at the department of health, for their use. Do not be surprised if they ask for permission to upload the project to their Web site!

## Step 8

Congratulate yourself for rewarding work well done!

### Resources

This assignment was inspired by epidemiological work of the County of Ventura (California) Public Health Department, whose Health Data/Statistics page can be seen online at http://www.vchca.org/ph/stats/index.htm.

The presentation of epidemiology and surveillance at http://www.vchca.org/ph/stats/CDR_April2003_1.ppt may also assist you in creating your report.

CHAPTER

# 7

# African Americans

## From Segregation to Modern Institutional Discrimination and Modern Racism

AT THE DAWN OF THE 20TH CENTURY, AFRICAN AMERICANS WERE PRIMARILY A SOUTHERN rural peasantry, victimized by de jure segregation, enmeshed in the sharecropping system of agriculture, and blocked from the better paying industrial and manufacturing jobs in urban areas. Segregation had disenfranchised them and stripped them of the legal and civil rights they had briefly enjoyed during Reconstruction. As we saw in chapter 6, the huge majority of African Americans had very limited access to quality education; few political rights; few occupational choices; and few vehicles for expressing their views, grievances, and concerns.

Today, at the beginning of the 21st century, African Americans are highly urbanized, dispersed throughout the United States, and represented in virtually every occupational grouping. Members of the group are visible at the highest levels of American society: from the Supreme Court to corporate boardrooms to the most prestigious universities. Some of the best known, most successful and respected (and wealthiest) people in the world have been African Americans: Martin Luther King, Jr., Malcolm X, Michael Jordan, Shirley Chisholm, Jesse Jackson, Bill Cosby, Toni Morrison, Maya Angelou, Muhammad Ali, Oprah Winfrey, Barbara Jordan, Colin Powell, and Condoleezza Rice, to name just a  few. Furthermore, some of the most important and prestigious American corporations (including Merrill Lynch, American Express, and Time Warner) have been led by African Americans.

How did these changes come about, and what do they signify? What problems are obscured by these glittering success stories? Do racism, prejudice, and discrimination continue to be significant problems? Is there any support for the view that the barriers to racial equality have been eliminated? How do the Noel and Blauner hypotheses and the other concepts developed earlier in this text help us understand contemporary black-white relations?

To understand the trajectories of change that have led to the present, we must deal with the watershed events in black-white relations: the end of de jure segregation, the triumph (and the limitations) of the **Civil Rights movement** of the 1950s and 1960s, the urban riots and **Black Power movement** of the 1960s, and the continuing racial divisions within U.S. society since the 1970s. Behind these events lie the powerful pressures of industrialization and modernization, the shift from rigid to fluid competitive group relations, changing distributions of power and forms of intergroup competition, declining levels of traditional prejudice, and new ideas about assimilation and pluralism. In less abstract terms, black-white relations changed as a direct result of protest, resistance, and the concerted actions of thousands of individuals, both blacks and whites.

## THE END OF DE JURE SEGREGATION

As a colonized minority group, African Americans entered the 20th century facing extreme inequality, relative powerlessness, and sharp limitations on their freedom. Their most visible enemy was the system of de jure segregation in the South, the rigid competitive system of group relations that controlled the lives of most African Americans.

Why and how did de jure segregation come to an end? Recall from chapter 6 that dominant-minority relationships change as the larger society and its subsistence technology change. As the United States industrialized and urbanized during the 20th century, a series of social, political, economic, and legal processes were set in motion that ultimately destroyed Jim Crow segregation.

The mechanization and modernization of agriculture in the South had a powerful effect on race relations. As farm work became less labor intensive and machines replaced people, the need to maintain a large, powerless workforce declined (Geschwender, 1978, pp. 175-177). Thus one of the primary motivations for maintaining Jim Crow segregation and the sharecropping system of farming lost force.

In addition, the modernization of Southern agriculture helped to spur the migration northward and to urban areas, as we discussed in chapter 6. Outside the rural South, African Americans found it easier to register to vote and pursue other avenues for improving their situations. The weight of the growing African American vote was first felt in the 1930s and was large enough to make a difference in local, state, and even national elections by the 1940s. In 1948, for example, President Harry Truman recognized that he could not be reelected without the support of African American voters. As a result, the Democratic Party adopted a civil rights plank in the party platform, the first time since Reconstruction that a national political party had taken a stand on race relations (Wilson, 1973, p. 123).

The weight of these changes accumulated slowly, and no single date or specific event marks the end of de jure segregation. The system ended as it had begun: gradually and in a series of discrete episodes and incidents. By the mid-20th century, resistance to racial change was weakening, and the power resources of African Americans were increasing. This enhanced freedom and strength fueled a variety of efforts that sped the demise of Jim Crow segregation. Although a complete historical autopsy is not necessary here, a general understanding of the reasons for the death of Jim Crow segregation is essential for an understanding of modern black-white relations.

# Wartime Developments

One of the first successful applications of the growing stock of black power resources occurred in 1941, as the United States was mobilizing for war against Germany and Japan. Despite the crisis atmosphere, racial discrimination was common, even in the defense industry. A group of African Americans, led by labor leader A. Philip Randolph, head of the Brotherhood of Sleeping Car Porters, threatened to march on Washington to protest the discriminatory treatment.

To forestall the march, President Franklin D. Roosevelt signed an executive order banning discrimination in defense-related industries and created a watchdog federal agency, the Fair Employment Practices Commission, to oversee compliance with the new antidiscriminatory policy (Franklin & Moss, 1994, pp. 436-437; Geschwender, 1978, pp. 199-200). President Roosevelt's actions were significant in two ways. First, a group of African Americans not only had their grievances heard at the highest level of society but also succeeded in getting what they wanted. Underlying the effectiveness of the planned march was the rising political and economic power of the Northern African American community and the need to mobilize all segments of the population for a world war. Second, the federal government made an unprecedented commitment to fair employment rights for African Americans. This alliance between the federal government and African Americans was tentative, but it foreshadowed some of the dynamics of racial change in the 1950s and 1960s.

# The Civil Rights Movement

The civil rights movement was a multifaceted campaign to end legalized segregation and ameliorate the massive inequalities faced by African Americans. The campaign lasted for decades and included lawsuits and courtroom battles as well as protest marches and demonstrations. We begin our examination with a look at the movement's successful challenge to the laws of racial segregation.

**Brown v. Board of Education of Topeka.** Undoubtedly, the single most powerful blow to de jure segregation was delivered by the U.S. Supreme Court in *Brown v. Board of Education of Topeka* in 1954. The Supreme Court reversed the Plessy v. Ferguson decision of 1896 and ruled that racially separate facilities are inherently unequal and therefore unconstitutional. Segregated school systems—and all other forms of legalized racial segregation—would have to end. The landmark Brown decision was the culmination of decades of planning and effort by the NAACP and individuals such as Thurgood Marshall, the NAACP's chief counsel (who was appointed to the Supreme Court in 1967).

The strategy of the NAACP was to attack Jim Crow by finding instances in which the civil rights of an African American had been violated and then bringing suit against the relevant governmental agency. These lawsuits were intended to extend far beyond the specific case being argued. The goal was to persuade the courts to declare segregation unconstitutional not only in the specific instance being tried but in all similar cases. The Brown (1954) decision was the ultimate triumph of this strategy. The significance of the Supreme Court's decision was not that Linda Brown—the child in whose name the case was argued—would attend a different school or even that the school system of Topeka, Kansas, would be integrated. Instead, the significance lies in the rejection of the *principle* of de jure segregation in the South and, by implication, throughout the nation. The Brown decision changed the law and dealt a crippling blow to Jim Crow segregation.

The blow was not fatal, however. Southern states responded to the Brown (1954) decision by stalling and mounting campaigns of massive resistance. Jim Crow laws remained on the books for years. White Southerners actively defended the system of racial privilege and attempted to forestall change through a variety of means, including violence and intimidation. The Ku Klux Klan (KKK), largely dormant since the 1920s, reappeared along with other racist and terrorist groups, such as the White Citizens' Councils. White politicians and other leaders competed with each other to express the most adamant statements of racist resistance (Wilson, 1973, p. 128). One locality, Prince Edward County in central Virginia, chose to close its public schools rather than integrate. The schools remained closed for 5 years. During that time, the white children attended private, segregated academies, and the county provided no education at all for African American children (Franklin, 1967, p. 644).

**Nonviolent Direct Action Protest.** The principle established by Brown (1954) was assimilationist: It ordered the educational institutions of the dominant group to be opened up freely and equally to all. Southern states and communities overwhelmingly rejected the principle of equal access and shared facilities. Centuries of racist tradition and privilege were at stake, and considerable effort would be required to overcome Southern defiance and resistance. The central force in this struggle was a protest movement, the beginning of which is often traced to Montgomery, Alabama, where on December 1, 1955, Rosa Parks, a seamstress and NAACP member, rode the city bus home from work, as she usually did. As the bus filled, she was ordered to surrender her seat to a white male passenger. When she refused, the police were called, and Rosa Parks was jailed for violating a local segregation ordinance.

Although Mrs. Parks was hardly the first African American to be subjected to such indignities, her case stimulated a protest movement in the African American community, and a boycott of the city buses was organized. Participants in the boycott set up car pools, shared taxis, and walked (in some cases, for miles) to and from work. They stayed off the buses for more than a year, until victory was achieved and the city was ordered to desegregate its buses. The Montgomery boycott was led by the Reverend Martin Luther King, Jr., the new minister of a local Baptist church.

From these beginnings sprang the protest movement that eventually defeated de jure segregation. The central strategy of the movement involved **nonviolent direct action**, a method by which the system of de jure segregation was confronted head on, not in the courtroom or in the state legislature, but in the streets. The movement's principles of nonviolence were adopted from the tenets of Christianity and from the teachings of Mohandas Gandhi, Henry David Thoreau, and others. Dr. King expressed the philosophy in a number of books and speeches (King, 1958, 1963, 1968). Nonviolent protest was intended to confront the forces of evil rather than the people who happened to be doing evil, and it attempted to win the friendship and support of its enemies rather than to defeat or humiliate them. Above all, nonviolent protest required courage and discipline; it was not a method for cowards (King, 1958, pp. 83-84).

The movement used different tactics for different situations, including sit-ins at segregated restaurants, protest marches and demonstrations, prayer meetings, and voter registration drives. The police and terrorist groups such as the KKK often responded to these protests with brutal repression and violence, and protesters were routinely imprisoned, beaten, and attacked by police dogs. The violent resistance sometimes escalated to acts of murder, including the 1963 bombing of a black church in Birmingham, Alabama, which took the lives of four little girls, and the 1967 assassination of Dr. King. Resistance to racial change in the South was intense. It would take more than protests and marches to finally extirpate de jure segregation, and the U.S. Congress finally provided the necessary tools (see D'Angelo, 2001; Killian, 1975; King, 1958, 1963, 1968; Morris, 1984).

**Landmark Legislation.** The successes of the protest movement, combined with changing public opinion and the legal principles established by the Supreme Court, coalesced in the mid-1960s to stimulate the passage of two laws that, together, ended Jim Crow segregation. In 1964, at the urging of President Lyndon B. Johnson, the U.S. Congress passed the Civil Rights Act of 1964, banning discrimination on the grounds of race, color, religion, national origin, or gender. The law applied to publicly owned facilities such as parks and municipal swimming pools, businesses and other facilities open to the public, and any programs that received federal aid. Congress followed this up with the Voting Rights Act in 1965, also initiated by President Johnson, which required that the same standards be used to register all citizens in federal, state, and local elections. The act banned literacy tests, whites-only primaries, and other practices that had been used to prevent African Americans from registering to vote. This law gave the franchise back to black Southerners and laid the groundwork for increasing black political power. This landmark federal legislation, in combination with court decisions and the protest movement, finally succeeded in crushing Jim Crow.

**The Success and Limitations of the Civil Rights Movement.** Why did the civil rights movement succeed? A comprehensive list of reasons would be legion, but we can cite some of the most important causes of its success, especially those consistent with the general points about dominant-minority relations that have been made in previous chapters.

The continuing industrialization and urbanization of the society as a whole—and the South in particular—weakened the Jim Crow, rigid competitive system of minority group control and segregation.

Following World War II, the United States enjoyed a period of prosperity that lasted into the 1960s. Consistent with the Noel hypothesis, this was important, because it reduced the intensity of intergroup competition, at least outside the South. During prosperous times, resistance to change tends to weaken. If the economic "pie" is expanding, the "slices" claimed by minority groups can increase without threatening the size of anyone else's portions, and the prejudice generated during intergroup competition (à la Robber's Cave, chapter 3) is held in check. Thus, these "good times" muted the sense of threat experienced in the dominant group by the demands for equality made by the Civil Rights movement.

Also, some of the economic prosperity found its way into African American communities and increased their pool of economic and political resources. Networks of independent, African American–controlled organizations and institutions, such as churches and colleges, were created or grew in size and power. The increasingly elaborate infrastructure of the black community included protest organizations, such as the NAACP (see chapter 6), and provided material resources, leadership, and "people power" to lead the fight against segregation and discrimination.

The goals of the Civil Rights movement were assimilationist; the movement embraced the traditional American values of liberty, equality, freedom, and fair treatment. It demanded civil, legal, and political rights for African Americans, rights available to whites automatically. Thus many whites did not feel threatened by the movement because they saw it as consistent with mainstream American values, especially in contrast with the intense, often violent resistance of Southern whites.

The perceived legitimacy of the goals of the movement also opened up the possibility of alliances with other groups (white liberals, Jews, college students). The support of others was crucial because black Southerners had few resources of their own other than their numbers and their courage. By mobilizing the resources of other, more powerful groups, black Southerners forged alliances and created sympathetic support that was brought to bear on their opposition.

Finally, widespread and sympathetic coverage from the mass media, particularly television, was crucial to the success of the movement. The oft-repeated scenario of African Americans being brutally attacked while demonstrating for their rights outraged many Americans and reinforced the moral consensus that eventually rejected "old-fashioned" racial prejudice along with Jim Crow segregation (see chapter 4).

The Southern Civil Rights movement ended de jure segregation but found it difficult to survive the demise of its primary enemy. The confrontational tactics that had been so effective against the Jim Crow system proved less useful when attention turned to the actual distribution of jobs, wealth, political power, and other valued goods and services. Outside the South, the allocation of opportunity and resources had always been the central concern of the African American community. Let's take a look at these concerns.

## DEVELOPMENTS OUTSIDE THE SOUTH

### De Facto Segregation

Chapter 6 discussed some of the difficulties encountered by African Americans as they left the rural South. Discrimination by labor unions, employers, industrialists, and white ethnic groups was common. Racial discrimination outside the South was less blatant but was still pervasive, especially in housing, education, and employment.

The pattern of racial separation and inequality outside the South is often called **de facto segregation**: segregation resulting from the apparently voluntary choices of dominant and minority groups alike. Theoretically, no person, law, or specific group is responsible for de facto segregation; it "just happens" as people and groups make decisions about where to live and work.

The distinction between de facto and de jure segregation can be misleading, however, and the de facto variety is often the de jure variety in thin disguise. Although cities and states outside the South may not have had actual Jim Crow laws, de facto segregation was often the direct result of intentionally racist decisions made by governmental and quasi-governmental agencies such as real estate boards, school boards, and zoning boards (see Massey & Denton, 1993, pp. 74-114). For example, shortly after World War I, the Real Estate Board in the city of Chicago adopted a policy that required its members, on penalty of "immediate expulsion," to follow a policy of racial residential segregation (Cohen & Taylor, 2000, p. 33).

Regardless of who or what was responsible for these patterns, African Americans living outside the South faced more poverty, higher unemployment, and lower quality housing and schools than did whites, but there was no clear equivalent of Jim Crow to attack or to blame for these patterns of inequality. In the 1960s, the African American community outside the South expressed its frustration over the slow pace of change in two ways: urban unrest and a movement for change that rose to prominence as the Civil Rights movement faded.

# Urban Unrest

In the mid-1960s, the frustration and anger of urban African American communities erupted into a series of violent uprisings. The riots began in the summer of 1965 in Watts, a neighborhood in Los Angeles, and over the next 4 years, virtually every large black urban community experienced similar outbursts. Racial violence was hardly a new phenomenon in America. Race riots had existed as early as the Civil War, and various time periods had seen racial violence of considerable magnitude. The riots of the 1960s were different, however. Most race riots in the past had involved attacks by whites against blacks, often including the invasion and destruction of African American neighborhoods (see, e.g., D'Orso, 1996; Ellsworth, 1982). The urban unrest of the 1960s, in contrast, consisted largely of attacks by blacks against the symbols of their oppression and frustration. The most obvious targets were white-owned businesses operating in black neighborhoods and the police, who were seen as an army of occupation and whose excessive use of force was often the immediate precipitator of riots (Conot, 1967; National Advisory Commission, 1968).

# The Black Power Movement

The urban riots of the 1960s were an unmistakable sign that the problems of race relations had not been resolved with the end of Jim Crow segregation. Outside the South, the problems were different and called for different solutions. Even as the civil rights movement was celebrating its victory in the South, a new protest movement rose to prominence. The Black Power movement was a loose coalition of organizations and spokespersons that encompassed a variety of ideas and views, many of which differed sharply from those of the Civil Rights movement. Some of the central ideas included racial pride ("Black is beautiful" was a key slogan of the day), interest in African heritage, and black nationalism. In contrast to the assimilationist goals of the Civil Rights movement, Black Power groups worked to increase African American control over schools, police, welfare programs, and other public services operating in black neighborhoods.

Most adherents of the Black Power movement felt that white racism and institutional discrimination, forces buried deep in the core of American culture and society, were the causes of racial inequality in America. Thus, if African Americans were ever to be truly empowered, they would have to liberate themselves and do it on their own terms. Some Black Power advocates specifically rejected the goal of assimilation into white society, arguing that integration would require blacks to become part of the very system that had for centuries oppressed, denigrated, and devalued them and other peoples of color.

**The Nation of Islam.** The themes of Black Power voiced so loudly in the 1960s were decades, even centuries, old. Marcus Garvey had popularized many of these ideas in the 1920s, and they were espoused and further developed by the Nation of Islam, popularly known as the Black Muslims, in the 1960s.

One of the best known organizations within the Black Power movement, the Black Muslims were angry, impatient, and outspoken. They denounced the hypocrisy, greed, and racism of American society and advocated staunch resistance and racial separation. The Black Muslims did more than talk, however. Pursuing the goals of autonomy and self-determination, they worked hard to create a separate, independent, African American economy within the United States. They opened businesses and stores in African American neighborhoods and tried to deal only with other Muslim-owned firms. Their goal was to develop the African American community economically and supply jobs and capital for expansion solely by using their own resources (Essien-Udom, 1962; Lincoln, 1961; Wolfenstein, 1993; X, 1964).

The Nation of Islam and other black power groups distinguished between racial *separation* and racial *segregation*. The former is a process of empowerment whereby a group becomes stronger as it becomes more autonomous and self-controlled. The latter is a system of inequality in which the African American community is powerless and is controlled by the dominant group. Thus the Black Power groups were working to find ways in which African Americans could develop their own resources and deal with the dominant group from a more powerful position, a strategy similar to that followed by minority groups that form ethnic enclaves (see chapter 2).

The best known spokesman for the Nation of Islam was Malcolm X, one of the most charismatic figures of the 1960s. Malcolm X forcefully articulated the themes of the Black Power movement. Born Malcolm Little, he converted to Islam and joined the Nation of Islam while serving a prison term. He became the chief spokesperson for the Black Muslims and a well-known but threatening figure to the white community. After a dispute with Elijah Muhammad, the leader of the Nation of Islam, Malcolm X founded his own organization in which he continued to express and develop the ideas of black nationalism. Like so many other protest leaders of the era, Malcolm X was assassinated, in 1965.

Black power leaders such as Malcolm X advocated autonomy, independence, and a pluralistic direction for the African American protest movement. They saw the African American community as a colonized, exploited population in need of liberation from the unyielding racial oppression of white America, not integration into the system that was the source of its oppression.

## PROTEST, POWER, AND PLURALISM
## The Black Power Movement in Perspective

By the end of the 1960s, the riots had ended, and the most militant and dramatic manifestations of the Black Power movement had faded. In many cases, the passion of Black Power activists had been countered by the violence of the police and other agencies, and many of the most powerful spokespersons of the movement were dead; others were in jail or in exile. The nation's commitment to racial change wavered and weakened as other concerns, such as the Vietnam War, competed for attention. Richard M. Nixon was elected president in 1968 and made it clear that his administration would not ally itself with the **black protest movement**. Pressure from the federal government for racial equality was reduced. The boiling turmoil of the mid-1960s faded, but the idea of Black Power had become thoroughly entrenched in the African American community.

In some part, the pluralistic themes of Black Power were a reaction to the failure of assimilation and integration in the 1950s and 1960s. Laws had been passed; court decisions had been widely publicized; and promises and pledges had been made by presidents, members of Congress, ministers, and other leaders. For many African Americans, though, little had changed. The problems of their parents and grandparents continued to constrain and limit their lives and, as far into the future as they could see, the lives of their children. The pluralistic Black Power ideology was a response to the failure to go beyond the repeal of Jim Crow laws and fully implement the promises of integration and equality.

Black nationalism, however, was, and remains, more than simply a reaction to a failed dream. It was also a different way of defining what it means to be black in America. In the context of black-white relations in the 1960s, the Black Power movement served a variety of purposes. First, along with the Civil Rights movement, it helped carve out a new identity for African Americans. The cultural stereotypes of black Americans (see chapters 3 and 4) stressed laziness, irresponsibility, and inferiority. This image needed to be refuted, rejected, and buried. The black protest movements supplied a view of African Americans that emphasized power, assertiveness, seriousness of purpose, intelligence, and courage.

Second, Black Power served as a new rallying cry for solidarity and unified action. Following the success of the Civil Rights movement, these new themes and ideas helped to focus attention on "unfinished business": the black-white inequalities that remained in U.S. society.

Finally, the ideology provided an analysis of the problems of American race relations in the 1960s. The Civil Rights movement had, of course, analyzed race relations in terms of integration, equality of opportunity, and an end to exclusion. After the demise of Jim Crow, that analysis became less relevant. A new language was needed to describe and analyze the continuation of racial inequality. Black Power argued that the continuing problems of U.S. race relations were structural and institutional, not individual or legal. To take the next steps toward actualizing racial equality and justice would require a fundamental and far-reaching restructuring of the society. Ultimately, white Americans, as the beneficiaries of the system, would not support such restructuring. The necessary energy and commitment had to come from African Americans pursuing their own self-interest.

The nationalistic and pluralistic demands of the Black Power movement evoked defensiveness and a sense of threat in white society. By questioning the value of assimilation and celebrating a separate African heritage equal in legitimacy with white European heritage, the Black Power movement questioned the legitimacy and worth of Anglo-American values. In fact, many Black Power spokespersons condemned Anglo-American values fiercely and openly and implicated them in the creation and maintenance of a centuries-long system of racial repression. Today, 40 years after the success of the Civil Rights movement, assertive and critical demands by the African American community continue to be perceived as threatening.

## Gender and Black Protest

Both the Civil Rights movement and the Black Power movement tended to be male dominated. African American women were often viewed as supporters of men rather than as equal partners in liberation. Although African American women were heavily involved in the struggle, they were often denied leadership roles or decision-making positions in favor of men. In fact, the women in one organization, the Student Nonviolent Coordinating Committee, wrote position papers to protest their relegation to lowly clerical positions and the frequent references to them as "girls" (Andersen, 1993, p. 284). The Nation of Islam emphasized female subservience, imposing a strict code of behavior and dress for women and separating the sexes in many temple and community activities. Thus, the battle against racism and the battle against sexism were separate struggles with separate and often contradictory agendas, as the black protest movement continued to subordinate women (Amott & Matthaei, 1991, p. 177).

When the protest movements began, however, African American women were already heavily involved in community and church work, and they often used their organizational skills and energy to further the cause of black liberation. In the view of many, African American women were the backbone of the movement, even if they were often relegated to less glamorous but vital organizational work (Evans, 1979).

Fannie Lou Hamer of Mississippi, an African American who became a prominent leader in the black liberation movement, illustrates the importance of the role played by women. Born in 1917 to sharecropper parents, Hamer's life was so circumscribed that until she attended her first rally at the beginning of the Civil Rights movement, she was unaware that blacks could—even theoretically—register to vote. The day after the rally she quickly volunteered to register:

> I guess I'd had any sense I'd a-been a little scared, but what was the point of being scared? The only thing they could do to me was kill me and it seemed like they'd been trying to do that a little bit at a time ever since I could remember. (Evans, 1989, p. 271)

As a result of her activism, Hamer lost her job, was evicted from her house, and was jailed and beaten on a number of occasions. She devoted herself entirely to the Civil Rights movement and founded the Freedom Party, which successfully challenged the racially segregated Democratic Party and the all-white political structure of the State of Mississippi (Evans, 1979; Hamer, 1967).

## BLACK-WHITE RELATIONS SINCE THE 1960s

By the 1970s, the outlines of present-day black-white relations had been established. Since that time, progress has been made in integrating the society and eliminating racial inequality in some areas. In other areas, however, the progress of the African American community has stagnated, and the problems that remain are enormous, deep rooted, and inextricably mixed with the structure and functioning of modern American society. As was the case in earlier eras, racism and racial inequality today cannot be addressed apart from the trends of change in the larger society, especially changes in subsistence technology. This section examines the racial separation that continues to characterize so many areas of U.S. society and applies many of the concepts from previous chapters to present-day black-white relations.

## Continuing Separation, Continuing Violence

More than 35 years ago, a presidential commission charged with investigating black urban unrest warned that the United States was "moving towards two societies, one black, one white, separate and unequal" (National Advisory Commission, 1968). We could object to the commission's use of the phrase "moving towards," with its suggestion that U.S. society was at one time racially unified, but the warning still seems prophetic. Without denying the progress toward integration that has been made, African Americans and white Americans continue to live in worlds that are indeed separate and unequal.

Both groups have committed violence and hate crimes against the other, but the power differentials and the patterns of inequality that are the legacy of our racist past guarantee that African Americans will more often be seen as "invaders" pushing into areas where they do not belong and are not wanted. Sometimes the reactions to these perceived intrusions are immediate and bloody, but other, subtler attempts to maintain the exclusion of African Americans continue to be part of everyday life, even at the highest levels of society. For example, in a lawsuit reminiscent of Jim Crow days, a national restaurant chain was accused of discriminating against African American customers by systematically providing poor service. In 2004, the company agreed to pay $8.7 million to settle the lawsuit (McDowell, 2004). In another example, Texaco, in 1996, was sued for discrimination by several of its minority employees. The case was settled out of court after a tape recording of company executives plotting to destroy incriminating documents and making racist remarks was made public (Eichenwald, 1996).

Many African Americans mirror the hostility of whites, and as the goals of full racial equality and justice continue to seem remote, frustration and anger continue to run high. The unrest and discontent has been manifested in violence and riots; the most widely publicized example was the racial violence that began with the 1991 arrest and beating of Rodney King by police officers in Los Angeles. The attack on King was videotaped and shown repeatedly on national and international news, and contrary to the expectations of most who saw the videotape, the police officers were acquitted of almost all charges in April 1992. On hearing word of the acquittals, African American communities in several cities erupted in violence. The worst disturbance occurred in the Watts section of Los Angeles, where 58 people lost their lives, and millions of dollars of property damage was done (Wilkens, 1992).

In some ways, the riot following the 1992 King verdict was different from the riots of the 1960s. The more recent event was multiracial and involved Hispanics as well as African Americans. In fact, most of the 58 fatalities were from these two groups. Also, many of the businesses looted and burned were owned by Korean Americans, and many of the attacks were against whites directly, as in the beating of truck driver Reginald Denny (also, ironically, captured on videotape).

In other ways, the events were similar. Both were spontaneous and expressed diffuse but bitter discontent with the racial status quo. Both signaled the continuing racial inequality, urban poverty and despair, and the reality of separate nations, unequal and hostile (for more on these urban uprisings, see Gooding-Williams, 1993).

## The Criminal Justice System and African Americans

No area of race relations is more volatile and controversial than the relationship between the black community and the criminal justice system. There is considerable mistrust and resentment of the police among African Americans, and the perception that the entire criminal justice system is stacked against them is widespread. These perceptions are not without justification, as black people continue to be victimized by the police in a variety of ways—some petty, some involving deadly violence. The scenario of the police viciously attacking Rodney King mentioned earlier is echoed in the more recent deaths of Amadou Diallo in New York City, in 1999, and a young African American man in Cincinnati, in 2001. Mr. Diallo, an unarmed immigrant from West Africa, was gunned down in a hail of 41 bullets fired by four undercover police officers on a drug stakeout. The officers testified that they believed that Mr. Diallo was reaching for a gun when they opened fire, a defense that led to their acquittal. In the Cincinnati case, the shooting of Timothy Thomas, an unarmed 19-year-old black man, by a white police officer set off a storm of protest and days of rioting in the city.

On another level, more pervasive if less dramatic, is the issue of racial profiling: the police use of race as an indicator when calculating whether a person is suspicious or dangerous (Kennedy, 2001, p. 3). The tendency to focus more on blacks and to disproportionately stop, question, and follow them is a form of discrimination that generates resentment and increases the distrust (and fear) many African Americans feel toward their local police forces. According to some, humiliating encounters with police (for example, being stopped and questioned for "driving while black") are virtually a rite of passage for black men (Kennedy, 2001, p. 7). According to one national survey, more than half of all black men and 25% of black females feel that they have been unfairly stopped by police (Morin & Cottman, 2001).

Black males are much more likely to be involved in the criminal justice system than white males, and in many communities, a third or more of young African American men are under the supervision of the system: in jail or prison or on probation or parole (Mauer & Huling, 2000, p. 417). This phenomenal level of imprisonment is largely the result of a national "get tough" policy on drugs and especially on crack cocaine that began in the 1980s. Crack cocaine is a cheap form of the drug that has devastated certain largely minority neighborhoods, and the street-level dealers who have felt the brunt of the national antidrug campaign have been disproportionately young African American males. Some see this crackdown as a not-so-subtle form of racial discrimination. For example, a 1986 federal law required a minimal prison sentence of 10 years for anyone convicted of possession with intent to distribute 50 grams or more of crack, a drug much more likely to be dealt by blacks. At the same time, comparable levels of sentencing for dealing powder cocaine—the more expensive form of the drug—was not reached until the accused possessed a minimum of 5000 grams (Kennedy, 2001, p. 15). The result was a double victimization of the African American community: first from the drug itself and then from the attempt to police the drug.

The scope of the relationship between the African American community and the criminal justice system is documented in a recent study (Pettit & Western, 2004). Focusing on men born between 1965 and 1969, the study found that 3% of whites, compared to 20% of blacks, had been imprisoned by the time they were 30 years old. Also, the study found that education was a key variable affecting the probability of imprisonment: Nearly 60% of African American men in this cohort who had not completed high school went to prison.

The charges of racial profiling and discrimination in the war against drugs are controversial. Many argue that racial profiling is at some level based on the fact that blacks are statistically more likely to be involved in street crime and in the illegal drug trade (for example, see Taylor & Whitney, 1999, an excerpt from which is included in the Current Debates at the end of chapter 3). At another level, these patterns sustain the ancient perceptions of African Americans as dangerous outsiders, and they feed the tradition of resentment and anger toward the police in the African American community.

## Urbanization and Increasing Class Differentiation

As black Americans moved out of the rural South and as the repressive force of de jure segregation receded, social class inequality within the African American population increased. Since the 1960s, the black middle class has grown, but black poverty continues to be a serious problem.

**The Black Middle Class.** A small, African American middle class, based largely on occupations and businesses serving only the African American community, had been in existence since before the Civil War (Frazier, 1957). Has this more affluent segment benefited from increasing tolerance in the larger society, civil rights legislation, and affirmative action programs? Is the African American middle class growing in size and affluence?

The answers to these questions are not entirely clear. Although the percentage of African Americans who might be considered middle class has apparently increased, research suggests that the size and affluence of this group is less than is often assumed. The relatively smaller size of the African American middle class is suggested by continuing substantial inequalities between blacks and whites in income, wealth, and net worth that have been documented by researchers. For example, one recent study (Kochlar, 2004) found that the median net worth (home equity, stocks, savings, cars, etc.) of African American households ($5988) was less than 7% of white households ($88,651) In other words, for every dollar of wealth and assets controlled by the median white household, the median black household controls 7 cents. The relatively smaller size of the African American middle class is also suggested by Exhibit 7.1, which shows the distribution of black and white households across four levels of wealth. The majority of African American households (58%) were in the "low wealth" category, and fewer than 25% were in the "upper middle" and "high" wealth categories, both of which could be considered to be indicators of middle-class status. The pattern for whites is very different: Only 27% are in the low wealth category, and 58% could be considered "middle class." By this measure, the white middle class is more than twice as large, proportionally, as the black middle class.

Other studies corroborate the point that the African American middle class is proportionally smaller and lags far behind middle-class whites in economic resources (Avery & Rendall, 2002; Oliver & Shapiro, 2001, Pollard & O'Hare, 1999, pp. 37-38). These economic differences are due partly to discrimination in the present and partly to the racial gaps in income, wealth, and economic opportunity in past generations. Economically more advantaged white families can pass

**EXHIBIT 7.1**   Wealth of Non-Hispanic Black and White Households, 2002

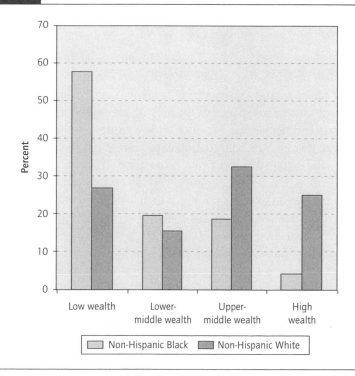

NOTE: Low wealth indicates net worth less than 25% of the national median net worth; lower middle wealth, net worth between 25% of the national median net worth and the median wealth; upper middle wealth, net worth between the national median net worth and four times the median wealth; high wealth, more than four times the median wealth.

along a larger store of resources, wealth, and property to the present generation. Thus the greater economic marginality of the African American middle class today is a form of "past-in-present" institutional discrimination (see chapter 6). It reflects the greater ability of white parents (and grandparents) to finance higher education and to subsidize business ventures and home mortgages (Oliver & Shapiro, 2001).

Not only is their economic position more marginal, middle-class African Americans commonly report that they are unable to escape the narrow straitjacket of race. No matter what their level of success, occupation, or professional accomplishments, race continues to be seen as their primary defining characteristic in the eyes of the larger society (Cose, 1993; Hughes & Thomas, 1998). Without denying the advances of some, many analysts argue that the stigma of race continues to set sharp limits on the life chances of African Americans.

There is also a concern that greater class differentiation may decrease solidarity and cohesion within the African American community. There is greater income inequality among African Americans than ever before, with the urban poor at one extreme and some of the wealthiest, most recognized figures in the world at the other: millionaires, celebrities, business moguls, politicians, and sports and movie stars. Will the more affluent segment of the African American community disassociate itself from the plight of the less fortunate and move away from the urban neighborhoods, taking with it its affluence, articulateness, and leadership skills? If this happens, it would reinforce the class division and further seal the fate of impoverished African Americans, who are largely concentrated in urban areas.

**Urban Poverty.** African Americans have become an urban minority group, and the fate of the group is inextricably bound to the fate of America's cities. The issues of black-white relations cannot be successfully addressed without dealing with urban issues, and vice versa.

As we saw in chapter 6, automation and mechanization in the workplace have eliminated many of the manual labor jobs that sustained city dwellers in earlier decades (Kasarda, 1989). The manufacturing, or secondary, segment of the labor force has declined in size, and the service sector has continued to expand (see Exhibit 6.3). The more desirable jobs in the service sector have increasingly demanding educational prerequisites. The service sector jobs available to people with lower educational credentials pay low wages and offer little in the way of benefits, security, and links to more rewarding occupations. This form of past-in-present institutional discrimination constitutes a powerful handicap for colonized groups such as African Americans, who have been excluded from educational opportunities for centuries.

Furthermore, many of the blue-collar jobs that have escaped automation have migrated away from the cities. Industrialists have been moving their businesses to areas where labor is cheaper, unions have less power, and taxes are lower. This movement to the suburbs, to the "sunbelt," and "offshore" has been devastating for the inner city. Poor transportation systems, lack of car ownership, the absence of affordable housing outside the center city, and outright housing discrimination have combined to keep urban poor people of color confined to center-city neighborhoods, distant from opportunities for jobs and economic improvement (Feagin, 2001, pp. 159-160; Kasarda, 1989; Massey & Denton, 1993).

These industrial and economic forces affect all poor urbanites, not just minority groups or African Americans in particular. The dilemma facing many African Americans is in some part not only racism or discrimination; the impersonal forces of evolving industrialization and social class structures contribute as well. However, when immutable racial stigmas and centuries of prejudice (even disguised as modern racism) are added to these economic and urban developments, the forces limiting and constraining many African Americans become extremely formidable.

For the past 60 years, the African American poor have been increasingly concentrated in narrowly delimited urban areas ("the ghetto") in which the scourge of poverty has been compounded and reinforced by a host of other problems, including joblessness, high rates of school dropout, crime, drug use, teenage pregnancy, and welfare dependency. These increasingly isolated neighborhoods are fertile grounds for the development of oppositional cultures, which reject or invert the values of the larger society. The black urban counterculture may be most visible in music, fashion, speech, and other forms of popular culture, but it is also manifest in widespread lack of trust in the larger society and whites in particular. An **urban underclass**, barred from the mainstream economy and the primary labor force and consisting largely of poor African Americans and other minority groups of color, is quickly becoming a permanent feature of the American landscape (Kasarda, 1989; Massey & Denton, 1993; Wilson, 1987, 1996).

Consider the parallels and contrasts between the plight of the present urban underclass and black Southerners under de jure segregation:

- In both eras, a large segment of the African American population was cut off from opportunities for success and growth.
- In the earlier era, African Americans were isolated in rural areas; now they are isolated in urban areas, especially center cities.
- In the past, escape from segregation was limited primarily by political and legal restrictions and blatant racial prejudice; escape from poverty in the present is limited by economic and educational deficits and a more subtle and amorphous prejudice.

The result is the same: Many African Americans remain a colonized minority group, isolated, marginalized, and burdened with a legacy of powerlessness and poverty.

**Race Versus Class.** One of the livelier debates in contemporary race relations concerns the relative importance of race and class in shaping the lives of African Americans and other minority groups. One position argues that race is no longer the primary controlling influence in the lives of African Americans and that blacks and whites at the same social class level or with the same credentials have the same opportunities. The playing field is level, it is argued, and what matters is competence and willingness to work hard, not skin color. The apparent increase in the size of the African American middle class has frequently been used as proof that modern American society is open and fair.

This position is often associated with *The Declining Significance of Race,* a book written in the late 1970s by William J. Wilson, an African American and prominent sociologist. Wilson concluded that there is a segmented job market for African Americans. The black urban underclass is restricted to the low-wage sector and faces high rates of unemployment and crushing poverty. Talented and educated African Americans, in contrast, have job prospects that are "at least comparable to those of whites with equivalent qualifications" (Wilson, 1980, p. 151). Wilson attributed the improved situation of the African American middle class partly to the expansion of white-collar occupations and partly to affirmative action programs and pressure from the federal government to include African Americans and other minorities in colleges, universities, professional schools, and the job market.

Wilson's assessment may have been accurate for the 1970s. It follows, however, that these improvements would be sustained only to the extent that white-collar jobs continued to grow and affirmative action programs continued to be enforced. In the decade following the publication of Wilson's book, neither of these conditions was fulfilled. Economic growth slowed in the 1980s and 1990s, the racial gap in wages actually widened (especially among younger workers), and, under the administrations of Presidents Reagan and Bush, federal affirmative action programs were de-emphasized (Cancio, Evans, & Maume, 1996, pp. 551-554). There is some evidence of a closing of the race/gender gaps during the economic boom of the 1990s (see Exhibits 7.2 and 7.8, later in this chapter) but these gains may not persist beyond the end of these good times. At any rate, Wilson's conclusion that race is declining in significance seems, at best, premature (Hughes & Thomas, 1998; Thomas, 1993; Wilson, 1997).

Other critics of Wilson's thesis argue that the forces of institutional discrimination and racism remain strong in modern America, even though they may be less blatant than in the past. Race remains the single most important feature of a person's identity and the most important determinant of life chances. Contrary to the beliefs of many white Americans, reports of the death of racism and the coming of a color-blind society have been greatly exaggerated (Feagin, 2001; Margolis, 1989, p. 99; Willie, 1989).

## The Family Institution and the Culture of Poverty

The nature of the African American family institution has been a continuing source of concern and controversy. On one hand, some analysts see the African American family as structurally weak, a cause of continuing poverty and a variety of other problems. No doubt the most famous study in this tradition was the Moynihan report (1965), which focused on the higher rates of divorce, separation, desertion, and illegitimacy among African American families and the fact that black families were far more likely to be female-headed than were white families. Moynihan concluded that the fundamental barrier facing African Americans was a family structure that he saw as crumbling, a condition that would perpetuate the cycle of poverty entrapping African Americans (p. iii). Today, most of the differences between black and white family institutions identified by Moynihan are even more pronounced. Exhibit 7.2, for example, compares the percentage of households headed by females (black and white) with the percentage of households headed by married couples.

The line of analysis implicit in the Moynihan (1965) report locates the problem of urban poverty in the characteristics of the African American community, particularly in the African American family. These structures are "broken" in important ways and need to be "fixed." This argument is consistent with the **culture of poverty theory**, which argues that poverty is perpetuated by the particular characteristics of the poor. Specifically, poverty is said to encourage **fatalism** (the sense that one's destiny is beyond one's control) and an orientation to the present rather than the future. The desire for instant gratification is a central trait of the culture of poverty, as opposed to the ability to defer gratification, which is thought to be essential for middle-class success. Other characteristics include violence, authoritarianism, and high rates of alcoholism and family desertion by males (Lewis, 1959, 1965, 1966).

The culture of poverty theory leads to the conclusion that the problem of urban poverty would be resolved if female-headed family structures and other cultural characteristics correlated with poverty could be changed. Note that this approach is consistent with the traditional assimilationist perspective and human capital theory: The poor have "bad" or inappropriate

## Condoleezza Rice: From Acorns to Oaks

*Condoleezza Rice is the second African American and the first African American female to be Secretary of State. She (as well as her predecessor, Colin Powell) has often been "the first," and her life exemplifies the opportunities available in the new, more open, U.S. society. Still, her life has been shaped by the forces of race, class, and gender: She was born in the Jim Crow South and witnessed the Southern Civil Rights movement directly and personally. Her parents were solidly middle class and shielded her from the worst excesses of racism and the turmoil of the times. Still, the struggle was so intense and pervasive that it eventually touched everyone and she lost at least one friend to the violence.*

*After pursuing an academic career, Rice served in the administration of President George Bush, Sr., and as National Security Advisor under the second President Bush before being appointed Secretary of State in 2005. This excerpt summarizes some of her experiences as a successful African American woman. How do these experiences illustrate the influences of race, class, and gender? Does her biography suggest that success is equally available to all or is Condoleezza Rice simply a rare exception to the usual realities of discrimination, racism, and inequality?*

### CONDOLEEZZA RICE'S JOURNEY FROM THE JIM CROW SOUTH TO THE WHITE HOUSE

**Arthur Hernstein**

Condoleezza Rice has experienced a wide range of life. . . . She is descended from slaves on both sides of her family. Her maternal great-grandfather was a white plantation owner who had children with his black house slave. Her paternal great-grandmother was a . . . house slave who had the opportunity to learn to read and write, she married John Wesley Rice, a former slave from South Carolina who was also literate. That desire for education would become a family theme. . . .

Rice's parents instilled in her a love for excellence and achievement. . . . They believed that only through such self-imposed discipline would it be possible to rise out of the oppression of the segregated South. "My parents were very strategic," she said. "I was going to be so well prepared, and I was going to do all of those things that were revered in white society so well,

that I would be armored somehow from racism. I would be able to confront white society on its own terms."

An only child, Rice was home-schooled for her first year, took ballet lessons, and started studying piano at age 3. . . .

During [her childhood in] the 1950s and early '60s, life for Birmingham's black citizens had many negative aspects. Segregation, bigotry, and discrimination were daily fare. A . . . number of middle-class families, like the Rices, moved to the suburbs and set high standards for their children, but they could never completely eliminate the degrading system known as Jim Crow. . . .

Birmingham was also dangerous. . . . In 1963, the Sixteenth Street Baptist Church was bombed on a busy Sunday morning, and the blast could be felt for miles. Rice, attending services at her family church a few miles away, actually felt the floor shake. Four girls aged 11 to 14 were killed instantly. She and the youngest girl, Denise McNair, had been friends since kindergarten. Rice attended the funeral and recalls, "I remember more than anything the coffins, the small coffins. And the sense that Birmingham wasn't a very safe place."

In 1965, . . . her father . . . became the dean of Stillman College [and], after three years . . . [he] was offered a position as assistant director of admissions at the University of Denver. The family moved again, this time far from the South and many of its difficulties.

Rice attended . . . an all-girls high school, where she was one of only three black students out of seventy in her class. During this time, she took up tennis and ice-skating. She would awake at 4:30 each weekday morning to practice at the rink.

Rice's fascination with sports came from her father. . . . Rice and her dad would "talk football" incessantly, and she developed a lifelong passion for the game. This interest would serve her well later on when she met George W. Bush, who was intrigued by her knowledge of football and baseball.

While still a senior in high school, Rice enrolled at the University of Denver. . . . She became a piano performance major . . . and was convinced she was headed for a career as a concert pianist. But . . . she came to realize she was not good enough for the concert stage. "I met 11-year-olds who could play from sight what had taken me all year to learn," she said. . . .

She . . . decided to . . . [switch to] international politics. She became inspired by her professor, Josef Korbel, a Jewish Czechoslovakian émigré (and the father of Madeleine Albright, [Secretary of State under President Clinton]). He took her under his wing, and Rice credits him with her decision to pursue international politics.

At 19, Rice graduated cum laude and . . . decided to continue her education at the University of Notre Dame . . . At the time, it was not common for a young black woman to pursue a graduate degree in [Soviet Studies], but Rice's strong desire to succeed and her intellectual capacity endeared her to the program's faculty, especially Dr. George Brinkley. He recalled, "Most students had little background, so we had to teach them basics. . . . But she was extremely bright, so she came better prepared than most. . . ." . . . Upon gaining her master's degree, Rice . . . decided . . . to return to the University of Denver and pursue an advanced degree. . . .

After she received her doctorate in 1981, Stanford University offered her a research fellowship . . . Just a few months [later] . . . , however, she was . . . offered a teaching position under an affirmative action program. The position would last three years and could be renewed based on her merits, not her minority status as a black person or woman. She would have to prove herself.

Rice . . . soon became known as a committed teacher and scholar. At the end of her three-year term she was rated highly, and her professorship was renewed. In 1987 she advanced to associate professor.

Rice [met] . . . Brent Scowcroft when he visited Stanford. He was so impressed with her that when he became the national security adviser to President George Bush in 1989, he asked Rice to . . . work with him . . . in Washington. She accepted and spent two years working closely with [President] George Bush Sr. . . . as an expert in Soviet affairs. . . .

After the intensity of that term of service, Rice was anxious to get back to her students and Stanford. . . . In 1993 she became a full professor [and], just a few months later, she was . . . asked to become the school's provost. As second in command, she would be responsible for the university's entire $1.5 billion budget.

When Rice took over as provost, the school had severe financial problems, including a $20 million deficit. She crafted a plan to correct the situation . . . Within just a few years, she was happy to announce that the school was out of the red . . .

Rice had met George W. Bush in 1995 while he was the governor of Texas. They hit it off. He was impressed with her expertise in foreign policy, and they found they had a mutual love for sports. When he was planning his presidential campaign in 1999, he enlisted her help as his foreign policy adviser. When he entered the White House, she was named his national security adviser [and, in 2005, Secretary of State].

To understand Condoleezza Rice more completely, one would have to view her philanthropic nature as well as her accomplishments in academia and government. One program she started . . . was the Center for a New Generation, an after school program in East Palo Alto, California. . . . The program . . . served third- through eighth-graders in a poor school district by providing enrichment studies in computers, foreign languages, math, and science. . . . Rice has said, "Ever since I've been out of school, most of my efforts outside work have dealt with trying to give kids an opportunity." . . .

SOURCE: Herstein, Arthur. 2004. "Acorns to Oaks: Condoleezza Rice's Journey From the Jim Crow South to the White House." *American Clergy.*

EXHIBIT 7.2

Percentage of Family Households With Married Couples and Headed by Females, by Race, 1970 to 2003

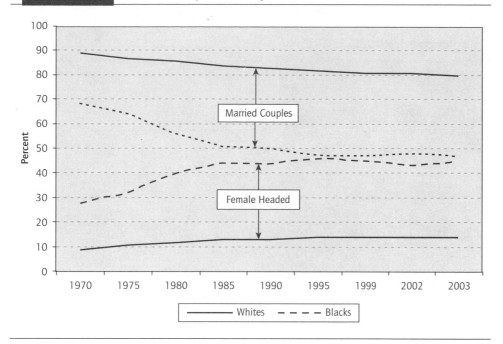

SOURCE: U.S. Bureau of the Census (1977, p. 43; 2005, p. 52).

values. If they could be equipped with "good" (i.e., white, middle-class) values, the problem would be resolved.

An opposed perspective, more consistent with the concepts and theories that underlie this text, sees the matriarchal structure of the African American family as the result of urban poverty—rather than a cause—and a reflection of racial discrimination and the scarcity of jobs for urban African American males. In impoverished African American urban neighborhoods, the supply of men able to support a family is reduced by high rates of unemployment, incarceration, and violence, and these conditions are in turn created by the concentration of urban poverty and the growth of the "underclass" (Massey & Denton, 1993; Wilson, 1996). Thus, the burden of child rearing tends to fall on females, and female-headed households are more common than in more advantaged neighborhoods.

Female-headed African American families tend to be poor, not because of any structural weakness but because of the lower wages accorded to women in general and to African American women in particular (see Exhibit 7.3). The poverty reflects the interaction of sexism and racism rather than a weak or pathological family structure. Sociologist John Farley (2000) concludes:

> Black . . . female-householder families experience a double disadvantage in income—the low wages and high unemployment rates associated with minority group status *and* the low wages of women. Significantly, neither of these has anything to do with the effects of one-parent, female-headed families per se. (Farley, 2000, p. 94)

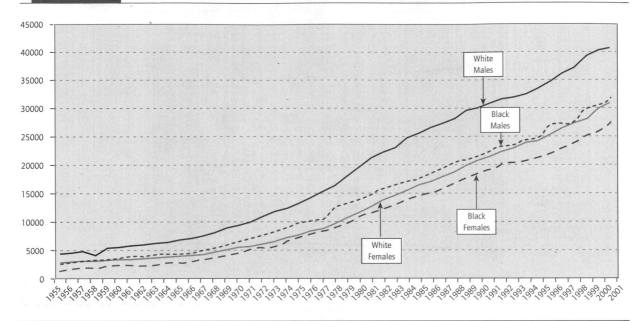

SOURCE: U.S. Bureau of the Census (2004).

This view locates the cause of African American urban poverty in the complex forces of past and present institutional discrimination, American racism and prejudice, the precarious position of African American women in the labor force, and continuing urbanization and industrialization. The African American family is not in need of "fixing," and the attitudes and values of the urban underclass are more the results of impoverishment than they are the causes. The solution to African American urban poverty lies in fundamental changes in the urban-industrial economy and sweeping alterations in the distribution of resources and opportunities.

## Prejudice and Discrimination

Modern racism, the more subtle form of prejudice that seems to dominate contemporary race relations, was discussed in chapter 4. Although the traditional, more overt forms of prejudice have certainly not disappeared, contemporary expressions of prejudice are often amorphous and indirect. For example, the widespread belief among whites that racial discrimination has been eliminated in the United States may be a way of blaming African Americans for the continuing patterns of racial inequality.

A parallel process of evolution from blunt and overt forms to more subtle and covert forms has occurred in patterns of discrimination. The clarity of Jim Crow has yielded to the ambiguity of modern institutional discrimination and the continuing legacy of past discrimination in the present.

The dilemmas of the African American urban underclass provide a clear, if massive, example of modern institutional discrimination. As long as American businesses and financial and political institutions continue to operate as they do, jobs will continue to migrate, cities will continue to lack the resources to meet the needs of their poorer citizens, and urban poverty will continue to sustain itself, decade after decade. The individual politicians, bankers, industrialists, and others who perpetuate and benefit from this system are not necessarily prejudiced and may not even be aware of these minority group issues. Yet their decisions can and do have profound effects on the perpetuation of racial inequality in America.

The effects of past discrimination on the present can be illustrated by the relatively low level of African American business ownership. From the beginning of slavery through the end of Jim Crow segregation less than 40 years ago, the opportunities for African Americans to start their own businesses were severely restricted (even forbidden) by law. The black-owned businesses that did exist were confined to the relatively less affluent market provided by the African American community, a market they had to share with firms owned by dominant group members. At the same time, customs and laws prevented the black-owned businesses from competing for more affluent white customers. The lack of opportunity to develop and maintain a strong business base in the past—and the consequent inability to accumulate wealth, experience, and other resources—limits the ability of African Americans to compete successfully for economic opportunities in the present (Oliver & Shapiro, 2001, p. 239).

## Assimilation and Pluralism

**Acculturation.** The Blauner hypothesis states that the culture of groups created by colonization will be attacked, denigrated, and, if possible, eliminated, and this assertion seems well validated by the experiences of African Americans. African cultures and languages were largely eradicated under slavery. As a powerless, colonized minority group, slaves had few opportunities to preserve their heritage even though traces of African homelands have been found in black language patterns, kinship systems, music, folk tales, or family legends (see Levine, 1977; Stuckey, 1987).

Cultural domination continued under the Jim Crow system, albeit through a different structural arrangement. Under slavery, slaves and their owners worked together, and interracial contact was common. Under de jure segregation, intergroup contact diminished, and blacks and whites generally became more separate. After slavery ended, the African American community had somewhat more autonomy (although still few resources) to define itself and develop a distinct culture.

The centuries of cultural domination and separate development have created a unique black experience in America. African Americans share language, religion, values, beliefs, and norms with the dominant society but have developed distinct variations on the general themes.

The acculturation process may have been slowed (or even reversed) by the Black Power movement. Beginning in the 1960s, on one hand, there has been an increased interest in African culture, language, clothing, and history and a more visible celebration of unique African American experiences (e.g., Kwanzaa) and the innumerable contributions of African Americans to the larger society. On the other hand, many of those traditions and contributions have been in existence all along. Perhaps all that really changed was the degree of public recognition.

**Secondary Structural Assimilation.** Structural assimilation, or integration, involves two different phases. Secondary structural assimilation refers to integration in more public areas, such as the job market, schools, and political institutions. We can assess integration in this area by comparing residential patterns, income distributions, job profiles, political power, and

**EXHIBIT 7.4**    Urban-Rural Residence for Black and White Americans

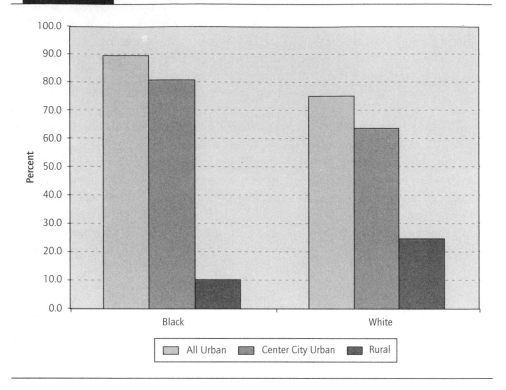

levels of education of the different groups. Each of these areas is addressed next. We then discuss the second phase of primary structural assimilation (integration in intimate associations, such as friendship) and intermarriage.

*Residential Patterns.* After a century of movement out of the rural South, African Americans today are highly urbanized and much more spread out across the nation. As displayed in Exhibit 7.4, about 90% of African Americans are urban and over 80% reside in center city areas. A slim majority of African Americans continues to reside in the South (about 55% today vs. almost 90% in 1910). About 37% of African Americans now live in the Northeast and Midwest (overwhelmingly in urban areas), and about 9% live in the West. Exhibit 7.5 clearly shows the concentration of African Americans in the states of the old Confederacy, the urbanized East Coast corridor from Washington, DC, to Boston, the industrial centers of the Midwest, and to a lesser extent, in California.

In the decades since Jim Crow segregation ended in the 1960s, residential integration has advanced slowly, if at all. Black and white Americans continue to live in separate areas, and racial residential segregation has been the norm. This pattern is reinforced by the fact that African Americans are more urbanized than whites and especially concentrated in densely populated center city areas (see Exhibit 7.4). Today, the extent of residential segregation varies around the nation, but African Americans continue to be residentially isolated, especially in the older industrial cities of the Northeast and Midwest and in the South (Pollard & O'Hare, 1999, p. 29). Is racial residential segregation increasing or decreasing? Looking at the nation as a whole, the answer to this question is somewhat unclear, because the studies that have been done use different methodologies, definitions, and databases and come to different conclusions (for different views,

EXHIBIT 7.5    Number of People, 2000: Black or African American

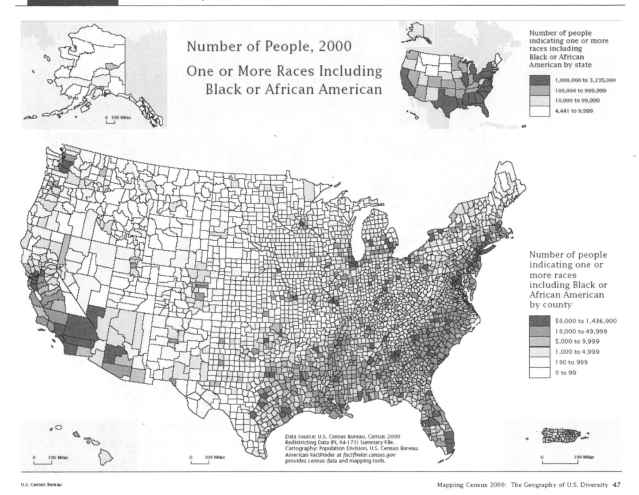

Number of People, 2000

One or More Races Including
Black or African American

Number of people indicating one or more races including Black or African American by state

- 1,000,000 to 3,235,000
- 100,000 to 999,999
- 10,000 to 99,999
- 4,441 to 9,999

Number of people indicating one or more races including Black or African American by county

- 50,000 to 1,436,000
- 10,000 to 49,999
- 5,000 to 9,999
- 1,000 to 4,999
- 100 to 999
- 0 to 99

Data Source: U.S. Census Bureau, Census 2000 Redistricting Data (PL 94-171) Summary File. Cartography: Population Division, U.S. Census Bureau. American FactFinder at *factfinder.census.gov* provides census data and mapping tools.

U.S. Census Bureau

Mapping Census 2000: The Geography of U.S. Diversity **47**

SOURCE: U.S. Bureau of the Census (2000h).

see Glaeser & Vigdor, 2001, and Lewis Mumford Center, 2001). One illustrative study (Charles, 2003) focused on the 50 largest metropolitan areas of the United States. In total, these areas encompass well over half the total African American population. The areas were divided into five regions and residential segregation statistics were calculated within each region. Exhibit 7.6 presents a measure of segregation called the dissimilarity index for African Americans for 1980 and 2000. This index indicates the degree to which a group is not evenly spread across neighborhoods or census tracts. Specifically, the index is the percentage of each group that would have to move to a different tract or area to achieve integration,[2] and scores over 60 are considered to indicate extreme segregation.

In 1980, the metro areas in all five regions averaged well over 60, further reinforcing the point that racial residential segregation has been the norm. The most segregated metro areas were in the Midwest: Chicago had an index of 89, followed by Detroit (88) and Cleveland (85).

**EXHIBIT 7.6** | Racial Residential Segregation, by Region

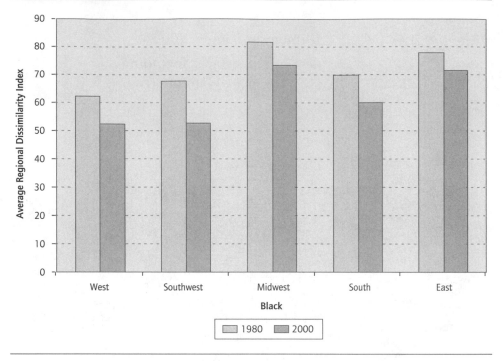

SOURCE: Calculated from Charles (2003).

By 2000, there were noticeable declines in all five regions, and three (the South, Southwest, and West) were at or below the 60% mark. Thus, according to this study, racial residential segregation is declining but remains quite high across most of the nation and continues to average in the "extreme" range in 2 of the 5 regions. The conclusion that residential segregation is decreasing holds for only the 50 metropolitan areas included in this study: smaller towns, suburbs, and other areas may be experiencing different patterns.

The continuing patterns of residential segregation are reinforced by a variety of practices, including racial steering (guiding clients to same-race housing areas) by realtors and barely disguised discrimination. For example, in an investigation of housing discrimination in the rental apartment market conducted over the telephone, Massey demonstrated that compared to speakers of "white English," speakers of "black English" were less likely to be told that an advertised unit was available, more likely to be required to pay an application fee, and more likely to have credit mentioned as an issue (Massey, 2000, p. 4). Also, banks and other financial institutions are more likely to refuse home mortgages to black applicants than to white applicants and are more likely to "redline," or deny, home improvement loans for houses in minority group neighborhoods (Feagin, 2001, pp. 155-159). "White flight" away from integrated areas also contributes to the pattern of racial separation, as whites flee from even minimal neighborhood integration. These practices are sometimes supplemented with harassment and even violence against African Americans who move into white-majority neighborhoods.

Contrary to popular belief among whites, African American preference for living in same-race neighborhoods plays a small role in perpetuating these patterns. For example, one study of representative samples of African Americans from four major American cities (Atlanta, Boston, Detroit, and Los Angeles) found that African Americans overwhelmingly preferred to live in areas split 50-50 between blacks and whites (Krysan & Farley, 2002, p. 949). Finally, the social class and income differences between blacks and whites are also relatively minor factors in perpetuating residential segregation, as the African American middle class is just as likely to be segregated as the African American poor (Stoll, 2004, p. 26).

*School Integration.* In 1954, the year of the landmark Brown desegregation decision, the great majority of African Americans lived in states operating segregated school systems. Compared with white schools, Jim Crow schools were severely underfunded and had fewer qualified teachers, shorter school years, and inadequate physical facilities. Today, 70% of African American children still attend schools with an African American majority, and one third attend schools that are 90% to 100% African American. The pressure from the federal government to integrate the schools has eased over the past several decades, and one recent report found that schools are being resegregated today at the fastest rate since the 1950s. For example, schools in the Southern states actually reached their highest levels of racial integration in the mid-1980s—almost 20 years ago—when 44% of black students attended white majority schools. Since that time, this percentage has drifted downward and reached a low of about 33% in 1998 (Orfield, 2001).

Exhibit 7.7 shows the extent of school segregation (percentage of students attending a majority white school) by race and region for 1991 and 2002. The trends are clear: Across all regions, African Americans are far less likely to attend a majority white school, and the percentage in integrated schools has declined over the 11-year period.

Underlying and complicating the difficulty of school integration is the widespread residential segregation mentioned previously. The challenges for school integration are especially evident in those metropolitan areas, such as Washington, D.C., that consist of a largely black inner city surrounded by largely white rings of suburbs. Even with busing, political boundaries would have to be crossed before the school systems could be substantially integrated. Without a renewed commitment to integration, American schools will continue to resegregate. This is a particularly ominous trend, because it directly affects the quality of education. For example, years of research demonstrate that the integration of schools—by social class as well as by race—is related to improved test scores (Orfield, 2001).

In terms of the quantity of education, the gap between whites and blacks has generally decreased over the century. Exhibit 7.8 displays the percentage of the population over 25 years old, by race and sex, who have high school diplomas. It clearly shows a shrinking (though still noticeable) racial gap in education. Part of the remaining difference in educational attainment is due to social class factors. For example, African American students are more likely to drop out of high school. Research has shown that "students are more likely to drop out . . . when they get poor grades, are older than their classmates, come from a single-parent family, have parents who dropped out . . . or live in a central city" (O'Hare, Pollard, Mann, & Kent, 1991, p. 21). On the average, African American students are more exposed to these risk factors than are white students. When the effects of social class background are taken into account, differences in dropout rates nearly disappear (O'Hare et al., 1991, p. 21).

At the college level, the trends somewhat parallel the narrowing gap in levels of high school education, as shown in Exhibit 7.9. For example, in 1960, white males were about 3½ times more likely to have a college degree than were African American males. By 2002, the advantage of white males had shrunk to a factor of less than 2. These racial differences are larger with more advanced degrees, however, and differences such as these will be increasingly

**EXHIBIT 7.7** School Integration by Race, 1991 and 2002: Percentage of Students in Majority White Schools

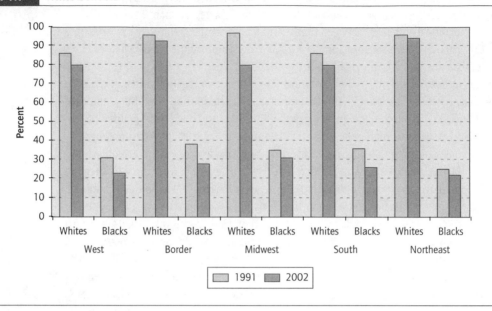

SOURCE: Lee (2004).

**EXHIBIT 7.8** Percentage of Persons 25 Years of Age and Older Completing High School by Sex and Race, 1960-2003

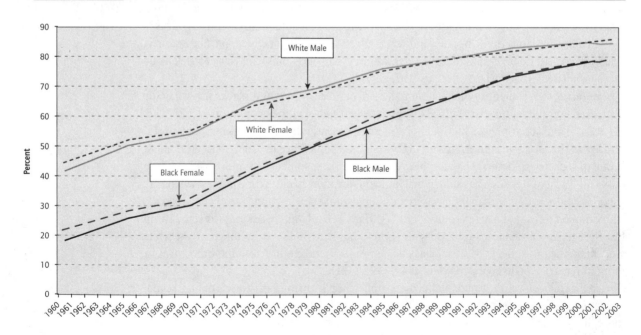

SOURCE: U.S. Bureau of the Census (2005), p. 141.

EXHIBIT 7.9

Percentage of Persons 25 Years Old and Older With College Degree, 1960-2003

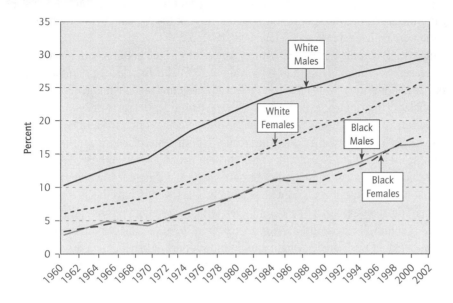

SOURCE: U.S. Bureau of the Census (2005), p. 141.

serious in an economy in which jobs increasingly require an education beyond high school (Pollard & O'Hare, 1999, p. 30).

*Political Power.* Two trends have increased the political power of African Americans since World War II. One is the movement out of the rural South, a process that concentrated African Americans in areas in which it was easier to get people registered to vote. The first African American representative to the U.S. Congress (other than those elected during Reconstruction) was elected in 1928. By 1954, there were still only three African American members in the House of Representatives (Franklin, 1967, p. 614), and in 2003, there were 39, about 9% of the total (U.S. Bureau of the Census, 2005, p. 250). In 2004, Barak Obama was elected to the U.S. Senate from the State of Illinois, the third African American senator since Reconstruction (the other two were Edward Brooke, R-Massachusetts, who served 2 terms beginning in 1967, and Carol Mosely-Braun, D-Illinois, who served one term beginning in 1993).

The number of African American elected officials at all levels of government increased from virtually zero at the turn of the century to more than 9000 in 2001 (U.S. Bureau of the Census, 2005, p. 255). In Virginia in 1989, Douglas Wilder became the first African American to be elected to a state governorship, and both Colin Powell and Condoleezza Rice have served as secretary of state, the highest governmental office—along with Supreme Court justice—ever held by African Americans.

African American communities are virtually guaranteed some political representation by their high degree of geographical concentration at the local level. Today, most large American cities, including Los Angeles, Chicago, Atlanta, New York, and Washington, D.C., have elected African American mayors.

The other trend is the dismantling of the institutions and practices that disenfranchised Southern blacks during Jim Crow segregation (see chapter 6). In particular, the Voting

Rights Act of 1965 specifically prohibited many of the practices (poll taxes, literacy tests, and whites-only primaries) traditionally used to keep African Americans politically powerless. The effect of these repressive policies can be seen in the fact that as late as 1962, only 5% of the African American population of Mississippi and 13% of the African American population of Alabama were registered to vote (O'Hare et al., 1991, p. 33).

Since the 1960s, the number of African Americans in the nation's voting age population has increased from slightly less than 10% to about 13%. This increasing potential for political power was not fully mobilized in the past, however, and actual turnout has generally been much lower for blacks than for whites. In the hotly contested presidential races of 2000 and 2004, however, a variety of organizations (such as the NAACP) made a concerted and largely successful effort to increase turnout for African Americans. In both years, black turnout was comparable to that of whites. In 2000, for example, black turnout nationally was only 3% lower than white turnout and, in the view of many, might have made the difference in the razor-close race in Florida had the votes been counted differently. Black voters have been a very important constituent for the Democratic Party and, even with low turnout, figured prominently in the elections of John F. Kennedy in 1960, Jimmy Carter in 1976, and Bill Clinton in 1992 and 1996. In 2004, President Bush made a slight gain in the support of black voters for the Republican Party, and African Americans may perhaps amplify their political power if the rivalry between the parties for this small but potentially crucial vote increases.

*Jobs and Income.* Integration in the job market and racial equality in income follow the trends established in other areas of social life: The situation of African Americans has improved since the end of de jure segregation but has stopped well short of equality. Exhibits 7.10a and 7.10b show the differences in occupation by race and sex. White males are much more likely to be employed in the highest rated occupational area, whereas black males are overrepresented in the service sector and in unskilled labor. Neither black nor white males are likely to be employed in agriculture, a reflection of continuing industrialization and mechanization. Although huge gaps remain, we should also note that the present occupational distribution represents a rapid and significant upgrading, given the fact that as recently as the 1930s, the majority of African American males were unskilled agricultural laborers (Steinberg, 1981, pp. 206-207).

A similar improvement has occurred for African American females. In the 1930s, about 90% of employed African American women worked in agriculture or in domestic service (Steinberg, 1981, pp. 206-207). The percentage of African American women in these categories has dropped dramatically, and the majority of African American females is employed in the two highest occupational categories, although typically at the lower levels of these categories. For example, in the "managerial and professional" category, women are more likely to be concentrated in less-well-paid occupations, such as nurse or elementary school teacher (see Exhibit 6.5), whereas men are more likely to be physicians and lawyers.

Unemployment has been at least twice as high for blacks as for whites since the 1940s. Unemployment rates vary by sex and by age, and African American males frequently have higher unemployment rates than do African American females. Among white Americans, females have always had a higher unemployment rate. The reasons for greater unemployment among African Americans are various and complex. As we have seen, lower levels of education and concentration in the job-poor center cities play a part. So, too, does lower seniority (because integration is so recent, African American workers have less seniority and are more often the victims of the "last hired, first fired" pattern) and the concentration of African Americans in positions more likely to become obsolete in a developing economy. At the core of these patterns of

EXHIBIT 7.10a Differences in Occupation by Race, 2000: Males

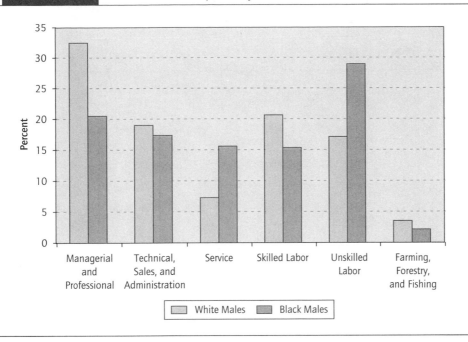

White Males    Black Males

EXHIBIT 7.10b Differences in Occupation by Race, 2000: Females

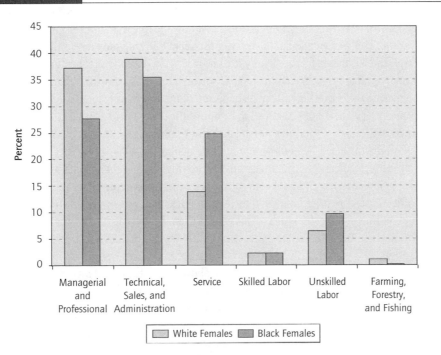

White Females    Black Females

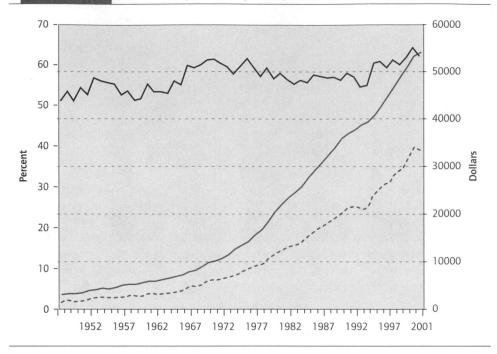

unemployment and disadvantage, however, are discrimination, both individual and institutional, and the continuing presence of prejudice and racism (Feagin, 2001, pp. 159-166).

The differences in education and jobs are reflected in a persistent racial income gap, as shown in Exhibit 7.11. In 1947, African American median family income was about 51% of white median family income. This percentage fluctuated over the years but gradually rose and reached a high point of 64% in 2000 before falling slightly to 62% in 2001. In the early 21st century, after 50 years of tumultuous change, African American family income remains far below white family income.

Also, as we saw in Exhibit 7.3, the distribution of income is affected by sex as well as race, and African American females continue to be one of the lowest paid groups in the society. Also as we noted earlier, when total net worth (including savings, stocks, real estate, etc.) is taken into account, the racial gap widens dramatically (Kochlar, 2004).

Finally, poverty affects African Americans at much higher rates than it does white Americans. Exhibit 7.12 shows the percentage of white and black Americans living below the federally established, "official" poverty level from 1970 through 2003. The poverty rate for African Americans runs about 3 times greater than the rate for whites, even though the rate for both groups trends down. For example, in 1970, African American poverty was more than 3.3 times the rate of white poverty (about 33% vs. 10%). By 2003, fewer families of both races were living in poverty (about 22% for blacks and 8% for whites), but the racial differential was still almost 3 times greater poverty for African American families. Tragically, although they are also declining, the highest rates of poverty continue to be found among children, especially African American children.

**Primary Structural Assimilation.** Interracial contact in the more public areas of society, such as schools or the workplace, is certainly more common today, and as Gordon's model of

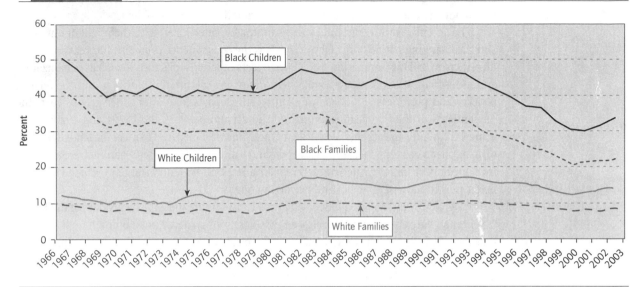

assimilation predicts, this has led to increases in more intimate contacts across racial lines. For example, the percentage of African Americans who say they have "good friends" who are white increased from 21% in 1975 to 78% in 1994. Comparable increases have occurred for whites: In 1975, only 9% said they had "good friends" who were black, and that percentage rose to 73% in 1995 (Thernstrom & Thernstrom, 1997, p. 521). More recent figures from a comparably worded survey question show that 82% of whites and 88% of African Americans claim to have friends "not of their own race" (Mazzuca, 2004). These figures are from public opinion polls, and they may very well exaggerate the actual number of interracial friendships (see Lach, 2000). Nonetheless, they document an increase in integration at the primary level. On the other hand, further increases in this area are limited by continuing structural pluralism and separate black and white institutional and organizational structures.

Interracial marriages are increasing in number but still make up a tiny percentage of all marriages. According to the U.S. Bureau of the Census (2002), there were 65,000 black-white married couples in 1970 (including persons of Hispanic origin), about .1 of 1% of all married couples. By 2003, the number of black-white married couples had increased more than sixfold, to 416,000, but this is still only about .7 of 1% of all married couples (U.S. Bureau of the Census, 2005, p. 50).

## IS THE GLASS HALF EMPTY OR HALF FULL?

The contemporary situation of African Americans is perhaps what might be expected for a group so recently "released" from exclusion and subordination. The average situation of African Americans improved vastly during the latter half of the 20th century in virtually every area of social life. As demonstrated by the data presented in this chapter, however, racial progress stopped well short of equality. In assessing the present situation, one might stress the improved situation of the group (the glass is half full) or the challenges that remain before full racial equality and justice are achieved (the glass is half empty). Perhaps the most reasonable approach is to recognize that in many ways, the overall picture of racial progress is "different" rather than "better" and that a large percentage of the African American population has traded rural peasantry for urban poverty and faces an array of formidable and deep-rooted problems.

The situation of African Americans is intimately intermixed with the plight of our cities and the changing nature of the labor force. It is the consequence of nearly 400 years of prejudice, racism, and discrimination, but it also reflects broader social forces, such as urbanization and industrialization. Consistent with their origin as a colonized minority group, the relative poverty and powerlessness of African Americans persists long after other groups (e.g., the descendents of the European immigrants who arrived between the 1820s and 1920s) have achieved equality and acceptance. African Americans were enslaved to meet the labor demands of an agrarian economy, became a rural peasantry under Jim Crow segregation, were excluded from the opportunities created by early industrialization, and remain largely excluded from the better jobs in the emerging postindustrial economy.

Progress toward racial equality has slowed considerably since the heady days of the 1960s, and in many areas, earlier advances seem hopelessly stagnated. Public opinion polls indicate that there is little support or sympathy for the cause of African Americans (see Chapter 4). Traditional prejudice has declined, only to be replaced by modern racism. In the court of public opinion, African Americans are often held responsible for their own plight. Biological racism has been replaced by indifference to racial issues or by blaming the victims.

Of course, in acknowledging the challenges that remain, we should not downplay the real improvements that have been made in the lives of African Americans. Compared with the days of Jim Crow, African Americans are on the average more prosperous and more politically powerful, and some are among the most revered of current popular heroes (the glass is half full). However, the increases in average income and education and the glittering success of the few obscures a tangle of problems for the many, problems that may well grow worse as America moves further into the postindustrial era. Poverty, unemployment, a failing educational system, residential segregation, racism, discrimination, and prejudice continue to be inescapable realities for millions of African Americans. In many African American neighborhoods, crime, drugs, violence, poor health care, malnutrition, and a host of other factors compound these problems (the glass is half empty).

Given this gloomy situation, it should not be surprising to find significant strength in pluralistic, nationalistic thinking, as well as resentment and anger in the African American community. Black nationalism and black power remain powerful ideas, but their goals of development and autonomy for the African American community remain largely rhetorical sloganeering without the resources to bring them to actualization.

The situation of the African American community in the early days of the 21st century might be characterized as structural pluralism combined with inequality. The former characterization testifies to the failure of assimilation and the latter to the continuing effects, in the present, of a colonized origin. The problems that remain are less visible (or perhaps just better hidden from the average white middle-class American) than those of previous eras. Responsibility is more diffused, the moral certainties of opposition to slavery or to Jim Crow laws are long gone, and contemporary racial issues must be articulated and debated in an environment of subtle prejudice and low levels of sympathy for the grievances of African Americans. Urban poverty, modern institutional discrimination, and modern racism are less dramatic and more difficult to measure than an overseer's whip, a lynch mob, or a sign that says "Whites Only," but they can be just as real and just as deadly in their consequences.

## Reparations

*Should African Americans be compensated for the losses they suffered as a result of their kidnapping from Africa, their centuries of slavery, and their continuing oppression under de jure segregation? What, if anything, does American society owe for the centuries of uncompensated labor performed by African Americans and the oppression and coerced inequality of the Jim Crow era? Should present-day Americans be held accountable for the actions of their ancestors? What about the families and businesses that grew rich from the labor of African Americans (and other minorities) in the past? To what extent are they responsible for the continuing racial gaps in income and wealth documented in this chapter?*

*The idea that America owes reparations to African Americans is not new but has been gaining momentum in recent years (Smith, 2001). The movement has been spurred by a best-selling book (Robinson, 2001), and in March 2002, a reparations lawsuit was filed against several large U.S. corporations, including the Aetna insurance company, alleging that they had profited from slave labor. Also, the issue promises to receive a great deal of attention on college campuses, in part as a serious issue worthy of discussion and in part as a focus of activism, as students question the relationship between their schools' endowment and slavery.*

*In the excerpts below, Manning Marable (2001) and John McWhorter (2001) present some of the central arguments for and against reparations. Both men are prominent African American academics.*

### Reparations Are an Idea Whose Time Has Come

**MANNING MARABLE**

In 1854 my great-grandfather, Morris Marable, was sold on an auction block in Georgia for $500. For his white slave master, the sale was just "business as usual." But to Morris Marable and his heirs, slavery was a crime against our humanity. This pattern of human-rights violations against enslaved African Americans continued under Jim Crow segregation for nearly another century.

The fundamental problem of American democracy in the 21st century is the problem of "structural racism": the deep patterns of socioeconomic inequality and accumulated disadvantage that are coded by race, and constantly justified in public discourse by both racist stereotypes and white indifference. Do Americans have the capacity and vision to dismantle these structural barriers that deny democratic rights and opportunities to millions of their fellow citizens?

This country has previously witnessed two great struggles to achieve a truly multicultural democracy. The First Reconstruction (1865-1877) . . . briefly gave black men voting rights, but gave no meaningful compensation for two centuries of unpaid labor. The promise of "40 acres and a mule" was for most blacks a dream deferred.

The Second Reconstruction (1954-1968), or the modern civil-rights movement, outlawed legal segregation in public accommodations and gave blacks voting rights. But these successes paradoxically obscure the tremendous human costs of historically accumulated disadvantage that remain central to black Americans' lives.

The disproportionate wealth that most whites enjoy today was first constructed from centuries of unpaid black labor. Many white institutions, including Ivy League universities, insurance companies and banks, profited from slavery. This pattern of white privilege and black inequality continues today.

Demanding reparations is not just about compensation for slavery and segregation. It is, more important, an educational campaign to highlight the contemporary reality of "racial deficits" of all kinds, the unequal conditions that impact blacks regardless of class. Structural racism's barriers include "equity inequity," the absence of black capital formation that is a direct consequence of America's history. One third of all black households actually have negative net wealth. In 1998 the typical black family's net wealth was $16,400, less than one fifth that of white families. Black families are denied home loans at twice the rate of whites.

Blacks remain the last hired and first fired during recessions. During the 1990-91 recession, African Americans suffered disproportionately. At Coca-Cola, 42 percent of employees who lost their jobs were black. At Sears, 54 percent were black. Blacks have significantly shorter life expectancies, in part due to racism in the health establishment. Blacks are statistically less likely than whites to be referred for kidney transplants or early-stage cancer surgery.

In criminal justice, African Americans constitute only one seventh of all drug users. Yet we account for 35 percent of all drug arrests, 55 percent of drug convictions and 75 percent of prison admissions for drug offenses. . . .

White Americans today aren't guilty of carrying out slavery and segregation. But whites have a moral and political responsibility to acknowledge the continuing burden of history's structural racism.

A reparations trust fund could be established, with the goal of closing the socioeconomic gaps between blacks and whites. Funds would be targeted specifically toward poor, disadvantaged communities with the greatest need, not to individuals.

Let's eliminate the racial unfairness in capital markets that perpetuates black poverty. A national commitment to expand black homeownership, full employment and quality health care would benefit all Americans, regardless of race.

Reparations could begin America's Third Reconstruction, the final chapter in the 400-year struggle to abolish slavery and its destructive consequences. As Malcolm X said in 1961, hundreds of years of racism and labor exploitation are "worth more than a cup of coffee at a white cafe. We are here to collect back wages."

SOURCE: Marable, Manning. August 27, 2001. "An Idea Whose Time Has Come. . . . Whites Have an Obligation to Recognize Slavery's Legacy." Newsweek, p. 22.

## Why I Don't Want Reparations for Slavery

### JOHN MCWHORTER

My childhood was a typical one for a black American in his mid-thirties. I grew up middle class in a quiet, safe neighborhood in Philadelphia. [My] mother taught social work at Temple University and my father was a student activities administrator there. My parents were far from wealthy, . . . but I had everything I needed plus some extras. . . .

Contrary to popular belief, I was by no means extraordinarily "lucky" or "unusual" among black Americans of the post-Civil Rights era. . . . today, there are legions of black adults in the United States who grew up as I did. As a child, I never had trouble finding black peers, and as an adult, meeting black people with life histories like mine requires no searching. In short, in our moment, black success is a norm. Less than one in four black families now live below the poverty line, and the black underclass is at most one out of five blacks. This is what the Civil Rights revolution helped make possible, and I grew up exhilarated at belonging to a race that had made such progress in the face of many obstacles.

Yet today, numerous black officials tell the public that lives like mine are statistical noise, that the overriding situation for blacks is one of penury, dismissal, and spiritual desperation. Under this analysis, the blood of slavery remains on the hands of mainstream America until it allocates a large sum of money to "repair" the . . . damage done to our race over four centuries. . . .

The shorthand version of the reparations idea is that living blacks are "owed" the money that our slave ancestors were denied for their unpaid servitude. But few black Americans even know the names or life stories of their slave ancestors; almost none of us have pictures or keepsakes from that far back. . . . Yes, my slave ancestors were "blood" to me; yes, what was done to them was unthinkable. But the 150 years between me and them has rendered our tie little more than biological. Paying anyone for the suffering of long-dead strangers . . . would be more a matter of blood money than "reparation." . . .

Perhaps recognizing this, the reparations movement is now drifting away from the "back salary" argument to justifications emphasizing the effects of slavery since Emancipation. It is said blacks deserve payment for residual echoes of their earlier disenfranchisement and segregation. This justification, however, is predicated upon the misconception that in 2001, most blacks are "struggling."

This view denies the stunning success that the race has achieved over the past 40 years. It persists because many Americans, black and white, have accepted the leftist notion which arose in the mid-1960s that blacks are primarily victims in this country, that racism and structural injustice hobble all but a few individual blacks. Based on emotion, victimologist thought ignores the facts of contemporary black success and progress, because they do not square with the "blame game."

Reparations cannot logically rely on a depiction of black Americans as a race still reeling from the brutal experience of slavery and its after effects. The reality is that, by any estimation, in the year 2001 there are more middle-class blacks than poor ones. The large majority of black Americans, while surely not immune to the slings and arrows of the eternal injustices of life on earth, are now leading dignified lives as new variations on what it means to be American. . . .

Any effort to repair problems in black America must focus on helping people to help themselves. Funds must be devoted to ushering welfare mothers into working for a living, so that their children do not grow up learning that employment is something "other people" do. Inner city communities should be helped to rebuild themselves, in part through making it easier for residents to buy their homes. Police forces ought to be trained to avoid brutality, which turns young blacks against the mainstream today, and to work with, rather than against, the communities they serve.

Finally, this country must support all possible efforts to liberate black children from the soul-extinguishing influence of ossified urban public schools, and to move them into experimental or all-minority schools where a culture of competition is fostered. This will help undo the sense that intellectual excellence is a "white" endeavor. Surely we must improve the public schools as well, including increasing the exposure of young black children to standardized tests. But we also must make sure another generation of black children are not lost during the years it will take for these schools to get their acts together. . . .

Ultimately, a race shows its worth not by how much charity it can extract from others, but in how well it can do in the absence of charity. Black America has elicited more charity from its former oppressors than any race in human history—justifiably in my view. However, this can only serve as a spark—the real work is now ours.

SOURCE: McWhorter, John. 2001. "Blood Money, An Analysis of Slavery Reparations." American Enterprise, 12: 18.

## Debate Questions to Consider

1. Do Marable's points agree with the analysis of racial income and wealth differentials presented in this chapter? How? Cite specific points of agreement. Marable says that whites share responsibility for the "continuing burden of history's structural racism." Evaluate this argument in light of the racial gaps documented in this chapter and the analysis of slavery and segregation presented in chapters 5 and 6.

2. Does McWhorter's assessment of African American success make sense in terms of the data presented in this chapter? Is he seeing the glass half full and ignoring the problems that remain? Is he a modern racist? He advocates programs of improvement (workfare, schools, etc.). How are these different from "reparations?"

3. Consider Marable's point that the reparations issue can be used as an educational tool. Could the campaign for reparations be used to counteract modern racism or white indifference? How?

# MAIN POINTS

- At the beginning of the 20th century, the racial oppression of African Americans took the form of a rigid competitive system of group relations, de jure segregation. This system ended because of changing economic and political conditions, changing legal precedents, and a mass movement of protest initiated by African Americans.

- The U.S. Supreme Court decision in *Brown v. Board of Education of Topeka* (1954) was the single most powerful blow struck against legalized segregation. A nonviolent direct action campaign was launched in the South to challenge and defeat segregation. The U.S. Congress delivered the final blows to de jure segregation in the 1964 Civil Rights Act and the 1965 Voting Rights Act.

- Outside the South, the concerns of the African American community had centered on access to schooling, jobs, housing, health care, and other opportunities. African Americans' frustration and anger were expressed in the urban riots in the 1960s. The Black Power movement addressed the massive problems of racial inequality remaining after the victories of the Civil Rights movement.

- Black-white relations since the 1960s have been characterized by continuing inequality, separation, and hostility, along with substantial improvements in status for some African Americans. Class differentiation within the African American community is greater than ever before.

- The African American family has been perceived as weak, unstable, and a cause of continuing poverty. Culture of poverty theory attributes poverty to certain characteristics of the poor. An alternative view sees problems such as high rates of family desertion by men as the result of poverty rather than the cause.

- Antiblack prejudice and discrimination are manifested in more subtle, covert forms (modern racism and institutional discrimination) in contemporary society.

- African Americans are largely acculturated, but centuries of separate development have created a unique black experience in American society.

- Despite real improvements in their status, the overall secondary structural assimilation of African Americans remains low. Evidence of racial inequalities in residence, schooling, politics, jobs, income, unemployment, and poverty is massive and underlines the realities of the urban underclass.

- In the area of primary structural assimilation, interracial interaction and friendships appear to be rising. Interracial marriages are increasing, although they remain a tiny percentage of all marriages.

- Compared with their situation at the start of the 20th century, African Americans have made considerable improvements in quality of life. The distance to true racial equality remains enormous.

- As suggested by the Blauner hypothesis, the legacy of racial inequality extens far beyond the matters of income, occupation, and poverty documented in this chapter. Public sociology Assignment 2 on pages 220–221 will permit you to document racial inequalities in health in your area. Are these comparable in magnitude to the racial inequalities documented in this chapter?

## Study Site on the Web

Don't forget the interactive quizzes and other resources and learning aids at www.www.pineforge.com/healeystudy4.

## For Further Reading

Feagin, Joe. 2001. *Racist America: Roots, Current Realities, and Future Reparations.* New York: Routledge.

Hacker, Andrew. 1992. *Two Nations: Black and White, Separate, Hostile, and Unequal.* New York: Scribner's. *(Two very readable overviews of contemporary race relations.)*

Massey, Douglas, & Denton, Nancy. 1993. *American Apartheid: Segregation and the Making of the Underclass.* Cambridge, MA: Harvard University Press. *(The authors argue powerfully that residential segregation is the key to understanding urban black poverty.)*

Morris, Aldon D. 1984. *The Origins of the Civil Rights Movement.* New York: Free Press. *(An indispensable source.)*

Thernstrom, Stephan, & Thernstrom, Abigail. 1997. *America in Black and White.* New York: Simon & Schuster. *(A comprehensive review of American race relations.)*

Smelser, N., Wilson, W., & Mitchell, F. (Eds.). 2001. *America Becoming: Racial Trends and Their Consequences.* Washington, DC: National Academy Press. *(A two-volume collection of articles by leading scholars that presents a comprehensive analysis of black-white relations in America.)*

Williams, Juan. 1987. *Eyes on the Prize: America's Civil Rights Years 1954-1965.* New York: Penguin. *(Commentaries and accounts. See also the acclaimed television documentary of the same name.)*

## Questions for Review and Study

1. What forces led to the end of de jure segregation? To what extent was this change a result of broad social forces (e.g., industrialization), and to what extent was it the result of the actions of African Americans acting against the system (e.g., the Southern Civil Rights movement)? By the 1960s and 1970s, how had the movement for racial change succeeded, and what issues were left unresolved? What issues remain unresolved today?

2. What are the differences between de jure segregation and de facto segregation? What are the implications of these differences for movements to change these systems? That is, how must movements against de facto segregation differ from movements against de jure segregation in terms of tactics and strategies?

3. Describe the differences between the Southern Civil Rights movement and the Black Power movement. Why did these differences exist? Do these movements remain relevant today? How?

4. How does gender affect contemporary black-white relations and the African American protest movement? Is it true that African American women are a "minority group within a minority group?" How?

5. What are the implications of increasing class differentials among African Americans? Does the greater affluence of middle-class blacks mean that they are no longer a part of a minority group? Will future protests by African Americans be confined only to working-class and lower-class blacks?

6. Regarding contemporary black-white relations, is the glass half empty or half full? Considering the totality of evidence presented in this chapter, with which of the following statements would you agree? Why? (1) American race relations are the best they've ever been; racial equality has been essentially achieved (even though some problems remain). (2) American race relations have a long way to go before society achieves true racial equality.

## Internet Research Project

Additional information and a list of relevant Web sites are included in the Appendix (Internet Resources).

In the year 2000, a team of reporters from the New York Times conducted a year-long investigation of how black-white relations are being lived out by ordinary people in churches, schools, neighborhoods, and other venues. A series of 15 articles detailing and analyzing these experiences were published, and all are available online at http://www.nytimes.com/library/national/race/. Read at least three or four of these stories and analyze them in terms of the concepts and conclusions presented in this chapter. What do these stories imply about black-white inequality, prejudice, discrimination, assimilation, pluralism, and racial separation? Is the glass half empty or half full?

**Notes**

1. Wilkerson (2002), p. 144.
2. Charles defines the index of dissimilarity as "the percentage of either group that would have to move to another tract in order to achieve within-tract population distributions that mirrored that of the metropolitan region" (Charles, 2003, p. 170).

# American Indians

## From Conquest to Tribal
## Survival in a Postindustrial Society

THE CONTACT PERIOD FOR AMERICAN INDIANS BEGAN IN EARLIEST COLONIAL DAYS AND LASTED nearly 300 years, ending only with the final battles of the Indian Wars in the late 1800s. The Indian nations fought for their land and to preserve their cultures and ways of life. The tribes had enough power to win many battles, but they eventually lost all the wars. The superior resources and power of the burgeoning white society made the eventual defeat of American Indians inevitable, and by 1890, the last of the tribes had been conquered, their leaders had been killed or were in custody, and their people were living on government-controlled reservations.

At the dawn of the 20th century, American Indians were, in Blauner's (1972) terms, a conquered and colonized minority group. Like the slave plantations, the reservations were paternalistic systems that controlled American Indians with federally mandated regulations and government-appointed Indian agents.

For much of the 20th century, during the days of Jim Crow segregation and while industrialization and urbanization transformed the situations of other minority groups, American Indians subsisted on the fringes of development and change, marginalized, relatively powerless, and isolated. Their relationship with the larger society changed and in some ways improved, especially in the most recent decades. Compared with other minority groups, however, their links with the larger society remained weaker, and they were less affected by its economic and social evolution.

At the dawn of the 21st century, American Indians remain among the most disadvantaged, poorest, and most isolated of minority groups. Their present status reflects the long, bitter competition with the dominant group, their colonized origins, and their lengthy exclusion from mainstream society. As we shall see, however, the group is not without resources and strategies for improving their situation.

# AMERICAN INDIAN CULTURES

The dynamics of American Indian and Anglo-American relationships have been shaped by the vast differences in culture, values, and norms between the two groups. These differences have hampered communication in the past and continue to do so in the present. A comprehensive analysis of American Indian cultures is well beyond the scope of this text, but the past experiences and present goals of the group can be appreciated only with some understanding of their views of the world. We must note here, as we did in chapter 5, that there were (and are) hundreds of different tribes in what is now the United States, each with its own language and heritage, and that a complete analysis of American Indian culture would have to take this diversity into account. However, some patterns and cultural characteristics are widely shared across the tribes, and we will concentrate on these similarities.

Perhaps the most obvious difference between American Indian and Western cultures lies in their respective conceptions of the relationship between human beings and the natural world. In the traditional view of many American Indian cultures, the universe is a unity. Humans are simply a part of a larger reality, no different from or more important than other animals, plants, trees, and the earth itself. The goal of many American Indian tribes was to live in harmony with the natural world, not "improve" it or use it for their own selfish purposes, views that differ sharply from Western concepts of development, commercial farming, and bending the natural world to the service of humans. The gap between the two worldviews is evident in the reaction of one American Indian to the idea that his people should become farmers: "You ask me to plow the ground.... Shall I take a knife and tear my mother's bosom? You ask me to cut grass and make hay ... but how dare I cut my mother's hair?" (Brown, 1970, p. 273).

The concept of private property, or the ownership of things, was not prominent in American Indian cultures and was, from the Anglo-American perspective, most notably absent in conceptions of land ownership. The land simply existed, and the notion of owning, selling, or buying it was foreign to American Indians. In the words of Tecumseh, a chief of the Shawnee, a man could no more sell the land than the "sea or the air he breathed" (Josephy, 1968, p. 283).

American Indian cultures and societies also tended to be more oriented toward groups (e.g., the extended family, clan, or tribe) than toward individuals. The interests of the self were subordinated to those of the group, and child-rearing practices strongly encouraged group loyalty (Parke & Buriel, 2002, p. 22). Cooperative, group activities were stressed over those of a competitive, individualistic nature. The bond to the group was (and is) so strong that "students go hungry rather than ask their parents for lunch money, for in asking they would be putting their needs in front of the group's needs" (Locust, 1990, p. 231).

Many American Indian tribes were organized around egalitarian values that stressed the dignity and worth of every man, woman, and child. Virtually all tribes had a division of labor based on gender, but women's work was valued, and they often occupied far more important positions in tribal society than was typical for women in Anglo-American society. In many of the American Indian societies that practiced gardening, women controlled the land. In other tribes, women wielded considerable power and held the most important political and religious offices. Among the Iroquois, for example, a council of older women appointed the chief of the tribe and made decisions about when to wage war (Amott & Matthaei, 1991, pp. 34-35).

These differences in values, compounded by the power differentials that emerged, often placed American Indians at a disadvantage when dealing with the dominant group. The American Indian conception of land ownership and their lack of experience with deeds, titles, contracts, and other Western legal concepts often made it difficult for them to defend their resources from Anglo Americans. At other times, cultural differences led to disruptions of traditional practices, further weakening American Indian societies. For example, Christian missionaries and government representatives tried to reverse the traditional American Indian division of labor in which women were responsible for the gardening. In the Western view, only males did farm work. Also, the military and political representatives of the dominant society usually ignored female tribal leaders and imposed Western notions of patriarchy and male leadership on the tribes (Amott & Matthaei, 1991, p. 39).

## RELATIONS WITH THE FEDERAL GOVERNMENT AFTER THE 1890s

By the end of the Indian Wars in 1890, Americans Indians had few resources with which to defend their self-interest. In addition to being confined to the reservations, the group was scattered throughout the western two thirds of the United States and split by cultural and linguistic differences. Politically, the power of the group was further limited by the facts that the huge majority of American Indians were not U.S. citizens and that most tribes lacked a cultural basis for understanding representative democracy as practiced in the larger society.

Economically, American Indians were among the most impoverished groups in the society. Reservation lands were generally of poor quality, traditional food sources such as buffalo and other game had been destroyed, and traditional hunting grounds and gardening plots had been lost to white farmers and ranchers. The tribes had few means of satisfying even their most basic needs. Many became totally dependent on the federal government for food, shelter, clothing, and other necessities.

Prospects for improvement seemed slim. Most reservations were in remote areas, far from sites of industrialization and modernization, and American Indians had few of the skills (knowledge of English, familiarity with Western work habits and routines) that would have enabled them to compete for a place in the increasingly urban and industrial American society of the early 20th century. Off the reservations, racial prejudice and strong intolerance limited them. On the reservations, they were subjected to policies designed either to maintain their powerlessness and poverty or to force them to Americanize. Either way, the future of American Indians was in serious jeopardy, and their destructive relations with white society continued in peace as they had in war.

## Reservation Life

As would be expected for a conquered and still hostile group, the reservations were intended to closely supervise American Indians and maintain their powerlessness. Relationships with the federal government were paternalistic and featured a variety of policies designed to coercively acculturate the tribes.

**Paternalism and the Bureau of Indian Affairs.** The reservations were run not by the tribes but by an agency of the federal government: the **Bureau of Indian Affairs** (BIA) of the U.S. Department of the Interior. The BIA and its local superintendent controlled virtually all aspects of everyday life, including the reservation budget, the criminal justice system, and the schools. The BIA (again, not the tribes) even determined tribal membership.

The traditional leadership structures and political institutions of the tribes were ignored as the BIA executed its duties with little regard for, and virtually no input from, the people it supervised. The BIA superintendent of the reservations "ordinarily became the most powerful influence on local Indian affairs, even though he was a government employee, not responsible to the Indians but to his superiors in Washington" (Spicer, 1980, p. 117). The superintendent controlled the food supply and communications to the world outside the reservation. This control was used to reward tribal members who cooperated and to punish those who did not.

### Coercive Acculturation: The Dawes Act and Boarding Schools.

Consistent with the Blauner hypothesis, American Indians on the reservations were subjected to coercive acculturation or forced Americanization. Their culture was attacked, their languages and religions were forbidden, and their institutions were circumvented and undermined. The centerpiece of U.S. Indian policy was the Dawes Allotment Act of 1887, a deeply flawed attempt to impose white definitions of land ownership and to transform American Indians into independent farmers by dividing their land among the families of each tribe. The intention of the act was to give each Indian family the means to survive like their white neighbors.

Although the law might seem benevolent in intent (certainly thousands of immigrant families would have been thrilled to own land), it was flawed by a gross lack of understanding of American Indian cultures and needs, and in many ways, it was a direct attack on those cultures. Most American Indian tribes did not have a strong agrarian tradition, and little or nothing was done to prepare the tribes for their transition to peasant yeomanry. More important, American Indians had little or no concept of land as private property, and it was relatively easy for settlers, land speculators, and others to separate Indian families from the land allocated to them by this legislation. By allotting land to families and individuals, the legislation sought to destroy the broader kinship, clan, and tribal social structures and replace them with Western systems that featured individualism and the profit motive (Cornell, 1988, p. 80).

About 140 million acres were allocated to the tribes in 1887. By the 1930s, nearly 90 million of those acres—almost 65%—had been lost. Most of the remaining land was desert or otherwise nonproductive (Wax, 1971, p. 55). From the standpoint of the Indian Nations, the Dawes Allotment Act was a disaster and a further erosion of their already paltry store of resources (for more details, see Josephy, 1968; Lurie, 1982; McNickle, 1973; Wax, 1971).

Coercive acculturation also operated through a variety of other avenues. Whenever possible, the BIA sent American Indian children to boarding schools, sometimes hundreds of miles away from parents and kin, where they were required to speak English, convert to Christianity, and become educated in the ways of Western civilization. Consistent with the Blauner (1972) hypothesis, tribal languages, dress, and religion were forbidden, and to the extent that native cultures were mentioned at all, they were attacked and ridiculed. Children of different tribes were mixed together as roommates to speed the acquisition of English. When school was not in session, children were often boarded with local white families, usually as unpaid domestic helpers or farm hands, and prevented from visiting their families and revitalizing their tribal ties (Hoxie, 1984; Spicer, 1980; Wax, 1971).

American Indians were virtually powerless to change the reservation system or avoid the campaign of acculturation. Nonetheless, they resented and resisted coerced Americanization, and many languages and cultural elements survived the early reservation period, although often in altered form. For example, the traditional tribal religions remained vital through the period despite the fact that by the 1930s, the great majority of Indians had affiliated with one Christian

## Native Americans by *Eric Margolis*

There were three groups who became Americans involuntarily. African Americans were brought to these shores in chains, as individuals, and every attempt was made to strip them of their tribal and family identities. Many Latinos became Americans as a result of the territorial expansion called "Manifest Destiny" which annexed the Southwest and later Puerto Rico to the growing nation. Wars to displace Native Americans began with the first colonists, and any discussion of Indians must begin with the

recognition that they became Americans as a conquered people. Thus, each of these groups were subjected to different processes of "Americanization." While African captives were denied access to schools, and in the South it was illegal to teach them to read and write, Native Americans were subjected to a specific regime of schooling that was designed to strip them of their Indian culture. As early as the 1630s the Puritan colony in what is present-day Boston accompanied military conquest with attempts to school and Christianize the Indians. Missionary John Elliot helped create a government commission that allocated land to establish "Praying Villages" to segregate Christianized Indians from the rest. Initial attempts to school and Christianize Native Americans were sporadic and often overshadowed by warfare, genocide, and relocation. But as the Indian wars in the West came to an end in the 19th century, Indian re-education became a mainstay of American policy.

The Carlisle Indian School was established in 1879 by ex-Indian fighter captain Richard Pratt who believed that "The Indian must die as an Indian and live as a man." Like many other Anglo Americans, Pratt

viewed tribal societies as "communistic," "indolent," "dirty," and "ignorant," contrasting with western civilization, which he characterized as "virile," "peaceable," "industrious," and "individualistic." Pratt articulated a systematic program of cultural extinction; he believed in subjecting Native American youth to quasi-military discipline—uniforms and drill exercises alongside instruction in English and industrial training. Half of the day was devoted to labor, designed to instill industrial discipline in people thought to be naturally lazy. Sports and regimented band practice were likewise part of the Indian School regime. From humble beginnings in Carlisle, Pennsylvania, Indian Schools evolved into the only system of *federal* schools the United States has ever developed. By 1890, nineteen large Indian boarding schools were in operation. Although there is no accurate count of the number of students, some estimates suggest nearly eighteen thousand in 1900. In addition to Carlisle, major institutions included: Albuquerque, New Mexico; Flandreau, South Dakota; Chemawa, Oregon; Haskell, Kansas; Mt. Pleasant, Michigan; Riverside, California; and Phoenix, Arizona.[1]

Indian schools and students were frequently photographed for purposes of documentation, and preserved as official records. Carlisle students were photographed individually and in groups when they arrived from the reservation in native dress. They were re-photographed after they had lived in cloudy Pennsylvania long enough to have lost their sun tan, and they had been "scrubbed," had their hair cut, and were dressed in military uniform. These "before and after" photos reinforced the Anglo viewers' perception that a "civilizing process" was taking place. Pratt consciously employed these paired portraits to

demonstrate the change from "Indian" to "man," from barbarism to civilization; he intended "Transformation of the body (to stand) for transformation of the soul." The photo of Chiricahua Apaches at the bottom of page 265, contrasted with that shown here, lower right, is indicative of this effort.

The Indian schools practiced harsh punishment to strip students of their Indian identity. Students were punished if they spoke their own languages; many schools used jails to lock up runaways; they also promoted older children to "officer" rank and allowed them to administer punishment. Whips were used to punish students. In the 1920s a national outcry arose to reform the Indian schools. Corporal punishment and jails were prohibited in 1929, and the boarding schools began to change in the 1930s during the Roosevelt administration. A controversial social worker, John Collier Sr., was appointed Indian Commissioner and began a "New Deal" for the American Indian. Collier set out to end the land allotment process that was breaking up the reservations, and to restore economic and cultural control to the tribes. The Indian Reorganization Act of 1934 ended the Dawes General Allotment Act of 1887, which had sought to privatize Indian lands.

The Johnson-O'Malley Act of that same year provided federal assistance to public schools to educate Indian children, and created a revenue source to cover the fact that Indian lands did not generate property taxes which are the basis for school finance in the United States. Slowly and in fits and starts boarding schools began to move away from military discipline and forced acculturation toward self determination. Native arts and crafts were taught, and some ceremonies were allowed on school grounds[2].

In 1966 the Rough Rock Demonstration school was begun on the Navajo Reservation. It became the model for many other tribally run schools. It taught reverence for Navajo ways along with a typical grade school curriculum of English and mathematics skills.

## Notes

1. Malmsheimer, L. M. (1985). Imitation white man: Images of transformation at the Carlisle Indian School. *Studies in Visual Communication, 11*(4), 56, 59, 66n. See also Margolis, E. & J. Rowe (2003). Images of assimilation: Photographs of Indian schools in Arizona. *History of Education 32*(6), 629-660. There is an excellent documentary on the Indian Boarding schools called "In the White Man's Image" Lesiak, C. A. M. J. (1991). *In the white man's image: An episode of the PBS series* The American Experience, PBS Video. The Denver public Library Photograph Collection can be searched at http://www.photoswest.org/

2. Margolis, E. (2004). Looking at discipline, Looking at labor: Photographic representations of Indian boarding schools. *Visual Studies 19*(1).

## Civilize Them With a Stick

*In recent decades, boarding schools for American Indian children have been much improved. Facilities have been modernized and faculties upgraded. The curriculum has been updated and often includes elements of American Indian culture and language. Still, it was not that long ago that coercive acculturation at its worst was the daily routine.*

*In the following passage, Mary Crow Dog, a member of the Sioux tribe who became deeply involved in the Red Power movement that began in the 1960s, recalls some of the horrors of her experiences at a reservation boarding school. As you read her words, keep in mind that she was born in 1955 and started school in the early 1960s, just a generation or two ago.*

### LAKOTA WOMAN

**Mary Crow Dog**

It is almost impossible to explain to a sympathetic white person what a typical old Indian boarding school was like; how it affected the Indian child suddenly dumped into it like a small creature from another world, helpless, defenseless, bewildered, trying desperately to survive and sometimes not surviving at all. Even now, when these schools are so much improved, when . . . the teachers [are] well-intentioned, even trained in child psychology—unfortunately the psychology of white children, which is different from ours—the shock to the child upon arrival is still tremendous. . . .

In the traditional Sioux family, the child is never left alone. It is always surrounded by relatives, carried around, enveloped in warmth. It is treated with the respect due to any human being, even a small one. It is seldom forced to do anything against its will, seldom screamed at, and never beaten. . . . And then suddenly a bus or car arrives full of strangers, who yank the child out of the arms of those who love it, taking it screaming to the boarding school. The only word I can think of for what is done to these children is kidnapping. . . .

The mission school at St. Francis was a curse for our family for generations. My grandmother went there, then my mother, then my sisters and I. At one time or another, every one of us tried to run away. Grandma told me about the bad times she experienced at St. Francis. In those days they let students go home only for one week every year. Two days were used up for transportation, which meant spending just five days out of every 365 with her family. . . . My mother had much the same experiences but never wanted to talk about them, and then there was I, in the same place. . . . Nothing had changed since my grandmother's days. I have been told that even in the '70s they were still beating children at that school. All I got out of school was being taught how to pray. I learned quickly that I would be beaten if I failed in my devotions or, God forbid, prayed the wrong way, especially prayed in Indian to Wakan Tanka, the Indian creator....

My classroom was right next to the principal's office and almost every day I could hear him swatting the boys. Beating was the common punishment for not doing one's homework, or for being late to school. It had such a bad effect upon me that I hated and mistrusted every white person on sight, because I met only one kind. It was not until much later that I met sincere white people I could relate to and be friends with. Racism breeds racism in reverse.

SOURCE: Crow Dog, Mary. 1990. *Lakota Woman.* New York: HarperCollins. Pp. 28-34.

faith or another. Furthermore, many new religions were founded, some combining Christian and traditional elements (Spicer, 1980, p. 118).

## The Indian Reorganization Act

By the 1930s, the failure of the reservation system and the policy of forced assimilation had become obvious to all who cared to observe. The quality of life for American Indians had not improved, and there was little economic development and fewer job opportunities on the reservations. Health care was woefully inadequate, and education levels lagged far behind national standards.

The plight of American Indians eventually found a sympathetic ear in the administration of Franklin D. Roosevelt, who was elected president in 1932, and John Collier, the man he appointed to run the Bureau of Indian Affairs. Collier was knowledgeable about American Indian issues and concerns and was instrumental in securing the passage of the **Indian Reorganization Act (IRA)** in 1934.

This landmark legislation contained a number of significant provisions for American Indians and broke sharply with the federal policies of the past. In particular, the IRA rescinded the Dawes Act of 1887 and the policy of individualizing tribal lands. It also provided means by which the tribes could expand their landholdings. Many of the mechanisms of coercive Americanization in the school system and elsewhere were dismantled. Financial aid in various forms and expertise were made available for the economic development of the reservations. In perhaps the most significant departure from earlier policy, the IRA proposed an increase in American Indian self-governance and a reduction of the paternalistic role of the BIA and other federal agencies.

Although sympathetic to American Indians, the IRA had its limits and shortcomings. Many of its intentions were never realized, and the empowerment of the tribes was not unqualified. The move to self-governance generally took place on the dominant group's terms and in conformity with the values and practices of white society. For example, the proposed increase in the decision-making power of the tribes was contingent on their adoption of Anglo-American political forms, including secret ballots, majority rule, and written constitutions. These were alien concepts to those tribes that selected leaders by procedures other than popular election (e.g., leaders might be chosen by councils of elders) or that made decisions by open discussion and consensus building (i.e., decisions required the agreement of everyone with a voice in the process, not a simple majority). The incorporation of these Western forms illustrates the basically assimilationist intent of the IRA.

The IRA had variable effects on American Indian women. In tribes that were male dominated, the IRA gave women new rights to participate in elections, run for office, and hold leadership roles. In other cases, new political structures replaced traditional forms, some of which, as in the Iroquois culture, had accorded women considerable power. Although the political effects were variable, the programs funded by the IRA provided opportunities for women on many reservations to receive education and training for the first time. Many of these opportunities were oriented toward domestic tasks and other traditionally Western female roles, but some prepared American Indian women for jobs outside the family and off the reservation, such as clerical work and nursing (Evans, 1989, pp. 208-209).

In summary, the Indian Reorganization Act of 1934 was a significant improvement over prior federal Indian policy but was bolder and more sympathetic to American Indians in intent than in execution. On one hand, not all tribes were capable of taking advantage of the opportunities provided by the legislation, and some ended up being further victimized. For example, in the Hopi tribe, located in the Southwest, the act allowed a westernized group of Indians to be elected to leadership roles, with the result that dominant group firms were allowed to have access to the mineral resources, farmland, and water rights controlled by the tribe. The resultant development generated wealth for the white firms and their Hopi allies, but most of the tribe continued to languish in poverty (Churchill, 1985, pp. 112-113). On the other hand, some tribes prospered (at least comparatively speaking) under the IRA. One impoverished, landless group of Cherokee in Oklahoma acquired land, equipment, and expert advice through the IRA, and between 1937 and 1949, they developed a prosperous, largely debt-free farming community (Debo, 1970, pp. 294-300). Many tribes remained suspicious of the IRA, and by 1948, fewer than 100 tribes had voted to accept its provisions.

## Termination and Relocation

The IRA's stress on the legitimacy of tribal identity seemed "un-American" to many. There was constant pressure on the federal government to return to an individualistic policy that encouraged (or required) Americanization. Some viewed the tribal structures and communal property-holding patterns as relics of an earlier era and as impediments to modernization and development. Not so incidentally, some elements of dominant society still coveted the remaining Indian lands and resources, which could be more easily exploited if property ownership were individualized.

In 1953, the assimilationist forces won a victory when Congress passed a resolution calling for an end to the reservation system and to the special relationships between the tribes and the federal government. The proposed policy, called **termination**, was intended to get the federal government "out of the Indian business." It rejected the IRA and proposed a return to the system of private land ownership imposed on the tribes by the Dawes Act. Horrified at the notion of termination, the tribes opposed the policy strongly and vociferously. Under this policy, all special relationships—including treaty obligations—between the federal government and the tribes would end. Tribes would no longer exist as legally recognized entities, and tribal lands and other resources would be placed in private hands (Josephy, 1968, pp. 353-355).

About 100 tribes, most of them small, were terminated. In virtually all cases, the termination process was administered hastily, and fraud, misuse of funds, and other injustices were common. The Menominee of Wisconsin and the Klamath on the West Coast were the two largest tribes to be terminated. Both suffered devastating economic losses and precipitous declines in quality of life. Neither tribe had the business or tax base needed to finance the services (e.g., health care and schooling) formerly provided by the federal government, and both were forced to sell land, timber, and other scarce resources to maintain minimal standards of living. Many poor American Indian families were forced to turn to local and state agencies, which placed severe strain on welfare budgets. The experience of the Menominee was so disastrous that at the concerted request of the tribe, reservation status was restored in 1973 (Deloria, 1969, pp. 60-82; McNickle, 1973, pp. 103-110; Raymer, 1974). The Klamath reservation was restored in 1986 (Snipp, 1996, p. 394).

At about the same time that the termination policy came into being, various programs were established to encourage American Indians to move to urban areas. The movement to the city had already begun in the 1940s, spurred by the availability of factory jobs during World War II. In the 1950s, the movement was further encouraged with programs of assistance and by the declining government support for economic development on the reservation, the most dramatic example of which was the policy of termination (Green, 1999, p. 265). Centers for American Indians were established in many cities, and various services (e.g., job training, housing assistance, English instruction) were offered to assist in the adjustment to urban life. The urbanization of the American Indian population is displayed in Exhibit 8.1. Note the rapid increase in the movement to the city that began in the 1950s. Almost 60% of all American Indians are now urbanized, and since 1950, Indians have urbanized faster than the general population. Nevertheless, American Indians are still the least urbanized minority group. The population as a whole is about 80% urbanized; in contrast, African Americans (see Exhibit 7.4) are about 90% urbanized.

As with African Americans, American Indians arrived in the cities after the mainsream economy had begun to de-emphasize blue-collar or manufacturing jobs. Because of their relatively low average levels of educational attainment and their racial and cultural differences, American Indians in the city tended to encounter the same problems experienced by African Americans and other minority groups of color: high rates of unemployment, inadequate housing, and all of the other travails of the urban underclass.

American Indian women also migrated to the city in considerable numbers. The discrimination, unemployment, and poverty of the urban environment often made it difficult for the men of the group to fulfill the role of breadwinner; thus the burden of supporting the family tended to fall on the women. The difficulties inherent in combining child rearing and a job outside the home are compounded by isolation from the support networks provided by extended family and clan back on the reservations. Nevertheless, one study found that American Indian women in the city continue to practice their traditional cultures and maintain the tribal identity of their children (Joe & Miller, 1994, p. 186).

American Indians living in the city are, on the average, better off than those living on reservations, where unemployment can reach 80% or even 90%. The improvement is relative, however. Although many individual Indians prosper in the urban environment, income figures for urban Indians as a whole are comparable to those for African Americans and well below those for whites. American Indian unemployment rates run about twice the national average (Cornell, 1988, p. 132). Thus a move to the city often means trading rural poverty for the urban variety, with little net improvement in life chances.

American Indians will probably remain more rural than other minority groups for years to come. Despite the poverty and lack of opportunities for schooling and jobs, the

**EXHIBIT 8.1**   Urbanization of American Indians, 1900-2000

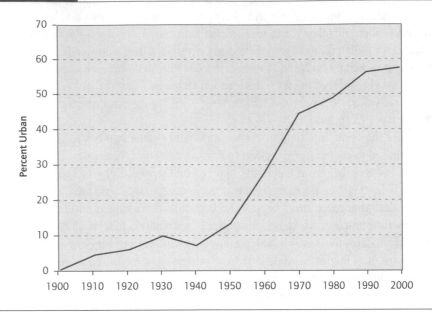

SOURCE: 1900-1990, Thornton (2001), p. 142; 2000 calculated from U.S. Bureau of the Census (n.d.).

reservation offers some advantages in services and lifestyle. On the reservation, there may be opportunities for political participation and leadership roles that are not available in the cities, where American Indians are a tiny minority. Reservations also offer kinfolk, friends, religious services, and tribal celebrations (Snipp, 1989, p. 84). Lower levels of education, work experience, and financial resources combine with the prejudice, discrimination, and racism of the larger society to lower the chances of success in the city and will probably sustain a continuing return to the reservations.

Although the economic benefits of urbanization have been slim for the group as whole, other advantages have accrued from life in the city. It was much easier to establish networks of friendship and affiliation across tribal lines in the cities, and urban Indians have been one of the sources of strength and personnel for a movement of protest that began early in the 20th century. Virtually all of the organizational vehicles of American Indian protest have had urban roots.

## Self-Determination

The termination policy aroused so much opposition from American Indians and was such an obvious disaster that the pressure to push tribes to termination faded in the late 1950s, although the act itself was not repealed until 1975. Since the 1960s, federal Indian policy has generally returned to the tradition set by the IRA. Termination and forced assimilation continue to be officially rejected, and within limits, the tribes have been granted more freedom to find their own way, at their own pace, of relating to the larger society.

Several federal programs and laws have benefited the tribes during the past few decades, including the antipoverty and "Great Society" campaigns launched in the 1960s. In 1970, President Richard Nixon affirmed the government's commitment to fulfilling treaty obligations and the right of the tribes to govern themselves. The Indian Self-Determination and Education Assistance Act was passed in 1975. This legislation increased aid to reservation schools and American Indian students and increased tribal control over the administration of the reservations, from police forces to schools to road maintenance.

The Self-Determination Act primarily benefited the larger tribes and those that had well-established administrative and governing structures. Smaller and less well-organized tribes have continued to rely heavily on the federal government (Snipp, 1996, p. 394). Nonetheless, at least in some cases, this new phase of federal policy has allowed American Indian tribes to plot their own courses free of paternalistic regulation, and just as important, it gave them the tools and resources to address their problems and improve their situations. We will look at some of these developments after examining the American Indian protest movement.

# PROTEST AND RESISTANCE
## Early Efforts

As BIA-administered reservations and coercive Americanization came to dominate tribal life in the 20th century, new forms of Indian activism appeared. The modern protest movement was tiny at first and, with few exceptions, achieved a measure of success only in recent decades. In fact, the American Indian protest movement in the past was not so much unsuccessful as simply ignored. The movement has focused on several complementary goals: protecting American Indian resources and treaty rights, striking a balance between assimilation and pluralism, and finding a relationship with the dominant group that would permit a broader array of life chances without sacrificing tribal identity and heritage.

Formally organized, American Indian protest organizations have existed since the 1910s, but the modern phase of the protest movement began during World War II. Many American Indians served in the military or moved to the city to take jobs in aid of the war effort and were thereby exposed to the world beyond the reservation. Also, political activism on the reservation, which had been stimulated by the IRA, continued through the war years, and the recognition that many problems were shared across tribal lines grew.

These trends helped to stimulate the founding of the National Congress of American Indians (NCAI) in 1944. This organization was pantribal (i.e., included members from many different tribes); its first convention was attended by representatives of 50 different tribes and reservations (Cornell, 1988, p. 119). The leadership consisted largely of American Indians educated and experienced in the white world. However, the NCAI's program stressed the importance of preserving the old ways and tribal institutions as well as protecting Indian welfare. An early victory for the NCAI and its allies came in 1946 when an Indian Claims Commission was created by the federal government. This body was authorized to hear claims brought by the tribes with regard to treaty violations. The commission has settled hundreds of claims, resulting in awards of millions of dollars to the tribes, and it continues its work today (Weeks, 1988, pp. 261-262).

In the 1950s and 1960s, the protest movement was further stimulated by the threat of termination and by the increasing number of American Indians living in the cities who developed friendships across tribal lines. Awareness of common problems, rising levels of education, and the examples set by the successful protests of other minority groups also increased readiness for collective action.

## Red Power

By the 1960s and 1970s, American Indian protest groups were finding ways to express their grievances and problems to the nation. The Red Power movement, like the Black Power movement (see chapter 7), encompassed a coalition of groups, many considerably more assertive than the NCAI, and a varied collection of ideas, most of which stressed self-determination and pride in race and cultural heritage. Red Power protests included a "fish-in" in Washington state in 1965, an episode that also illustrates the nature of American Indian demands. The State of Washington had tried to limit the fishing rights of several different tribes on the grounds that the supply of fish was diminishing and needed to be protected. The tribes depended on fishing for subsistence and survival and argued that their right to fish had been guaranteed by treaties signed in the 1850s and that it was the pollution and commercial fishing of the dominant society that had depleted the supply of fish. They organized a "fish-in" in violation of the state's policy and were met by a contingent of police officers and other law officials. Violent confrontations and mass arrests ensued. Three years later, after a lengthy and expensive court battle, the tribes were vindicated, and the U.S. Supreme Court confirmed their treaty rights to fish the rivers of Washington State (Nabakov, 1999, pp. 362-363).

Another widely publicized episode took place in 1969, when American Indians from various tribes occupied Alcatraz Island in San Francisco Bay, the site of a closed federal prison. The protesters were acting on an old law that granted American Indians the right to reclaim abandoned federal land. The occupation of Alcatraz was organized in part by the American Indian Movement (AIM), founded in 1968. More militant and radical than the previously established protest groups, AIM aggressively confronted the BIA, the police, and other forces that were seen as repressive. With the backing of AIM and other groups, Alcatraz was occupied for nearly 4 years and generated a great deal of publicity for the Red Power movement and the plight of American Indians.

In 1972, AIM helped to organize a march on Washington, DC, called the "Trail of Broken Treaties." Marchers came from many tribes and represented both urban and reservation Indians. The intent of the marchers was to dramatize the problems of the tribes. The leaders demanded the abolition of the BIA, the return of illegally taken land, and increased self-governance for the tribes, among other things. When they reached Washington, some of the marchers forcibly occupied the BIA offices. Property was damaged (by which side is disputed), and records and papers were destroyed. The marchers eventually surrendered, but none of their demands were met. The following year, AIM occupied the village of Wounded Knee in South Dakota to protest the violation of treaty rights. Wounded Knee was the site of the last armed confrontation between Indians and whites in 1890 and was selected by AIM for its deep symbolic significance. The occupation lasted more than 2 months and involved several armed confrontations with federal authorities. Again, the protest ended without achieving any of the demands made by the Indian leadership (Olson & Wilson, 1984, pp. 172-175). Since the early 1970s, the level of protest activity has declined, just as it has for the African American protest movement. Lawsuits and court cases have predominated over dramatic, direct confrontations.

Ironically, the struggle for red power encouraged assimilation as well as pluralism. The movement linked members of different tribes and forced Indians of diverse heritages to find common ground, often in the form of a "generic" American Indian culture. Inevitably, the protests were conducted in English and the grievances were expressed in ways that were understandable to white society, thus increasing the pressure to acculturate even while arguing for the survival of the tribes. Furthermore, successful protest required that American Indians be fluent in English, trained in the law and other professions, skilled in dealing with bureaucracies, and knowledgeable about the formulation and execution of public policy. American Indians who became proficient in these areas thereby took on the characteristics of their adversaries (Hraba, 1979, p. 235).

As the pantribal protest movement forged ties between members of diverse tribes, the successes of the movement and changing federal policy and public opinion encouraged a rebirth of commitment to tribalism and "Indian-ness." American Indians were simultaneously stimulated to assimilate (by stressing their common characteristics and creating organizational forms that united the tribes) and to retain a pluralistic relationship with the larger society (by working for self-determination and enhanced tribal power and authority). Thus part of the significance of the Red Power movement was that it encouraged both pantribal unity and a continuation of tribal diversity (Olson & Wilson, 1984, p. 206). Today, American Indians continue to seek a way of existing in the larger society that merges assimilation with pluralism.

Exhibit 8.2 summarizes this discussion of federal policy and Indian protest. The four major policy phases since the end of overt hostilities in 1890 are listed on the left. The thrust of the government's economic and political policies are listed in the next two columns, followed by a brief characterization of tribal response. The last column shows the changing bases for federal

**EXHIBIT 8.2**   Federal Indian Policy and Indian Response

| Period | Economic Impact | Political Impact | Indian Response | Government Approach |
|---|---|---|---|---|
| *Reservation.* Late 1800s–1930s | Land loss (Dawes Act) and Welfare dependency | Government control of reservation and coerced acculturation | Some resistance, growth of religious movements | Individualistic, creation of self-sufficient farmers |
| *Reorganization* (IRA). 1930s and 1940s | Stabilize land base and support some development of reservation | Establish federally sponsored tribal governments | Increased political participation in many tribes; some pantribal activity | Incorporate tribes as groups, creation of self-sufficient "Americanized" communities |
| *Termination and relocation.* Late 1940s–early 1960s | Withdrawal of government support for reservations; promotion of urbanization | New assault on tribes, new forms of coercive acculturation | Increased pantribalism, widespread and intense opposition to termination | Individualistic, dissolve tribal ties and promote incorporation into the modern, urban labor market |
| *Self-determination* 1960s-present | Develop reservation economies, increased integration of Indian labor force | Support for tribal governments | Greatly increased political activity | Incorporate tribes as self-sufficient communities with access to federal programs of support and welfare |

SOURCE: Based on Cornell, Kalt, Krepps, and Taylor (1998), p. 5.

policy, sometimes aimed at weakening tribal tribes and individualizing American Indians and sometimes (including most recently) aimed at working with and preserving tribal structures.

# THE CONTINUING STRUGGLE FOR DEVELOPMENT IN CONTEMPORARY AMERICAN INDIAN–WHITE RELATIONS

Conflicts between American Indians and the larger society are far from over. Although the days of deadly battle are (with occasional exceptions) long gone, the issues that remain are serious, difficult to resolve, and, in their way, just as much matters of life and death. American Indians face enormous challenges in their struggle to improve their status, but largely as a result of their greater freedom from stifling federal control since the 1970s, they also have some resources, some opportunities, and a leadership that is both talented and resourceful (Bordewich, 1996, p. 11).

## Natural Resources

Ironically, land allotted to American Indian tribes in the 19th century sometimes turned out to be rich in resources that became valuable in the 20th century. These resources include 3% of oil and natural gas reserves, 15% of U.S. coal reserves, and 55% of uranium reserves (Amott & Matthaei, 1991, p. 54). In addition (and despite the devastation wreaked by the Dawes Act of 1887), some tribes hold title to water rights, fishing rights, woodlands that could sustain a lumbering industry, and wilderness areas that could be developed for camping, hunting, and other forms of recreation. These resources are likely to become more valuable as the earth's natural resources and undeveloped areas are further depleted in the future.

The challenge faced by American Indians is to retain control of these resources and to develop them for the benefit of the tribes. Threats to the remaining tribal lands and assets are common. Mining and energy companies continue to cast envious eyes on American Indian land, and other tribal assets are coveted by real estate developers, fishermen (recreational as well as commercial), backpackers and campers, and cities facing water shortages (Harjo, 1996).

Some tribes have succeeded in developing their resources for their own benefit. For example, the White Mountain Apaches of Arizona operate nine tribally owned enterprises, including a major ski resort, a logging operation and sawmill, and a small casino. These businesses are the primary economic engines of the local area, and unemployment on the White Mountain reservation is only a quarter of the national reservation average (Cornell & Kalt, 2000, pp. 445-446). On many other reservations, however, even rich stores of resources lie dormant, awaiting the right combination of tribal leadership, expertise, and development capital. The Crow tribe of Montana, for example, controls a huge supply of coal and has extensive timber, water, mineral, and other resources. Yet unemployment on the reservation runs nearly 80%, and more than half of the tribe gets public assistance of some kind. "The last two tribal chief executives have been convicted of federal felonies, and the current chief executive has had to have armed guards surrounding her when addressing the tribal council" (Cornell & Kalt, 2000, p. 444).

On a broader level, tribes are banding together to share expertise and negotiate more effectively with the larger society. For example, 25 tribes founded the Council of Energy Resource Tribes in 1975 to coordinate and control the development of the mineral resources on reservation lands. Since its founding, the council has successfully negotiated a number of agreements with dominant group firms, increasing the flow of income to the tribes and raising their quality of life (Cornell, 1988; Snipp, 1989).

## Attracting Industry to the Reservation

Many efforts to develop the reservations have focused on creating jobs by attracting industry through such incentives as low taxes, low rents, and a low-wage pool of labor—not unlike the package of benefits offered to employers by less developed nations in Asia, South America, and Africa. With some notable exceptions, these efforts have not been particularly successful (for a review, see Vinje, 1996). Reservations are often so geographically isolated that transportation costs become prohibitive. The jobs that have materialized are typically low wage and have few benefits; usually, non-Indians fill the more lucrative managerial positions. Thus the opportunities for building economic power or improving the standard of living from these jobs are sharply limited. These new jobs may transform "the welfare poor into the working poor" (Snipp, 1996, p. 398), but their potential for raising economic vitality is low.

To illustrate the problems of developing reservations by attracting industry, consider the Navajo, the second-largest American Indian tribe. The Navajo reservation spreads across Arizona, New Mexico, and Utah and encompasses about 20 million acres, an area a little smaller than either Indiana or Maine. Although the reservation seems huge on a map, much of the land is desert not suitable for farming or other uses. As they have for the past several centuries, the Navajo today rely heavily on the cultivation of corn and sheepherding for sustenance.

Most wage-earning jobs on the reservation are with the agencies of the federal government (e.g., the BIA) or with the tribal government. Tourism is large and growing, but the jobs available in that sector are typically low wage and seasonal. There are reserves of coal, uranium, and oil on the reservation, but these resources have not generated many jobs. In some cases, the Navajo have resisted the damage to the environment that would be caused by mines and oil wells because of their traditional values and respect for the land. When exploitation of these resources has been permitted, the companies involved often use highly automated technologies that generate few jobs (Oswalt & Neely, 1996, pp. 317-351).

Exhibits 8.3 and 8.4 contrast Navaho income, poverty, and education with national norms. Median income for the Navaho is about 58% of the national average, and the poverty rate is almost three times greater than the rate of the nation as a whole. The tribe runs an extensive school system, and almost all Navajo children attend day school (as opposed to the boarding schools of the past). The schools mix a standard curriculum with Navajo culture and language. However, the tribe is far below national standards in terms of levels of high school and college education.

On the other hand, some tribes have managed to achieve relative prosperity by bringing jobs to their people. The Choctaw Nation of Mississippi, for example, has become one of the largest employers in the state. Tribal leaders have been able to attract companies such as Xerox and Harley-Davidson by promising (and delivering) high-quality labor for relatively low wages. Incomes have risen, unemployment is relatively low, and the tribe has built schools, hospitals, and a television station and administers numerous other services for its members (Bordewich, 1996, pp. 300-305). The median income for Choctaw households, although still only about 80% of the national figure, is $10,000 greater than that of the Navaho (see Exhibit 8.4). The Choctaw poverty rate is half that of the Navaho, and Choctaws actually exceed the national figure for

| EXHIBIT 8.3 | Poverty Rates and Education for Navaho, Choctaw, and the United States, 2000 |

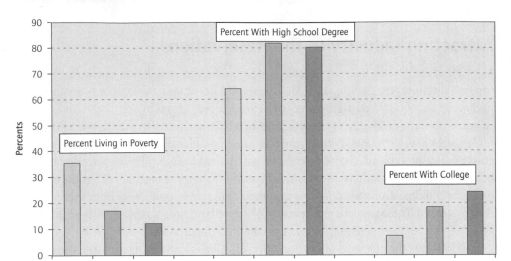

SOURCE: U.S. Bureau of the Census (n.d.).

| EXHIBIT 8.4 | Median Income Data for Navaho, Choctaw, and the United States, 2000 |

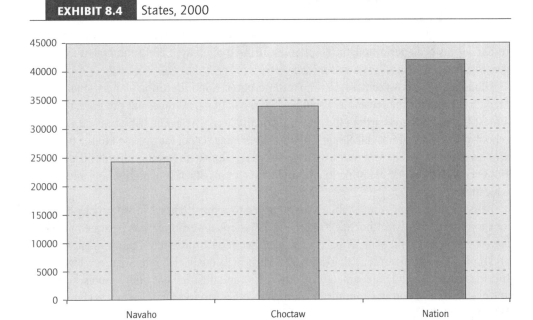

SOURCE: U.S. Bureau of the Census (n.d.).

high school education. Almost 19% of the Choctaw are college educated, more than twice the comparable figure for the Navaho.

The Choctaw are not the most affluent tribe, and the Navajo are far from being the most destitute. They illustrate the mixture of partial successes and failures that typify efforts to bring prosperity to the reservations; together, these two cases suggest that attracting industry and jobs to the reservations is a possible—but difficult and uncertain—strategy for economic development.

## Broken Treaties

For many tribes, the treaties signed with the federal government in the 19th century offer another potential resource. These treaties were often violated by white settlers, the military, state and local governments, the BIA, and other elements and agencies of the dominant group, and many tribes are pursuing this trail of broken treaties and seeking compensation for the wrongs of the past. For example, in 1972, the Passamaquoddy and Penobscot tribes filed a lawsuit demanding the return of 12.5 million acres of land—more than half the state of Maine—and $25 billion in damages. The tribes argued that this land had been illegally taken from them more than 150 years earlier. After 8 years of litigation, the tribes settled for a $25 million trust fund and 300,000 acres of land. Although far less than their original demand, the award gave the tribes control over resources that could be used for economic development, job creation, upgrading educational programs, and developing other programs that would enhance human and financial capital (Worsnop, 1992, p. 391).

Virtually every tribe has similar grievances, and if pursued successfully, the long-dead treaty relationship between the Indian nations and the government could be a significant fount of economic and political resources. Of course, lawsuits require considerable (and expensive) legal expertise and years of effort to bring to fruition. Because there are no guarantees of success, this avenue has some sharp limitations and risks.

## Gambling and Other Development Possibilities

Another potential resource for American Indians is the gambling industry, the development of which was made possible by federal legislation passed in 1988. There are currently more than 200 tribes with gaming establishments (National Indian Gaming Commission, n.d.a), and the industry has grown nearly 80 times over, from $212 million in revenues in 1988 (Spilde, 2001) to almost $17 billion in 2000 (National Indian Gaming Commission, n.d.b). In 2000, total revenues from American Indian gaming ($10.4 billion) exceeded all riverboat gambling ($9 billion) and approached the combined revenues from all casinos in Nevada and Atlantic City ($13.7 billion) (Evans & Topoleski, 2002). Exhibit 8.5 charts the growth of revenues from gaming on American Indian reservations from 1995 to 2003.

The single most profitable Indian gambling operation is the Foxwoods Casino in Connecticut, operated by the Pequot tribe. The casino attracts as many as 35,000 gamblers per day and generates more revenue than the casinos of Atlantic City. The profits from the casino are used to benefit tribal members in a variety of ways, including the repurchase of tribal lands, housing assistance, medical benefits, educational scholarships, and public services, such as a tribal police force (Bordewich, 1996, p. 110). Other tribes have used gambling profits to purchase restaurants and marinas and to finance the development of outlet malls, aquacultural programs, manufacturing plants, and a wide variety of other businesses and enterprises (Spilde, 2001).

**EXHIBIT 8.5**   Revenues From Gaming, 1995-2003

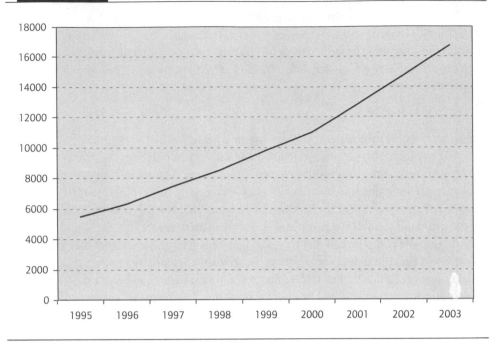

SOURCE: National Indian Gaming Commission (n.d.).

Various tribes have sought other ways to capitalize on their freedom from state regulation and taxes. Some have established small but profitable businesses selling cigarettes tax-free. Also, because they are not subject to state and federal environmental regulations, some reservations are exploring the possibility of housing nuclear waste and other refuse of industrialization— a somewhat ironic and not altogether attractive use of the remaining Indian lands.

Clearly, the combination of increased autonomy, treaty rights, natural resources, and gambling means that American Indians today have an opportunity to dramatically raise their standards of living and creatively take control of their own destinies. For many tribes, however, these assets remain a potential waiting to be actualized (Vinje, 1996). Without denying the success stories, such as the Choctaw and the Pequot, the lives of most American Indians continue to be limited by poverty and powerlessness, prejudice, and discrimination. We document these patterns in the next section.

## CONTEMPORARY AMERICAN INDIAN–WHITE RELATIONS

This section uses many of the terms and concepts we have developed over the first seven chapters to analyze the contemporary situation of American Indians. Compared with other groups, information about American Indians is scant. Nonetheless, a relatively clear picture emerges. The portrait stresses many of the themes of this chapter: continued colonization, marginalization, and impoverishment for a large segment of the group; continuing discrimination and exclusion; and the search for a meaningful course between integration and separation.

# Prejudice and Discrimination

Anti-Indian prejudice has been a part of American society from the beginning. Historically, negative feelings such as hatred and contempt have been widespread and strong, particularly during the heat of war, and various stereotypes of Indians have been common. One stereotype, especially strong during periods of conflict, depicts Indians as bloodthirsty, ferocious, cruel savages capable of any atrocity. The other image of American Indians is that of "the noble Red Man" who lives in complete harmony with nature and symbolizes goodwill and pristine simplicity (Bordewich, 1996, p. 34). Although the first stereotype tended to fade away as hostilities drew to a close, the latter image retains a good deal of strength in modern views of Indians found in popular culture and among environmentalist and "new age" spiritual organizations.

A variety of studies have documented continued stereotyping of Native Americans in the popular press, textbooks, the media, cartoons, and various other places (for example, see Bird, 1999; Rouse & Hanson, 1991). In the tradition of "the noble Red Man," American Indians are often portrayed as bucks and squaws, complete with headdresses, bows, tepees, and other such "generic" Indian artifacts. These portrayals obliterate the diversity of American Indian culture and lifestyles. American Indians are often referred to in the past tense, as if their present situation were of no importance or, worse, as if they no longer existed. Many history books continue to begin the study of American history in Europe or with the "discovery" of America, omitting the millennia of civilization prior to the arrival of European explorers and colonizers. Contemporary portrayals of American Indians, such as in the movie *Dances With Wolves* (1990), are more sympathetic but still treat the tribes as part of a bucolic past forever lost, not as peoples with real problems in the present.

The persistence of stereotypes and the extent to which they have become enmeshed in modern culture is illustrated by continuing controversies surrounding nicknames for athletic teams (the Washington Redskins, the Cleveland Indians, and the Atlanta Braves) and the use of American Indian mascots, tomahawk "chops," and other practices offensive to many American Indians (see the Current Debates section at the end of this chapter for more). Protests have been staged at some athletic events to increase awareness of these derogatory depictions, but as was the case so often in the past, the protests have been attacked, ridiculed, or simply ignored. Public opinion polls indicate that the public sees the issue as trivial and regards the protesters as attention-seeking troublemakers (Giago, 1992).

There are relatively few studies of anti-Indian prejudices in the social science literature, and it is therefore difficult to characterize changes over the past several decades. We do not know whether there has been a shift to more symbolic or "modern" forms of anti-Indian racism, as there has been for antiblack prejudice, or if the stereotypes of American Indians have declined in strength or changed in content.

One of the few records of national anti-Indian prejudice over time is that of social distance scale results (see Exhibit 3.5). When the scales were first administered in 1926, American Indians were ranked in the middle third of all groups (18th out of 28), at about the same level as Southern and Eastern Europeans and slightly above Mexicans, another colonized group. The ranking of American Indians remained stable until 1977, when there was a noticeable rise in their position relative to other groups. In the most recent polls, the social distance scores of American Indians fell (indicating less prejudice), but the relative ranking still placed them with other racial minority groups. These shifts may reflect a decline in levels of prejudice, a change from more overt forms to more subtle modern racism, or both. Remember, however, that the samples for the social distance research were college students for the most part and do not necessarily reflect trends in the general population (see also Hanson & Rouse, 1987; Smith & Dempsey, 1983).

Research is also unclear about the severity or extent of discrimination against American Indians. Certainly, the group's lower average levels of education limit their opportunities for upward mobility, choice of occupations, and range of income. This is a form of institutional discrimination in the sense that the opportunities to develop human capital are much less available to American Indians than to much of the rest of the population. In terms of individual discrimination or more overt forms of exclusion, there is simply too little evidence to sustain clear conclusions (Snipp, 1992, p. 363). The situation of American Indian women is also under-researched, but Snipp (1992) reports that, like their counterparts in other minority groups and the dominant group, they "are systematically paid less than their male counterparts in similar circumstances" (p. 363).

The very limited evidence available from social distance scales suggests that overt anti-Indian prejudice has declined, perhaps in parallel with antiblack prejudice. A great deal of stereotyping remains, however, and demeaning, condescending, or negative portrayals of American Indians are common throughout the dominant culture. Institutional discrimination is a major barrier for American Indians, who have not had access to opportunities for education and employment.

## Assimilation and Pluralism

**Acculturation.** Despite more than a century of coercive Americanization, many tribes have been able to preserve a large portion of their traditional cultures. For example, many tribal languages continue to be spoken on a daily basis. The huge majority (75%) of American Indians in the continental U.S. speaks only English, but a sizeable minority (18%) speaks a tribal language as well. Exhibit 8.6 suggests the extent of language acculturation. For most of the 10 largest tribes, less than 10% speak the tribal language in addition to English. In some tribes, however, the picture is dramatically different. For example, about two thirds of the Navaho speak the tribal language at least occasionally, and about 2% speak no English at all.

Traditional culture is retained in other forms besides language. Religions and value systems, political and economic structures, cuisine, and recreational patterns have all survived the military conquest and the depredations of reservation life; each pattern has been altered, however, by contact with the dominant group. Cornell (1987), for example, argues that although American Indians have been affected by the "American dream" of material success through hard, honest work, their individual values continue to reflect their greater orientation to the group rather than to the individual.

The tendency to filter the impact of the larger society through continuing, vital American Indian culture is also illustrated by the Native American Church. The Native American Church is an important American Indian religion, with congregations across the nation (Wax, 1971, pp. 141-144). This religion combines elements from both cultures, and church services freely mix Christian imagery and the Bible with attempts to seek personal visions by using peyote, a hallucinogenic drug. The latter practice is consistent with the spiritual and religious traditions of many tribes but clashes sharply with the laws and norms of the larger society. The difference in traditions has generated many skirmishes with the courts and, as recently as 2004, the right of the Native American Church to use peyote was upheld by the Supreme Court of Utah ("Utah Supreme Court," 2004).

American Indians have been considerably more successful than African Americans in preserving their traditional cultures. The differences in the relationship between each

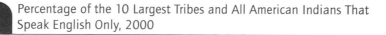

**EXHIBIT 8.6** Percentage of the 10 Largest Tribes and All American Indians That Speak English Only, 2000

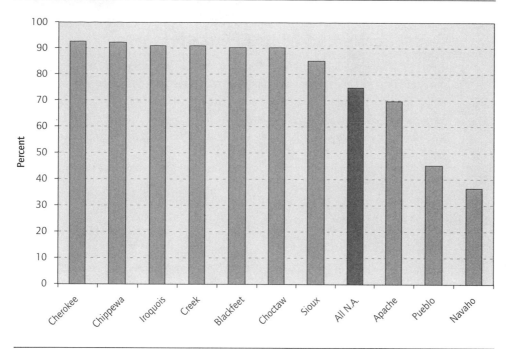

SOURCE: U.S. Bureau of the Census (n.d.).

minority group and the dominant group help explain this pattern. African Americans were exploited for labor, whereas the competition with American Indians involved land. African cultures could not easily survive, because the social structures that transmitted the cultures and gave them meaning were destroyed by slavery and sacrificed to the exigencies of the plantation economy.

In contrast, American Indians confronted the dominant group as tribal units, intact and whole. The tribes maintained integrity throughout the wars and throughout the reservation period. Tribal culture was indeed attacked and denigrated during the reservation era, but the basic social unit that sustained the culture survived, albeit in altered form. The fact that American Indians were placed on separate reservations, isolated from one another and the "contaminating" effects of everyday contact with the larger society, also abetted the preservation of traditional languages and culture (Cornell, 1990).

Indian cultures seem healthy and robust in the current atmosphere of greater tolerance and support for pluralism in the larger society combined with increased autonomy and lower government regulation on the reservations. However, a number of social forces are working against pluralism and the survival of tribal cultures. Pantribalism may threaten the integrity of individual tribal cultures even as it successfully represents American Indian grievances and concerns to the larger society. Opportunities for jobs, education, and higher incomes draw American Indians to more developed urban areas and will continue to do so as long as the reservations are underdeveloped. Many aspects of the tribal cultures can be fully expressed and practiced only

## An Indian View of White Civilization

*Who's the savage? One stereotype of American Indians portrays them as "cruel, barbaric, and savage." Is it possible, however, that American Indians are more advanced than the dazzling sophisticates of urban America? In a 1972 interview, John Lame Deer, a Sioux, gives his view of the technologically advanced society that surrounds him. Through his words, we can hear the voices of the Indian cultures that have survived.*

### LISTENING TO THE AIR

**John Lame Deer**

You have made it hard for us to experience nature in the good way by being part of it. Even here [a Sioux reservation in South Dakota] we are conscious that somewhere out in those hills there are missile silos and radar stations. White men always pick the few unspoiled, beautiful, awesome spots for these abominations. You have raped and violated these lands, always saying, "gimme, gimme, gimme," and never giving anything back. . . . You have not only despoiled the earth, the rocks, the minerals, all of which you call "dead" but which are very much alive; you have even changed the animals, . . . changed them in a horrible way, so no one can recognize them. There is power in a buffalo—spiritual, magic power—but there is no power in an Angus, in a Hereford.

There is power in an antelope, but not in a goat or a sheep, which holds still while you butcher it, which

will eat your newspaper if you let it. There was great power in a wolf, even in a coyote. You made him into a freak—a toy poodle, a Pekinese, a lap dog. You can't do much with a cat, which is like an Indian, unchangeable. So you fix it, alter it, declaw it, even cut its vocal cords so you can experiment on it in a laboratory without being disturbed by its cries. . . .

You have not only altered, declawed, and malformed your winged and four-legged cousins; you have done it to yourselves. You have changed men into chairmen of boards, into office workers, into time-clock punchers. You have changed women into housewives, truly fearful creatures. . . . You live in prisons which you have built for yourselves, calling them "homes," offices, factories. We have a new joke on the reservations: "What is cultural deprivation?" Answer: "Being an upper-middle-class white kid living in a split-level suburban home with a color TV." . . .

I think white people are so afraid of the world they created that they don't want to see, feel, smell, or hear it. The feeling of rain or snow on your face, being numbed by an icy wind and thawing out before a smoking fire, coming out of a hot sweat bath and plunging into a cold stream, these things make you feel alive, but you don't want them anymore. Living in boxes that shut out the heat of the summer and the chill of winter, living inside a body that no longer has a scent, hearing the noise of the hi-fi rather than listening to the sounds of nature, watching some actor on TV have a make-believe experience when you no longer experience anything for yourself, eating food without taste—that's your way. It's no good.

SOURCE: Lame Deer, John (Fire), & Erdoes, Richard. 1972. "Listening to the Air." In *Lame Deer, Seeker of Visions.* New York: Simon and Schuster. Pp. 119-121.

with other tribal members on the reservations. Thus many American Indians must make a choice between "Indian-ness" on the reservation and "success" in the city. The younger, more educated American Indians will be most likely to confront this choice, and the future vitality of traditional American Indian cultures and languages will hinge on which option is chosen.

**Secondary Structural Assimilation.** This section assesses the degree of integration of American Indians into the various institutions of public life, following the general outlines of the parallel section in chapter 7.

*Population Size.* The changing fortunes of American Indians are reflected in their population size. As I mentioned in Chapter 5, in 1492, the group numbered at least 1 million in what is now the continental United States (Snipp, 1992, p. 354). Losses suffered during the contact period reduced the population to less than 250,000 by 1900, a loss of at least 75%. Since that time, the population has generally increased, dramatically so in recent decades. Exhibit 8.7 charts the growth of the American Indian population over the 20th century. Recent increases are partly due to higher birth rates. Mainly, however, the growth is a result of changing definitions of race in the larger society and a much greater willingness of people to claim Indian ancestry (Thornton, 2001, p. 137). The 2000 census, as you recall, allowed people to classify themselves in more than one racial group. If we included people who choose American Indian as their "second race," the number of Indians would increase by over 60%, from 2.5 million to over 4 million (U.S. Bureau of the Census, 2001b). These patterns again underscore the basically social nature of race (see Chapter 1).

*Residence.* Since the Indian Removal Act of 1830 (see Chapter 5), American Indians have been concentrated in the western two thirds of the nation, as illustrated in Exhibit 8.8, although some pockets of population still can be found in the East. The states with the largest concentrations of American Indians—California, New Mexico, and Arizona—together include about one third of all American Indians, and another 10% live in Oklahoma. American Indians belong to hundreds of different tribes, the 10 largest of which are listed in Exhibit 8.9.

*Education.* As a result of the combined efforts of missionaries and federal agencies, American Indians have had a long but not necessarily productive acquaintance with Western education. Until the last few decades, schools for American Indians were primarily focused on Americanizing children, not on educating them. Although the percentage of high school graduates has increased dramatically in the recent past, levels of education are still lower than for the nation as a whole. According to the 2000 census, there was a relatively small gap between American Indians and national norms in high school graduates (75% vs. 80%) but a much larger gap in college graduates (14% vs. 24%). There is quite a bit of variation in educational

EXHIBIT 8.7  American Indian Population, 1900-2000

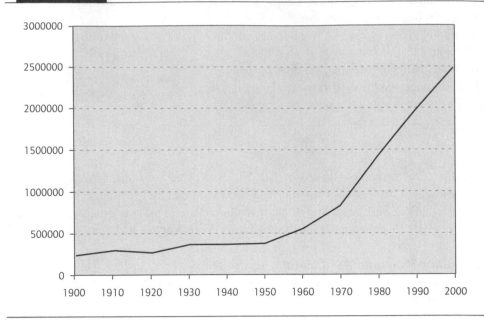

SOURCE: 1900-1990, Thornton (2001), p. 137; 2000, U.S. Bureau of the Census (2001b).

attainment across the tribes, with the Navaho considerably below and some tribes actually exceeding national norms at the high school level. None of the 10 largest tribes matches national norms at the college level.

The educational levels of American Indians are displayed in Exhibit 8.10. The differences in schooling are especially important because the lower levels of educational attainment limit mobility and job opportunities in the postindustrial job market.

One positive development for the education of American Indians is the rapid increase in tribally controlled colleges, more than 30 of which have been built since the 1960s. These institutions are mostly 2-year community colleges located on or near reservations, and some have been constructed with funds generated in the gaming industry. They are designed to be more sensitive to the educational and cultural needs of the group, and tribal college graduates who transfer to 4-year colleges are more likely to graduate than other American Indian students (Pego, 1998; see also American Indian Higher Education Consortium, 2001).

*Political Power.* The ability of American Indians to exert power as a voting bloc or to otherwise directly affect the political structure is very limited by group size; they are a tiny percentage of the electorate. Furthermore, their political power is limited by their lower average levels of education, language differences, lack of economic resources, and fractional differences within and between tribes and reservations. The number of American Indians holding elected office is minuscule, far less than 1% (Pollard & O'Hare, 1999, p. 41). In 1992, however, Ben Nighthorse Campbell of Colorado became the first American Indian to be elected to the U.S. Senate, and he still held his seat as of 2004.

*Jobs and Income.* Some of the most severe challenges facing American Indians relate to work and income. The problems are especially evident on the reservations, where jobs have traditionally been scarce and affluence rare. As in the case of African Americans, the

**EXHIBIT 8.8**

Percentage of People Choosing American Indian or Alaska Native
Designations, Alone or in Combination, 2000

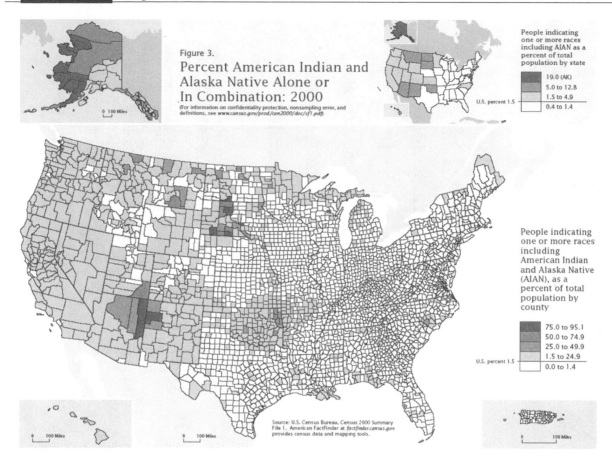

Figure 3.

## Percent American Indian and Alaska Native Alone or In Combination: 2000

(For information on confidentiality protection, nonsampling error, and definitions, see www.census.gov/prod/cen2000/doc/sf1.pdf)

People indicating one or more races including AIAN as a percent of total population by state

- 19.0 (AK)
- 5.0 to 12.8
- 1.5 to 4.9
- 0.4 to 1.4

U.S. percent 1.5

People indicating one or more races including American Indian and Alaska Native (AIAN), as a percent of total population by county

- 75.0 to 95.1
- 50.0 to 74.9
- 25.0 to 49.9
- 1.5 to 24.9
- 0.0 to 1.4

U.S. percent 1.5

Source: U.S. Census Bureau, Census 2000 Summary File 1. American FactFinder at *factfinder.census.gov* provides census data and mapping tools.

SOURCE: Ogunwole (2002).

---

**EXHIBIT 8.9**     Population of the 10 Largest Tribes (American Indians Alone and in Combination)

| Tribe | Population | Percentage of all American Indians |
|-------|-----------|-----------------------------------|
| Cherokee | 729,533 | 18 |
| Navaho | 298,197 | 7 |
| Choctaw | 158,774 | 4 |
| Sioux | 153,360 | 4 |
| Chippewa | 149,669 | 4 |
| Apache | 96,833 | 2 |
| Blackfeet | 85,750 | 2 |
| Iroquois | 80,822 | 2 |
| Pueblo | 74,085 | 2 |
| Creek | 71,310 | 2 |
| All American Indians | 4,119,301 | 46 |

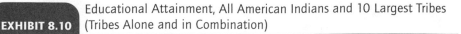

**EXHIBIT 8.10** Educational Attainment, All American Indians and 10 Largest Tribes (Tribes Alone and in Combination)

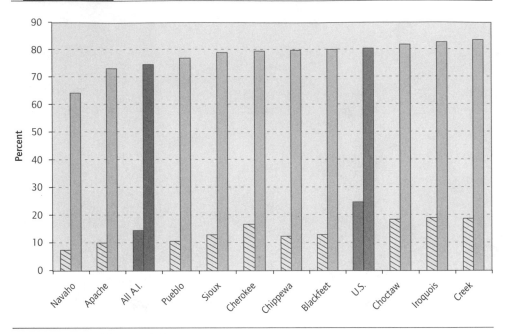

SOURCE: U.S. Bureau of the Census (n.d.).

NOTE: Solid bars indicate percentage older than 25 with high school degree; striped bars, percentage older than 25 with college degree.

overall unemployment rate for all American Indians is about double the rate for whites. For Indians living on or near reservations, however, the rate is much higher. It averaged 50% in 1997 (U.S. Bureau of Indian Affairs, 1997) but ranged up to 70% to 80% on the smaller, more isolated reservations.

Nationally, American Indians are underrepresented in the higher status, more lucrative professions and overrepresented in unskilled labor and service jobs. As is the case for African Americans, American Indians who hold white-collar jobs are more likely than whites to work in relatively low-level occupations such as typist or retail salesperson (Pollard & O'Hare, 1999, p. 33).

Income data reflect the higher levels of unemployment and lower levels of education. In 1979, median household income for American Indians was $20,500, which was 68% of the median household income for non-Hispanic whites (O'Hare, 1992, p 34). By the 2000 census, this figure had risen to 32,225, still only 76% of the median household income nationally. In 1969, about one third of all American Indian families had incomes below the federal poverty line, and the percentage living in poverty was higher on the reservations (Snipp, 1992, pp. 362-363). By 2000, the percentage had fallen to 22%, almost double the national rate (see Exhibits 8.11 and 8.12).

The interlocking forces of past discrimination, lack of development on the reservation, and lower levels of educational attainment have severely limited the range of job opportunities and

EXHIBIT 8.11

Median Household Income, All American Indians and 10 Largest
Tribes (Tribes Alone and in Combination)

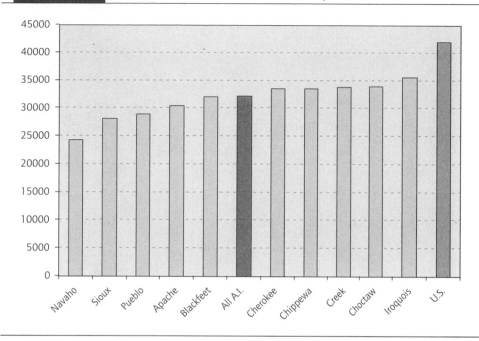

SOURCE: U.S. Bureau of the Census (n.d.).

career possibilities for American Indians. However, the rural isolation of the reservations and their distance from the centers of growth and development limit possibilities for improvement and raise the likelihood that many reservations will remain the rural counterparts to urban underclass ghettoes.

**Primary Structural Assimilation.** Rates of intermarriage for American Indians are quite high compared with other groups. In 1980, only about half of all married Indians were married to other Indians. In contrast, the rate of within-group marriage for whites and blacks was about 99%. The higher rate of marriage outside the group for American Indians is partly the result of the small size of the group. In New England, which has the lowest relative percentage of American Indians in any region, less than 10% of Indian marriages are within the group. By contrast, in the mountain states, which have a greater number of American Indians who are also highly concentrated on reservations, more than 60% of Indian marriages are within the group (Snipp, 1989, pp. 156-159).

The higher rate of marriage outside the group is also an indication of the extent of acculturation and integration for American Indians. Marriages with non-Indians are much more common in metropolitan areas, away from the reservations. They are also associated with higher levels of education, greater participation in the labor force, higher income levels, and lower rates of poverty (Snipp, 1989, pp. 160-164). Thus marriage with non-Indians is more characteristic for American Indians who have left the reservation to pursue opportunities for education and careers in the cities.

EXHIBIT 8.12

**Percentage of Poor, All American Indians and 10 Largest Tribes (Tribes Alone and in Combination)**

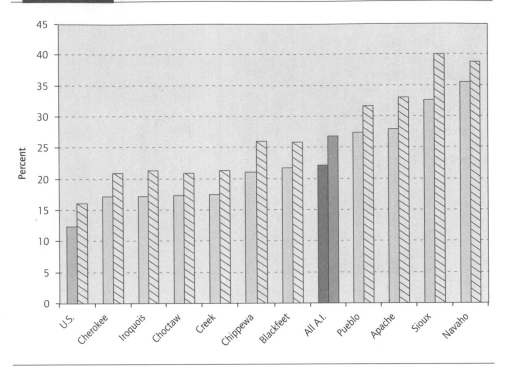

SOURCE: U.S. Bureau of the Census (n.d.).

NOTE: Solid bars indicate percentage of all people below poverty line; striped bars, percentage of children (younger than 18 years) below poverty line.

## Comparing Minority Groups

This chapter has focused on American Indians, but comparing their experiences with other groups will further our understanding of the complexities of dominant-minority relationships and permit us to test the explanatory power of the concepts and theories that are central to this text. No two minority groups have had the same experiences, and our concepts and theories should help us understand the differences and the similarities. We begin by comparing American Indians with African Americans.

First, note the differences in the stereotypes attached to the two groups during the early years of European colonization. While Indians were seen as "cruel savages," African Americans under slavery were seen as "lazy, irresponsible, and in constant need of supervision and direction." The two stereotypes are consistent with the outcomes of the contact period. The supposed irresponsibility of blacks under slavery helped justify their subordinate, highly controlled status, and the alleged savagery of American Indians helped to justify their near extermination by white society.

Second, both American Indians and African Americans were colonized minority groups, but their contact situations were governed by very different dynamics (competition for labor vs. land) and a very different dominant group agenda (the capture and control of a large, powerless work force vs. the elimination of a military threat). These differing contact situations shaped subsequent relationships with the dominant group and the place of the groups in the larger society.

For example, consider the situations of the two groups a century ago. For African Americans, their most visible enemy was de jure segregation, the elaborate system of repression in the South that controlled them politically, economically, and socially (see chapters 6 and 7). In particular, the Southern system of agriculture needed the black population—but only as a powerless, cheap work force. The goals of African Americans centered on dismantling this oppressive system, assimilation, and equality.

American Indians, in contrast, were not viewed as a source of labor and were far too few in number and too dispersed geographically to constitute a political threat. Thus there was little need to control them in the same way African Americans were controlled. The primary enemies of the tribes were the reservation system, various agencies of the federal government (especially the Bureau of Indian Affairs), rural isolation, and the continuing attacks on their traditional cultures and lifestyles, which are typical for a colonized minority group. American Indians had a different set of problems, different resources at their disposal, and different goals in mind. They have always been more oriented toward a pluralistic relationship with the larger society and preserving what they could of their autonomy, their institutions, and their heritage. African Americans spent much of the 20th century struggling for inclusion and equality; American Indians were fighting to maintain or recover their traditional cultures and social structures. This difference in goals reflects the different histories of the two groups and the different circumstances surrounding their colonization.

## PROGRESS AND CHALLENGES

What does the future hold for American Indians? Their situation has certainly changed over the past 100 years, but is it "better" or just "different," as is the case for large segments of the African American community? The answer seems to be a little of both, as the group grows in size and becomes even more diversified. To reach some conclusions, we will look at several aspects of the situation of American Indians and assess the usefulness of our theoretical models and concepts.

Since the 1960s, the decline of intolerance in the society at large, the growth of pride in ancestry in many groups (e.g., black power), and the shift in federal government policy to encourage self-determination have all helped to spark a reaffirmation of commitment to tribal cultures and traditions. As was the case with African Americans and the Black Power movement, the Red Power movement asserted a distinct and positive Indian identity, a claim for the equal validity of American Indian cultures within the broad framework of the larger society. During the same time period, the favorable settlements of treaty claims, the growth in job opportunities, and the gambling industry have enhanced the flow of resources and benefits to the reservations. In popular culture, American Indians have enjoyed a strong upsurge of popularity and sympathetic depictions. This enhanced popularity accounts for much of the growth in population size as people of mixed ancestry resurrect and reconstruct their Indian ancestors and their own ethnic identities.

Linear or simplistic views of assimilation do not fit the current situation or the past experiences of American Indians very well. Some American Indians are intermarrying with whites and integrating into the larger society; others strive to retain a tribal culture in the midst of an

## Australian Aborigines and American Indians

The history of American Indians—their conquest and domination by a larger, more powerful society—has a number of parallels from around the globe, a reflection of the rise of European societies to power and their frequent conquest of indigenous societies in Africa, North and South America, and Asia. A comparative analysis of these episodes suggests that similar dynamics have come into play, even though each has its own unique history. To illustrate, we will use some of the concepts developed in this text to compare the impact of European domination on Australian Aborigines and the indigenous peoples of North America.

Australia came under European domination in the late 1700s, nearly two centuries after the establishment of Jamestown and the beginning of Anglo-American Indian relations. In other ways, however, the two contact situations shared many features. In both cases, the colonial power was Great Britain, and first contacts occurred in the preindustrial era (although Britain had begun to industrialize by the late 1700s). Also, the indigenous peoples of both North America and Australia were thinly spread across vast areas and were greatly inferior to the British in their technological development.

The Aboriginal peoples had lived in Australia for 50,000 years by the time the British arrived. Estimates of their population size vary, but there may have been as many as a million Aborigines at the time of contact with the British ("A Sorry Tale," 2000). They were organized into small, nomadic, hunting-and-gathering bands and were generally much less developed than the tribes of North America, lacking the population base, social organization, and resources that would have permitted sustained resistance to the invasion of their land. There was plenty of violence in the contact situation, but unlike the situation in North America, no sustained military campaigns pitting large armies against each other.

The initial thrust of colonization was motivated by Great Britain's need for a place to send its convicts after losing the Revolutionary War to the fledgling United States. The European population in Australia grew slowly at first and consisted mostly of prisoners. The early economic enterprises centered on subsistence farming and sheepherding, not large-scale enterprises that required forced labor (at least not on the same scale as in North America).

Relations between the English and the Aborigines were hostile and centered on competition for land. In their ethnocentrism, the invaders denied that the Aborigines had any claims to the land and simply pushed them aside or killed them if they resisted. As in the Americas, European diseases took their toll, and the indigenous population declined rapidly. Because they were not desired as laborers (although many became semi-unfree servants), they were pushed away from the areas of white settlement into the fringes of development, where they and their grievances could be ignored. As in North America, they were seen as "savages," a culture that would (and in the view of the emerging dominant group, should) wither away and disappear.

To the extent that there was contact with the larger society, it was often in the form of coercive acculturation. For example, throughout much of the 20th century, the Australian government, aided by various church organizations, actually removed children of mixed parentage from their

Aboriginal mothers and placed them in orphanages. The idea behind this program was to give these children a chance to leave their Aboriginal culture behind, marry whites, and enter the larger society. This policy, abandoned only in the 1960s, resulted in the state-sponsored orphaning of thousands of Aboriginal children. Some of the angriest and most militant members of the current generation of Aborigines belong to this "stolen generation" (for a report on this program, see Australian Human Rights and Equal Opportunity Commission, 1997).

The contemporary situation of Australian Aborigines has many parallels with American Indians, as does their past. The group is largely rural and continues to live on land that is less desirable. After the initial—and dramatic— declines, their numbers have been increasing of late, partly because of higher birth rates and partly because of changing perceptions, growing sympathy for their plight, and increased willingness of people to claim their aboriginal heritage. The population fell to a low of less than 100,000 at the start of the 20th century but is now put at 427,000, or about 2% of the total population (Australian Bureau of Statistics, 2002).

Just as in North America, there is a huge gap between the indigenous population and the rest of society on every statistic that measures quality of life, equality, and access to resources. Life expectancy for Aborigines is as much as 20 years lower than the general population, and their infant mortality rate is 2 to 3 times higher. They have much less access to health care, and Aboriginal communities are much more afflicted with alcoholism, suicide, and malnutrition than the general population. Unemployment rates are double the rate in the general population, average income is about 65% of the national average, and only about a third as many Aboriginal people (13.6%) as the national population (34.4%) are in school at age 19 (Brace, 2001; see also Australian Bureau of Statistics, 2002). The issues animating Aboriginal affairs have a familiar ring for anyone familiar with American Indians. They include concerns for the preservation of Aboriginal culture, language, and identity; self-determination and autonomy; the return of lands illegally taken by the Anglo invaders; and an end to discrimination and unequal treatment.

As in North America, Aboriginal relations are in flux, and the overall picture is mixed. For example, in 1998, the federal government of Australia was condemned by the United Nations Committee on the Elimination of Racial Discrimination for its handling of Aboriginal land claims. Australia is the only developed nation to have ever received this censure (Pilger, 2000). On the other hand, the opening ceremonies of the 2000 Olympic games in Sydney featured a celebration of Aboriginal culture, dance, music, and art, and Aboriginal athlete Cathy Freeman lit the Olympic flame.

The Aboriginal peoples of Australia, like American Indians, face many—often overwhelming—challenges to secure a better future for themselves and for their children. Their history and their present situation clearly validate both the Blauner and Noel hypotheses: They are a colonized minority group, victims of European domination, with all that that status implies.

urbanized, industrialized society; and still others labor to use the profits from gaming and other enterprises for the benefit of the tribe as a whole. Members of the group can be found at every degree of acculturation and integration, and the group seems to be moving toward assimilation in some ways and away from it in others.

From the standpoint of the Noel and Blauner hypotheses, we can see that American Indians have struggled with conquest and colonization, experiences made more difficult by the loss of so much of their land and other resources and by the concerted, unrelenting attacks on their culture and language. The legacy of conquest and colonization was poor health and housing, an inadequate and misdirected education system, and slow (or nonexistent) economic development. For most of this century, American Indians were left to survive as best they could on the margins of the larger society, too powerless to establish meaningful pluralism and too colonized to pursue equality.

Today, the key to further progress for many, if not all, members of this group is economic development on reservation lands and the further strengthening of the tribes as functioning social units. Some tribes do have assets—natural resources, treaty rights, and the gambling industry—that could fuel development. However, they often do not have the expertise or the capital to finance the exploitation of these resources. They must rely, in whole or in part, on non-Indian expertise and white-owned companies and businesses. Thus, non-Indians, rather than the tribes, may be the primary beneficiaries of some forms of development (this would, of course, be quite consistent with American history). For those reservations for which gambling is not an option and for those without natural resources, investments in human capital (education) may offer the most compelling direction for future development.

Even though research is scant, it is clear that urban Indians confront the same patterns of discrimination and racism that confront other minority groups of color. Members of the group with lower levels of education and job skills face the prospects of becoming a part of a permanent urban underclass. More educated and skilled American Indians share with African Americans the prospect of a middle-class lifestyle that is more partial and tenuous than that of comparable segments of the dominant group.

The situation of American Indians today is superior to the status of the group a century ago. Given the depressed and desperate conditions of the reservations in the early 20th century, however, it would not take much to show an improvement. American Indians are growing rapidly in numbers and are increasingly diversified by residence, education, and degree of assimilation. Some tribes have made dramatic progress over the past several decades, but enormous problems remain, both on and off the reservations. The challenge for the future, as it was in the past, is to find a course between pluralism and assimilation, pantribalism and traditional lifestyles that will balance the issues of quality of life against the importance of retaining an Indian identity.

## Are Indian Sports Team Mascots Offensive?

American Indians face many challenges as they address persistent problems such as unemployment and poverty. Some of the issues they face are not about money and jobs but are, rather, symbolic and perceptual. How are American Indians seen by the larger society? What stereotypes linger in American popular culture? How might these stereotypes affect the ability of American Indians to argue their causes?

The controversies over using Indian mascots for athletic teams illustrate these symbolic battles. Is there any real harm in using team names such as Indians, Seminoles, or Braves? Are people who object to these names carrying political correctness and sensitivity too far?

The excerpts below present both sides of this argument. Journalists Price and Woo, in the March 4, 2002 issue of Sports Illustrated (SI), argue that the team names are not offensive to sports fans and, in fact, to most American Indians. The opposing point of view is presented by a group of five academics and Indian activists. They raise a number of issues about the SI article, including its use of polling and what they see as a profound bias on the part of the authors and the magazine. In this selection, their analysis of stereotypes and American Indians is presented.

## Indian Symbols and Mascots are not Offensive

### S. L. PRICE AND ANDREA WOO

[The thorniest word problem in sports today is] the use of Native American names and mascots by high school, college and professional teams. For more than 30 years the debate has been raging over whether names such as Redskins, Braves, Chiefs and Indians honor or defile Native Americans, whether clownish figures like the Cleveland Indians' Chief Wahoo have any place in today's racially sensitive climate and whether the sight of thousands of non-Native Americans doing the tomahawk chop at Atlanta's Turner Field is mindless fun or mass bigotry. It's an argument that, because it mixes mere sports with the sensitivities of a people who were nearly exterminated, seems both trivial and profound....

[The case of Betty Ann Gross, a member of the Sisseton-Wahpeton Sioux tribe] illustrates how slippery the issue can be. She grew up on a reservation in South Dakota and went to Sisseton High, a public school on the reservation whose teams are called the Redmen. Gross, 49, can't recall a time when people on the reservation weren't arguing about the team name, evenly divided between those who were proud of it and those who were ashamed. Gross recently completed a study that led the South Dakota state government to change the names of 38 places and landmarks around the state, yet she has mixed feelings on the sports issue. She wants Indian mascots and the tomahawk chop discarded, but she has no problem with team names like the Fighting Sioux (University of North Dakota) or even the Redskins. "There's a lot of division," Gross says....

Although most Native American activists and tribal leaders consider Indian team names and mascots offensive, neither Native Americans in general nor a cross-section of U.S. sports fans agree. That is one of the findings of a poll conducted for SI.... The pollsters interviewed 351 Native Americans (217 living on reservations and 134 living off) and 743 fans. Their responses were weighted according to U.S. census figures for age, race and gender and for distribution of Native Americans on and off reservations. With a margin of error of ± 4%, 83% of the Indians said that professional teams should not stop using Indian nicknames, mascots or symbols, and 79% of the fans agreed with them.... When pollsters asked about the Washington Redskins, they found no great resentment toward the name. Instead, they again found agreement between Native Americans and fans (69% of the former and 74% of the latter do not object to the name)....

Regardless, the campaign to erase Indian team names and symbols nationwide has been a success. Though Native American activists have made little progress at the highest level of pro sports ... their single-minded pursuit of the issue has literally changed the face of sports in the U.S. Since 1969 ... more than 600 school teams and minor league professional clubs have dropped nicknames deemed offensive by Native American groups....

While those who support names such as Seminoles (Florida State) and [Atlanta] Braves can argue that the words celebrate Native American traditions, applying that claim to the Redskins is absurd. Nevertheless, Redskins vice president Karl Swanson says the name "symbolizes courage, dignity and leadership and has always been employed in that manner"—conveniently ignoring the fact that in popular usage dating back four centuries, the word has been a slur based on skin color.... Many experts on Native American history point out that ... the word redskin was first used by whites who paid and received bounties for dead Indians....

However, what's most important, Swanson counters, is intent: Because the Redskins and their fans mean nothing racist by using the nickname, it isn't racist or offensive. Not so, says Suzan Harjo (a Native American activist): "There's no more derogatory word that's used against us ... in the English language.... Everyone knows that it has never been an honorific. It's a terrible insult."...

That the name is offensive to Native Americans is easy for non-Natives to presume. It resonates when an Olympic hero and former Marine Corps captain such as Billy Mills (a Native American and a Gold Medal winner in the 1964 Olympics), who speaks out against Indian names and mascots at schools around the country, insists that a team named Redskins in the capital of the nation that committed genocide against Native Americans is the equivalent of a soccer team in Germany being called the Berlin Kikes.

Somehow that message is lost on most of Mills's fellow Native Americans. Asked if they were offended by the name Redskins, 75% of Native American respondents in SI's poll said they were not, and even on reservations, where Native American culture and influence are perhaps felt most intensely, 62% said they weren't offended.... Only 29% of Native Americans ... thought [the owner of the Redskins] should change his team's name. Such indifference implies a near total disconnect between Native American activists and the general Native American population on this issue....

The Utes' experience with the University of Utah might serve as a model for successful resolution of conflicts over Indian nicknames. Four years ago the council met with university officials, who made it clear that they would change their teams' name, the Running Utes, if the tribe found it objectionable.... The council was perfectly happy to have the Ute name continue to circulate in the nations' sports pages.... Florida State, likewise, uses the name Seminoles for its teams with the express approval of the Seminole nation.... Like the Ute tribe, most Native Americans have no problem with teams using [Indian] names....

SOURCE: Price, S. L. Woo, Andrea. March 4, 2002. "Poles Apart," *Sports Illustrated*, *96*(10). March 4, 2002. "The Indian Wars." *Sports Illustrated*, *96*(10): 66-73.

## Mascots are Offensive

C. RICHARD KING, ELLEN J. STAUROWSKY, LAWRENCE BACA, R. DAVIS, AND CORNEL PEWEWARDY

To fully understand both the SI article and ongoing controversy about mascots, one must grasp the history of Indian symbols in sports.... Native American mascots emerged (mainly) in the early 1900s, after [the end of military hostilities] . . . These mascots were part of a larger phenomena of increased prevalence of Native American images in U.S. popular culture, including Western movies, symbols for beer and butter, and art in homes. One of the reasons why most Americans find the mascots unremarkable . . . is because of the prevalence of similar images throughout U.S. popular culture. . . .

Historically, the most popular sport mascots have been animals associated with aggression (e.g., Tigers) and Native Americans (e.g., Indians, Chiefs, Braves, and so forth). Although other ethnic groups have been occasionally used as mascots, these mascots differ from Native American mascots in several ways: [these mascots] are often (a) a people that do not exist today (e.g., Spartans); (b) less associated with aggression (e.g., Scots); (c) selected by people from the same ethnicity (e.g., Irish Americans at Notre Dame); and (d) not mimicked to nearly the same degree.

Native American mascots emerged in a context in which many non–Native Americans were "playing Indian." Still today, children don "Indian" costumes at Halloween, "act like Indians" during "Cowboy and Indian" games, "become Indian Princesses" at the YMCA, and perform "Indian rituals" at summer camps. Adults belong to organizations that involve learning "Indian ways" and performing "Indian rituals." Non–Native Americans have created an imaginary version of Indianness that they sometimes enact, and they expect real Native Americans to either ignore, affirm, or validate such myths and practices. Similar practices applied to other races/ethnicities, such as "playing Black" or "playing Jewish," would not be accepted in our society today.

Activism against Native American mascots has been evident for more than 30 years. Since the early 1990s, this activism has become more widespread [and] emerged from Native American individuals, groups, and communities that work on a variety of other issues, such as treaty, economic, cultural, environmental, health, and educational issues. Although many U.S. citizens see the mascot issue as emerging "out of the blue," many Native American organizations see the elimination of such mascots as part of a larger agenda of reducing societal stereotyping about Native Americans (in the media, school curriculums, and so forth) and informing the public about the realities of Native American lives. An increase in accurate information about Native Americans is viewed as necessary for the achievement of other goals such as poverty reduction, educational advancements, and securing treaty rights.

Anti-mascot activists articulate many different arguments against the mascots. First, they assert that the mascots stereotype Native Americans as only existing in the past, having a single culture, and being aggressive fighters. Second, they hold that these stereotypes influence the way people perceive and treat Native Americans. Such imagery is seen as affecting Native American images of themselves, creating a hostile climate for many Native Americans, and preventing people from understanding current Native American realities, which affects public policy relative to Native Americans. Third, the activists state that no racial/cultural group should be mimicked (especially in regard to sacred items/practices), even if such mimicking is "culturally accurate." And fourth, they argue that Native Americans should have control over how they are represented. . . .

Native American mascots are rooted in the bloodthirsty savage stereotype, as it is this stereotype that is linked to desirable athletic qualities such as having a fighting spirit and being aggressive, brave, stoic, proud, and persevering. . . .

Of course, even [this] so-called positive stereotype [is] ultimately negative. [All] stereotypes fail to recognize diversity among the people who are being stereotyped. . . . Most people deny that they believe any racial stereotypes. . . . When we do notice our own stereotyping, it is often because our beliefs are very negative (e.g., believing that African Americans are criminal or Puerto Ricans are lazy). When our stereotypes are "positive" (e.g., Jews as good at business or Asians as smart), we tend to think that these beliefs are not stereotypical and thus not racist.

Sport mascots are based on what is today perceived as "positive" ideas about Native Americans: that they are brave, principled, persevering, good fighters. This "positive cast" to the mascot stereotype leads most to conclude that the mascots are not racist. In fact, it is this "positive cast" to the mascot stereotype that leads many mascot supporters to think that the mascots actually counter racism by "honoring" Native Americans. . . .

It is not surprising that some Native Americans embrace "positive" stereotypes of Native Americans, and thus that some are not critical of Native American mascots. There are several factors that encourage Native Americans to accept, internalize, celebrate, and even capitalize on, "positive" stereotypes of Native Americans. First, many people do not define so-called positive stereotypes as stereotypes or racist. In fact, a group that experiences a great deal of inequality may be especially attracted to any imagery that is positive, as such imagery might be a relief from the negative. Second, throughout much of U.S. history, Native people have faced intense pressures to acculturate and have been exposed to many of the same stereotypical images of Native Americans as non-Natives have. These pressures have certainly resulted in some Natives adopting "dominant/White/outsider views" of Native Americans. Third, given the destruction of Native economies and the resulting economic destitution, some Native people have turned to the marketing of their ethnicity, or an acceptable Hollywood version of their ethnicity, to survive, including teaching "Native spirituality" to non-Native Americans; selling Native jewelry and art; and managing Native tourist establishments.

In conclusion, to understand the Native American mascot issue, and the SI article, one needs to understand the social context surrounding the mascots. Most important, one must understand the historically rooted, but contemporarily alive, stereotypes of Native Americans. Native American mascots emerged from these stereotypes, and these mascots continue to reinforce these stereotypes. The continued prevalence of these stereotypes inhibits social changes that would better contemporary Native American lives.

SOURCE: King, C. Richard, Staurowsky, Ellen J., Baca, Lawrence, Davis, R., and Pewewardy, Cornel. 2002. "Of Polls and Race Prejudice: *Sports Illustrated*'s Errant "Indian Wars." *Journal of Sport and Social Issues,* 26: 381-403.

## Debate Questions to Consider

1. Price and Woo argue that the majority of American Indians polled did not object to the use of Indian team mascots. How relevant is this point to the debate? Should questions such as these be decided by "popular vote," or are there deeper principles that should guide public policy? If so, what are those principles and how should they be applied?

2. Price and Woo quote an official of the Washington Redskins franchise as arguing that the team uses the term to honor American Indians for their courage and dignity. Should "intent" matter in deciding if a term is insulting or offensive? Who should decide these matters? The team? The tribes? Someone else?

3. What arguments do King et al. make about why these matters are important? What *real* harm comes from using Indian team mascots? Are their arguments convincing? Why or why not? What are "positive stereotypes," and how do they differ (if at all) from negative stereotypes? Are positive stereotypes less harmful than negative stereotypes?

4. Is there a gender dimension to these arguments? Price and Woo mention the controversy about a South Dakota High School using "Redmen" as a team name. What do you suppose the women's teams at this school were called? Lady Redmen? Redwomen? How is this handled on your campus? Are the women's athletic teams distinguished by adding the modifier "Lady" or "Women"? What issues arise from this (very common) pattern? How do these issues matter?

5. Ultimately, is all of this just a matter of political correctness? What is at stake here (if anything)?

# MAIN POINTS

■ American Indian and Anglo-American cultures are vastly different, and these differences have hampered communication and understanding, usually in ways that harmed American Indians or weakened the integrity of their tribal structures.

■ At the beginning of the 20th century, American Indians faced the paternalistic reservation system, poverty and powerlessness, rural isolation and marginalization, and the BIA. American Indians continued to lose land and other resources.

■ The Indian Reorganization Act (IRA) of 1934 attempted to increase tribal autonomy and to provide mechanisms for improving the quality of life on the reservations. The policy of termination was proposed in the 1950s. The policy was a disaster, and the tribes that were terminated suffered devastating economic losses and drastic declines in quality of life.

■ American Indians began to urbanize rapidly in the 1950s but are still less urbanized than the population as a whole. They are the least urbanized American minority group.

■ The Red Power movement rose to prominence in the 1960s and had some successes but was often simply ignored. The Red Power movement was partly assimilationist even though it pursued pluralistic goals and greater autonomy for the tribes.

■ Current conflicts between American Indians and the dominant group center on control of natural resources, preservation of treaty rights, and treaties that have been broken in the past. Another possible source of development and conflict is in the potentially lucrative gambling industry.

■ There is some indication that anti-Indian prejudice has shifted to more "modern" forms. Institutional discrimination and access to education and employment remain major problems confronting American Indians.

■ American Indians have preserved much of their traditional culture, although in altered form. The secondary structural assimilation of American Indians is low and, on many measures of quality of life, they are the most impoverished American minority group. Primary structural assimilation is comparatively high.

■ Over the course of the last 100 years, American Indians have struggled from a position of powerlessness and isolation. Today, the group faces an array of problems similar to those faced by all American colonized minority groups of color as they try to find ways to raise their quality of life and continue their commitment to their tribes and to an Indian identity.

■ The public sociology assignment on page 218 will acquaint you with the history of Indian loss of land in your area and with the continuing unique relationship between American Indian tribes and the federal government. How did the loss of land you will document contribute to the present status of the tribe?

### Study Site on the Web

Don't forget the interactive quizzes and other resources and learning aids at www.www.pineforge.com/healeystudy4.

## For Further Reading

Amott, Teresa, & Matthaei, Julie. 1991. "I Am the Fire of Time: American Indian Women." In T. Amott & J. Matthaei (Eds.), *Race, Gender, and Work: A Multicultural History of Women in the United States* (pp. 31-62). Boston: South End Press. *(Good overview of the history and present situation of American Indian women.)*

Bordewich, Fergus. 1996. *Killing the White Man's Indian.* New York: Doubleday. *(A comprehensive, dispassionate analysis of current problems and future possibilities.)*

Brown, Dee. 1970. *Bury My Heart at Wounded Knee.* New York: Holt, Rinehart, & Winston. *(A passionately written, highly readable account of the military defeat and the establishment of dominance over American Indians.)*

Deloria, Vine. 1995. *Red Earth, White Lies.* New York: Scribner's.

Deloria, Vine. 1970. *We Talk, You Listen.* New York: Macmillan.

Deloria, Vine. 1969. *Custer Died for Your Sins.* New York: Macmillan. *(The three major works of the well-known American Indian activist, writer, and professor of Indian studies.)*

Nabakov, Peter (Ed.). 1999. *Native American Testimony.* New York: Penguin. *(A collection of personal accounts by American Indians from pre-Colombian times to the present day.)*

Snipp, C. Matthew. 1989. *American Indians: The First of This Land.* New York: Russell Sage Foundation. *(A valuable scholarly study covering a variety of aspects of the American Indian condition.)*

Wax, Murray. 1971. *Indian Americans: Unity and Diversity.* Englewood Cliffs, NJ: Prentice Hall. *(A leading authority's view of the history and contemporary situation of American Indians.)*

## Questions for Review and Study

1. What were the most important cultural differences between American Indian tribes and the dominant society? How did these affect relations between the two groups?

2. Compare and contrast the effects of paternalism and coercive acculturation on American Indians after the end of the contact period with those of African Americans under slavery. What similarities and differences existed in the two situations? Which system was more oppressive and controlling? How? How did these different situations shape the futures of the groups?

3. How did federal Indian policy change over the course of the 20th century? What effects did these changes have on the tribes? Which were more beneficial? Why? What was the role of the Indian protest movement in shaping these policies?

4. What options do American Indians have for improving their position in the larger society and developing their reservations? Which strategies seem to have the most promise? Which seem less effective? Why?

5. Compare and contrast the contact situations of American Indians, African Americans, and Australian Aborigines. What are the most crucial differences in the situations? What implications did these differences have for the development of each group's situation after the initial contact situation?

6. Characterize the present situation of American Indians in terms of acculturation and integration. How do they compare to African Americans? What factors in the experiences of the two groups might help explain contemporary differences?

7. What gender differences can you identify in the experiences of American Indians? How do these compare to the gender differences in the experiences of African Americans?

8. Given the information and ideas presented in this chapter, speculate about the future of American Indians. How likely are American Indian cultures and languages to survive? What are the prospects for achieving equality?

## Internet Research Projects

Additional information and a list of relevant Web sites are included in the Appendix (Internet Resources).

Use the Internet to develop a profile of American Indians by answering the questions asked here. Some addresses are provided as starting points, but you will have to use your own initiative to cruise the Internet and answer all questions fully.

**A. Numbers (U.S. Bureau of the Census: http://www.census.gov; Bureau of Indian Affairs: http://www.doi.gov/bureau-indian-affairs.html)**

1. Counting people who select only one racial category, how many American Indians are there?

2. How does the number change when people who selected more than one category are counted as members of the group?

3. Which of these two totals (if either) should be regarded as the "true" number of American Indians? Why?

4. How many separate tribes are recognized by the federal government?

5. How many federal reservations are there? In what regions of the nation are they concentrated? Which is the largest? Which is the smallest?

**B. Gambling (National Indian Gaming Association: http://www .indiangaming.org/)**

1. How many reservations are involved in gaming or gambling?

2. What is the approximate annual revenue from these enterprises?

3. How is that revenue used?

**C. Health (Indian Health Services: http://www.ihs.gov)**

1. What are the birth rates and death rates for American Indians?

2. Are these higher or lower than national norms or the rates for white Americans?

3. What are the mortality rates for various age groups compared with national norms?

|  | Death Rates | National Norms |
|---|---|---|
| Infants (ages 0–1) | | |
| Young adults (18–25) | | |
| Senior citizens (65+) | | |

4. Select two age groups and find the five most common causes of death for the group.

| Age Group 1 | Age Group 2 |
|---|---|
| 1. _____ | 1. _____ |
| 2. _____ | 2. _____ |
| 3. _____ | 3. _____ |
| 4. _____ | 4. _____ |
| 5. _____ | 5. _____ |

5. Describe how these patterns vary from national norms.

**D. Issues (National Congress of American Indians: http://www.ncai.org. Also, search for American Indian newspapers or periodicals that are online. For example, Indian Country Today, "America's Leading Indian News Source," is available at http://www.indiancountry.com)**

1. Cite and briefly explain three current issues in *Indian Country Today* or whatever newspaper or periodical you've found.

2. Analyze each issue in terms of the concepts used in the text (especially assimilation, pluralism, self-determination or development of the reservation, institutional discrimination, protest and resistance, and inequality).

3. How would members of other groups (e.g., white or black Americans) view each issue?

# 9

# Hispanic Americans

## Colonization, Immigration, and Ethnic Enclaves

THE UNITED STATES IS HOME TO MANY DIFFERENT SPANISH-ORIGIN GROUPS. BEFORE THE Declaration of Independence was signed, before slavery began, even before Jamestown was founded, the ancestors of some of these groups were already in North America. Other Hispanic groups are recent immigrants and new members of U.S. society. The label Hispanic American includes a number of groups that are diverse and distinct from each other. These groups connect themselves to a variety of traditions; like the larger society, they are dynamic and changeable, unfinished and evolving. Hispanic Americans share a language and some cultural traits but do not generally think of themselves as a single social entity. Many identify with their national-origin groups (e.g., Mexican American) rather than broader, more encompassing labels, and politically, the group has not acted as a united voting bloc (Camarillo & Bonilla, 2001, p. 119).

In this chapter, we look at the development of Hispanic American groups over the past century, examine their contemporary relations with the larger society, and assess their current status. We focus on the three largest Hispanic groups: Mexican Americans, Puerto Ricans, and Cuban Americans: Exhibit 9.1 shows the size of these groups and some information on growth since 1980. Although Mexican Americans are more than 7% of the total U.S. population (and about two thirds of all Hispanic Americans), the other groups are small in size. Considered as a single group, however, Hispanic Americans are 12.5% of the total population, and they became the largest U.S. minority group, surpassing African Americans, in the spring of 2004. The relative sizes of the major subgroups of Latino Americans are displayed in Exhibit 9.2, and Exhibit 9.3 shows the countries of origin of the three largest Hispanic American groups.

Latinos are growing rapidly, partly because of their relatively high birth rates, but mainly because of immigration. The number of Mexican Americans increased almost 2½ times between 1980 and 2000, and all Hispanic groups are growing at rates above the national average. The growth in both absolute numbers and in relative size is projected to continue well into the century, and Hispanic Americans will become an increasingly

**EXHIBIT 9.1** Size and Recent Growth of Hispanic American Groups Percentage

| Group | 1980 | 1990 | 2000 | Growth (Number of times larger), 1980–2000 | Percentage of Total Population, 2000 |
|---|---|---|---|---|---|
| Mexican Americans | 8,740,000 | 13,496,000 | 20,641,000 | 2.4 | 7.3 |
| Puerto Ricans[a] | 2,014,000 | 2,728,000 | 3,406,000 | 1.7 | 1.2 |
| Cuban Americans | 803,000 | 1,044,000 | 1,242,000 | 1.6 | 0.4 |
| Other Hispanics[b] | 3,051,000 | 5,086,000 | 10,017,000 | 3.3 | 3.6 |
| Total U.S. population | 226,546,000 | 248,710,000 | 281,422,000 | 1.2 | |

SOURCE: 1980 and 1990, Del Pinal and Singer (1997), p. 13; 2000, U.S. Bureau of the Census (2005), p. 25.

a. Living on U.S. mainland only.

b. Includes people from the Dominican Republic, El Salvador, Columbia, Peru, and many other nations.

important part of American life and culture. Today, about 1 out of every 10 Americans is Hispanic, but by 2050, this ratio will increase to 1 out of every 4 (see Exhibit 1.1).

It is appropriate to discuss Hispanic Americans at this point because they include both colonized and immigrant groups, and in that sense, they combine elements of the polar extremes of Blauner's typology of minority groups. We would expect that the Hispanic groups that were more colonized in the past would have much in common with African Americans and Native Americans today. Hispanic groups whose experiences more closely model those of immigrants would have different characteristics and follow different pathways of adaptation. We test these ideas by reviewing the histories of the groups and by analyzing their current status and degree of acculturation and integration.

Two additional introductory comments can be made about Hispanic Americans:

• Hispanic Americans are partly an ethnic minority group (i.e., identified by cultural characteristics such as language) and partly a racial minority group (identified by their physical appearance). Latinos bring a variety of racial backgrounds to U.S. society. For example, most Mexican Americans combine European and Native American ancestry and are identifiable by their physical traits as well as by their cultural and linguistic characteristics. Puerto Ricans, in contrast, are a mixture of white and black ancestry. The original inhabitants of the island, the Arawak and Caribe tribes, were decimated by the Spanish conquest, and the proportion of Native American ancestry is much smaller in Puerto Rico than it is in Mexico. Africans were originally brought to the island as slaves, and there has been considerable intermarriage between whites and blacks. The Puerto Rican population today varies greatly in its racial characteristics, combining every conceivable combination of white and African ancestry. Hispanic Americans are often the victims of racial discrimination in the United States. Racial differences often (but not always) overlap with cultural distinctions and reinforce the separation of Hispanic Americans from Anglo-American society. Even members of the group who are completely acculturated may still experience discrimination based on their physical appearance.

• As is the case with most American minority groups, labels and group names are important. The term Hispanic American is widely applied to this group and might seem neutral and inoffensive to non-Hispanics. In fact, a recent survey shows that a sizeable majority (67%) of

EXHIBIT 9.2    Hispanic Americans by Group

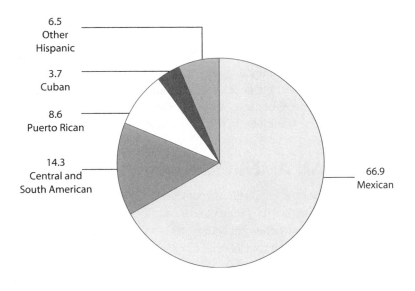

- 6.5 Other Hispanic
- 3.7 Cuban
- 8.6 Puerto Rican
- 14.3 Central and South American
- 66.9 Mexican

EXHIBIT 9.3    Points of Origin for Mexican Americans, Cuban Americans, and Puerto Ricans

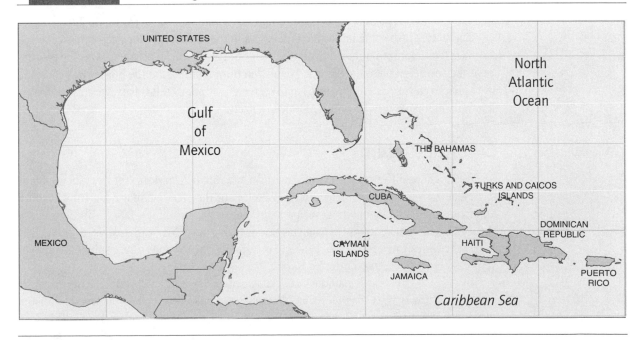

the group prefer this label to Latino (Jones, 2001). However, depending on context, the term can have negative meanings and controversial connotations. For one thing, this label is similar to "American Indian" in that it was invented and applied by the dominant group and may reinforce the mistaken perception that all Spanish-speaking peoples are the same. Also, the term "Hispanic" highlights Spanish heritage and language but does not acknowledge the roots of these groups in African American and Native American civilizations Also, the label is sometimes mistakenly applied to immigrant groups that bring French, Portuguese, or English traditions (e.g., Haitians, Brazilians, and Jamaicans, respectively). On the other hand, the Latino[1] label stresses the common origins of these groups in Latin America and the fact that each culture is a unique blend of diverse traditions. In this chapter, Latino and Hispanic are used interchangeably.

## MEXICAN AMERICANS

We applied the Noel and Blauner hypotheses to this group in chapter 5. Mexicans were conquered and colonized in the 19th century and used as a cheap labor force in agriculture, ranching, mining, railroad construction, and other areas of the dominant group economy in the Southwest. In the competition for control of land and labor, they became a minority group, and the contact situation left them with few power resources with which to pursue their self-interest.

By the dawn of the 20th century, the situation of Mexican Americans resembled that of American Indians in some ways. Both groups were small, numbering about one half of 1% of the total population (Cortes, 1980, p. 702). Both differed from the dominant group in culture and language, and both were impoverished, relatively powerless, and isolated in rural areas distant from the centers of industrialization and modernization. In other ways, Mexican Americans resembled African Americans in the South in that they also supplied much of the labor power for the agricultural economy of their region and both were limited to low-paying occupations and subordinate status in the social structure. All three groups were colonized and, at least in the early decades of the 20th century, lacked the resources to end their exploitation and protect their cultural heritages from continual attack by the dominant society (Mirandé, 1985, p. 32).

There were also some important differences in the situation of Mexican Americans and the other two colonized minority groups. Perhaps the most crucial difference was the proximity of the sovereign nation of Mexico. Population movement across the border was constant, and Mexican culture and the Spanish language were continually rejuvenated, even as they were attacked and disparaged by Anglo-American society.

## Cultural Patterns

Besides language differences, Mexican American and Anglo-American cultures differ in many ways. Whereas the dominant society is largely Protestant, the overwhelming majority of Mexican Americans are Catholic, and the church remains one of the most important institutions in any Mexican American community. Religious practices also vary; Mexican Americans (especially men) are relatively inactive in church attendance, preferring to express their spiritual concerns in more spontaneous, less routinized ways.

In the past, everyday life among Mexican Americans was often described in terms of the "culture of poverty" (see chapter 7), an idea originally based on research in several different Hispanic communities (see Lewis, 1959, 1965, 1966). This perspective asserts that Mexican Americans suffer from an unhealthy value system that includes a weak work ethic, fatalism, and other negative attitudes. Today, this characterization is widely regarded as exaggerated or simply mistaken. More recent research shows that the traits associated with the culture of poverty tend to characterize people who are poor and uneducated, rather than any particular racial or ethnic group. In fact, a number of studies show that there is little difference between the value systems of Mexican Americans and other Americans of similar length of residence in the United States, social class, and educational backgrounds (e.g., see Buriel, 1993; Moore & Pinderhughes, 1993; Valentine & Mosley, 2000).

Another area of cultural difference involves **machismo**, a value system that stresses male dominance, honor, virility, and violence. The stereotypes of the dominant group exaggerate the negative aspects of machismo and often fail to recognize that machismo can also be expressed through being a good provider, a respected father, and in other nondestructive ways. In fact, the concern for male dignity is not unique to Hispanics and can be found in many cultures in varying strengths and expressions, including Anglo-American. Thus this difference is one of degree rather than kind (Moore & Pachon, 1985).

Compared with Anglo-Americans, Mexican Americans tend to place more value on family relations and obligations (see Exhibit 2.4). Strong family ties can be the basis for support networks and cooperative efforts but can also conflict with the emphasis on individualism and individual success in the dominant culture. For example, strong family ties may inhibit geographical mobility and people's willingness to pursue educational and occupational opportunities distant from their home communities (Moore, 1970, p. 127).

These cultural and language differences have inhibited communication with the dominant group and have served as the basis for excluding Mexican Americans from the larger society. However, they also have provided a basis for group cohesion and unity that has sustained common action and protest activity.

# Immigration

Although Mexican Americans originated as a colonized minority group, their situation since the early 1900s (and especially since the 1960s) has been largely shaped by immigration. The numbers of legal border crossings from Mexico to the United States are shown in Exhibit 9.4. The fluctuations in the rate of immigration can be explained by conditions in Mexico, the varying demand for labor in the low-paying, unskilled sector of the U.S. economy, and by changing federal immigration policy. As you will see, competition, one of the key variables in Noel's hypothesis, has shaped the relationships between Mexican immigrants and the larger American society.

**Leaving Mexico.** Since the early 1900s, a variety of events in Mexico have motivated people to immigrate. The Mexican Revolution began in 1910, and the resulting political turmoil and instability created a strong "push" to the North. Mexico also began to industrialize at about this time, and its rural population was displaced by the mechanization of agriculture. Over the course of the 20th century, the population of Mexico grew, and unemployment was frequently widespread (Cortes, 1980, p. 702; Moore, 1970, pp. 39-41). In recent years, the rising levels of immigration have been sustained by the strong demand for cheap labor in the United States and the continuing wage gap between the two nations that makes even menial work in the North attractive.

**Fluctuating Demand for Labor and Federal Immigration Policy.** For the last century, Mexico has served as a reserve pool of cheap labor for the benefit of U.S. businesses, agricultural interests, and other groups, and the volume of immigration reflects changing economic

### The Meaning of Macho

*Words as well as people can immigrate, and in both cases, the process can be transforming. In the following passage, Rose Guilbault (1993), a newspaper editor and columnist, reflects on the meaning of one term that has become central to the dominant group's view of Hispanic males. The image evoked by the term macho changed from positive to negative as it found its way into American English, a process that reflects dominant-minority relations and partly defines them.*

### AMERICANIZATION IS TOUGH ON MACHO

**Rose Del Castillo Guilbault**

What is macho? That depends on which side of the border you come from. . . . The negative connotations of macho in this country are troublesome to Hispanics.

The Hispanic macho is manly, responsible, hardworking, a man in charge, a patriarch. A man who expresses strength through silence. . . .

The American macho is a chauvinist, a brute, uncouth, loud, abrasive, capable of inflicting pain, and sexually promiscuous.

Quintessential macho models in this country are Sylvester Stallone, Arnold Schwarzenegger, and Charles Bronson. . . . They exude toughness, independence, masculinity. But a closer look reveals their machismo is really violence masquerading as courage, sullenness disguised as silence and irresponsibility camouflaged as independence. . . .

In Spanish, macho ennobles Latin males. In English it devalues them. This pattern seems consistent with the conflicts ethnic minority males experience in this country. Typically the cultural traits other societies value don't translate as desirable characteristics in America.

I watched my own father struggle with these cultural ambiguities. He worked on a farm for 20 years. He laid down miles of irrigation pipe, carefully plowed long, neat rows in fields, . . . stoically worked 20-hour days during the harvest season, accepting the long hours as part of agricultural work. When the boss complained or upbraided him for minor mistakes, he kept quiet, even when it was obvious that the boss had erred.

He handled the most menial tasks with pride. At home he was a good provider. . . . Americans regarded my father as decidedly un-macho. His character was interpreted as non-assertive, his loyalty non-ambition, and his quietness, ignorance. I once overheard the boss's son blame him for plowing crooked rows. . . . My father merely smiled at the lie, knowing the boy had done it, . . . confident his good work was well-known. . . . Seeing my embarrassment, my father dismissed the incident, saying "They're the dumb ones. Imagine me fighting with a kid."

I tried not to look at him with American eyes because sometimes the reflection hurt. . . .

In the United States, I believe it was the feminist movement of the early '70s that changed macho's meaning. Perhaps my generation of Latin women was in part responsible. I recall Chicanas complaining about the chauvinistic nature of Latin men and the notion they wanted their women barefoot, pregnant, and in the kitchen. The generalization that Latin men embodied chauvinistic traits led to this . . . twist of semantics. Suddenly a word that represented something positive in one culture became a negative stereotype in another. . . .

The impact of language in our society is undeniable. And the misuse of macho hints at a deeper cultural misunderstanding that extends beyond mere word definitions.

SOURCE: Guilbault, Rose Del Castillo. 1993. "Americanization is Tough on 'Macho.'" In D. La Guardia & H. Guth (Eds.), *American Voices*. Mountain View, CA: Mayfield Press. Pp. 163-165. First published in "This World," *San Francisco Chronicle*, August 20, 1989.

**EXHIBIT 9.4** Legal Immigration From Mexico

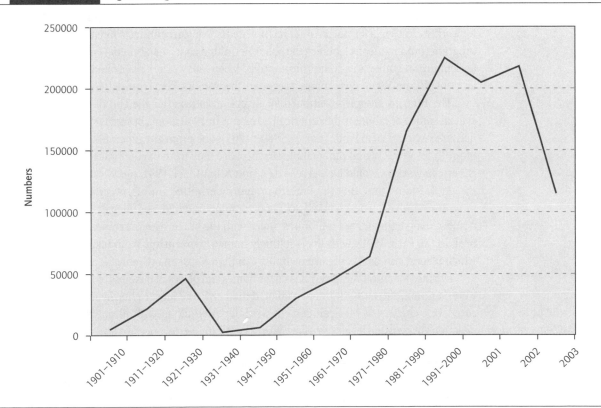

SOURCE: U.S. Department of Homeland Security (2004), pp. 13-14.

NOTE: Numbers are average per year for each decade except for 2001, 2002, and 2003, which are the actual number of immigrants for each year.

conditions in the United States. By and large, the policies of the federal government have responded to these conditions and have encouraged immigration during good times and clamped down during hard times.

In the earliest decades of the 20th century, movement across the United States' southern border was informal and largely unrestricted (Grebler, Moore, & Guzman, 1970, p. 63). In the 1910s and 1920s, the demand for cheap labor from Mexico increased because World War I and restrictive immigration legislation (see chapter 12) reduced or eliminated the flow of labor from Europe and Asia. Whereas employers in the East recruited African American workers from the South, those in the West, Southwest, and even the Midwest turned to Mexico to solve the labor shortages. During this time, Mexicans were not only encouraged to immigrate, U.S. employers actively recruited them.

When hard times came to the United States (and the world) during the Great Depression of the 1930s, demand for labor decreased, the flow of immigration slowed, recruiting stopped, and Mexicans in the United States returned home, sometimes voluntarily, often by force. As unemployment rates soared and competition for jobs increased, efforts began to expel Mexican laborers, just as the Noel hypothesis would predict. The federal government instituted a **repatriation** campaign aimed specifically at deporting illegal Mexican immigrants. In many localities, repatriation was pursued with great zeal, and the campaign intimidated many legal immigrants and native-born Mexican Americans into moving to Mexico. The result was that the Mexican American population of the United States declined by an estimated 40% during the 1930s (Cortes, 1980, p. 711).

When the depression ended and U.S. society began to mobilize for World War II, federal policy toward immigrants from Mexico changed once more as employers again turned to Mexico for workers. In 1942, a formal program was initiated to bring in contract laborers. Called the Bracero program (*bracero* means laborer), the policy permitted contract laborers—usually employed in agriculture and other areas requiring unskilled labor—to work in the United States for a limited amount of time. When their contracts expired, the workers were required to return to Mexico.

The Bracero program continued for several decades after the end of the war and was a crucial source of labor for the American economy. In 1960 alone, braceros supplied 26% of the nation's seasonal farm labor (Cortes, 1980, p. 703). The program generated millions of dollars of profit for growers and other employers, because they were paying braceros much less than American workers would have received (Amott & Matthaei, 1991, pp. 79-80).

At the same time that the Bracero program permitted immigration from Mexico, other programs and agencies worked to deport undocumented (or illegal) immigrants, large numbers of whom entered the United States with the braceros. Government efforts reached a peak in the early 1950s with the insultingly named "**Operation Wetback**," a program under which federal authorities deported almost 4 million Mexicans (Grebler et al., 1970, p. 521).

During Operation Wetback, raids on the homes and places of business of Mexican Americans were common, and authorities often ignored their civil and legal rights. In an untold number of cases, U.S. citizens of Mexican descent were deported along with illegal immigrants. These violations of civil and legal rights have been a continuing grievance of Mexican Americans (and other Latinos) for decades (Mirandé, 1985, pp. 70-90).

In 1965, a new U.S. immigration policy came into effect that gave a high priority to immigrants who were family and kin of U.S. citizens. The immediate family (parents, spouses, children) of U.S. citizens could enter without numerical restriction. Some numerical restrictions were placed on the number of immigrants from each sending country, but about 80% of these restricted visas were reserved for other close relatives of citizens. The remaining 20% of the visas went to people who had skills needed in the labor force. Also, people who were classified as political refugees could enter without regard to the numerical limits (Bouvier & Gardner, 1986, pp. 13-15; Rumbaut, 1991, p. 215).

Immigrants had always tended to move along chains of kinship and other social relationships, and the new policy reinforced those tendencies. The social networks connecting Latin America with the United States expanded, and the rate of immigration from Mexico increased sharply after 1965 (see Exhibit 9.4). Immigrants sent for other family members as finances permitted, and a chain was established. Once citizenship had been obtained, immediate family members could enter without numerical restrictions, and other close relatives would receive a high priority within the numerically restricted category.

Most of the Mexican immigrants, legal as well as undocumented, who have arrived since 1965 continue the pattern of seeking work in the low-wage, unskilled sectors of the labor market in the cities and fields of the Southwest. For many, work is seasonal or temporary. When the work ends, they often return to Mexico, commuting across the border as has been done for decades (for estimates of the circular nature of Mexican immigration, see Massey & Singer, 1995).

In 1986, Congress attempted to deal with illegal immigrants, most of whom are thought to be Mexican, by passing the Immigration Reform and Control Act. This legislation allowed illegal immigrants who had been in the country continuously since 1982 to legalize their status. According to the U.S. Immigration and Naturalization Service (1993, p. 17), about 3 million people, 75% of them Mexican, have taken advantage of this provision, but this program has not slowed the volume of illegal immigration. In 1988, at the end of the amnesty application period, there were still almost 3 million undocumented immigrants in the United States, and this number grew to an estimated 5 million in 1996 (Del Pinal & Singer, 1997, pp. 20, 22). In 2000, the number may have been as high as 8.5 million people (Martin & Widgren, 2002).

**Immigration, Colonization, and Intergroup Competition.** Three points can be made about Mexican immigration to the United States. First, the flow of population from Mexico was and is stimulated and sustained by powerful political and economic interests in the United States. Systems of recruitment and networks of communication and transportation have been established to routinize the flow of people and make it a predictable source of labor for the benefit of U.S. agriculture and other employers. The movement of people back and forth across the border was well established long before current efforts to regulate and control it. Depending on U.S. policy, this immigration is sometimes legal and encouraged and sometimes illegal and discouraged. Regardless of the label, the river of people has been steadily flowing for decades in response to opportunities for work in the North (Portes, 1990, pp. 160-163).

Second, Mexican immigrants enter a social system in which a colonized status for the group has already been established. The paternalistic traditions and racist systems that were established in the 19th century shaped the positions that were open to Mexican immigrants in the 20th century. Mexican Americans continued to be treated as a colonized group despite the streams of new arrivals, and the history of the group in the 20th century has many parallels with African Americans and American Indians. Thus Mexican Americans might be thought of as a colonized minority group that happens to have a large number of immigrants or, alternatively, as an immigrant group that incorporates a strong tradition of colonization.

Third, this brief review of the twisting history of U.S. policy on Mexican immigration should serve as a reminder that levels of prejudice, racism, and discrimination increase as competition and the sense of threat between groups increases. The very qualities that make

Mexican labor attractive to employers have caused bitter resentment among those segments of the Anglo population who feel that their own jobs and financial security are threatened. Often caught in the middle, Mexican immigrants and Mexican Americans have not had the resources to avoid exploitation by employers or rejection and discrimination by others. The ebb and flow of the efforts to regulate immigration (and sometimes even deport U.S. citizens of Mexican descent) can be understood in terms of competition, differentials in power, and prejudice.

## Developments in the United States

As the flow of immigration from Mexico fluctuated with the need for labor, Mexican Americans struggled to improve their status. In the early decades of the 20th century, like other colonized minority groups, they faced a system of repression and control in which they were accorded few rights and had little political power.

**Continuing Colonization.** Throughout much of the 20th century, Mexican Americans have been limited to less desirable, low-wage jobs. Split labor markets, in which Mexican Americans are paid less than Anglos for the same jobs, have been common. The workforce has often been further split by gender, with Mexican American women assigned to the worst jobs and receiving the lowest wages in both urban and rural areas (Takaki, 1993, pp. 318-319).

Men's jobs often took them away from their families to work in the mines and fields. In 1930, 45% of all Mexican American men worked in agriculture, with another 28% in unskilled nonagricultural jobs (Cortes, 1980, p. 708). The women were often forced by economic necessity to enter the job market; in 1930, they were concentrated in farm work (21%), unskilled manufacturing jobs (25%), and domestic and other service work (37%) (Amott & Matthaei, 1991, pp. 76-77). They were typically paid less than both Mexican American men and Anglo women. In addition to their job responsibilities, Mexican American women had to maintain their households and raise their children, often facing these tasks without a spouse (Baca Zinn & Eitzen, 1990, p. 84).

As the United States industrialized and urbanized during the century, employment patterns became more diversified. Mexican Americans found work in manufacturing, construction, transportation, and other sectors of the economy. Some Mexican Americans, especially those of the third generation or later, moved into middle- and upper level occupations, and some began to move out of the Southwest. Still, Mexican Americans in all regions (especially recent immigrants) tended to be concentrated at the bottom of the occupational ladder. Women increasingly worked outside the home, but their employment was largely limited to agriculture, domestic service, and the garment industry (Amott & Matthaei, 1991, pp. 76-79; Cortes, 1980, p. 708).

Like African Americans in the segregated South, Mexican Americans were excluded from the institutions of the larger society by law and by custom for much of the 20th century. There were separate (and unequal) school systems for Mexican American children, and in many communities, Mexican Americans were disenfranchised and accorded few legal or civil rights. There were "whites-only" primary elections modeled after the Jim Crow system, and residential segregation was widespread. The police and the court system generally abetted or ignored the rampant discrimination against the Mexican American community. Discrimination in the criminal justice system and civil rights violations have been continual grievances of Mexican Americans throughout the century.

**Protest and Resistance.** Like all minority groups, Mexican Americans have attempted to improve their collective position whenever possible. The beginnings of organized resistance and protest stretch back to the original contact period in the 19th century, when protest was usually organized on a local level. Regional and national organizations made their appearance in the 20th century (Cortes, 1980, p. 709).

As with African Americans, Mexican Americans' early protest organizations were integrationist and reflected the assimilationist values of the larger society. For example, one of the earlier and more significant groups was the League of United Latin American Citizens (LULAC), founded in Texas in 1929. LULAC promoted Americanization and greater educational opportunities for Mexican Americans. The group also worked to expand civil and political rights and to increase equality for Mexican Americans. LULAC fought numerous court battles against discrimination and racial segregation (Moore, 1970, pp. 143-145).

The workplace has been a particularly conflictual arena for Mexican Americans. Split labor market situations increased anti–Mexican American prejudice; some labor unions tried to exclude Mexican immigrants from the United States along with immigrants from Asia and Southern and Eastern Europe (Grebler et al., 1970, pp. 90-93).

At the same time, Mexican Americans played important leadership roles in the labor movement. Since early in the century, Mexican Americans have been involved in union organizing, particularly in agriculture and mining. When excluded by Anglo labor unions, they often formed their own unions to work for the improvement of working conditions. As the 20th century progressed, the number and variety of groups pursuing the Mexican American cause increased. During World War II, Mexican Americans served in the armed forces, and as with other minority groups, this experience increased their impatience with the constraints on their freedoms and opportunities. After the war ended, a number of new Mexican American organizations were founded, including the Community Service Organization in Los Angeles and the American GI Forum in Texas. Compared with older organizations such as LULAC, the new groups were less concerned with assimilation per se, addressed a broad range of community problems, and attempted to increase Mexican American political power (Grebler et al., 1970, pp. 543-545).

**Chicanismo.** The 1960s were a time of intense activism and militancy for Mexican Americans. A protest movement guided by an ideology called **Chicanismo** began at about the same time as the Black Power and Red Power movements. Chicanismo encompassed a variety of organizations and ideas, united by a heightened militancy and impatience with the racism of the larger society and strongly stated demands for justice, fairness, and equal rights. The movement questioned the value of assimilation and sought to increase awareness of the continuing exploitation of Mexican Americans; it adapted many of the tactics and strategies (marches, rallies, voter registration drives, etc.) of the Civil Rights movement of the 1960s.

Chicanismo is similar in some ways to the black power ideology (see chapter 7). It is partly a reaction to the failure of U.S. society to implement the promises of integration and equality. It rejected traditional stereotypes of Mexican Americans, proclaimed a powerful and positive group image and heritage, and analyzed the group's past and present situation in American society in terms of victimization, continuing exploitation, and institutional discrimination. The inequalities that separated Mexican Americans and the larger society were seen as the result of deep-rooted, continuing racism and the cumulative effects of decades of exclusion. According to Chicanismo, the solution to these problems lay in group empowerment, increased militancy, and group pride, not in assimilation to a culture that had rationalized and abetted the exploitation of Mexican Americans (Acuna, 1988, pp. 307-358; Grebler et al., 1970, p. 544; Moore, 1970, pp. 149-154).

Some of the central thrusts of the 1960s protest movement are captured in the widespread adoption of **Chicanos**, which had been a derogatory term, as a group name for Mexican Americans. Other minority groups underwent similar name changes at about the same time. For example, African Americans shifted from *Negro* to *Black* as a group designation. These name changes were not merely cosmetic; they marked fundamental shifts in group goals and desired relationships with the larger society. The new names came from the minority groups themselves, not from the dominant group, and they expressed the pluralistic themes of group pride, self-determination, militancy, and increased resistance to exploitation and discrimination.

**Organizations and Leaders.** The Chicano movement saw the rise of many new groups and leaders, one of the most important of whom was Reies Lopez Tijerina, who formed the Alianza de Mercedes (Alliance of Land Grants) in 1963. The goal of this group was to correct what Tijerina saw as the unjust and illegal seizure of land from Mexicans during the 19th century. The Alianza was militant and confrontational, and to bring attention to their cause, members of the group seized and occupied federal lands. Tijerina spent several years in jail as a result of his activities, and the movement eventually lost its strength and faded from view in the 1970s.

Another prominent Chicano leader was Rodolfo Gonzalez, who founded the Crusade for Justice in 1965. The crusade focused on abuses of Mexican American civil and legal rights and worked against discrimination by police and the criminal courts. In a 1969 presentation at a symposium on Chicano liberation, Gonzalez expressed some of the nationalistic themes of Chicanismo and the importance of creating a power base within the group (as opposed to assimilating or integrating):

> Where [whites] have incorporated themselves to keep us from moving into their neighborhoods, we can also incorporate ourselves to keep them from controlling our neighborhoods. We . . . have to understand economic revolution. . . . We have to understand that liberation comes from self-determination, and to start to use the tools of nationalism to win over our barrio brothers. . . . We have to understand that we can take over the institutions within our community. We have to create the community of the Mexicano here in order to have any type of power. (Moquin & Van Doren, 1971, pp. 381-382)

A third important leader was José Angel Gutierrez, organizer of the La Raza Unida (People United) party. La Raza Unida offered alternative candidates and ideas to Democrats and Republicans. Its most notable success was in Crystal City, Texas, where in 1973 it succeeded in electing its entire slate of candidates to local office (Acuna, 1988, pp. 332-451).

Without a doubt, the best-known Chicano leader of the 1960s and 1970s was the late Cesar Chávez, who organized the United Farm Workers, the first union to successfully represent migrant workers. Chávez was as much a labor leader as a leader of the Mexican American community, and he also organized African Americans, Filipinos, and Anglo-Americans. Migrant farm workers have few economic or political resources, and the migratory nature of their work isolates them in rural areas and makes them difficult to contact. In the 1960s (and still today), many were undocumented immigrants who spoke little or no English and who returned to the cities or to their country of origin at the end of the season. As a group, farm workers were nearly invisible in the social landscape of the United States in the 1960s, and organizing this group was a demanding task. Chávez's success in this endeavor is one of the more remarkable studies in group protest.

Like Dr. Martin Luther King, Jr., Chávez was a disciple of Gandhi and a student of nonviolent direct protest (see chapter 7). His best known tactic was the boycott; in 1965, he organized a grape pickers' strike and a national boycott of grapes. The boycott lasted 5 years and ended when the growers recognized the United Farm Workers as the legitimate representative of farm workers. Chávez and his organization achieved a major victory, and the agreement provided for significant improvements in the situation of the workers (for a biography of Chávez, see Levy, 1975).

**Gender and the Chicano Protest Movement.** Mexican American women were heavily involved in the Chicano protest movement. Jessie Lopez and Dolores Huerta were central figures in the movement to organize farm workers and worked closely with Cesar Chávez. However, as was the case for African American women, Chicano women encountered sexism and gender discrimination within the movement even as they worked for the benefit of the group as a whole. Their dilemmas are described by activist Sylvia Gonzales:

> Along with her male counterpart, she attended meetings, organized boycotts, did everything asked of her. . . . But, if she [tried to assume leadership roles], she was met with the same questioning of her femininity which the culture dictates when a woman is not self-sacrificing and seeks to fulfill her own needs. . . . The Chicano movement seemed to demand self-actualization for only the male members of the group. (Amott & Matthaei, 1991, p. 83)

Despite these difficulties, Chicano women contributed to the movement in a variety of areas. They helped to organize poor communities and worked for welfare reform. Continuing issues include domestic violence, child care, the criminal victimization of women, and the racial and gender oppression that limits women of all minority groups (Amott & Matthaei, 1991, pp. 82-86; see also Mirandé & Enriquez, 1979, pp. 202-243).

# Mexican Americans and Other Minority Groups

Like the Black Power and Red Power movements, Chicanismo began to fade from public view in the 1970s and 1980s. The movement could claim some successes, but perhaps the clearest victory was in raising the awareness of the larger society about the grievances and problems of Mexican Americans. Today, many Chicanos continue to face poverty and powerlessness and continuing exploitation as a cheap agricultural labor force. The less educated, urbanized segments of the group share the prospect of becoming a permanent urban underclass with other minority groups of color.

Over the course of the 20th century, the ability of Chicanos to pursue their self-interest has been limited by both internal and external forces. Like African Americans, the group has been systematically excluded from the institutions of the larger society. Continuing immigration from Mexico has increased the size of the group, but these immigrants bring few resources with them that could be directly or immediately translated into economic or political power in the United States.

Unlike immigrants from Europe, who settled in the urban centers of the industrializing East Coast, Mexican Americans tended to work and live in rural areas distant from and marginal to urban centers of industrialization and opportunities for education, skill development, and upward mobility. They were a vitally important source of labor in agriculture and other segments of the economy but only to the extent that they were exploitable and powerless. As Chicanos moved to the cities, they continued to serve as a colonized, exploited labor force concentrated at the lower end of the stratification system. Thus the handicaps created by discrimination in the past were reinforced by continuing discrimination and exploitation in the present, perpetuating the cycles of poverty and powerlessness.

At the same time, however, the flow of immigration and the constant movement of people back and forth across the border kept Mexican culture and the Spanish language alive. Unlike African Americans under slavery, Chicanos were not cut off from their homeland and native culture. Mexican American culture was attacked and disparaged, but it was not destroyed to the same extent as African culture.

Clearly, the traditional model of assimilation does not describe the experiences of Mexican Americans very well. They have experienced less social mobility than European immigrant groups and have maintained their traditional culture and language more completely. Like African Americans, the group is split along lines of social class. Although many Mexican Americans (particularly of the third generation and later) have acculturated and integrated, a large segment of the group continues to fill the same economic role as their ancestors: an unskilled labor force for the development of the Southwest, augmented with "immigrants" from Mexico at the convenience of U.S. employers. Today, nearly 40% of employed Mexican American males—nearly double the percentage for non-Hispanic whites—remain in the "unskilled labor" and "farm" sectors of the labor force (see Exhibit 9.9a later in this chapter). For the less educated and for recent immigrants, cultural and racial differences combine to increase their social visibility, mark them for exploitation, and rationalize their continuing exclusion from the larger society.

# PUERTO RICANS

Puerto Rico became a territory of the United States after the defeat of Spain in the Spanish-American War of 1898. The island was small and impoverished, and it was difficult for Puerto Ricans to avoid domination by the United States. Thus the initial contact between Puerto Ricans and U.S. society was made in an atmosphere of war and conquest. By the time Puerto Ricans began to migrate to the mainland in large numbers, their relationship to U.S. society was largely that of a colonized minority group, and they generally retained that status on the mainland.

## Migration (Push and Pull) and Employment

At the time of initial contact, the population of Puerto Rico was overwhelmingly rural and supported itself by subsistence farming and by exporting coffee and sugar. As the century wore on, U.S. firms began to invest in and develop the island economy, especially the sugarcane industry. These agricultural endeavors took more and more of the land. Opportunities for economic survival in the rural areas declined, and many peasants were forced to move into the cities (Portes, 1990, p. 163).

Movement to the mainland began gradually and increased slowly until the 1940s. In 1900, there were about 2000 Puerto Ricans living on the mainland. By the eve of World War II, this number had grown to only 70,000, a tiny fraction of the total population.

Then, during the 1940s, the number of Puerto Ricans on the mainland increased more than fourfold, to 300,000, and during the 1950s, it nearly tripled, to 887,000 (U.S. Commission on Civil Rights, 1976, p. 19).

This massive and sudden population growth was the result of a combination of circumstances. First, Puerto Ricans became citizens of the United States in 1917, so their movements were not impeded by international boundaries or immigration restrictions. Second, unemployment was a major problem on the island. The sugarcane industry continued to displace the rural population, urban unemployment was high, and the population continued to grow. By the 1940s, a considerable number of Puerto Ricans were available to seek work off the island and, like Chicanos, could serve as a cheap labor supply for U.S. employers.

Third, Puerto Ricans were "pulled" to the mainland by the same labor shortages that attracted Mexican immigrants during and after World War II. Whereas the latter responded to job opportunities in the West and Southwest, Puerto Ricans moved to the Northeast. The job profiles of these two groups were similar; both were concentrated in the low-wage, unskilled sector of the job market. However, the Puerto Rican migration began many decades after the Mexican migration, at a time when the United States was much more industrialized and urbanized. As a result, Puerto Ricans have been more concentrated in urban labor markets than Mexican immigrants (Portes, 1990, p. 164).

Movement between the island and the mainland was facilitated by the commencement of affordable air travel between San Juan and New York City in the late 1940s. New York had been the major center of settlement for Puerto Ricans on the mainland even before annexation. A small Puerto Rican community had been established in the city, and as with many groups, organizations and networks were established to ease the transition and help newcomers with housing, jobs, and other issues. Although they eventually dispersed to other regions and cities, Puerto Ricans on the mainland remain centered in New York City. More than two thirds currently reside in the cities of the Northeast (U.S. Bureau of the Census, 2000c).

Economics and jobs were at the heart of the move to the mainland. The rate of Puerto Rican migration has followed the cycle of boom and bust, just as it has for Mexican immigrants. The 1950s, the peak decade for Puerto Rican migration, was a period of rapid U.S. economic growth. Migration was encouraged, and job recruiters traveled to the island to attract workers. By the 1960s, however, the supply of jobs on the island had expanded appreciably, and the average number of migrants declined from the peak of 41,000 per year in the 1950s to about 20,000 per year. In the 1970s, the U.S. economy faltered, unemployment grew, and the flow of Puerto Rican migration actually reversed itself, with the number of returnees exceeding the number of migrants in various years (U.S. Commission on Civil Rights, 1976, p. 25). The migrations continue: A little more than 3.4 million Puerto Ricans, or about 47% of all Puerto Ricans, were living on the mainland in 1999.

As the U.S. economy expanded and migration accelerated after World War II, Puerto Ricans moved into a broad range of jobs and locations in the society, and the group grew more economically diversified and more regionally dispersed. Still, the bulk of the group remains concentrated in lower status jobs in the larger cities of the Northeast. Puerto Rican men have often found work as unskilled factory laborers or in the service sector, particularly in areas where English language facility was not necessary (e.g., janitorial work). The women have often been employed as domestics or seamstresses for the garment industry in New York City (Portes, 1990, p. 164).

# Transitions

Although Puerto Ricans are not "immigrants," the move to the mainland does involve a change in culture and language (Fitzpatrick, 1980, p. 858). Despite nearly a century of political affiliation, Puerto Rican and Anglo cultures differ along many dimensions. Puerto Ricans are overwhelmingly Catholic, but the religious practices and rituals on the mainland are quite different from those on the island. Mainland Catholic parishes often reflect the traditions and practices of other cultures and groups. On the island, "Religious observance reflects the spontaneous and expressive practices of the Spanish and the Italian and not the restrained and well-organized worship of the Irish and Germans" (Fitzpatrick, 1980, p. 865). Also, there are few Puerto Rican priests or even Spanish-speaking clergy on the mainland; thus, members of the group often feel estranged from and poorly served by the Church (Fitzpatrick, 1987, pp. 117-138).

A particularly unsettling cultural difference between the island and the mainland involves skin color and perceptions of race. Puerto Rico has a long history of racial intermarriage. Slavery was less monolithic and total, and the island had no periods of systematic, race-based segregation like the Jim Crow system. Thus, although skin color prejudice still exists in Puerto Rico, it has never been as categorical as on the mainland. On the island, race is perceived as a continuum of possibilities and combinations, not as a simple dichotomous split between white and black. Furthermore, in Puerto Rico, other factors, such as social class, are considered to be more important than race as criteria for judging and classifying others. In fact, social class can affect perceptions of skin color, and regardless of actual color, people of higher status might be seen as "whiter" than those of lower status. Coming from this background, Puerto Ricans find the rigid racial thinking of U.S. culture disconcerting and even threatening.

The confusion and discomfort that can result was documented and illustrated by a study of Puerto Rican college students in New York City. Dramatic differences were found between the personal racial identification of the students and their perceptions of how Anglos viewed them. When asked for their racial identification, most of the students classified themselves as "tan," with one third labeling themselves "white" and only 7% considering themselves "black." When asked how they thought they were racially classified by Anglos, however, none of the students used the "tan" classification: 58% felt that they were seen as "white," and 41% felt that they were seen as "black" (Rodriguez, 1989, pp. 60-61; see also Rodriguez & Cordero-Guzman, 1992).

In the racially dichotomized U.S. culture, many Puerto Ricans feel they have no clear place. They are genuinely puzzled when they first encounter prejudice and discrimination based on skin color and are uncertain about their own identity and self-image. The racial perceptions of the dominant culture can be threatening to Puerto Ricans to the extent that they are victimized by the same web of discrimination and disadvantage that affects African Americans. There are still clear disadvantages to being classified as black in U.S. society. Institutionalized racial barriers can be extremely formidable, and in the case of Puerto Ricans, they may combine with cultural and linguistic differences to sharply limit opportunities and mobility.

# Puerto Ricans and Other Minority Groups

Puerto Ricans arrived in the cities of the Northeast long after the great wave of European immigrants and several decades after African Americans began migrating from the South. They have often competed with other minority groups for housing, jobs, and other resources. A pattern of ethnic succession can be seen in some neighborhoods and occupational areas in which Puerto Ricans have replaced other groups that have moved out (and sometimes up).

Because of their more recent arrival, Puerto Ricans on the mainland were not subjected to the more repressive paternalistic or rigid competitive systems of race relations like slavery or Jim Crow. Instead, the subordinate status of the group is manifested in their occupational, residential, and educational profiles and by the institutionalized barriers to upward mobility that they face. Puerto Ricans share many problems with other urban minority groups of color: poverty, failing educational systems, and crime. Like African Americans, their fate is dependent on the future of the American city, and a large segment of the group is in danger of becoming part of a permanent urban underclass.

Like Mexican Americans, Puerto Ricans on the mainland combine elements of both an immigrant and a colonized minority experience. The movement to the mainland is voluntary in some ways, but in others, it is strongly motivated by the transformations in the island economy that resulted from modernization and U.S. domination. Like Chicanos, Puerto Ricans tend to enter the labor force at the bottom of the occupational structure and face similar problems of inequality and marginalization. Also, Puerto Rican culture retains a strong vitality and is continually reinvigorated by the considerable movement back and forth between the island and the mainland.

## CUBAN AMERICANS

The contact period for Cuban Americans, like Puerto Ricans, dates back to the Spanish-American War. At that time, Cuba was a Spanish colony but became an independent nation as a result of the war. Despite its nominal independence, the United States remained heavily involved in Cuban politics and economics for decades, and U.S. troops actually occupied the island on two different occasions.

The development of a Cuban American minority group bears little resemblance to the experience of either Chicanos or Puerto Ricans. As recently as the 1950s, there had not been much immigration from Cuba to the United States, even during times of labor shortages, and Cuban Americans were a very small group, numbering no more than 50,000 (Perez, 1980, p. 256).

## Immigration (Push and Pull)

The conditions for a mass immigration were created in the late 1950s when a Marxist revolution brought Fidel Castro to power in Cuba. Castro's government was decidedly anti-American and began to restructure Cuban society along socialist lines. The middle and upper classes lost political and economic power, and the revolution made it difficult, even impossible, for Cuban capitalists to remain in business. Thus the first Cuban immigrants to the United States tended to come from the more elite classes and included affluent and powerful people who controlled many resources.

The United States was a logical destination for those displaced by the revolution. Cuba is only 90 miles from southern Florida, the climates are similar, and the U.S. government, which was as anti-Castro as Castro was anti-American, welcomed the new arrivals as political refugees fleeing from communist tyranny. Prior social, cultural, and business ties also pulled the immigrants in the direction of the United States. Since gaining its independence in 1898, Cuba has been heavily influenced by its neighbor to the north, and U.S. companies helped to develop the

## Gender Images of Latinas

*One part of the minority group experience is learning to deal with the stereotypes, images, and expectations of the larger society. Of course, everyone (even white males) has to respond to the assumptions of others, but given the realities of power and status, minority group members have fewer choices and a narrower range in which to maneuver: The images imposed by the society are harder to escape and more difficult to deny.*

*In her analysis, Judith Ortiz Cofer (1995), a writer, poet, professor of English, and Puerto Rican, describes some of the images and stereotypes of Latinas with which she has had to struggle and some of the dynamics that have created and sustained those images. She writes from her own experiences, but the points she makes illustrate many of the sociological theories and concepts that guide this text.*

### "THE ISLAND TRAVELS WITH YOU"

**Judith Ortiz Cofer**

On a bus trip from London to Oxford University . . .
a young man, obviously fresh from a pub, spotted me
and as if struck by inspiration went down on his knees
in the aisle. With both hands over his heart he broke
into an Irish tenor's rendition of "Maria" from West
Side Story. My politely amused fellow passengers gave
his lovely voice the round of gentle applause that it
deserved. Though I was not quite as amused, I
managed my version of an English smile: no show of
teeth, no extreme contortions of the facial muscles—
I was at this time in my life practicing reserve and
cool. . . . But Maria had followed me to London,
reminding me of a prime fact of my life: You can leave
the island, master the English language, and travel as
far as you can, but if you are a Latina, . . . the Island
travels with you.

This is sometimes a very good thing—it may win
you the extra minute of somebody's attention. But
with some people, the same things can make you an
island—not so much a tropical paradise as an
Alcatraz, a place nobody wants to visit. As a Puerto
Rican girl growing up in the United States and
wanting like most children to "belong," I resented the
stereotypes that my Hispanic appearance called forth
from many people I met.

Our family lived in a large urban center in New
Jersey during the sixties, where life was designed as a
microcosm of my parents' casas on the island. We
spoke Spanish, we ate Puerto Rican food bought at the
bodega, and we practiced strict Catholicism. . . .

As a girl, I was kept under strict surveillance,
since virtue and modesty were, by cultural equation,
the same as family honor. As a teenager, I was
instructed on how to behave as a proper senorita. But
it was a conflicting message girls got, since the Puerto

320 UNDERSTANDING U.S. DOMINANT-MINORITY RELATIONS

Rican mothers also encouraged their daughters to look and act like women and to dress in clothes our Anglo friends found too "mature" for our age. . . . At a Puerto Rican festival, neither the music nor the colors we wore could be too loud. I still experience a vague sense of letdown when I'm invited to a "party" and it turns out to be a marathon conversation in hushed tones rather than a fiesta with salsa, laughter, and dancing—the kind of celebration I remember from my childhood. . . .

Mixed cultural signals have perpetuated certain stereotypes—for example, that of the "Hot Tamale" or sexual firebrand. It is a . . . view that the media have found easy to promote. In their special vocabulary, advertisers have designated "sizzling" and "smoldering" as the adjectives of choice for describing not only the foods but the women of Latin America. . . .

It is custom, however, not chromosomes, that leads us to choose scarlet over pale pink. As young girls, we were influenced in our decisions about clothes and colors by the women . . . who had grown up on a tropical island where the natural environment was a riot of primary colors, where showing your skin was one way to keep cool as well as to look sexy. Most important of all, on the island, women perhaps felt freer to dress and move more provocatively, since . . . they were protected by the traditions, mores, and laws of a Spanish/Catholic system of morality and machismo whose main rule was: You may look at my sister, but if you touch her I will kill you. The extended family and church structure could provide a young woman with a circle of safety in her small pueblo on the Island; if a man "wronged" a girl, everyone would close in to save her family honor. . . .

Because of my education and proficiency with the English language, I have acquired many mechanisms for dealing with the anger I experience. This was not true for my parents, nor is it true for the many Latin women working at menial jobs who must put up with stereotypes about our ethnic group such as: "They make good domestics." This is another facet of the myth of the Latin women in the United States. . . . The myth of the Hispanic menial has been maintained by the same media phenomenon that made "Mammy" from *Gone With the Wind* America's idea of a black woman for generations: Maria, the housemaid or counter girl, is now indelibly etched into the national psyche. The big and little screens have presented us with the picture of the funny Hispanic maid, mispronouncing words and cooking up a spicy storm in the kitchen. . . .

I am one of the lucky ones. My parents made it possible for me to acquire a stronger footing in the mainstream culture by giving me the chance at an education. . . . There are thousands of Latinas without the privilege of an education or the entrée into society that I have. For them, life is a struggle against the misconceptions perpetuated by the myth of the Latina as whore, domestic, or criminal. My personal goal in my public life is to try to replace the old pervasive stereotypes and myths about Latinas with a much more interesting set of realities. Every time I give a reading [of my poetry], I hope the stories I tell, the dreams and fears I examine in my work, can achieve some universal truth which will get my audience past the particulars of my skin color, my accent, or my clothes.

SOURCE: Cofer, Judith Ortiz. 1995. "The Myth of the Latin Woman: I Just Met a Girl Named Maria." In her *The Latin Deli: Prose and Poetry*. Athens, GA: University of Georgia Press. Pp. 148-154.

Cuban economy. At the time of Castro's revolution, the Cuban political leadership and the more affluent classes were profoundly Americanized in their attitudes and lifestyles (Portes, 1990, p. 165). Furthermore, many Cuban exiles viewed southern Florida as an ideal spot from which to launch a counterrevolution to oust Castro.

Immigration was considerable for several years. More than 215,000 Cubans arrived between the end of the revolution and 1962, when an escalation of hostile relations resulted in the cutoff of all direct contact between Cuba and the United States. In 1965, an air link was reestablished, and an additional 340,000 Cubans made the journey. When the air connection was terminated in 1973, immigration slowed to a trickle once more. In 1980, however, the Cuban government permitted another period of open immigration. Using boats of every shape, size, and degree of seaworthiness, about 124,000 Cubans crossed to Florida. These immigrants are often referred to as the **Marielitos**, after the port of Mariel from which many of them debarked. This wave of immigrants generated a great deal of controversy in the United States, because the Cuban government used the opportunity to rid itself of a variety of convicted criminals and outcasts. However, the Marielitos also included people from every segment of Cuban society, a fact that was lost in the clamor of concern about the "undesirables" (Portes & Manning, 1986, p. 58).

## Regional Concentrations

The overwhelming majority of Cuban immigrants settled in southern Florida, especially in Miami and the surrounding Dade County. Today, Cuban Americans remain one of the most spatially concentrated minority groups in the United States, with 67% of all Cuban Americans residing in Florida, and 52% in the Miami area alone (U.S. Bureau of the Census, 2000f). This dense concentration has led to a number of disputes and conflicts between the Hispanic, Anglo-, and African American communities in the area. Issues have centered on language (see the Current Debates section in Chapter 2), jobs, and discrimination by the police and other governmental agencies. The conflicts have often been intense, and on more than one occasion, they have erupted into violence and civil disorder.

## Socioeconomic Characteristics

Compared with other streams of immigrants from Latin America, Cubans are, on the average, unusually affluent and well educated. Among the immigrants in the early 1960s were large numbers of professionals, landowners, and businesspeople. In later years, as Cuban society was transformed by the Castro regime, the stream included fewer elites, largely because there were fewer left in Cuba, and more political dissidents and working-class people. Today (as will be displayed in the Exhibits presented later in this chapter), Cuban Americans rank higher than other Latino groups on a number of dimensions, a reflection of the educational and economic resources they brought with them from Cuba and the favorable reception they enjoyed from the United States (Portes, 1990, p. 169).

These assets gave Cubans an advantage over Chicanos and Puerto Ricans, but the differences between the three Latino groups run deeper and are more complex than a simple accounting of initial resources would suggest. Cubans adapted to U.S. society in a way that is fundamentally different from the other two Latino groups.

## The Ethnic Enclave

The minority groups we have discussed to this point have been concentrated in the unskilled, low-wage segments of the economy in which jobs are not secure and not linked to opportunities for upward mobility. Many Cuban Americans have bypassed this sector of the economy and much of the discrimination and limitations associated with it. Like several other groups, Cuban Americans are an enclave minority (see chapter 2). An ethnic enclave is a social, economic, and cultural subsociety controlled by the group itself. Located in a specific geographical area or neighborhood inhabited solely or largely by members of the group, the enclave encompasses sufficient economic enterprises and social institutions to permit the group to function as a self-contained entity, largely independent of the surrounding community.

The first wave of Cuban immigrants brought with them considerable resources and business expertise. Although much of their energy was focused on ousting Castro and returning to Cuba, they generated enough economic activity to sustain restaurants, shops, and other small businesses that catered to the exile community.

As the years passed and the hope of a return to Cuba dimmed, the enclave economy grew. Between 1967 and 1976, the number of Cuban-owned firms in Dade County increased nine-fold, from 919 to about 8,000. Six years later, the number had reached 12,000. Most of these enterprises are small, but some factories employ hundreds of workers (Portes & Rumbaut, 1996, pp. 20-21). In addition to businesses serving their own community, Cuban-owned firms are involved in construction, manufacturing, finance, insurance, real estate, and an array of other activities. Over the decades, Cuban-owned firms have become increasingly integrated into the local economy and increasingly competitive with firms in the larger society. The growth of economic enterprises has been paralleled by a growth in the number of other types of groups and organizations and in the number and quality of services available (schools, law firms, medical care, funeral parlors, etc.). The enclave has become a largely autonomous community capable of providing for its members from cradle to grave (Logan, Alba, & McNulty, 1994; Peterson, 1995; Portes & Bach, 1985, p. 59).

The fact that the enclave economy is controlled by the group itself is crucial; it separates the ethnic enclave from "the ghetto," or neighborhoods that are impoverished and segregated. In ghettoes, members of other groups typically control the local economy; the profits, rents, and other resources flow out of the neighborhood. In the enclave, profits are reinvested and kept in the neighborhood. Group members can avoid the discrimination and limitations imposed by the larger society and can apply their skills, education, and talents in an atmosphere free from language barriers and prejudice. Those who might wish to venture into business for themselves can use the networks of cooperation and mutual aid for advice, credit, and other forms of assistance. Thus the ethnic enclave provides a platform from which Cuban Americans can pursue economic success independent of their degree of acculturation or English language ability.

The effectiveness of the ethnic enclave as a pathway for adaptation is illustrated by a study of Cuban and Mexican immigrants, all of whom entered the United States in 1973. At the time of entry, the groups were comparable in levels of skills, education, and English language ability. The groups were interviewed on several different occasions, and although they remained comparable on many variables, there were dramatic differences between the groups that reflected their different positions in the labor market. The majority of the Mexican immigrants were employed in the low-wage job sector. Less than 20% were self-employed or employed by another person of Mexican descent. Conversely, 57% of the Cuban immigrants were self-employed or employed by another Cuban (i.e., they were involved in the enclave economy). Among the subjects in the study, self-employed Cubans reported the highest monthly incomes ($1495), and Cubans otherwise employed in the enclave earned the second-highest incomes ($1111). The lowest incomes ($880) were earned by Mexican immigrants employed in small, nonenclave firms; many of these people worked as unskilled laborers in seasonal, temporary, or otherwise insecure jobs (Portes, 1990, p. 173; see also Portes & Bach, 1985).

The ability of the Mexican immigrants to rise in the class system and compete for place and position was severely constrained by the weight of past discrimination, the preferences of employers in the present, and their own lack of economic and political power. Cuban immigrants who found jobs in the enclave did not need to expose themselves to American prejudices or rely on the job market of the larger society. They entered an immigrant context that had networks of mutual assistance and support and linked them to opportunities more consistent with their ambitions and their qualifications.

The fact that success came faster to the group that was less acculturated reverses the prediction of many theories of assimilation. The pattern has long been recognized by some leaders of other groups, however, and is voiced in many of the themes of black power, red power, and Chicanismo that emphasize self-help, self-determination, nationalism, and separation. However, ethnic enclaves cannot be a panacea for all immigrant or other minority groups. They develop only under certain limited conditions; namely, when business and financial expertise and reliable sources of capital are combined with a disciplined labor force willing to work for low wages in exchange for on-the-job training, future assistance and loans, or other delayed benefits. Enclave enterprises usually start on a small scale and cater only to other ethnics. Thus the early economic returns are small and prosperity follows only after years of hard work, if at all. Most important, eventual success and expansion beyond the boundaries of the enclave depend on the persistence of strong ties of loyalty, kinship, and solidarity. The pressure to assimilate might easily weaken these networks and the strength of group cohesion (Portes & Manning, 1986, pp. 61-66).

## Cuban Americans and Other Minority Groups

The adaptation of Cuban Americans contrasts sharply with the experiences of colonized minority groups and with the common understanding of how immigrants are "supposed" to acculturate and integrate. Cuban Americans are neither the first nor the only group to develop an ethnic enclave, and their success has generated prejudice and resentment from the dominant group and from other minority groups. Whereas Puerto Ricans and Chicanos have been the victims of stereotypes labeling them "inferior," higher status Cuban Americans have been stereotyped as "too successful," "too clannish," and "too ambitious." The former stereotype commonly emerges to rationalize exploitative relationships; the latter expresses disparagement and rejection of groups that are more successful in the struggle to acquire resources (see chapter 3). Nonetheless, the stereotype of Cubans is an exaggeration and a misperception that obscures the fact that poverty and unemployment are major problems for many members of this group.

## CONTEMPORARY HISPANIC-WHITE RELATIONS

As in previous chapters, we will use the central concepts of this text to review the status of Latinos in the United States. Where relevant, comparisons are made between the major Latino groups and the minority groups discussed in previous chapters.

## Prejudice and Discrimination

The American tradition of prejudice against Latinos was born in the 19th-century conflicts that created minority group status for Mexican Americans. The themes of the original anti-Mexican stereotypes and attitudes were consistent with the nature of the contact situation: As Mexicans were conquered and subordinated, they were characterized as inferior, lazy, irresponsible, low in intelligence, and dangerously criminal (McWilliams, 1961, pp. 212-214). The prejudice and racism, supplemented with the echoes of the racist ideas and beliefs brought to the Southwest by many Anglos, helped to justify and rationalize the colonized, exploited status of the Chicanos.

These prejudices were incorporated into the dominant culture and were transferred to Puerto Ricans when they began to arrive on the mainland. As we have already mentioned, this stereotype does not fit Cuban Americans. Instead, their affluence has been exaggerated and perceived as undeserved or achieved by unfair or "un-American" means, a characterization similar to the traditional stereotype of Jews but just as prejudiced as the perception of Latino inferiority.

There is some evidence that the level of Latino prejudice has been affected by the decline of explicit American racism (discussed in chapter 4). For example, social distance scale results show a decrease in the scores of Mexicans, although their group ranking tends to remain stable. On the other hand, prejudice and racism against Latinos tend to increase during times of high immigration.

Although discrimination of all kinds, institutional as well as individual, has been common against Latino groups, it has not been as rigid or as total as the systems that controlled African American labor under slavery and segregation. However, discrimination against Latinos has not dissipated to the same extent as it has against European immigrant groups and their descendants. Because of their longer tenure in the United States and their original status as a rural labor force, Mexican Americans have probably been more victimized by the institutionalized forms of discrimination than have other Latino groups.

## Assimilation and Pluralism

**Acculturation.** Latino groups are highly variable in their extent of acculturation but are often seen as "slow" to change, learn English, and adopt Anglo customs. This perception is partly based on the assumption that Hispanics would follow the assimilation patterns of European immigrants and their descendants. Whereas white ethnic groups were largely acculturated after three or four generations, some Latino groups have been part of American society for many decades, and their language and culture remain prominently "unmelted."

Contrary to this perception, research shows that Hispanic groups are following many of the same patterns of assimilation as European groups. Their rates of acculturation increase with length of residence and are higher for the native born (Espinosa & Massey, 1997; Godstein & Suro, 2000; Valentine & Mosley, 2000). One national study, for example, showed that Mexican Americans who are citizens of the United States are very similar to Anglos in terms of their support for economic individualism and patriotism (de la Garza, Falcon, & Garcia, 1996). English language fluency increases as the generations pass, and most Hispanic Americans speak English or a combination of English and Spanish. Even those who speak Spanish at home report that they also speak English well or very well (de la Garza, DeSipio, Garcia, Garcia, & Falcon, 1992, p. 41; Portes & Rumbaut, 1996, pp. 199-231), and the percentage of Hispanics who are fluent in English increases with length of residence (e.g., see Saenz, 1999, p. 223). The pattern of language acculturation and changing values by generation was documented in Exhibit 2.4.

Even while acculturation continues, however, Hispanic culture and the Spanish language are revitalized by immigration. By its nature, assimilation is a slow process that can require decades or generations to complete. In contrast, immigration can be fast, often accomplished in less than a day. Thus, even as Hispanic Americans acculturate and integrate, Hispanic culture and language are sustained and strengthened. What is perceived to be slow acculturation for these groups is mostly the result of fast and continuous immigration.

Furthermore, colonized minority groups such as Chicanos and Puerto Ricans were not encouraged to assimilate in the past. Valued primarily for the cheap labor they supplied, they were seen as otherwise inferior or undesirable and unfit for integration. Two sociologists put the point forcefully: "Non-white people were brought to this society precisely because of race: not to assimilate but to work in unfree, unskilled labor systems that were tightly controlled" (Baca Zinn & Eitzen, 1990, p. 73). For much of this century, Latinos were excluded from the institutions and experiences (e.g., school) that could have led to greater equality and higher rates of acculturation. Prejudice, racism, and discrimination combined to keep most Latino groups away from the centers of modernization and change and away from opportunities to improve their situation.

Racial factors have complicated and slowed the process of assimilation for many Latinos, especially perhaps for darker complexioned Puerto Ricans. Latinos who are less "Anglo" in appearance may retain or even emphasize their Spanish heritage to avoid classification as African American or Native American and all the disabilities associated with American racism. The same is true for Caribbean immigrants, such as Haitians and West Indians, who are seen as black (Fernandez-Kelly & Schauffler, 1994). Thus, the weight of our racist past (and present) may put some Latinos in a position in which they increase the salience of their ethnic identity and thus slow the process of Anglo conformity as a way of avoiding the disadvantages associated with their racial identity.

Finally, for many Cubans and other groups, cultural differences reflect the recency of their immigration. Their first generations are alive and well, and as is typical for immigrant groups, they keep the language and traditions alive. Cuban Americans have been a sizable group in the United States for only about 40 years, barely enough time for a third generation to develop.

**Secondary Structural Assimilation.** In this section, we survey the situation of Latinos in the public areas and institutions of American society, beginning with where people live.

*Residence.* Exhibit 9.5 shows the regional concentrations of Latinos in 2000. The legacies of their varied patterns of entry and settlement are evident. The higher concentrations in the Southwest reflect the presence of Mexican Americans; those in Florida are the result of the Cuban immigration, and those in the Northeast display the settlement patterns of Puerto Ricans.

Within each of these regions, Latino groups are highly urbanized, as shown in Exhibit 9.6. Virtually all Cuban Americans and Puerto Ricans are urbanized and concentrated in densely settled center city areas. Mexican Americans are more rural than the other two groups, but, in sharp contrast to their historical role as an agrarian workforce, the percentage of the group living outside urban areas is tiny today.

Hispanics are generally less residentially segregated than African Americans, as shown in Exhibit 9.7. This exhibit, like Exhibit 7.6, shows the average dissimilarity index for the 50 largest metro areas grouped into 5 regions for 1980 and 2000. Hispanic Americans are less residentially segregated in every region, but, in opposition to African Americans, residential segregation increased over the 20-year period. This is a reflection of high rates of immigration and "chain" patterns of settlement, among other factors.

*Education.* Levels of education for Hispanic Americans have risen in recent years but still lag behind national standards (see Exhibit 9.8). All three groups fall well below national norms for high school education. The percentage of college-educated Cuban Americans is comparable to non-Hispanic whites, but the percentages for the other groups are dramatically lower.

The lower levels of education are the cumulative results of decades of systematic discrimination and exclusion. These levels have been further reduced, in the case of Mexican Americans, by the high percentage of recent immigrants who have very modest educational backgrounds. Given the role that educational credentials have come to play in the job market, these figures

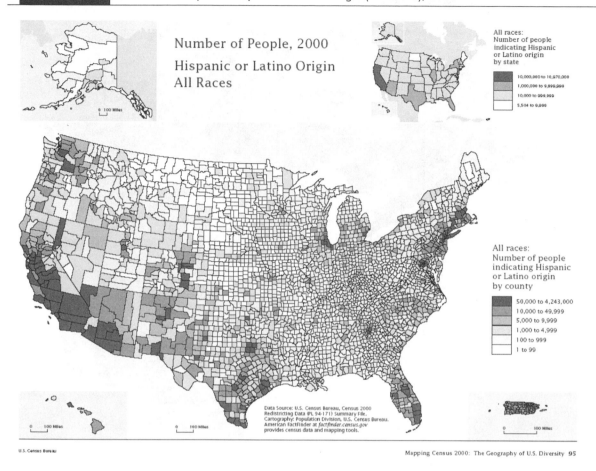

Number of People, 2000

Hispanic or Latino Origin

All Races

All races:
Number of people
indicating Hispanic
or Latino origin
by state

10,000,000 to 10,970,000
1,000,000 to 9,999,999
10,000 to 999,999
5,504 to 9,999

All races:
Number of people
indicating Hispanic
or Latino origin
by county

50,000 to 4,243,000
10,000 to 49,999
5,000 to 9,999
1,000 to 4,999
100 to 999
1 to 99

Data Source: U.S. Census Bureau, Census 2000
Redistricting Data (PL 94-171) Summary File.
Cartography: Population Division, U.S. Census Bureau.
American FactFinder at *factfinder.census.gov*
provides census data and mapping tools.

U.S. Census Bureau

Mapping Census 2000: The Geography of U.S. Diversity **95**

SOURCE: U.S. Bureau of the Census (2000e1), p. 93.

are consistent with the idea that assimilation may be segmented for these groups, with limited opportunities for upward mobility for some generations.

*Political Power.* The political resources available to Hispanic Americans have increased over the years, but the group is still proportionally underrepresented. Currently, there are no Hispanic Americans in the Senate and only 22 in the House of Representatives. However, the number of representatives of Hispanic origin has more than doubled since 1985 (U.S. Bureau of the Census, 2005, p. 250).

On the local and state level, the number of public officials identified as Hispanic increased by about 41% between 1985 and 2003, from 3147 to 4432 (U.S. Bureau of the Census, 2005, p. 255). Also, in February 2005, Hector Gonzalez, the grandson of Mexican immigrants, became the first Latino to serve as Attorney General of the United States.

The number of Hispanics of voting age has more than doubled in recent decades, and Hispanics today constitute more than 10% of the voting age population. Yet, because

EXHIBIT 9.6 Residential Patterns for Three Hispanic American Groups

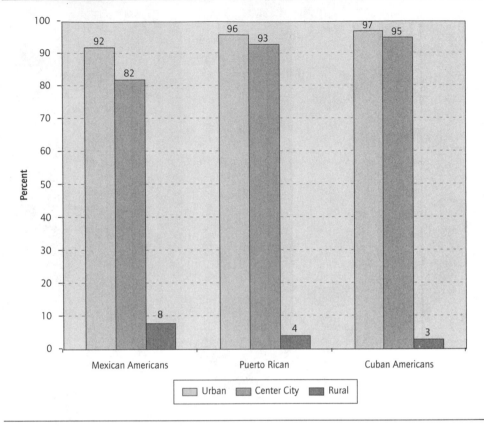

SOURCE: U.S. Census Bureau (n.d.), Summary File 4.

registration rates and actual turnout have been low, the Hispanic community has not had an impact on the political structure proportionate to its size. For example, in the presidential elections between 1980 and 2000, actual voter turnout for Hispanic Americans was generally lower than 30% of those registered to vote, about half of the comparable rate for non-Hispanic whites (U.S. Bureau of the Census, 2002, p. 251). These lower participation rates are due to many factors, including the younger average age of the Hispanic population (younger people are the least likely to register and vote) and the large percentage of recent immigrants in the group (Del Pinal & Singer, 1997, p. 42).

On a more positive note, Hispanic Americans are beginning to exert their political power as the 21st century begins. The Hispanic vote figured prominently in the 2000 and 2004 presidential elections, and President George W. Bush has relied on support from the Hispanic community throughout his career. For example, Bush attracted the support of 44% of Hispanic voters in the 2004 presidential election, up nine percentage points from 2000 (DuBose, 2004).

Hispanic voters could become a crucial element in the coalition that sustains the power of the Republican Party on a national level. Certainly, with their rapid population growth rate, it is clear that the Hispanic voters will have a much greater impact on politics in the future, especially as second- and third-generation children of the current wave of immigration reach voting age.

EXHIBIT 9.7

Residential Segregation in the 50 Largest Metro Areas, Grouped Into Five Regions, 1980 and 2000

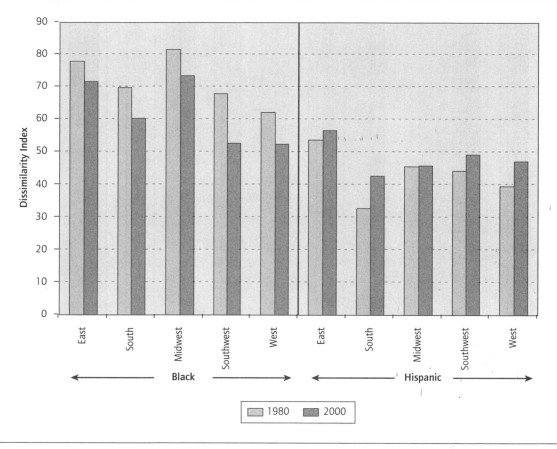

SOURCE: Calculated from data in Charles (2003).

**Jobs and Income.** The economic situation of Hispanic Americans is mixed. Many members of these groups, especially those who have been in the United States for several generations, are doing "just fine. They have, in ever increasing numbers, accessed opportunities in education and employment and have carved out a niche of American prosperity for themselves and their children" (Camarillo & Bonilla, 2001, pp. 130-131). For many others, however, the picture is not so promising. They face segmented assimilation (see chapter 2) and, like African Americans and other minority groups of color, the possibility of becoming members of an impoverished, powerless, and economically marginalized urban underclass.

Exhibit 9.9 displays occupational profiles for Hispanics. Looking first at males (see Exhibit 9.9a), we see that both Mexican Americans and Puerto Ricans are notably underrepresented in the highest status jobs and overrepresented in unskilled jobs. Also, Mexican Americans are over-represented in the agricultural sectors; Puerto Ricans are more overrepresented in the service sector, a difference that reflects the greater urbanization of Puerto Ricans. The profile for Cuban American males is similar to the other two groups, except that they are less underrepresented in the highest occupational category (managerial and professional) and, along with Puerto

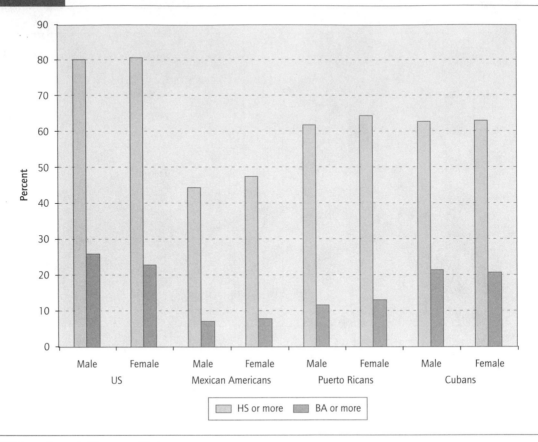

SOURCE: U.S. Census Bureau (n.d.), summary File 4.

Ricans, are actually overrepresented in the next-highest occupational category (technical, sales, and administration). The females of all three groups (see Exhibit 9.9b), as well as dominant group females, are heavily concentrated in the technical, sales, and administration sector (mostly in clerical jobs) and in the service sector.

Unemployment, low income, and poverty continue to be issues for all three Hispanic groups. The unemployment rates for Hispanic Americans run about twice the rate for non-Hispanic whites, and the poverty rates for the group as a whole are comparable to those of African Americans (Camarillo & Bonilla, 2001, pp. 110-111). Exhibit 9.10 shows that all three groups, especially Mexican American females, have dramatically lower median incomes. Cuban American males have the highest incomes, followed closely by Puerto Rican males. Exhibit 9.11 shows that Cuban American households have the lowest poverty rates, and Puerto Ricans have the highest, especially for female-headed households.

The socioeconomic profiles of Mexican Americans and Puerto Ricans reflect their concentration in the low-wage sector of the economy, the long tradition of discrimination and exclusion, and the lower amounts of human capital (education, job training) controlled by these groups. The higher rates of unemployment for these two groups reflect not only discrimination

**EXHIBIT 9.9a** Occupation by Ethnicity, 2000: Males

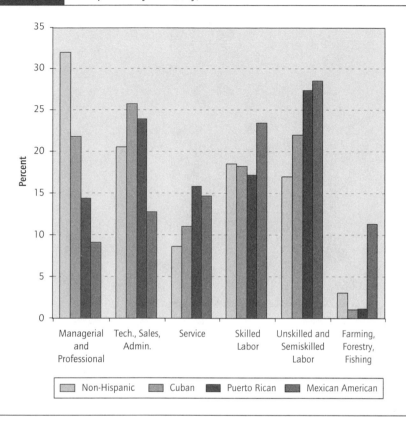

SOURCE: U.S. Bureau of the Census (n.d.).

but also the lack of security and seasonal nature of many of the jobs they hold. Cuban Americans, buoyed by a more privileged social class background and their enclave economy, rank higher on virtually all measures of wealth and prosperity.

These figures also point to a split labor market differentiated by gender, within the dual market differentiated by race and ethnicity. Hispanic women—like minority group women in general— are among the lowest paid, most exploitable, and least protected segments of the U.S. labor force. The impact of poverty is especially severe for Latino women, who often find themselves with the responsibility of caring for their children alone. The percentage of female-headed households ranges from 36% for Puerto Rican families to about 20% for Mexican American and Cuban American families (U.S. Bureau of the Census, 2000o). This pattern is the result of many factors, among them the status of Latino men in the labor force. The jobs available to Latino men often do not pay enough to support a family, and many jobs are seasonal, temporary, or otherwise insecure.

Female-headed Latino families are affected by a triple economic handicap: They have only one wage earner, whose potential income is limited by discrimination against both women and Latinos. The result of these multiple disadvantages is an especially high rate of poverty. Whereas less than 20% of non-Hispanic, white female-headed households fall below the poverty line, the percentage is nearly 40% for Mexican female-headed households and more than 45% for Puerto Rican female-headed households.

**EXHIBIT 9.9b** Occupation by Ethnicity, 2000: Females

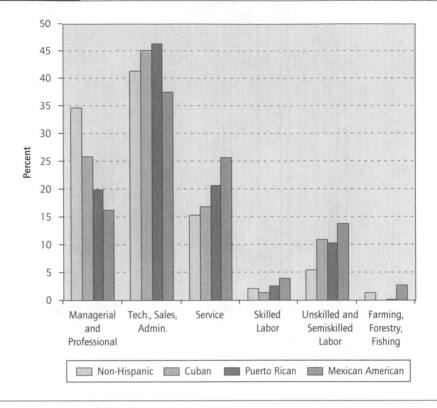

SOURCE: U.S. Bureau of the Census (n.d.).

*Wealth.* As was the case with African Americans and Native Americans, these economic differences are even wider when we consider wealth (savings, property, stocks and bonds, etc.) as opposed to income. Exhibit 9.12 shows the comparative wealth of Hispanic and white households in the same format that was used in Exhibit 7.1. The majority of Hispanic households (57%) are in the "low wealth" category, and only about 26% are in "upper middle" and "high" wealth categories. This pattern is similar to that of African American families and dramatically different from white American families, 58% of which are in the two highest wealth categories.

The contrasts in wealth also display some interesting patterns when we compare immigrants with those born in the United States. First, as displayed in Exhibit 9.13, the median wealth of immigrant Hispanic American households is about 65% of native-born Hispanic households, a difference that reflects the low levels of resources that Hispanic immigrants bring with them. Second, the exhibit shows a wealth gap between Hispanic and other immigrants (the latter control about 9 times as much wealth as Hispanic immigrants). This difference reflects the fact that Hispanic immigrants typically arrive with little education and few skills and compete for jobs in the lower levels of the service and manual labor sectors of the economy.

*Summary.* The socioeconomic situation of Latinos is complex and diversified. Although members of all groups have successfully entered the mainstream economy, poverty and exclusion continue to be major issues. Highly concentrated in deteriorated urban areas (barrios),

EXHIBIT 9.10  Median Income for Full-Time, Year-Round Workers

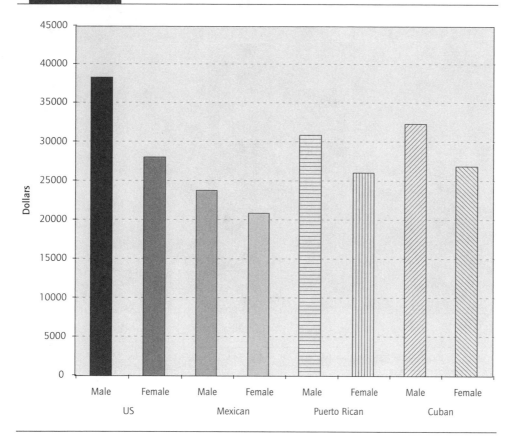

segments of these groups, like other minority groups of color, face the possibility of permanent poverty and economic marginality.

**Primary Structural Assimilation.** Overall, the extent of intimate contact between Hispanic Americans and the dominant group is probably higher than for either African Americans or American Indians (see, e.g., Quillian & Campbell, 2003, and Rosenfield, 2002). This pattern may reflect the fact that Latinos are partly ethnic minority groups and partly racial minority groups. Some studies report that contact is greater for the more affluent social classes, in the cities, and for the younger generations (who are presumably more Americanized) (Fitzpatrick, 1976; Grebler et al., 1970, p. 397; Rodriguez, 1989, pp. 70-72).

Rates of intermarriage are higher for Latinos than for African Americans, but neither are a very high percentage of all marriages. Black and white interracial couples make up less than 1% of all marriages, and the comparable figure for Latinos is 3.2% of all marriages (U.S. Bureau of the Census, 2005, p. 48).

## ASSIMILATION AND HISPANIC AMERICANS

As test cases for what we have called the traditional view of American assimilation, Latinos fare poorly. Mexican Americans continue to be concentrated in the low-wage sector of the labor

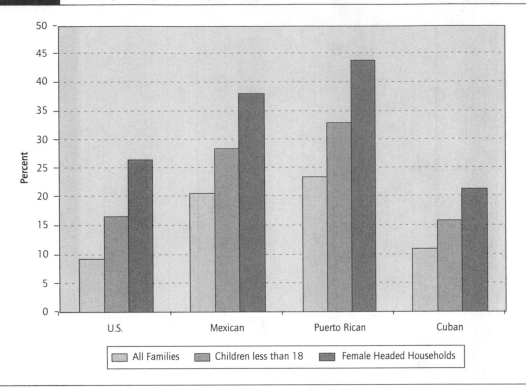

SOURCE: U.S. Bureau of the Census (n.d.).

market, a source of cheap labor for the dominant group's economy. Puerto Ricans, who are more recent arrivals, occupy a similar profile and position.

The fundamental reality faced by both groups, in their histories and in their present situations, is their colonized status in U.S. society. Both Mexican Americans and Puerto Ricans have struggled to rise from their subordinate positions in the United States, and some members have been successful. Yet both groups continue to resemble other colonized minority groups and share many problems with other urban minority groups of color.

The traditional views of the nature of assimilation likewise fail to describe the experiences of Cuban Americans. They are more prosperous, on the average, than either Mexican Americans or Puerto Ricans, but they became successful by remaining separate.

There is no single Hispanic American experience or pattern of adjustment to the larger society. We have focused on just three of the many Latino groups in the United States (others will be covered in Chapter 11), and the diversity of their experiences suggests the variety and complexity of what it means to be a minority group in this society. Their experiences also illustrate some of the fundamental forces that shape the experiences of minority groups: the split labor market and the U.S. appetite for cheap labor, the impact of industrialization, the dangers of a permanent urban underclass, the relationships between competition and levels of prejudice and rejection, and the persistence of race as a primary dividing line between people and groups.

**EXHIBIT 9.12** Wealth of Hispanic and White Non-Hispanic Households

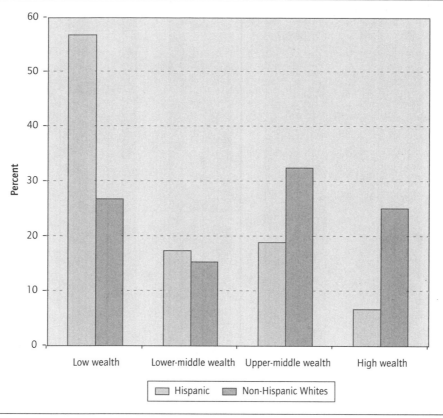

SOURCE: Kochlar (2004).

**EXHIBIT 9.13** Wealth of Immigrant and Native-Born Hispanic and White Non-Hispanic Households, 2002

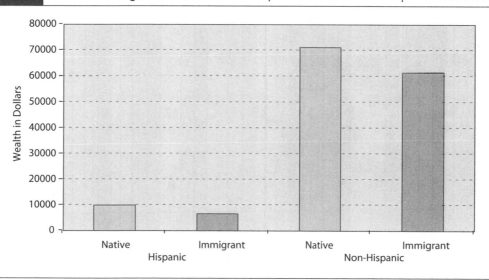

SOURCE: Kochlar (2004).

## Hispanic Americans by *Eric Margolis*

The Hispanic presence in America dates to the "discovery" of Puerto Rico by Christopher Columbus on his second voyage in 1493. Spain colonized the Caribbean almost immediately. Explorers from Spain, England, Holland, and France converged on the East Coast of North America at roughly the same time. By 1687, as the English consolidated their colonies along the East Coast, a Jesuit missionary named Eusebio F. Kino was building

missions north through Spanish Sonora. In Arizona the mission San Javier del Bac near Tucson began about 1701, when Francisco Gonzalvo arrived to be the first resident priest. Like all missions, it was built to advance evangelical conversion to Catholicism and intended to further an educational process of the "civilization" of native Indians. In California, the first Spanish mission was built by Padre Junipero Serra at San Diego de Alcala in 1769. Twenty other Spanish missions were built before 1823 when Mission San Francisco de Solano was completed. Spanish-speaking communities were thriving in California, Texas, New Mexico, Arizona, and Southern Colorado when Anglo American "pioneers" arrived from the East during the 19th century.

The photo above shows an adobe "ranchito" typical for small landholders in southern Colorado and northern New Mexico, late 19th to early 20th century. These communities date back to the 1500's when Spanish pioneers hiked north from Mexico and settled on the northern frontier. They settled in small farming and ranching communities and fought with and intermarried with the Pueblo, Apache, and other Native American communities, many of whom converted to Catholicism. Spanish and Mexican governments made large land grants to the people, and, along with private strips of farm lands along the streams and rivers, people had access to large common lands of mountain and prairie. The Hispanic population of the Southwest became Americans after 1848 when the U.S. won the Mexican War and annexed the territory north of the Rio Grande. Spanish land grants were contested in American courts and much of the common land that made the communities economically viable were whittled away. Some became private property owned by mining companies and large Anglo ranchers; vast tracts were taken over by the Forest Service and Bureau of Land Management.

The U.S.–Mexican border has always been porous; people and culture flow in both directions. This photo on the lower left of the page opposite was taken by the famous Depression era photographer Dorothea Lange in 1938. It shows several generations of Mexican women entering the United States at the El Paso, Texas, immigration station. Four years later, with the U.S. at war with Germany and Japan, the flow of immigrants became a flood. The "Bracero" program sought bring Mexican labor in to pick crops: "More than 80,000 braceros pass through the El Paso Center annually. They're part of an army of 350,000 or more that marches

across the border each year to help plant, cultivate, and harvest cotton and other crops throughout the United States" (*El Paso Herald Post,* April 28, 1956).

The conditions Mexican workers encountered in the American agricultural industry could be abysmal. The photo left shows the housing in a sugar beet camp in Northern Colorado. Tending the beets was labor intensive; the plants had to be thinned, weeded, and harvested during a long season. Jack Allison, the photographer, made these notes to go with the images he made:

A colony of twenty adobe houses built by the inhabitants with materials supplied by the Great Western Sugar Company. Thirteen of the houses are used; seven are unfit to use for inhabitation. In the thirteen houses live approximately fifty people. Being in the limits of an incorporated town (Hudson) there is a water system. However there is only one outlet (an outdoor spigot) for this whole colony. No electricity, gas or sewerage system. . . . Father and son before their house. Two girls from a neighboring house pose with them. "Those two girls are 'too old' to go to school, so they just play around with my boy." (Girls' ages, fourteen and sixteen; the older one has only one good eye). Hudson, Colorado.

In the 1960s, spurred on by the black civil rights movement, Mexican and Chicana/o (Mexican American) workers sought to organize both a union for agricultural workers and as a community seeking better schools and an end to discrimination. Caesar Chavez, the charismatic leader of the farmworkers union, led strikes and organized a boycott of table grapes that helped bring growers to the bargaining table. The Chicano movement organized for bilingual instruction, culturally sensitive curricula, and access to higher education. Lalo Delgado's poem "Stupid America" expressed the community's sense of frustration:

## Stupid America

stupid america, see that chicano
with a big knife
in his steady hand
he doesn't want to knife you
he wants to sit on a bench
and carve christfigures
but you won't let him.

stupid america, see that chicano
shouting curses on the street
he is a poet
without paper and pencil
and since he cannot write
he will explode.

stupid america, remember that chicanito
flunking math and english
he is the picasso
of your western states
but he will die
with one thousand masterpieces
hanging only from his mind.

Abelardo "Lalo" Berrientos Delgado, 1969

"Hispanic" was a term employed by the U.S. census to conglomerate all persons of Spanish heritage. Like the term "Asian" it describes groups of people who have had little historically or politically in common, although today Spanish media and close living conditions are helping to forge a "Latina/o" identity.

With several people hard at work, and cords crisscrossing about, the above photo is a typical garment factory/sweatshop

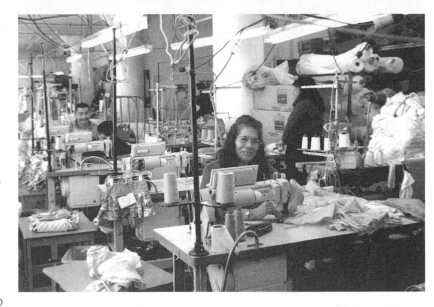

in LA from which emanates the distinct sound of whirring sewing machines and cutting scissors. This *maquila* is managed by an Argentinean woman and her husband. She tries to provide a clean environment and to work with her workers, after having spent years working in different and hostile LA sweatshops. The number of men in the LA garment industry has skyrocketed; several men, mostly Latino immigrants, work alongside their female counterparts. Workers come from Guatemala, Mexico, and other Latin American countries. One woman, a twelve-year veteran of the Los Angeles garment industry, puts in heavy overtime in order to save money to send her children to college.

Latino communities are found in many American cities. The photo on the page opposite shows the intersection of Main and Slater streets in Patterson, New Jersey. Lechonera Bayoman is a restaurant owned by a Puerto Rican, Ottavio Arios, who had previously owned the store across the street, now owned and operated by a Mexican family under the name Lissette's Grocery.

# Is Americanization Threatened by "Hispanization"?

*As we have seen in this chapter, immigration from Latin America—and especially from Mexico—is voluminous and shows no sign of slowing. How will these new immigrants shape American culture? Will traditional American values such as individualism, the Protestant Ethic, democracy, and loyalty and patriotism be compromised? Are we developing into two nations, one Anglo and the other Hispanic?*

*Many people are deeply concerned that American culture cannot survive in its present form. For example, political scientist Samuel Huntington, in his influential book* Who Are We? *( 2004), argues that large-scale immigration (particularly from Mexico) is leading the United States away from its historical roots and its central values. Others have taken up his argument and, in the article below, John Fonte presents a case for patriotic assimilation as an antidote to the threats presented by our growing cultural diversity.*

*In opposition to the alarms raised by Huntington and Fonte, Professor Francis Fukuyama, a leading American academic, argues that the immigrants are the true carriers of the "Protestant Ethic" and that the United States is corrupting their stronger family and traditional values, not the other way around.*

## How to make an American

JOHN FONTE

Browsing through my grandmother's citizenship textbook from the 1930s one day, I found Lesson 61 on the Americanization policies of Theodore Roosevelt:

> [Roosevelt] loved America above all else and his last public message was a plea for the "complete Americanization" of our people in which he said: ". . . [if] the immigrant who comes here in good faith

becomes an American and assimilates himself to us, he shall be treated on an exact equality with everyone else, for it is an outrage to discriminate against any such man because of creed, or birthplace, or origin. But this is predicated upon the man's becoming an American, and nothing but an American. There can be no divided allegiance here. We have room for but one soul (sic) loyalty and that is loyalty to the American people."

The textbook captured the spirit of Americanization – that immigrants are expected to assimilate patriotically and become loyal Americans. More than one hundred years earlier George Washington had written to John Adams that he envisioned immigrants "assimilated to our customs, measures, and laws," and because of this, Washington declared, native-born citizens and immigrants would "soon become one people."

This sentiment is roughly the view of the majority of Americans today, but clearly not the opinion of many American elites. As Samuel Huntington argues . . . , elites in government, business, education, academia, and the media have for decades been actively involved in efforts to "deconstruct"[2] the American nation and its traditional concepts of assimilation and citizenship.

Huntington explains in his new book, *Who Are We?*, that arguments over multiculturalism, bilingualism, ethnic and gender group preferences, dual citizenship, history standards, transnationalism—and immigration and assimilation—are all part of the same conflict over the nature of the American liberal democratic regime. He is right to maintain that a "deconstructionist coalition" challenges the core principles of the American nation on all fronts. At the end of the day, the deconstructionists would transform an American nation based on the principles of individual citizenship, equality of opportunity, and self-government within Constitutional limits, into a new form of regime built on ethnic, racial, and gender group rights with decision-making increasingly in the hands of unelected elites. . . . What is ultimately at stake is whether the traditional American regime will be transmitted to future generations intact or wholly transformed.

Clearly, all of this means that the issue of immigration/assimilation (and these two issues should always be considered as one) must be examined within the broader context of the leftist assault on traditional American political principles. To help clarify the problem, let us explore a series of assimilation-related issues that will soon confront both elite and popular opinion. These include initiatives to revise the oath of allegiance [and] design a new citizenship test. . . .

Implicit in Huntington's thesis is that just below the surface of the policy debate there exists unapologetic public support for vigorous Americanization policies that would explicitly promote the patriotic integration of immigrants into what was once called "the American way of life." Besides public support, there appears to be a bloc in Congress . . . strongly interested in patriotic, as well as economic and linguistic, integration. Last year when the United States Citizenship and Immigration Services (USCIS) wanted to simplify the citizenship oath, some members of Congress immediately protested, and the USCIS pulled back. Worried that the traditional oath (in which new citizens promise to "renounce" their old allegiances and "bear arms" on behalf of the United States) will be weakened, Senator Lamar Alexander (R-TN) and Congressman Jim Ryun (R-KS) have introduced legislation to codify it into law.

In addition, it appears that the forces of patriotic renewal are being heard in discussions over the development of a new citizenship test. . . . Advocates of patriotic integration in veterans groups, think tanks, and Congress . . . declare that we must start with first principles by asking: What is the purpose of the history/government citizenship test?

The law states that applicants for citizenship must have: 1) "a knowledge and understanding of the history, and of the principles and form of government of the United States" and 2) possess "good moral character, attachment to the principles of the Constitution, and be well disposed to the good order and happiness of the United States." This leads naturally to the conclusion that the purpose of the test as a whole is not merely to get new citizens to know certain facts, but also to be "attached" to the principles of the Constitution-evidence of the explicit normative purpose of naturalization.

The citizenship naturalization process should be a life-altering experience, a rite of passage, such as a wedding, graduation, first communion, or bar mitzvah, which fosters emotional attachment to our nation and strengthens patriotism. . . . The oath is especially crucial to American democracy, because citizenship in America is not based on race, religion, or ethnicity, but on political loyalty. In taking the oath, the new citizen transfers allegiance from the land of his birth to the United States.

Oath-takers have a moral obligation to give up all political loyalty to their birth nations. . . . The oath of allegiance, like wedding vows, represents not only a moral obligation for individuals, but a norm for our democracy. . . .

If it becomes routine for large numbers of new citizens to keep old political loyalties, the nature of American citizenship will be transformed, just as, say, legal polygamy would transform the nature of marriage. The principle that we are a people united by political allegiance rather than the ascriptive characteristics of race, ethnicity, and birth would be effectively repudiated.

"Patriotic Renewalists" on Capitol Hill could very well demand that . . . we should get serious about patriotic assimilation. . . . Like Theodore Roosevelt . . . , we should insist that immigration policy be combined with serious Americanization initiatives and that immigration levels remain dependent on how well we integrate newcomers patriotically. After all, we are a nation, not just a market.

SOURCE: Fonte, John. 2004. "How To Make an American." *The American Enterprise*: 15: pp. 4–5.

## Why We Shouldn't Worry About the "Hispanization" of the United States

FRANCIS FUKUYAMA

It is not politically correct today to say that America is fundamentally a Protestant country, or that a specific form of religion is critical to its success as a democracy. Yet as historical facts, these statements are undoubtedly true, and they are the premise of *Who Are We?,* Samuel Huntington's new book. The United States, he argues, is a liberal democracy based on certain universal political principles regarding liberty and equality, summed up traditionally as the American Creed. But the country's success as a free and prosperous democratic society was not due simply to the goodness of these principles or the strength of America's formal institutions. There was a crucial supplement: cultural values that Huntington describes as "Anglo-Protestant." . . .

Huntington is following in the path of innumerable observers of the United States [who] have noted that the dissident, sectarian nature of the Protestantism transplanted to North America was critical to shaping American values like individualism, anti-statism, tolerance, moralism, the work ethic, the propensity for voluntary association, and a host of other informal habits and customs that augment our Constitution and legal system. *Who Are We?* is also perfectly consistent with Huntington's [work] in arguing that liberal democracy is less a universalistic system for organizing political life than an outgrowth of a certain northern European Christian culture, the appeal and feasibility of which will be limited in other cultural settings.

Huntington goes on to argue that . . . immigration [is a] threat to that traditional American identity. In his view, the American elite, from corporate executives to professors to journalists, sees itself as cosmopolitan, secular, and attached to the principle of diversity as an end in itself. That elite no longer feels emotionally attached to America and is increasingly out of touch with the vast majority of non-elite Americans who remain patriotic, morally conservative, and Christian. . . .

On no issue are elites and ordinary Americans further apart than on immigration, and Huntington takes the latter's concerns about the threat posed by Mexican immigration very seriously. This is because of the numbers involved, . . . the concentration of Mexican immigrants in a few Southwestern states and cities, and the proximity of their country of origin. The wave has occurred, moreover, at a time when American elites have lost confidence in their own cultural values and are no longer willing to use the public school system to assimilate these new immigrants to Anglo-Protestant culture. Huntington worries that unchecked immigration will sow the seeds of a later backlash, and may even lead one day to something new in the American experience, an ethnolinguistic minority with strong ties to a neighboring country that could potentially make territorial claims on much of the Southwest.

I am glad that a scholar like Huntington has raised these issues, since they deserve serious discussion. . . . Huntington poses some real questions about whether the large Mexican immigrant population will assimilate as other immigrant groups have done before them. . . . He is right that "culture matters" and he is right that the thoughtless promotion of multiculturalism and identity politics threatens important American values. But his book, ironically, offers grist for a rather different perspective on the problem: *Who Are We?* suggests that the more serious threat to American culture comes perhaps from its own internal contradictions than from foreigners.

Let's begin with the question of who the true bearers of "Anglo-Protestant" values are. . . . His chapter describing "core" Anglo-Protestant values ends up focusing almost entirely on the work ethic: "from the beginning," he writes, "America's religion has been the religion of work." But who in today's world works hard? Certainly not contemporary Europeans with their six-week vacations. The real Protestants are those Korean grocery-store owners, or Indian entrepreneurs, or Taiwanese engineers, or

Russian cab drivers working two or three jobs in America's free and relatively unregulated labor market. I lived in Los Angeles for nearly a decade, and remember passing groups of Chicanos gathered at certain intersections at 7 A.M. waiting for work as day laborers. No lack of a work ethic here: That's why Hispanics have pushed native-born African-Americans out of low-skill jobs in virtually every city where they compete head-to-head. . . .

There are a number of grounds for thinking that the United States will assimilate Hispanic immigrants just as it has earlier ethnic groups. Most important is the fact that they are Christian—either Catholic or, to an increasing degree, Evangelical Protestant. When controlling for socioeconomic status, they have stronger traditional family values than their native-born counterparts. This means that culturally, today's Mexican immigrants are much less distant from mainstream "Anglos" than were, say, the southern Italian immigrants or Eastern European Jews from mainstream WASPs at the beginning of the 20th century. Their rates of second- and third-generation intermarriage are much closer to those of other European groups than for African-Americans. And, from Gen. Ricardo Sanchez on down, they are serving honorably today in the U.S. armed forces in numbers disproportionate to their place in the overall population.

The problem . . . is not that Mexican and other Latino immigrants come with the wrong values, but rather that they are corrupted by American practices. Many young Hispanics are absorbed into the underclass culture of American inner cities, which has then re-exported gang violence back to Mexico and Central America; or else their middle-class leaders have absorbed the American post-civil rights era sense of victimization and entitlement. There is a sharp divide between elites—organizations like the National Council of La Raza, or the Mexican-American Legal Defense Fund—and the general population of Hispanic immigrants. The latter, overall, tend to be socially conservative, want to learn English and assimilate into the American mainstream, and were even supportive initially of California's Proposition 187 (denying benefits to illegal immigrants) and 227 (ending bilingualism in public education). . . .

If it is the case that high levels of immigration are inevitable for developed societies, then what we need to do is to shift the focus from immigration per se to the issue of assimilation. . . .

This will be a huge challenge for the United States, but I am more confident than Huntington that we can meet it. Indeed, Hispanic immigrants will help to reinforce certain cultural values like the emphasis on family and work, and the Christian character of American society.

SOURCE: Fukuyama, Francis. 2004. "Identity Crisis: Why We Shouldn't Worry About Mexican Immigration." Retrieved April 2, 2005, from http://slate.msn.com/id/2101756/#continuearticle

## Debate Questions to Consider

1. Analyze these arguments in terms of assimilation and pluralism. Are these authors using Gordon's model of assimilation? Can these issues and concerns be expressed in terms of pluralism? How?

2. Is "patriotic assimilation" a reasonable policy to deal with the concerns over "Hispanization"? What would this policy look like if implemented in schools and other institutions?

3. What points does Fukuyama make in response to the arguments presented by Fonte and Huntington? What evidence does he present to back up his points? How convincing is the evidence?

4. Is it fair to say that Fonte is a pessimist and Fukuyama is an optimist about the future of American culture? Does immigration really threaten traditional American values?

# MAIN POINTS

- Hispanic Americans are a diverse and growing part of U.S. society. There are many distinct groups, but the three largest are Mexican Americans, Puerto Ricans, and Cuban Americans. The various Hispanic groups do not think of themselves as a single entity.

- Hispanic Americans have some characteristics of colonized groups and some of immigrant groups. Similarly, these groups are racial minorities in some ways and ethnic minorities in others.

- Since the beginning of the 20th century, Mexico has served as a reserve labor force for the development of the U.S. economy. Immigrants from Mexico entered a social system in which the colonized status of the group was already established. Mexican Americans remained a colonized minority group despite the large numbers of immigrants in the group and have been systematically excluded from opportunities for upward mobility by institutional discrimination and segregation.

- A Mexican American protest movement has been continuously seeking to improve the status of the group. In the 1960s, a more intense and militant movement emerged, guided by the ideology of Chicanismo.

- Puerto Ricans began to move to the mainland in large numbers only in recent decades. The group is concentrated in the urban Northeast, in the low-wage sector of the job market.

- Cubans began immigrating after Castro's revolution in the late 1950s. They settled primarily in southern Florida, where they created an ethnic enclave.

- The overall levels of anti-Hispanic prejudice and discrimination seem to have declined, along with the general decline in explicit, overt racism in American society. Recent high levels of immigration seem to have increased anti-Hispanic prejudice and discrimination, however, especially in areas with large numbers of immigrants.

- Levels of acculturation are highly variable from group to group and generation to generation. Acculturation increases with length of residence. The vitality of Latino cultures has been sustained by recent immigration.

- Secondary structural assimilation also varies from group to group. Poverty, unemployment, lower levels of educational attainment, and other forms of inequality continue to be major problems for Hispanic groups, even the relatively successful Cuban Americans.

- Primary structural assimilation with the dominant group is greater than for African Americans.

- Public Sociology Assignment 2 on pages 220–221 will permit you to document racial and ethnic inequalities in health in your area. What differences in health can you document between Hispanic groups and non-Hispanic whites? Are there differences between specific Hispanic groups? Do these differences parallel the patterns of inequality documented in this chapter?

## Study Site on the Web

Don't forget the interactive quizzes and other resources and learning aids at www.www.pineforge.com/healeystudy4.

## For Further Reading

Acuna, Rodolfo. 1999. *Occupied America* (4th ed.). New York: Harper & Row. *(The author reviews Mexican American history and argues that the experiences of this group resemble those of colonized groups.)*

Garcia, Maria Cristina. 1996. *Havana USA: Cuban Exiles and Cuban Americans in South Florida, 1959-1994.* Berkeley: University of California Press. *(A comprehensive history of the Cuban community in southern Florida.)*

Fitzpatrick, Joseph P. 1987. *Puerto Rican Americans: The Meaning of Migration to the Mainland* (2nd ed.). Englewood Cliffs, NJ: Prentice Hall. *(Good overview of the history and present situation of Puerto Ricans.)*

Mirandé, Alfredo. 1985. *The Chicano Experience: An Alternative Perspective.* Notre Dame, IN: University of Notre Dame Press. *(A passionate analysis of the Mexican American experience. Separate chapters on work, crime, education, the church, and family.)*

Portes, Alejandro, & Bach, Robert L. 1985. *Latin Journey: Cuban and Mexican Immigrants in the United States.* Berkeley: University of California Press. *(A landmark analysis of Latino immigration, ethnic enclaves, U.S. and assimilation.)*

## Questions for Review and Study

1. At the beginning of this chapter, it is stated that Hispanic Americans "combine elements of the polar extremes [immigrant and colonized] of Blauner's typology of minority groups" and that they are "partly an ethnic minority group and partly a racial minority group." Explain these statements in terms of the rest of the material presented in the chapter.

2. What important cultural differences between Mexican Americans and the dominant society shaped the relationships between the two groups?

3. How does the history of Mexican immigration demonstrate the usefulness of Noel's concepts of differentials in power and competition?

4. Compare and contrast the protest movements of Mexican Americans, American Indians, and African Americans. What similarities and differences existed in Chicanismo, Red Power, and Black Power? How do the differences reflect the unique experiences of each group?

5. In what ways are the experiences of Puerto Ricans and Cuban Americans unique compared with those of other minority groups? How do these differences reflect other differences, such as differences in contact situation?

6. The Cuban American enclave has resulted in a variety of benefits for the group. Why don't other minority groups follow this strategy?

7. What images of Latinas are common in U.S. society? How do these images reflect the experiences of these groups?

8. Describe the situation of the major Hispanic American groups in terms of acculturation and integration. Which groups are closest to equality? What factors or experiences might account for the differences between groups? In what ways might the statement "Hispanic Americans are remaining pluralistic even while they assimilate" be true?

## Internet Research Project

Additional information and a list of relevant Web sites are included in the Appendix (Internet Resources).

The Mexican Migration Project was created to learn more about the complex process of Mexican migration to the United States. The project is binational and has been gathering data since 1982. A number of individual stories of Mexican migrants are available online at http://mmp.opr.princeton.edu/expressions/stories-en.aspx. Read the introduction and then select several of the stories to read. Analyze each using the concepts developed in this chapter, especially the idea that Mexico serves as a reserve pool of cheap labor for the benefit of U.S. businesses.

### Notes

1. Latino refers to the group in general or to males. The correct form for females is Latina.

2. In this context, to "deconstruct" means to critically analyze values and traditions in order to expose contradictions and inconsistencies.

# 10

# Asian Americans

## Are Chinese Americans and Japanese Americans "Model Minorities"?

A VARIETY OF GROUPS FROM ASIA AND THE PACIFIC ISLANDS ARE BECOMING INCREASINGLY prominent in the United States. Although they are often seen as the same and classified into a single category in government reports, these groups vary in their language, in their cultural and physical characteristics, and in their experiences in the United States. Some of these groups are truly newcomers to America, but others have roots in this country stretching back for more than 150 years.

In this chapter, we will begin with an overview of the characteristics of the largest Asian American and Pacific Islander groups and then briefly examine the traditions and customs that they bring with them to America. We will then focus on the two oldest Asian American groups: Chinese Americans and Japanese Americans. The newer Asian and Pacific Islander groups will be covered in Chapter 11. We will explore the differences between Chinese Americans Japanese Americans, and the groups we have covered in previous chapters, but we will be especially concerned with the perception that Asian Americans in general and Chinese and Japanese Americans in particular are "**model minorities**": successful, affluent, highly educated people who do not suffer from the problems usually associated with minority group status. How accurate is this view? Have Asian Americans forged a pathway to upward mobility that could be followed by other groups? Do the concepts and theories that have guided this text (particularly the Blauner and Noel hypotheses) apply? Does the success of these groups mean that the United States is truly an open, fair, and just society? We explore these questions throughout the chapter.

EXHIBIT 10.1 Asian American and Pacific Islander (API) Population by Major Ethnicity: 1980, 1990, and 2000 Censuses

| Group | 1980 Number | 1980 % of Total Population | 1990 Number | 1990 % of Total Population | 2000 Number | 2000 % of Total Population |
|---|---|---|---|---|---|---|
| United States | 226,545,805 | | 248,709,873 | | 281,421,906 | |
| All API Groups | 3,259,519 | 1.4 | 6,908,638 | 2.8 | 11,070,913 | 3.9 |
| Chinese | 806,040 | 0.4 | 1,645,472 | 0.7 | 2,633,849 | 0.9 |
| Japanese | 700,974 | 0.3 | 847,562 | 0.3 | 958,945 | 0.3 |
| Filipino | 774,652 | 0.3 | 1,406,770 | 0.6 | 2,089,701 | 0.7 |
| Korean | 354,593 | 0.2 | 798,849 | 0.3 | 1,148,951 | 0.4 |
| Asian Indian | 361,531 | 0.2 | 815,447 | 0.3 | 1,785,336 | 0.6 |
| Vietnamese | 261,729 | 0.1 | 614,547 | 0.3 | 1,171,776 | 0.4 |
| Other API[a] | 806,040 | 0.4 | 2,425,463 | 1.0 | 3,916,204 | 1.4 |

SOURCE: Xie and Goyette (2004), p. 3.

a. Includes Native Hawaiians, Cambodians, Laotians, Hmong, Thais, Pakastanis, Samoans, and others.

## ASIAN AMERICANS AND PACIFIC ISLANDERS

Exhibit 10.1 lists the largest Asian American and Pacific Islander groups and illustrates their diversity. The six largest groups are distinct from each other in culture and physical appearance, and each has had its own unique experience in America. The "Other" groups further add to this diversity.

Several features of Exhibit 10.1 are worth noting. First, Asians and Pacific Islanders are tiny fractions of the total U.S. population. Even when aggregated, they account for slightly less than 4% of the total population. In contrast, African Americans and Hispanic Americans are each about 12% of the total population (see Exhibit 1.1). Second, most Asian American groups have grown dramatically in recent decades, largely because of high rates of immigration since the 1965 changes in U.S. immigration policy (Lee, 1998, p. 15). Each group listed in Exhibit 10.1, except Japanese Americans, grew faster than the total population between 1980 and 2000. The Japanese American population grew at the slowest rate (largely because immigration from Japan has been low in recent decades), but the number of Vietnamese Americans more than quadrupled, as did the number of Indian Americans. This rapid growth is projected to continue for decades to come, and the impact of Asian Americans on everyday life and American culture will increase accordingly. Today, fewer than 4 out of every 100 Americans are in this group, but this ratio will grow to nearly 10 out of every 100 by the year 2050.

## ORIGINS AND CULTURES

Asian Americans and Pacific Islanders have brought a wealth of traditions to the United States. They speak many different languages and practice religions as diverse as Buddhism, Confucianism, Islam, Hinduism, and Christianity. Asian cultures predate the founding of the United States by centuries or even millennia. Although no two of these cultures are the same, some general similarities can be identified. These cultural traits have shaped the behavior of Asian

Americans, as well as the perceptions of members of the dominant group, and compose part of the foundation on which Asian American experiences have been built.

Asian cultures tend to stress group membership over individual self-interest. For example, Confucianism, which was the dominant ethical and moral system in traditional China and had a powerful influence on many other Asian cultures, counsels people to see themselves as elements in larger social systems and status hierarchies. Confucianism emphasizes loyalty to the group, conformity to societal expectations, and respect for one's superiors. In traditional China, as in other Asian societies, the business of everyday life was organized around kinship relations, and most interpersonal relations were with family members and other relatives (Lyman, 1974, p. 9). The family or the clan often owned the land on which all depended for survival, and kinship ties determined inheritance patterns. The clan also performed a number of crucial social functions, including arranging marriages, settling disputes between individuals, and organizing festivals and holidays.

Asian cultures stress sensitivity to the opinions and judgments of others and the importance of avoiding public embarrassment and not giving offense. Especially when discussing Japanese culture, these cultural tendencies are often contrasted with Western practices in terms of "guilt versus shame" and the nature of personal morality (Benedict, 1946). In Western cultures, individuals are encouraged to develop and abide by a conscience, or an inner moral voice, and behavior is guided by one's personal sense of guilt. In contrast, Asian cultures stress the importance of maintaining the respect and good opinion of others and avoiding shame and public humiliation. Group harmony, or *wa* in Japanese, is a central concern, and displays of individualism are discouraged. These characteristics are reflected in the Japanese proverb: "The nail that sticks up must be hammered down" (Whiting, 1990, p. 70). Asian cultures emphasize proper behavior, conformity to convention and the judgments of others, and avoiding embarrassment and personal confrontations ("saving face").

Traditional Asian cultures were male dominated, and women were consigned to subordinate roles. A Chinese woman was expected to serve first her father, then her husband, and, if widowed, her eldest son. Confucianism also decreed that women should observe the Four Virtues: chastity and obedience, shyness, a pleasing demeanor, and skill in the performance of domestic duties (Amott & Matthaei, 1991, p. 200). Women of high status in traditional China symbolized their subordination by binding their feet. This painful, crippling practice began early in life and required women to wrap their feet tightly to keep them artificially small. The bones in the arch were broken so that the toes could be bent under the foot, further decreasing the size of the foot. Bound feet were considered beautiful, but they also immobilized women and were intended to prevent them from "wandering away" from domestic and household duties (Jackson, 2000; Takaki, 1993, pp. 209-210).

The experiences of Asian Americans in the United States modified these patriarchal values and traditional traits. For the groups with longer histories in U.S. society, such as Chinese Americans and Japanese Americans, the effects of these values on individual personality may be slight; for more recently arrived groups, the effects are more powerful. The cultural and religious differences among the Asian American groups also reflect the recent histories of each of the sending nations. For example, Vietnam was a colony of China for 1000 years, but for much of the past century, it was a colony of France. Although Vietnamese culture has been heavily influenced by China, many Vietnamese are Catholic, a result of the efforts of the French to convert them. The Philippines and India were also colonized by Western nations—the former by Spain and then by the United States and the latter by Great Britain. As a result, many Filipinos are Catholic, and many Indian immigrants are familiar with English and with Anglo culture.

**EXHIBIT 10.2** East Asia, Showing China and Japan

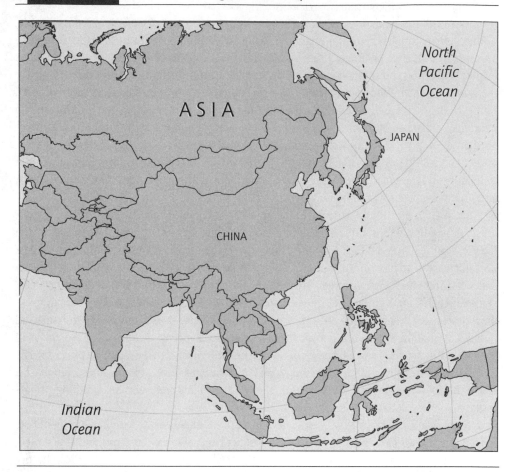

These examples are, of course, the merest suggestion of the diversity of these groups. In fact, Asian Americans and Pacific Islanders, who share little more than a slight physical resemblance and some broad cultural similarities, are much more diverse than Hispanic Americans, who are overwhelmingly Catholic and share a common language and a historical connection with Spain (Min, 1995, p. 25).

## CONTACT SITUATIONS AND THE DEVELOPMENT OF THE CHINESE AMERICAN AND JAPANESE AMERICAN COMMUNITIES

The earliest Asian groups to arrive in substantial numbers were from China and Japan. Their contact situations not only shaped their own histories but also affected the present situation of all Asian Americans and Pacific Islanders in many ways. As we will see, the contact situations for both Chinese Americans and Japanese Americans featured massive rejection and discrimination. Both groups adapted to the racism of the larger society by forming enclaves, a strategy that eventually produced some major benefits for their descendants.

# Chinese Americans

**Early Immigration and the Anti-Chinese Campaign.** Immigrants from China to the United States began to arrive in the early 1800s and were generally motivated by the same kinds of social and economic forces that have inspired immigration everywhere for the past two centuries. Chinese immigrants were "pushed" to leave their homeland by the disruption of traditional social relations, caused by the colonization of much of China by more industrialized European nations, and by rapid population growth (Chan, 1990; Lyman, 1974; Tsai, 1986). At the same time, these immigrants were "pulled" to the West Coast of the United States by the Gold Rush of 1849 and by other opportunities created by the development of the West.

The Noel hypothesis (see Chapter 5) provides a useful way to analyze the contact situation that developed between Chinese and Anglo-Americans in the mid-19th century. As you recall, Noel argues that racial or ethnic stratification will result when a contact situation is characterized by three conditions: ethnocentrism, competition, and a differential in power. Once all three conditions were met on the West Coast, a vigorous campaign against the Chinese began, and the group was pushed into a subordinate, disadvantaged position.

Ethnocentrism based on racial, cultural, and language differences was present from the beginning, but at first, competition for jobs between Chinese immigrants and native-born workers was muted by a robust, rapidly growing economy and an abundance of jobs. At first, politicians, newspaper editorial writers, and business leaders praised the Chinese for their industriousness and tirelessness (Tsai, 1986, p. 17). Before long, however, the economic boom slowed, and the supply of jobs began to dry up. The Gold Rush petered out, and the transcontinental railroad, which thousands of Chinese workers had helped to build, was completed in 1869. The migration of Anglo-Americans from the East continued, and competition for jobs and other resources increased. An anti-Chinese campaign of harassment, discrimination, and violent attacks began. In 1871, in Los Angeles, a mob of "several hundred whites shot, hanged, and stabbed 19 Chinese to death" (Tsai, 1986, p. 67). Other attacks against the Chinese occurred in Denver, Seattle, Tacoma, and Rock Springs, Wyoming (Lyman, 1974, p. 77).

As the West Coast economy changed, the Chinese came to be seen as a threat, and elements of the dominant group tried to limit competition. The Chinese were a small group—there were only about 100,000 in the entire country in 1870—and by law, they were not permitted to become citizens. Hence, they controlled few power resources with which to withstand these attacks. During the 1870s, Chinese workers were forced out of most sectors of the mainstream economy, and in 1882, the anti-Chinese campaign experienced its ultimate triumph when the U.S. Congress passed the Chinese Exclusion Act, banning virtually all immigration from China. The act was one of the first restrictive immigration laws and was aimed solely at the Chinese. It established a "rigid competitive" relationship between the groups (see Chapter 6) and eliminated the threat presented by Chinese labor by excluding Chinese from American society.

Consistent with the predictions of split labor market theory (see Chapter 2), the primary antagonists of Chinese immigrants were native-born workers and organized labor. White owners of small businesses, feeling threatened by Chinese-owned businesses, also supported passage of the Chinese Exclusion Act (Boswell, 1986). Other social classes, such as the capitalists who owned larger factories, might actually have benefited from the continued supply of cheaper labor created by immigration from China. Conflicts such as the anti-Chinese campaign can be especially intense because they confound racial and ethnic antagonisms with disputes between different social classes.

**EXHIBIT 10.3** Population Growth for Chinese and Japanese Americans

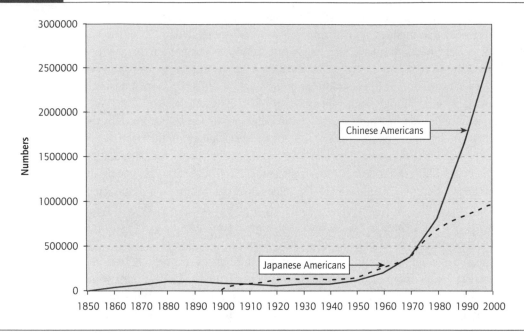

SOURCE: Kitano (1980), p. 562; Lee (1998), p. 15; Xie and Goyette (2004).

The ban on immigration from China remained in effect until World War II, when China was awarded a yearly quota of 105 immigrants in recognition of its wartime alliance with the United States. However, large-scale immigration from China did not resume until federal policy was revised in the 1960s.

**Population Trends and the "Delayed" Second Generation.** Following the Chinese Exclusion Act, the number of Chinese in the United States actually declined (see Exhibit 10.3), as some immigrants passed away or returned to China and were not replaced by newcomers. The huge majority of Chinese immigrants in the 19th century had been young adult male sojourners who intended to work hard, save money, and return to their homes in China (Chan, 1990, p. 66). After 1882, it was difficult for anyone from China, male or female, to immigrate, and the Chinese community in the United States remained overwhelmingly male for many decades. At the end of the 19th century, for example, males outnumbered females by more than 25 to 1, and the sex ratio did not approach parity for decades (Wong, 1995, p. 64; see also Ling, 2000). The scarcity of Chinese women in the United States delayed the second generation (the first born in the United States) and it wasn't until the 1920s, 80 years after immigration began, that as many as one third of all Chinese in the United States were native born (Wong, 1995, p. 64).

The delayed second generation may have reinforced the exclusion of the Chinese American community that began as a reaction to the overt discrimination of the dominant group (Chan, 1990, p. 66). The children of immigrants are usually much more acculturated, and their language facility and greater familiarity with the larger society often permits them to represent the group and speak for it more effectively. In the case of Chinese Americans (and other Asian groups), members of the second generation were citizens of the United States by birth, a status from which the immigrants were barred, and they had legal and political rights not available to their parents. Thus the decades-long absence of a more Americanized, English-speaking generation increased the isolation of Chinese Americans.

**The Ethnic Enclave.** The Chinese became increasingly urbanized as the anti-Chinese campaign and rising racism took their toll. Forced out of towns and smaller cities, they settled in larger urban areas, such as San Francisco, which offered the safety of urban anonymity and ethnic neighborhoods where the old ways could be practiced and contact with the hostile larger society minimized. Chinatowns had existed since the start of the immigration, and they now took on added significance as safe havens from the storm of anti-Chinese venom. The Chinese withdrew to these neighborhoods and became an "invisible minority" (Tsai, 1986, p. 67).

These early Chinatowns were ethnic enclaves like the more recently founded Cuban community in Miami, and a similar process formed them. The earliest urban Chinese included merchants and skilled artisans who, like the early wave of Cuban immigrants, were experienced in commerce (Chan, 1990, p. 44). They established businesses and retail stores that were typically small in scope and modest in profits. As the number of urban Chinese increased, the market for these enterprises became larger and more spatially concentrated. New services were required, the size of the cheap labor pool available to Chinese merchants and entrepreneurs increased, and the Chinatowns became the economic, cultural, and social centers of the community.

Within the Chinatowns, elaborate social structures developed that mirrored traditional China in many ways. The enforced segregation of the Chinese in America helped preserve much of the traditional food, dress, language, values, and religions of their homeland from the pressures of Americanization. The social structure was based on a variety of types of organizations, including family and clan groups and **huiguan**, or associations based on the region or district in China from which the immigrant had come. These organizations performed various, often overlapping, social and welfare services, including settling disputes, aiding new arrivals from their regions, and facilitating the development of mutual aid networks (Lai, 1980, p. 221; Lyman, 1974, pp. 32-37, 116-118). Life was not always peaceful in Chinatown, and there were numerous disputes over control of resources and the organizational infrastructure. In particular, secret societies called **tongs** contested the control and leadership of the merchant-led huiguan and the clan associations. These sometimes bloody conflicts were sensationalized in the American press as "Tong Wars," and they contributed to the popular stereotypes of Asians as exotic, mysterious, and dangerous (Lai, 1980, p. 222; Lyman, 1974, pp. 37-50).

Despite these internal conflicts, American Chinatowns evolved into highly organized, largely self-contained communities complete with their own leadership and decision-making structures. The internal "city government" of Chinatown was the Chinese Consolidated Benevolent Association (CCBA). Dominated by the larger huiguan and clans, the CCBA coordinated and supplemented the activities of the various organizations and represented the interests of the community to the larger society.

The local CCBAs, along with other organizations, also attempted to combat the anti-Chinese campaign, speaking out against racial discrimination and filing numerous lawsuits to contest racist legislation (Lai, 1980, p. 223). The effectiveness of the protest efforts was handicapped by the lack of resources in the Chinese community and by the fact that Chinese immigrants could not become citizens. Attempts were made to mobilize international pressure to protest the treatment of the Chinese in the United States. At the time, however, China was itself colonized and dominated by other nations (including the United States). China was further weakened by internal turmoil and could mount no effective assistance for its citizens in the United States (Chan, 1990, p. 62).

**Survival and Development.** The Chinese American community survived despite the widespread poverty, discrimination, and pressures created by the unbalanced sex ratio. Members of the group began to seek opportunities in other regions, and Chinatowns appeared and grew in New York, Boston, Chicago, Philadelphia, and many other cities.

The patterns of exclusion and discrimination that began during the 19th century anti-Chinese campaign were common throughout the nation and continued well into the 20th century. Chinese Americans responded by finding economic opportunity in areas where dominant group competition for jobs was weak, continuing their tendency to be an "invisible" minority group. Very often, they started small businesses that served either other members of their own group (restaurants, for example) or that relied on the patronage of the general public (laundries, for example). The jobs provided by these small businesses were the economic lifeblood of the community but were limited in the amount of income and wealth they could generate. Until recent decades, for example, most restaurants served primarily other Chinese, especially single males. Since their primary clientele was poor, the profit potential of these businesses was sharply limited. Laundries served the more affluent dominant group, but the returns from this enterprise declined as washers and dryers became increasingly widespread in homes throughout the nation. The population of Chinatown was generally too small to sustain more than these two primary commercial enterprises (Zhou, 1992, pp. 92-94).

As the decades passed, the enclave economy and the complex subsociety of Chinatown evolved. However, discrimination, combined with defensive self-segregation, ensured the continuation of poverty, limited job opportunities, and substandard housing. Relatively hidden from general view, Chinatown became the world in which the second generation grew to adulthood.

**The Second Generation.** Whereas the immigrant generation generally retained its native language and customs, the second generation was much more influenced by the larger culture. The institutional and organizational structures of Chinatown were created to serve the older, mostly male immigrant generation, but younger Chinese Americans tended to look beyond the enclave to fill their needs. They came in contact with the larger society through schools, churches, and voluntary organizations such as the YMCA and YWCA. They abandoned many traditional customs and were less loyal to and interested in the clan and regional associations that the immigrant generation had constructed. They founded organizations of their own that were more compatible with their Americanized lifestyles (Lai, 1980, p. 225).

As with other minority groups, World War II was an important watershed for Chinese Americans. During the war, job opportunities outside the enclave increased, and after the war, many of the 8000 Chinese Americans who served in the armed forces were able to take advantage of the GI Bill to further their education (Lai, 1980, p. 226). In the 1940s and 1950s, many second-generation Chinese Americans moved out of the enclave, away from the traditional neighborhoods, and pursued careers in the larger society. This group was mobile and Americanized, and with educational credentials comparable to the general population, they were prepared to seek success outside Chinatown.

In another departure from tradition, the women of the second generation also pursued education, and as early as 1960, median years of schooling for Chinese American women were slightly higher than for Chinese American men (Kitano & Daniels, 1995, p. 48). Chinese American women also became more diverse in their occupational profile as the century progressed. In 1900, three quarters of all employed Chinese American women worked in manufacturing (usually in garment industry sweatshops or in canning factories) or in domestic work. By 1960, less than 2% were in domestic work, 32% were in clerical occupations, and 18% held professional jobs, often as teachers (Amott & Matthaei, 1991, pp. 209-211).

**An American Success Story?** The men and women of the second generation achieved considerable educational and occupational success and helped to establish the idea that Chinese Americans are a "model minority." A closer examination reveals, however, that the old traditions of anti-Chinese discrimination and prejudice continued to limit the life chances of even the best educated members of this generation. Second-generation Chinese Americans earned less, on the average, and had less favorable occupational profiles than comparably educated white Americans, a gap between qualifications and rewards that reflects persistent discrimination. Kitano and Daniels (1995, p. 50) conclude, for example, that although well-educated Chinese Americans could find good jobs in the mainstream economy, the highest, most lucrative positions—and those that required direct supervision of whites—were still closed to them (see also Hirschman & Wong, 1984).

Furthermore, many Chinese Americans, including many of those who stayed in the Chinatowns to operate the enclave economy and the immigrants who began arriving after 1965, do not fit the image of success at all. A large percentage of these Chinese Americans face the same problems as other colonized, excluded, exploited minority groups of color. They rely for survival on low-wage jobs in the garment industry, the service sector, and the small businesses of the enclave economy and are beset by poverty and powerlessness, much like the urban underclass segments of other groups.

Thus Chinese Americans can be found at both ends of the spectrum of success and affluence, and the group is often said to be "bipolar" in its occupational structure (see Barringer, Takeuchi, & Levin, 1995; Takaki, 1993, pp. 415-416; Wong, 1995, pp. 77-78; Zhou & Logan, 1989). Although a high percentage are found in more desirable occupations—sustaining the idea of Asian success—others, less visible, are concentrated at the lowest levels of the society. Later in this chapter, we will again consider the socioeconomic status of Chinese Americans and the accuracy of the image of success and affluence.

# Japanese Americans

Immigration from Japan began to increase shortly after the Chinese Exclusion Act of 1882 took effect (see Exhibit 10.3), in part to fill the gap in the labor supply created by the restrictive legislation (Kitano, 1980). The 1880 census counted only a few hundred Japanese in the United States, but the group increased rapidly over the next few decades. By 1910, the Japanese in the United States outnumbered the Chinese and remained the larger of the two groups until large-scale immigration resumed in the 1960s (see Exhibit 10.2).

**The Anti-Japanese Campaign.** The contact situation for Japanese immigrants resembled that of the Chinese. They immigrated to the same West Coast regions as the Chinese, entered the labor force in a similar position, and were a small group with few power resources. Predictably, the feelings and emotions generated by the anti-Chinese campaign transferred to them. By the early 1900s, an anti-Japanese campaign to limit competition was in full swing. Efforts were being made to establish a rigid competitive system of group relations and to exclude Japanese immigrants in the same way the Chinese had been barred (Kitano, 1980, p. 563; Kitano & Daniels, 1995, pp. 59-60; Petersen, 1971, pp. 30-55).

Japanese immigration was partly curtailed in 1907 when a "gentlemen's agreement" was signed between Japan and the United States limiting the number of laborers Japan would allow to emigrate (Kitano & Daniels, 1995, p. 59). This policy remained in effect until the United States changed its immigration policy in the 1920s and barred immigration from Japan completely. The end of Japanese immigration is largely responsible for the slow growth of the Japanese American population displayed in Exhibit 10.2.

Most Japanese immigrants, like the Chinese, were young male laborers who planned to eventually return to their homeland or bring their wives after they were established in their new country (Duleep, 1988, p. 24). The agreement of 1907 curtailed the immigration of men, but because of a loophole, females were able to continue to immigrate until the 1920s. Japanese Americans were thus able to maintain a relatively balanced sex ratio, marry, and begin families, and a second generation of Japanese Americans began to appear without much delay. Native-born Japanese numbered about half of the group by 1930 and were a majority of 63% on the eve of World War II (Kitano & Daniels, 1995, p. 59).

The anti-Japanese movement also attempted to dislodge the group from agriculture. Many Japanese immigrants were skilled agriculturists, and farming proved to be their most promising avenue for advancement (Kitano, 1980, p. 563). In 1910, between 30% and 40% of all Japanese in California were engaged in agriculture; from 1900 to 1909, the number of independent Japanese farmers increased from fewer than 50 to about 6000 (Jibou, 1988, p. 358).

Most of these immigrant farmers owned small plots of land, and they comprised only a minuscule percentage of West Coast farmers (Jibou, 1988, pp. 357-358). Nonetheless, their presence and relative success did not go unnoticed and eventually stimulated discriminatory legislation, most notably the **Alien Land Act**, passed by the California legislature in 1913 (Kitano, 1980, p. 563). This bill declared aliens who were ineligible for citizenship (effectively meaning only immigrants from Asia) to be also ineligible to own land. The act did not achieve its goal of dislodging the Japanese from the rural economy. They were able to dodge the discriminatory legislation by various devices, mostly by putting titles of land in the names of their American-born children, who were citizens by law (Jibou, 1988, p. 359).

The Alien Land Act was one part of a sustained campaign against the Japanese in the United States. In the early decades of this century, the Japanese were politically disenfranchised and segregated from dominant group institutions in schools and residential areas. They were discriminated against in movie houses, swimming pools, and other public facilities (Kitano & Daniels, 1988, p. 56). The Japanese were excluded from the mainstream economy and confined to a limited range of poorly paid occupations (see Yamato, 1994). Thus there were strong elements of systematic discrimination, exclusion, and colonization in their overall relationship with the larger society.

**The Ethnic Enclave.** Spurned and disparaged by the larger society, the Japanese, like the Chinese, constructed a separate subsociety. The immigrant generation, called **Issei** (from the Japanese word *ichi*, meaning "one"), established an enclave in agriculture and related enterprises, a rural counterpart of the urban enclaves constructed by other groups we have examined.

By World War II, the Issei had come to dominate a narrow but important segment of agriculture on the West Coast, especially in California. Although they were never more than 2%

of the total population of California, Japanese American–owned farms produced as much as 30% to 40% of various fruits and vegetables grown in that state. As late as 1940, more than 40% of the Japanese American population was involved directly in farming and many more were dependent on the economic activity stimulated by agriculture, including the marketing of their produce (Jibou, 1988, pp. 359-360). Other Issei lived in urban areas, where they were concentrated in a narrow range of businesses and services, such as domestic service and gardening, some of which catered to other Issei and some of which served the dominant group (Jibou, 1988, p. 362).

Japanese Americans in both the rural and urban sectors maximized their economic clout by doing business with other Japanese-owned firms as often as possible. Gardeners and farmers purchased supplies at Japanese-owned firms, farmers used other members of the group to haul their products to market, and businesspeople relied on one another and mutual credit associations, rather than dominant group banks, for financial services. These networks helped the enclave economy to grow and also permitted the Japanese to avoid the hostility and racism of the larger society. However, these very same patterns helped sustain the stereotypes that depicted the Japanese as clannish and unassimilable. In the years before World War II, the Japanese American community was largely dependent for survival on their networks of cooperation and mutual assistance, not on Americanization and integration.

**The Second Generation (Nisei).** In the 1920s and 1930s, anti-Asian feelings continued to run high, and Japanese Americans continued to experience exclusion and discrimination despite (or perhaps because of) their relative success. Unable to find acceptance in Anglo society, the second generation—called **Nisei**—established clubs, athletic leagues, churches, and a multitude of other social and recreational organizations within their own communities (Kitano & Daniels, 1995, p. 63). These organizations reflected the high levels of Americanization of the Nisei and expressed values and interests quite compatible with those of the dominant culture. For example, the most influential Nisei organization was the Japanese American Citizens League, whose creed expressed an ardent patriotism that was to be sorely tested: "I am proud that I am an American citizen. . . . I believe in [American] institutions, ideas and traditions; I glory in her heritage; I boast of her history, I trust in her future" (Kitano & Daniels, 1995, p. 64).

Although the Nisei enjoyed high levels of success in school, the intense discrimination and racism of the 1930s prevented most of them from translating their educational achievements into better jobs and higher salaries. Many occupations in the mainstream economy were closed to even the best educated Japanese Americans, and anti-Asian prejudice and discrimination did not diminish during the hard times and high unemployment of the Great Depression in the 1930s. Many Nisei were forced to remain within the enclave, and in many cases, jobs in the produce stands and retail shops of their parents were all they could find. Their demoralization and anger over their exclusion were eventually swamped by the larger events of World War II.

**The Relocation Camps.** On December 7, 1941, Japan attacked Pearl Harbor, killing almost 2500 Americans. President Franklin D. Roosevelt asked Congress for a declaration of war the next day. The preparations for war stirred up a wide range of fears and anxieties among the American public, including concerns about the loyalty of Japanese Americans. Decades of exclusion and anti-Japanese prejudice had conditioned the dominant society to see Japanese Americans as sinister, clannish, cruel, unalterably foreign, and racially inferior. Fueled by the ferocity of the war itself and fears about a Japanese invasion of the mainland, the tradition of anti-Japanese racism laid the groundwork for a massive violation of civil rights.

Two months after the attack on Pearl Harbor, President Roosevelt signed Executive Order 9066, which led to the relocation of Japanese Americans living on the West Coast. By the late summer of 1942, more than 110,000 Japanese Americans, young and old, male and female—virtually the entire West Coast population—had been transported to **relocation camps** where they were imprisoned behind barbed-wire fences patrolled by armed guards. Many of these people were American citizens, yet no attempt was made to distinguish between citizen and alien. No trials were held, and no one was given the opportunity to refute the implicit charge of disloyalty.

The government gave families little notice to prepare for evacuation and secure their homes, businesses, and belongings. They were allowed to bring only what they could carry, and many possessions were simply abandoned. Businesspeople sold their establishments and farmers sold their land, at panic sale prices. Others locked up their stores and houses and walked away, hoping that the evacuation would be short-lived and their possessions undisturbed.

The internment lasted for nearly the entire war. At first, Japanese Americans were not permitted to serve in the armed forces, but eventually more than 25,000 escaped the camps by volunteering for military service. Nearly all of them served in segregated units or in intelligence work with combat units in the Pacific Ocean. Two all-Japanese combat units served in Europe and became the most decorated units in American military history (Kitano, 1980, p. 567). Other Japanese Americans were able to get out of the camps by means other than the military. Some, for example, agreed to move to militarily nonsensitive areas far away from the West Coast (and their former homes). Still, when the camps closed at the end of the war, about half of the original internees remained (Kitano & Daniels, 1988, p. 64).

The strain of living in the camps affected Japanese Americans in a variety of ways. Lack of activities and privacy, overcrowding, boredom, and monotony were all common complaints. The following personal narrative summarizes the experiences of one Japanese American.

The camps disrupted the traditional forms of family life, as people had to adapt to barracks living and mess hall dining. Conflicts flared between those who counseled caution and temperate reactions to the incarceration and those who wanted to protest in more vigorous ways. Many of those who advised moderation were Nisei intent on proving their loyalty and cooperating with the camp administration.

Despite the injustice and dislocations of the incarceration, the camps did reduce the extent to which women were relegated to a subordinate role. Like Chinese women, Japanese women were expected to devote themselves to the care of the males of their family. In Japan, for example, education for females was not intended to challenge their intellect so much as to make them better wives and mothers. In the camps, however, pay for the few jobs available was the same for both men and women, and the mess halls and small living quarters freed women from some of the burden of housework. Many took advantage of the free time to take classes to learn more English and other skills. The younger women were able to meet young men on their own, weakening the tradition of family-controlled, arranged marriages (Amott & Matthaei, 1991, pp. 225-229).

Some Japanese Americans protested the incarceration from the start and brought lawsuits to end the relocation program. Finally, in 1944, the Supreme Court ruled that detention was unconstitutional. As the camps closed, some Japanese American individuals and organizations began to seek compensation and redress for the economic losses the group had suffered. In 1948, Congress passed legislation to authorize compensation to Japanese Americans. About 26,500 people filed claims under this act. These claims were eventually settled for a total of about $38 million—less than one tenth the amount of the actual economic losses. Demand for meaningful

# Asian Americans by *Eric Margolis*

"Asians": it is one of those curious pan-ethnic terms like "Hispanic" or "White Ethnic" that lumps together huge groups of people who have little in common besides an Anglo American notion of race. The category "Asian," for instance, merges the fifth generation Japanese American with the most recent immigrant from Cambodia who arrived with little more than the clothes on her back. Koreans, Mainland and Taiwanese Chinese, and, if you include "South Asia," Indians and Bangladeshis, are conflated in our American imagination and census categories. The census category adds in "Pacific Islanders," thus including Filipinos, Native Hawaiians, and everyone in between, despite the fact that they come from different nations, speak different languages, have different histories, practice different religions, came to America for different reasons, and in some cases have animosity toward each other. Our image of Asians in America is similarly confusing, from Opium-smoking white slavers, to the brilliant detective Charlie Chan, from the Yellow Peril during World War II and cold war "Chicoms," to today's "model minority" and computer nerd.

THE CHINESE SCHOOL, IN MOTT STREET, NEW YORK.—Drawn by W. P. Snyder, from a Sketch by C. A. Keetels.

DOES NOT A MEETING LIKE THIS, ETC.
"Hello, Niggy man! Youlee golee West—Melee golee East."

Chinese have been "in" but not "of" the American imagined community for at least 150 years. Many were recruited to build the transcontinental railroads or to work in the California gold fields. The railroad was completed in 1869 and in the 1870s California was in an economic slump. Many Chinese came to New York where they opened steam laundries. When the image above was made in 1879 there were about 200 Chinese laundries in the city, a decade later there were 2000. Chinese schools taught old and young alike how to speak English. Still the Chinese remained outside mainstream society, clustered in communities called "Chinatowns."

Chinese and other Asians were subjected to great race prejudice and discrimination as seen in a cartoon from *Harper's Weekly* in 1879.

Alongside prejudice and social exclusion, there was murderous racism directed at Asians. The photograph at the top left of page 360 was taken in 1895 in Rock Springs, Wyoming. Chinese workers, who had been recruited to build the Union Pacific Railroad, were brought to the coal mining town to break a strike by English-speaking workers. A vigilante group of strikers attacked the Chinese section of town, burning it to the ground. This event came to be known as the Chinese

WAITING FOR THE CAR

Massacre. The men in the photo were part of the group investigating the massacre. Left to right: Lieutenant Groesbeck, Tsang Hoy [interpreter to the Chinese Legation], Colonel [Fred A.] Bee [Consul of China at San Francisco], Wong Sic Chen [Chinese Consul at New York], unidentified, and General [A. McD.] McCook.

Arnold Genthe created a collection of photographs of San Francisco's Chinatown before it was destroyed by the great earthquake of 1906. While occasionally overemphasizing the exotic, Genthe managed to capture many of the qualities of everyday life (above, right).

Two Japanese residents of Gardena, California, Sohei Hakehashi, 55, a storekeeper and Koichi Oriba, 58, a farmer, are shown being searched by deputy sheriffs after they were taken into custody on March 13, 1942 (photo top left), in a giant roundup staged by federal agents and other officers to intern persons of Japanese ancestry. After Pearl Harbor almost all of the Japanese on the West Coast were rounded up and sent to Relocation Camps further inland. In many cases their land and houses were taken and sold to Anglo Americans.

Most of the Japanese sent to the Relocation Camps were loyal Americans. The Raphael Weill School in San Francisco was well-integrated in 1941 when this photo was taken by the famous depression era photographer Dorothea Lange. But this would be the last day for the Japanese children who would be relocated with their parents.

# Narrative Portrait

## The Relocation

*Joseph Kurihara was born in Hawaii in 1895. He moved to California at age 20 and served with the U.S. Army in World War I, completed a college education and was a businessman working within the Japanese American enclave until World War II. He worked actively to promote acculturation and better relations with the larger society during the interwar years. He was sent to the relocation camp at Manzanar, California, in the spring of 1942 and continued to play an active role in the dislocated Japanese American community. Although he had never visited Japan and had no interest or connection with the country of his parents' birth, his experiences in the camp were so bitter that he renounced his American citizenship and expatriated to Japan following the war.*

### "WE WERE JUST JAPS"

**Joseph Kurihara**

[The evacuation] . . . was really cruel and harsh. To pack and evacuate in forty-eight hours was an impossibility. Seeing mothers completely bewildered with children crying from want and peddlers taking advantage and offering prices next to robbery made me feel like murdering those responsible without the slightest compunction in my heart.

The parents may be aliens but the children are all American citizens. Did the government of the United States intend to ignore their rights regardless of their citizenship? Those beautiful furnitures [sic] which the parents bought to please their sons and daughters, costing hundreds of dollars were robbed of them at the single command, "Evacuate!" Here my first doubt of American Democracy crept into the far corners of my heart with the sting that I could not forget. Having had absolute confidence in Democracy, I could not believe my very eyes what I had seen that day. America, the standard bearer of Democracy had committed the most heinous crime in its history. . . .

[The camp was in an area that is largely desert.] The desert was bad enough. The . . . barracks made it worse. The constant cyclonic storms loaded with sand and dust made it worst. After living in well furnished homes with every modern convenience and suddenly forced to live the life of a dog is something which one can not so readily forget. Down in our hearts we cried and cursed this government every time when we were showered with sand. We slept in the dust; we breathed the dust; and we ate the dust. Such abominable existence one could not forget, no matter how much we tried to be patient, understand the situation, and take it bravely. Why did not the government permit us to remain where we were? Was it because the government was unable to give us the protection? I have my doubt. The government could have easily declared Martial Law to protect us.

It was not the question of protection. It was because we were Japs! Yes, Japs!

After corralling us like a bunch of sheep in a hellish country, did the government treat us like citizens? No! We were treated like aliens regardless of our rights. Did the government think we were so without pride to work for $16.00 a month when people outside were paid $40.00 to $50.00 a week in the defense plants? Responsible government officials further told us to be loyal and that to enjoy our rights as American citizens we must be ready to die for the country. We must show our loyalty. If such is the case, why are the veterans corralled like the rest of us in the camps? Have they not proven their loyalty already? This matter of proving one's loyalty to enjoy the rights of an American citizen was nothing but a hocus-pocus.

My American friends. . . . no doubt must have wondered why I renounced my citizenship. This decision was not that of today or yesterday. It dates back to the day when General DeWitt [the officer in charge of the evacuation] ordered evacuation. It was confirmed when he flatly refused to listen even to the voices of the former World War Veterans and it was

doubly confirmed when I entered Manzanar. We who already had proven our loyalty by serving in the last World War should have been spared. The veterans asked for special consideration but their requests were denied. They too had to evacuate like the rest of the Japanese people, as if they were aliens.

I did not expect this of the Army. . . . I expected that at least the Nisei would be allowed to remain. But to General DeWitt, we were all alike. "A Jap's a Jap. Once a Jap, always a Jap." . . . I swore to become a Jap 100 percent and never to do another day's work to help this country fight this war. My decision to renounce my citizenship there and then was absolute.

[Just before he left for Japan (in 1946), Kurihara wrote:]

It is my sincere desire to get over there as soon as possible to help rebuild Japan politically and economically. The American Democracy with which I was infused in my childhood is still unshaken. My life is dedicated to Japan with Democracy my goal.

SOURCE: Swaine, Thomas, & Nishimoto, Richard S. (1946). *The Spoilage* (pp. 363-369). Berkeley: University of California Press. Retrieved February 11, 2005, from http://www.geocities.com/Athens/8420/kurihara.html

redress and compensation continued, and in 1988, Congress passed a bill granting reparations of about $20,000 in cash to each of the 60,000 remaining survivors of the camps. The law also acknowledged that the relocation program had been a grave injustice to Japanese Americans (Biskupic, 1989, p. 2879).

The World War II relocation devastated the Japanese American community and left it with few material resources. The emotional and psychological damage inflicted by this experience is incalculable. The fact that today, only six decades later, Japanese Americans are equal or superior to national averages on measures of educational achievement, occupational prestige, and income is one of the more dramatic transformations in minority group history.

**Japanese Americans After World War II.** In 1945, Japanese Americans faced a world very different from the one they had left in 1942. To escape the camps, nearly half of the group had scattered throughout the country and lived everywhere *but* on the West Coast. As Japanese Americans attempted to move back to their former homes, they found their fields untended, their stores vandalized, their possessions lost or stolen, and their lives shattered. In some cases, there was simply no Japanese neighborhood to return to; the Little Tokyo area of San Francisco, for example, was now occupied by African Americans who had moved to the West Coast to take jobs in the defense industry (Amott & Matthaei, 1991, p. 231).

Japanese Americans themselves had changed as well. In the camps, the Issei had lost power to the Nisei. The English-speaking second generation had dealt with the camp administrators and held the leadership positions. Many Nisei had left the camps to serve in the armed forces or to find work in other areas of the country. For virtually every American minority group, the war brought new experiences and a broader sense of themselves, the nation, and the world. A similar transformation occurred for the Nisei. When the war ended, they were unwilling to rebuild the Japanese community as it had been before.

Like second-generation Chinese Americans, the Nisei had a strong record of success in school, and they also took advantage of the GI Bill to further their education. When anti-Asian prejudice began to decline in the 1950s and the job market began to open, the Nisei were educationally prepared to take advantage of the resultant opportunities (Kitano, 1980, p. 567).

The Issei-dominated enclave economy did not reappear after the war. One indicator of the shift away from an enclave economy was the fact that the percentage of Japanese American women in California who worked as unpaid family laborers (i.e., worked in family-run businesses for no salary) declined from 21% in 1940 to 7% in 1950 (Amott & Matthaei, 1991, p. 231). Also, between 1940 and 1990, the percentage of the group employed in agriculture declined from about 50% to 3%, and the percentage employed in personal services fell from 25% to 5% (Nishi, 1995, p. 116).

By 1960, Japanese Americans had an occupational profile very similar to that of whites except that they were actually overrepresented among professionals. Many were employed in the primary economy, not in the ethnic enclave, but there was a tendency to choose "safe" careers (e.g., in engineering, optometry, pharmacy, accounting) that did not require extensive contact with the public or supervision of whites (Kitano & Daniels, 1988, p. 70).

Within these limitations, the Nisei, their children (**Sansei**), and their grandchildren (**Yonsei**) have enjoyed relatively high status, and their upward mobility and prosperity have contributed to the perception that Asian Americans are a "model minority." An additional factor contributing to the high status of Japanese Americans (and to the disappearance of Little Tokyos) is that unlike Chinese Americans, the number of immigrants from Japan has been quite small, and the community has not had to devote many resources to newcomers. Furthermore, recent immigrants from Japan tend to be highly educated professional people whose socioeconomic characteristics add to the perception of success and affluence.

The Sansei and Yonsei are highly integrated into the occupational structure of the larger society. Compared with their parents, their connections with their ethnic past are more tenuous, and in their values, beliefs, and personal goals, they resemble dominant group members of similar age and social class (Kitano & Daniels, 1995, pp. 79-81; also see Spickard, 1996).

# Comparing Minority Groups

What factors account for the differences in the development of Chinese Americans and Japanese Americans and other racial minority groups? First, unlike the situation of African Americans in the 1600s and Mexican Americans in the 1800s, the dominant group had no desire to control the labor of these groups. The contact situation featured economic competition (e.g., for jobs) during an era of rigid competition between groups (see Exhibit 6.4), and Chinese Americans and Japanese Americans were seen as a threat to security that needed to be eliminated, not as a labor pool that needed to be controlled. Second, unlike American Indians, Chinese Americans and Japanese Americans in the early 20th century presented no military danger to the larger society, so there was little concern with their activities once the economic threat had been eliminated. Third, Chinese Americans and Japanese Americans had the ingredients and experiences necessary to form enclaves. The groups were allowed to "disappear," but unlike other racial minority groups, the urban location of their enclaves left them with opportunities for schooling for later generations. As many scholars argue, the particular mode of incorporation developed by Chinese Americans and Japanese Americans is the key to understanding the present status of these groups.

## CONTEMPORARY RELATIONS

In this section, we once more use our guiding concepts to assess the situation of Chinese Americans and Japanese Americans. Other Asian American and Pacific Islander groups are discussed in the next chapter. This section is organized around the same concepts used in previous case study chapters.

## Prejudice and Discrimination

American prejudice against Asians first became prominent during the anti-Chinese movement of the 19th century. The Chinese were castigated as racially inferior, docile, and subservient, but also cruel and crafty, despotic, and threatening (Lai, 1980, p. 220; Lyman, 1974, pp. 55-58). The Chinese Exclusion Act of 1882 was justified by the idea that the Chinese were unassimilable and could never be part of U.S. society. The Chinese were seen as a threat to the working class, to American democracy, and to other American institutions. Many of these stereotypes and fears transferred to the Japanese later in the 19th century and then to other groups as they, in turn, arrived in the United States. The social distance scales presented in Exhibit 3.5 provide the only long-term record of anti-Asian prejudice in the society as a whole. In 1926, the five Asian groups included in the study were grouped in the bottom third of the scale, along with other racial and colonized minority groups. Twenty years later, in 1946, the Japanese had fallen to the bottom of the rankings, and the Chinese had risen seven positions, changes that reflect America's World War II conflict with Japan and alliance with China. This suggests that anti-Chinese prejudice may have softened during the war as distinctions were made between "good" and "bad" Asians. For example, an item published in a 1941 issue of *Time* magazine, "How to Tell Your Friends From the Japs," provided some tips for identifying "good" Asians: "The Chinese expression is likely to be more placid, kindly, open; the Japanese more positive, dogmatic, arrogant. . . . Japanese are nervous in conversation, laugh loudly at the wrong time" (p. 33).

In more recent decades, the average social distance scores of Asian groups have fallen even though the ranking of the groups remained relatively stable. The falling scores probably reflect the societywide increase in tolerance and the shift from blatant prejudice to modern racism that we discussed in Chapter 4. However, the relative position of Asians in the American hierarchy of group preferences has remained remarkably consistent since the 1920s. This stability may reflect the cultural or traditional nature of much of American anti-Asian prejudice.

Although prejudice against Asian and Pacific Island groups may have weakened overall, there is considerable evidence that it remains a potent force in American life. The continuing force of anti-Asian prejudice is marked most dramatically, perhaps, by hate crimes against members of the group. Asian Americans and Pacific Islanders of all types—citizens, immigrants, tourists—have been attacked, beaten, and even murdered in recent years. For example, in 1996, an unemployed meat cutter named Robert Page murdered a randomly selected Chinese American male. Page said that he hated the Chinese because they "got all the good jobs" (Fong, 2002, p. 162). Other attacks include the murder of an Indian gas station owner in Mesa, Arizona,

## Japan's "Invisible" Minority

One of the first things I did in this text was to list the five characteristics that, together, define a minority group. The first and most important of these characteristics was the disadvantage and inequality that minority groups face, and the second was visibility: Minority group members must be easily identifiable, either culturally (language, accent, dress) or physically (skin color, stature). These two traits work in tandem. Members of the dominant group must be able to determine a person's group membership quickly and easily, preferably at a glance, so that the systematic discrimination that is the hallmark of minority group status can be practiced.

Cultural and racial visibility is such an obvious precondition for discrimination that it almost seems unnecessary to state it. However, every generalization about human beings seems to have an exception, and there is at least one minority group, the *Buraku* of Japan, that has been victimized by discrimination and prejudice for hundreds of years but is virtually indistinguishable from the general population. That is, Buraku people are a minority and fit all parts of the definition stated in Chapter 1—except that there is no physical, cultural, religious, or linguistic difference between them and other Japanese. How could such an "invisible" minority come into being? How could the disadvantaged status be maintained through time?

The Buraku were created centuries ago, during feudal times in Japan. At that time, the society was organized into a caste system (see Chapter 5) based on occupation, and the

ancestors of today's Buraku people did work that brought them into contact with death (gravediggers, executioners) or required them to handle meat or meat products (leather workers, butchers). These occupations were regarded as very low in status, and their practitioners were seen as being "unclean" or polluted. In fact, an alternative name for the group, *eta*, means "extreme filth." The Buraku people were required to live in separate, segregated villages and to wear leather patches for purposes of identification (thus raising their social visibility). They were forbidden to marry outside their caste, and any member of the general population who touched a member of the Buraku class had to be ritually purified or cleansed of pollution (Lamont-Brown, 1993, p. 137).

The caste system was officially abolished in the 19th century, at about the time Japan began to industrialize. The Buraku today, however, continue to suffer from discrimination and rejection, even though most observers agree that the levels of discrimination today are lower than in the past and that the overall situation of the Buraku people is improving. The Buraku have much lower levels of education than the general population. For example, the enrollment rate of the Buraku in higher education is about 60% of the national average (Buraku Liberation League, 2001). Lower levels of education in Japan, as in the United States, limit occupational mobility and lead to higher unemployment rates. The educational deficits also help to maintain gaps between the Buraku and the general population in income and poverty rates.

The Buraku are a small group, about 2% or 3% of Japan's population. About 1 million still live in the thousands of traditional

Buraku areas that remain, and another 2 million or so live in non-Buraku areas, mostly in larger cities. They continue to be seen as "filthy," "not very bright," and "untrustworthy"—stereotypical traits that are often associated with minority groups mired in subordinate and unequal positions (see Chapter 3). Also, as is the case for many American minority groups, the Buraku have a vocal and passionate protest organization—the Buraku Liberation League (http://www.blhrri .org/index_e.htm)—that is dedicated to improving the conditions of the group.

The situation of the Buraku might seem puzzling. If it is disadvantageous to be a member of the group, and if the group is indistinguishable from the general population, why don't the Buraku simply blend into the larger society and avoid the discrimination and prejudice? What keeps them attached to their group? In fact, it is relatively easy for those who choose to do so to disappear into the mainstream and to "pass," as attested by the fact that two thirds of the group no longer live in the traditional Buraku areas. Why doesn't the group integrate into the larger society?

One answer to this question, at least for some Buraku, is that they are committed to their group identity and are proud of their heritage. They refuse to surrender to the dominant culture, insist on being accepted for who they are, and have no intention of trading their identity for acceptance or opportunity. For others, even those attempting to pass, the tie to the group and a subtle form of social visibility are maintained by the ancient system of residential segregation. The identity of the traditional Buraku villages and areas of residence are matters of public record, and it is this information—not race or culture—that establishes the boundaries of the group and forms the ultimate barrier to Buraku assimilation.

Japanese firms keep lists of local Buraku addresses and use the lists to screen out potential employees, even though this practice is now illegal. Also, the telltale information may be revealed when applying to rent an apartment (some landlords refuse to rent rooms to Buraku because of their alleged "filthiness") or purchase a home (banks may be reluctant to make loans to members of a group that is widely regarded as untrustworthy). A particularly strong line of resistance to the complete integration of the Buraku arises if they attempt to marry outside of the group. It is common practice for Japanese parents to research the family history of a child's fiancé, and any secret Buraku connections are very likely to be unearthed by this process. Thus members of the Buraku who pass undetected at work and in their neighborhood are likely to be "outed" if they attempt to marry into the dominant group.

This link to the traditional Buraku residential areas means that this group is not really invisible. Although their social visibility is much lower than racial and ethnic minority groups, there is a way to determine group membership, a mark or sign of who belongs and who doesn't. Consistent with the definition presented in Chapter 1, this "birthmark" is the basis for a socially constructed boundary that differentiates "us" from "them" and for systematic discrimination, prejudice, inequality, and all the other disabilities and disadvantages associated with minority group status.

in the aftermath of the September 11, 2001, attacks on the World Trade Center and the Pentagon (discussed in Chapter 3) and the murder of Filipino postman Joseph Ileto (Chapter 4). Incidents such as these suggest that the tradition of anti-Asian prejudice is close to the surface and could be activated under the right combination of competition and threat.

Asian Americans have also been the victims of "positive" stereotypes. The perception of Asian Americans as a "model minority" is exaggerated and, for some Asian American groups, simply false. This label has been applied to these groups by the media, politicians, and others. It is not an image that the Asian American groups themselves developed or particularly advocate. As you might suspect, people who apply these labels to Asian Americans have a variety of hidden moral and political agendas, and we explore these dynamics later in this chapter.

# Assimilation and Pluralism

**Acculturation.** The extent of acculturation of Asian Americans is highly variable from group to group. Japanese Americans represent one extreme. They have been a part of American society for more than a century, and the current generations are highly acculturated. Immigration from Japan has been low throughout the century and has not revitalized the traditional culture or language. As a result, Japanese Americans are probably the most acculturated of the Asian American groups.

Chinese Americans, in contrast, are highly variable in their extent of acculturation. Many are members of families who have been American for generations and are highly acculturated. Others, including many here illegally, are new immigrants who have little knowledge of English or of Anglo culture. In this dimension, as in occupations, Chinese Americans are "bipolar." This great variability within the group makes it difficult to characterize their overall degree of acculturation.

**Secondary Structural Assimilation.** We will cover this complex area in roughly the order followed in previous chapters.

*Residence.* Exhibit 10.4 shows the regional concentrations of all Asian Americans. The tendency to reside on either coast and around Los Angeles, San Francisco, and New York stands out clearly. Note also the sizable concentrations in a variety of metropolitan areas, including Chicago, Atlanta, Miami, Denver, and Houston.

Asian Americans in general are highly urbanized, a reflection of the entry conditions of recent immigrants as well as the appeal of ethnic neighborhoods, such as Chinatowns, with long histories and continuing vitality. The 2000 census showed that more than 96% of Asian Americans lived in urban areas (vs. about 80% of the total population), most living in more densely populated center city areas. Exhibit 10.5 shows the residential patterns of all Asian Americans, Chinese Americans, and Japanese Americans.

Asian American groups are generally less residentially segregated than either African American or Hispanic Americans. Exhibit 10.6 shows the pattern for the 50 largest metropolitan areas, grouped by region for 2000. The information in this graph was presented in slightly different formats in Chapters 7 and 9. In each region, Asian Americans are the least segregated groups (although the difference between Asian Americans and Hispanic Americans in three regions—the South, the Midwest, and the West—is not great). Unlike the other two groups, Asian Americans were not "extremely" segregated (dissimilarity index scores greater than 60) in any area in either 1980 or 2000, but they were generally more segregated in 2000 than in 1980, a reflection of the high rates of immigration and the strong tendency of newcomers to settle near their coethnics.

Asian Americans and Pacific Islanders are also moving away from their traditional neighborhoods and enclaves into the suburbs of metropolitan areas, most notably in the areas surrounding Los Angeles, San Francisco, New York, and other cities where the groups are highly concentrated. For example, Asian Americans have been moving in large numbers to the San Gabriel Valley, just east of downtown Los Angeles. Once a bastion of white, middle-class suburbanites, these areas have taken on a distinctly Asian flavor in recent years. Monterey Park, once virtually all white, is now 62% Chinese and is often referred to as "America's first suburban Chinatown" or the "Chinese Beverly Hills" (Fong, 2002, p. 49).

**EXHIBIT 10.4** Number of Asians, 2000

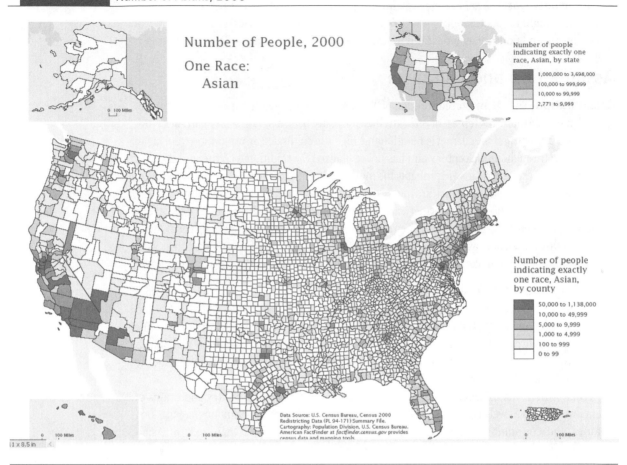

Number of People, 2000

One Race:
    Asian

Number of people
indicating exactly one
race, Asian, by state

- 1,000,000 to 3,698,000
- 100,000 to 999,999
- 10,000 to 99,999
- 2,771 to 9,999

Number of people
indicating exactly
one race, Asian,
by county

- 50,000 to 1,138,000
- 10,000 to 49,999
- 5,000 to 9,999
- 1,000 to 4,999
- 100 to 999
- 0 to 99

Data Source: U.S. Census Bureau, Census 2000
Redistricting Data (PL 94-171) Summary File.
Cartography: Population Division, U.S. Census Bureau.
American FactFinder at *factfinder.census.gov* provides
census data and mapping tools.

SOURCE: U.S. Bureau of the Census (2000e1), p. 63.

*Education.* The pattern of schooling for Asian Americans and for Chinese and Japanese Americans is very different from other U.S. racial minority groups. Considered as a whole, Asian Americans compare favorably with societywide standards for educational achievement, and they are above those standards on many measures. Exhibits 10.7 and 10.8 show that all Asian Americans and both subgroups are equal to national standards on high school education and exceed those standards on college education, a pattern that reinforces the label of "model minority." Remember, however, that Chinese Americans (and several other Asian American groups) are "bipolar" and have a sizeable underclass group. The image of the "model minority" needs to be balanced by the recognition that there is a full range of success and failure among Asian Americans and by the fact that average levels of achievement are "inflated" for some groups by recent immigrants who are highly educated, skilled professionals. Also, note that women generally do not fare as well as men (even though they exceed national standards for college education).

*Jobs and Income.* The image of success is also sustained by the occupational profiles of Asian American groups. Exhibits 10.9a and 10.9b show that both males and females are overrepresented in the highest occupational category, a reflection of the high levels of educational attainment for

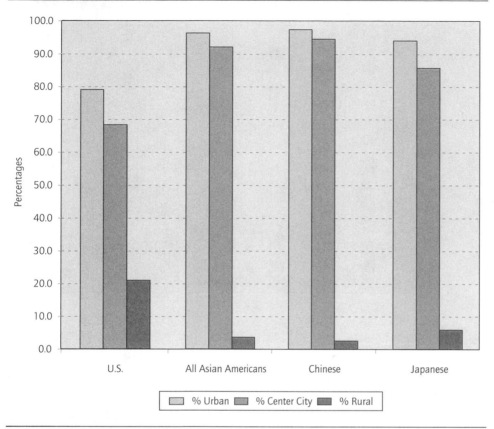

SOURCE: U.S. Bureau of the Census (n.d.).

the group. Asian American males are underrepresented among manual laborers, but otherwise, the occupational profiles of the groups are in rough proportion to the society as a whole.

Exhibit 10.10 shows the income distribution for Asian Americans, and, yet again, both the males and females of these groups are above national norms and Japanese American males have the highest relative incomes. This picture of success is marred, however, when we look at the poverty rates presented in Exhibit 10.11. Asian Americans as a whole and Chinese Americans in particular are well above national norms for both the percentage of families and the percentage of children living in poverty. This pattern directly contradicts the impression created by the income data in Exhibit 10.10 and reminds us that Chinese Americans are "bipolar" and include a large proportion of the disadvantaged and poor (especially among recent immigrants) along with the affluent and successful. For this group (and some other Asian American groups we will address in Chapter 11), the image of a "model minority," successful and affluent, presents only half the truth.

On the other hand, the profile of Japanese Americans is consistent with the image of success. Their poverty rate for families is about half the rate for the nation as a whole and the rate for children is 25% below the national norm.

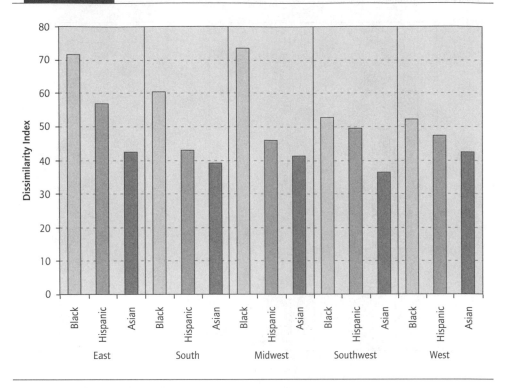

SOURCE: Compiled from Charles (2003).

Although these data generally support the image of economic success, we must examine some qualifications before coming to any conclusions. First, Asian Americans in general and Chinese and Japanese Americans in particular generally reside in areas with higher than average costs of living (e.g., San Francisco, Los Angeles, New York); thus, their higher incomes have relatively less purchasing power. Second, they are more likely than the general population to have multiple wage earners in each household, and differences in per capita income are smaller than differences in median family income (Lee, 1998, p. 28). Finally, many researchers have found that Asian Americans in general tend to be "underrewarded" for their occupational positions and earn less than comparably educated whites. This differential benefit from education has been documented as far back as the 1950 census for Japanese Americans (Woodrum, 1979) and is thought to reflect lingering anti-Asian racism and discrimination (Pollard & O'Hare, 1999, p. 37; see also Kitano & Daniels, 1995; Min, 1995). In contrast, using sample data from the various years of the census, Xie and Goyette (2004) found that the income differential largely disappears after 1989 and that Asian Americans now surpass non-Hispanic whites in income, even after adjusting for experience and education (Xie & Goyette, 2004, p. 17). If this finding is validated by other studies, it might signal that some forms of anti-Asian discrimination have ended.

*Political Power.* The ability of Asian Americans to pursue their group interests has been sharply limited by a number of factors, including their relatively small size, institutionalized discrimination, and the same kinds of racist practices that have limited the power resources of other minority groups of color. However, and contrary to the perception that Asian Americans

EXHIBIT 10.7 Percentage Older Than 25 With High School Degree, 2000

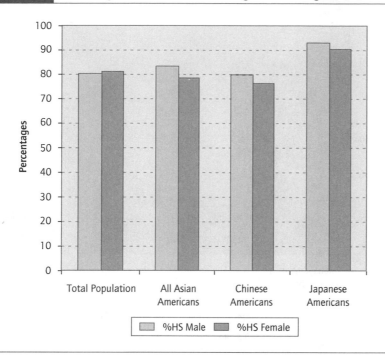

EXHIBIT 10.8 Percentage Older Than 25 With College Degree, 2000

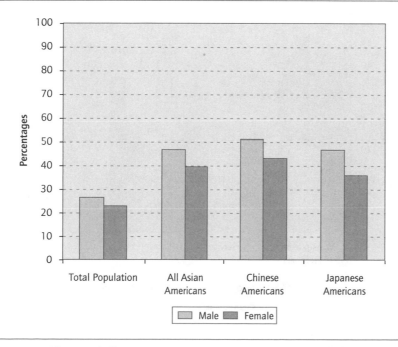

SOURCE: U.S. Bureau of the Census (n.d.).

EXHIBIT 10.9a   Occupations, Asian Americans, 2000: Males

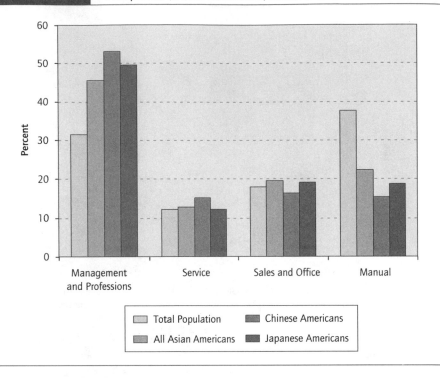

EXHIBIT 10.9b   Occupations, Asian Americans, 2000: Females

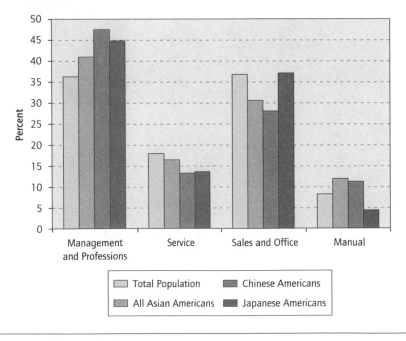

SOURCE: U.S. Bureau of the Census (n.d.).

EXHIBIT 10.10

Median Yearly Income of Full-Time, Year-Round Workers, by Sex and Group, 2000

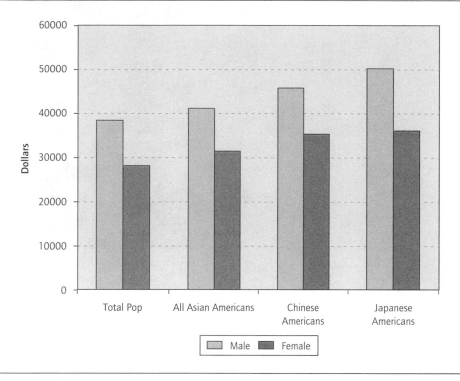

SOURCE: U.S. Bureau of the Census (n.d.).

are a "quiet" minority, the group has a long history of political action, including a civil rights movement in the 1960s and 1970s (Fong, 2002, pp. 273-281).

The political power of Asian Americans and Pacific Islanders today is also limited by their high percentage of foreign-born members. Rates of political participation for the group (e.g., voting in presidential elections) are somewhat lower than national norms but may rise as more members Americanize, learn English, and become citizens (Lee, 1998, p. 30). Even today, there are signs of the growing power of the group, especially in areas where they are most residentially concentrated. Of course, Asian Americans have been prominent in Hawaiian politics for decades, but they are increasingly involved in West Coast political life as well. For example, in 1996, the state of Washington elected Gary Locke as governor, the first Chinese American to hold this high office. Governor Locke was reelected in 2000.

**Primary Structural Assimilation.** Studies of integration at the primary level for Asian Americans generally find high rates of interracial friendship and intermarriage. For example, using 1980 census data, Lee and Yamanaka (1990) report higher rates of intermarriage for Asian Americans than for other minority groups. They report out-marriage rates at 2% for African Americans, 13% for Hispanic Americans, and from 15% to 34% for Asian Americans. They also found that native-born Asian Americans were much more likely to marry outside their group than the foreign born (see also Kitano & Daniels, 1995; Min, 1995; Sung, 1990). Some studies have found that the rate of intermarriage is decreasing in recent years in the nation as a whole

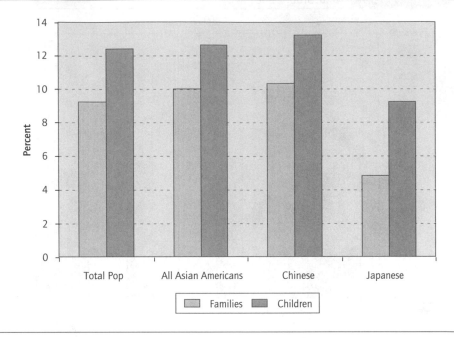

**EXHIBIT 10.11** Percentage of Families and Children Living in Poverty, 2000

SOURCE: U.S. Bureau of the Census (n.d.).

and specifically in California, a pattern that perhaps reflects the high rates of immigration, the tendency for the first generation to marry within the group, and the growing number of potential partners within Asian American groups (Lee & Fernandez, 1998; Shinagawa & Pang, 1996, see also Xie & Goyette, 2004).

## COMPARING MINORITY GROUPS: EXPLAINING ASIAN AMERICAN SUCCESS

To conclude this chapter, let's return to a question raised in the opening pages: How can we explain the apparent success of Asian Americans? Relative affluence and high status are not characteristic of the other racial minority groups we have examined, and at least at first glance, there seems to be little in our theories and concepts to help us understand the situation of Asian Americans. Even after we recognize that the "success" label is simplistic and even misleading, the relatively high status of many Asian Americans begs a closer look.

The Current Debates section at the end of this chapter presents several different views on the nature and causes of Asian American success. In this section, we compare Asian Americans with European immigrant groups and with colonized minority groups. What crucial factors differentiate the experiences of these groups? Can we understand these differences in terms of the framework provided by the Blauner and Noel hypotheses and the other concepts developed in this text?

The debate over the causes of Asian American success often breaks down into two different viewpoints. One view offers a *cultural* explanation, which accepts the evidence of Asian

American success at face value and attributes it to the "good values" of traditional Asian cultures that we briefly explored at the beginning of this chapter. These values—including respect for elders and for authority figures, hard work and thriftiness, and conformity and politeness—are highly compatible with U.S. middle-class Protestant value systems and presumably helped Asian Americans gain acceptance and opportunities. The cultural explanation is consistent with traditional assimilation theory and human capital theory, and an example of it can be found in the selection by Professor Harry Kitano in the Current Debates section.

The other point of view stresses the ways in which these groups entered American society and the reactions of Asian Americans to the barriers of racism and exclusion they faced. This approach could be called a *structural* explanation, and it emphasizes contact situations, modes of incorporation, enclave economies, group cohesion, position in the labor market, and institutionalized discrimination rather than cultural values. Also, this approach questions the whole notion that Asian Americans are successful and stresses the facts of Asian American poverty and the continuing patterns of racism and exclusion. The structural approach is more compatible with the theories and concepts used throughout this text, and it identifies several of the important pieces needed to solve the puzzle of Asian "success" and put it in perspective. This is not to suggest that the cultural approach is wrong or irrelevant, however. The issues we raise are complex and will probably require many approaches and perspectives before they are fully resolved.

## Asian and European Immigrants

Chinese and Japanese immigrants arrived in America at about the same time as immigrants from Southern and Eastern Europe (see Chapter 12). Both groups consisted mainly of sojourning young men who were largely unskilled, from rural backgrounds, and not highly educated. European immigrants, like Asian immigrants, encountered massive discrimination and rejection and were also victims of restrictive legislation. Yet the barriers to upward mobility for European immigrants (or, at least for their descendants) fell away more rapidly than the barriers for immigrants from Asia. Why?

Some important differences between the two immigrant experiences are clear, the most obvious being the greater racial visibility of Asian Americans. Whereas the cultural and linguistic markers that identified Eastern and Southern Europeans faded with each passing generation, the racial characteristics of the Asian groups continued to separate them from the larger society. Thus Asian Americans are not "pure immigrant" groups (see Blauner, 1972, p. 55). For most of this century, Chinese Americans and Japanese Americans remained in a less favorable position than European immigrants and their descendants, excluded by their physical appearance from the mainstream economy until the decades following World War II.

Another important difference relates to position in the labor market. Immigrants from Southern and Eastern Europe entered the industrializing East Coast economy, where they took industrial and manufacturing jobs. Although such jobs were poorly paid and insecure, this location in the labor force gave European immigrants and their descendants the potential for upward mobility in the mainstream economy. At the very least, these urban industrial and manufacturing jobs put the children and grandchildren of European immigrants in positions from which skilled, well-paid, unionized jobs were reachable, as were managerial and professional careers.

In contrast, Chinese and Japanese immigrants on the West Coast were forced into ethnic enclaves and came to rely on jobs in the small business and service sector and, in the case of the Japanese, in the rural economy. By their nature, these jobs did not link Chinese and

Japanese immigrants or their descendants to the industrial sector or to better paid, more secure, unionized jobs. Furthermore, their exclusion from the mainstream economy was reinforced by overt discrimination based on race from both employers and labor unions (see Fong & Markham, 1991).

## Asian Americans and Colonized Minority Groups

Comparisons between Asian Americans and African Americans, American Indians, and Hispanic Americans have generated a level of controversy and a degree of heat and passion that may be surprising at first. An examination of the issues and their implications, however, reveals that the debate involves some thinly disguised political and moral agendas and evokes sharply clashing views on the nature of U.S. society. What might appear on the surface to be merely an academic comparison of different minority groups turns out to be an argument about the quality of American justice and fairness and the very essence of the value system of U.S. society.

What is not in dispute in this debate is that some Asian groups (e.g., Japanese Americans) rank far above other racial minority groups on all the commonly used measures of secondary structural integration and equality. What is disputed is how to interpret these comparisons and assess their meanings. First, we need to recognize that gross comparisons between entire groups can be misleading. If we confine our attention to averages (mean levels of education or median income), the picture of Asian American success tends to be sustained. However, if we also observe the full range of differences within each group (e.g., the "bipolar" nature of occupations among Chinese Americans), we see that the images of success have been exaggerated and need to be placed in a proper context (see the selection by Takaki in the Current Debates section). Even with these qualifications, however, discussion often slides on to more ideological ground, and political and moral issues begin to cloud the debate. Asian American success is often taken as proof that American society is truly the land of opportunity and that people who work hard and obey the rules will get ahead: In America, anyone can be anything they want as long as they work hard enough.

When we discussed modern racism in Chapter 4, we pointed out that a belief in the openness and fairness of the United States can be a way of blaming the victim and placing the responsibility for change on the minority groups rather than on the structure of society. Asian success has become a "proof" of the validity of this ideology. The none-too-subtle implication is that other groups (African Americans, Hispanic Americans, American Indians) could achieve the same success Asian Americans have achieved but, for various reasons, choose not to. Thus the relative success of Chinese Americans and Japanese Americans has become a device for scolding other minority groups.

A more structural approach to investigating Asian success begins with a comparison of the history of the various racial minority groups and their modes of incorporation into the larger society. When Chinese Americans and Japanese Americans were building their enclave economies in the early part of the 20th century, African Americans and Mexican Americans were concentrated in unskilled agricultural occupations. American Indians were isolated from the larger society on their reservations, and Puerto Ricans had not yet begun to arrive on the mainland. The social class differences between these groups today flow from their respective situations in the past.

Many of the occupational and financial advances made by Chinese Americans and Japanese Americans have been due to the high levels of education achieved by the second generations.

Although education is traditionally valued in Asian cultures, the decision to invest limited resources in schooling is also quite consistent with the economic niche occupied by these immigrants. Education is one obvious, relatively low-cost strategy to upgrade the productivity and profit of a small business economy and improve the economic status of the group as a whole. An educated, English-speaking second generation could bring expertise and business acumen to the family enterprises and lead them to higher levels of performance. Education might also be the means by which the second generation could enter professional careers. This strategy may have been especially attractive to an immigrant generation that was itself relatively uneducated and barred from citizenship (Hirschman & Wong, 1986, p. 23; see also Bonacich & Modell, 1980, p. 152; Sanchirico, 1991).

The efforts to educate the next generation were largely successful. Chinese Americans and Japanese Americans achieved educational parity with the larger society as early as the 1920s. One study found that for men and women born after 1915, the median years of schooling completed were actually higher for Chinese Americans and Japanese Americans than for whites (Hirschman & Wong, 1986, p. 11). Before World War II, both Asian groups were barred from the mainstream economy and from better jobs. When anti-Asian prejudice and discrimination declined in the 1950s, however, the Chinese and Japanese second generations had the educational background necessary to take advantage of the increased opportunities.

Thus there was a crucial divergence in the development of Chinese Americans and Japanese Americans and the colonized minority groups. At the time that native-born Chinese Americans and Japanese Americans reached educational parity with whites, the vast majority of African Americans, American Indians, and Mexican Americans were still victimized by Jim Crow laws and legalized segregation and excluded from opportunities for anything but rudimentary education. The Supreme Court decision in *Brown v. Board of Education of Topeka* (1954) was decades in the future, and American Indian schoolchildren were still being subjected to intense Americanization in the guise of a curriculum. Today, these other racial minority groups have not completely escaped from the disadvantages imposed by centuries of institutionalized discrimination. African Americans have approached educational parity with white Americans only in recent years (see Chapter 7), and American Indians and Mexican Americans remain far below national averages (see Chapters 8 and 9).

The structural explanation argues that the recent upward mobility of Chinese Americans and Japanese Americans is the result of the methods by which they incorporated themselves into American society, not so much their values and traditions. The logic of their subeconomy led the immigrant generation to invest in the education of their children, who would be better prepared to develop the enclave businesses and seek opportunity in the larger society.

As a final point, note that the structural explanation is not consistent with traditional views of the assimilation process. The immigrant generation of Chinese Americans and Japanese Americans responded to the massive discrimination they faced by withdrawing, developing ethnic enclaves, and becoming "invisible" to the larger society. Like Cuban Americans, Chinese Americans and Japanese Americans used their traditional cultures and patterns of social life to create and build their own subcommunities, from which they launched the next generation. Contrary to traditional ideas about how assimilation is "supposed" to happen, we see again that integration can precede acculturation and that the smoothest route to integration may be the creation of a separate subsociety independent of the surrounding community.

# Asian American "Success": What are the Dimensions, Causes, and Implications for Other Minority Groups?

The following selections continue the discussion of the causes of Asian American success. The first selection, from the writings of sociologist Harry Kitano (1980), is consistent with cultural explanations for the upward mobility of Asian groups. It argues that the success of the Japanese in America is due in part to their culture and in part to their strength of character, resilience, and flexibility.

In opposition to Kitano's views are two other selections. The first counterargument, by sociologists Alejandro Portes and Min Zhou (1992), presents a structural analysis that links the success of Chinese Americans to their enclave economy. Portes and Zhou also draw some provocative comparisons between Chinese Americans and African Americans, suggesting that the "thorough acculturation" of the African American community has weakened its economic vitality.

The second counterargument, by sociologist Ronald Takaki, sharply questions the whole notion of the "model minority" and points out the limits and qualifications that need to be observed when comparing Asian Americans with other groups. Takaki (1993) also points to a hidden agenda of those who single out Asian Americans as a "model minority": the chastisement of other minority groups, particularly African Americans.

## The Success of Japanese Americans Is Cultural

**HARRY KITANO**

Social interaction among Japanese Americans is governed by behavioral norms such as enryo and amae. These derive from Confucian ideas about human relationships and define the dimensions of interaction and exchange between superior and inferior members of a social group. Although these forms of behavior were brought over by Issei immigrants, they still survive in attenuated form among the Nisei and even the Sansei.

Enryo prescribes the way in which a social inferior must show deference and self-abnegation before a superior. Hesitancy to speak out at meetings, the automatic refusal of a second helping, and selecting a less desired object are all manifestations of enryo. . . .

Amae behavior softens a power relationship through the acting out of dependency and weakness, and expresses the need for attention, recognition, acceptance, and nurture. A child displays amae to gain the sympathy and indulgence of a parent. A young, anxious-to-please employee in a business firm will act with exaggerated meekness and confusion to give his superior an opportunity to provide paternal advice and treat him as a protégé. Through the ritual display of weakness and dependency, reciprocal bonds of loyalty, devotion, and trust are formed. In this way amae creates strong emotional ties that strengthen cohesion within the family, business organization, and community.

Japanese Americans inherit an almost reverential attitude toward work. Their ancestors struggled for survival in a crowded island country with limited natural resources and they placed great value on industry and self-discipline. Certain traditional attitudes encourage resilient behavior in the face of setbacks and complement the moral imperative to work hard. Many Japanese Americans are familiar with the common expressions gaman and gambotte which mean "don't let it bother you," "don't give up." These dicta, derived from Buddhist teachings, encourage Japanese people to conceal frustration or disappointment and to carry on.

A tradition that places great value on work and persistence has helped many Japanese Americans to acquire good jobs and to get ahead.

The submerging of the individual to the interest of the group is another basic Japanese tradition, and one that produces strong social cohesion and an oblique style of behavior, one manifestation of which is the indirection or allusiveness of much communication between Japanese; another is the polite, consensual behavior expected in all social contacts. Both are common in Japan and visible among Japanese Americans. Today, even third- and fourth-generation Japanese Americans are apt to be seen by others as agreeable, unaggressive, willing to accept subordinate roles, and reluctant to put themselves forward. . . .

The history of the Japanese Americans in the United States is one of both resilience and adaptation. Suffering from discriminatory laws and racial hostility in the first half of the 20th century, Japanese Americans were nonetheless able to create stable ethnic communities and separate, but vital, social organizations. Since the end of World War II, with the disappearance of legal discrimination and the weakening of social restrictions, they have assimilated more readily into American society and shown rapid economic progress. Scholars have searched for the key to their remarkable record of adaptation. Some have pointed to the Japanese family, others to a strong group orientation, and still others to Japanese moral training; all of these theories often tend to overemphasize the degree to which Japanese traditions have been maintained. Japanese Americans have displayed a pragmatic attitude toward American life. [Rather] than rigidly maintaining their traditions, Japanese Americans have woven American values and behavior into the fabric of their culture and have seized new social, cultural, and economic avenues as they have become available, extending the limits of ethnicity by striking a workable balance between ethnic cohesion and accommodation.

SOURCE: Kitano, Harry. 1980. "Japanese." In S. Thornstrom et al. (Ed.), *Harvard Encyclopedia of Ethnic Groups*. Cambridge, MA: Harvard University Press. Pp. 570-571.

## The "Success" of Chinese Americans Is Structural

### ALEJANDRO PORTES AND MIN ZHOU

[What lessons for ethnic poverty can we find in the experiences of Chinese Americans and other groups that have constructed ethnic enclaves?] A tempting option—and one to which many experts have not been averse—is to resort to culturalistic explanations. According to these interpretations, certain groups do better because they possess the "right" kind of values. This view is, of course, not too different from assimilation theory except that, instead of learning the proper values after arrival, immigrants bring them ready made. A moment's reflection suffices to demonstrate the untenability of this explanation. . . .

The very diversity of [the] groups [that have constructed enclave economies] conspires against explanations that find the roots of economic mobility in the unique values associated with a particular culture. If we had to invoke a particular "ethic" to account for the business achievements of Chinese and Jews, Koreans and Cubans, Lebanese and Dominicans, we would wind up with a very messy theory. In terms of professed religions alone, we would have to identify those unique values leading Confucianists and Buddhists, Greek Orthodox and Roman Catholics into successful business ventures. In addition, culturalistic explanations have little predictive power since they are invoked only after a particular group has demonstrated its economic prowess. . . .

There is no alternative but to search for the relevant causal process in the social structure of the ethnic community. [Several] common aspects in the economic experience of the immigrant communities [are] relevant. . . .

[First is] the "bounded solidarity" created among immigrants by virtue of their foreignness and being treated as [different]. As consumers, immigrants manifest a consistent preference for items associated with the country of origin, both for their intrinsic utility and as symbolic representations of a distinct identity. As workers, they often prefer to work among "their own," interacting in their native language even if this means sacrificing some material benefits. As investors, they commonly opt for firms in the country of origin or in the ethnic community rather than trusting their money to impersonal outside organizations.

Bounded solidarity [is accompanied by] "enforceable trust" against malfeasance among prospective ethnic entrepreneurs. Confidence that business associates will not resort to double-dealing is cemented in something more tangible than generalized cultural loyalty since it also relies on the ostracism of violators, cutting them off from sources of credit and opportunity. [Enforceable trust] is the key mechanism underlying the smooth operation of rotating credit associations among Asian immigrant communities.

Bounded solidarity and enforceable trust as sources of social capital do not inhere in the moral convictions of individuals or in the value orientations in which they were socialized. [These benefits] accrue by virtue of [the group's] minority [status] in the host country and as a result of being subjected to mainstream pressure to accept their low place in the ethnic hierarchy. Such pressures prompt the revalorization of the symbols of a common nationality and the privileging of the ethnic community as the place where the status of underprivileged menial labor can be avoided. . . .

Black Americans, Mexican Americans, and mainland Puerto Ricans today lag significantly behind the immigrant groups in their entrepreneurial orientation. [This] lack of entrepreneurial presence is even more remarkable because of the large size of these minorities and the significant consumer market that they represent. . . .

We believe that the dearth of entrepreneurship among these groups is related to the dissolution of the structural underpinnings of the social capital resources noted above: bounded solidarity and enforceable trust. A thorough process of acculturation among U.S.-born members of each of these groups has led to a gradual weakening of their sense of community and to a re-orientation towards the values, expectations, and preferences of the cultural mainstream. [Complete] assimilation among domestic minorities leads to identification with the mainstream views, including a disparaging evaluation of their own group. . . .

[Even] groups with a modest level of human capital have managed to create an entrepreneurial presence when the necessary social capital, created by specific historical conditions, was present. This was certainly the case among turn-of-the-century Chinese. [It] was also true of segregated black communities during the same time period. The current desperate conditions in many inner-city neighborhoods have led some black leaders to recall wistfully the period of segregation. [As one black leader said]:

> [T]he same kind of business enclave that exists in the Cuban community or in the Jewish community existed in the black community when the consumer base was contained [i.e., segregated from the larger society] and needed goods and services that had to be provided by someone in the neighborhood. Today, blacks will not buy within their neighborhood if they can help it; they want to go to the malls and blend with mainstream consumers.

Hence, thorough acculturation and the formal end of segregation led to the dissipation of the social capital formerly present in restricted black enclaves and the consequent weakening of minority entrepreneurship. As blacks attempted to join the mainstream, they found that lingering discrimination barred or slowed down their progress in the labor market, while consumption of outside goods and services undermined their own community business base.

SOURCE: Portes, Alejandro, & Zhou, Min. 1992. "Gaining the Upper Hand: Economic Mobility Among Immigrant and Domestic Minorities." *Ethnic and Racial Studies*, 15: 513-518.

## The Success of Asian Americans has Been Exaggerated, in Part, to Criticize Other Minority Groups

RONALD TAKAKI

African American "failure" has been contrasted with Asian American "success." In 1984, William Raspberry of the Washington Post noted that Asian Americans on the West Coast had "in fact" "outstripped" whites in income. Blacks should stop blaming racism for their plight, he argued, and follow the example of the self-reliant Asian Americans. In 1986, NBC Nightly News and McNeil/Lehrer Report aired special segments on Asian Americans and their achievements. U.S. News and World Report featured Asian American advances in a cover story, and Newsweek focused a lead article on "Asian Americans: A 'Model Minority'" while Fortune applauded them as "America's super minority."

But in their celebration of this "model minority," these media pundits have exaggerated Asian American "success." Their comparisons of income between Asians and whites fail to recognize the regional location of the Asian American population. Concentrated in California, Hawaii, and New York, most Asian Americans reside in states with higher incomes but also higher costs of living than the national average. . . .

Asian American families have more persons working per family than white families. Thus, the family incomes of Asian Americans indicate the presence of more workers in each family rather than higher individual incomes. Actually, in terms of personal incomes, Asian Americans have not reached equality.

While many Asian Americans are doing well, others find themselves mired in poverty: They include southeast-Asian refugees such as the Hmong, as well as immigrant workers trapped in Chinatowns. Eighty percent of the people in New York Chinatown, 74% of San Francisco Chinatown, and 88% of Los Angeles Chinatown are foreign born. Like the nineteenth century Chinese immigrants in search of Gold Mountain, they came here to seek a better life. But what they found instead was work in Chinatown's low wage service and garment industries. . . .

The myth of the Asian American "model minority" has been challenged, yet it continues to be widely believed. One reason for this is its instructional value. For whom are Asian Americans supposed to be a "model"? . . .

Asian Americans are being used to discipline blacks. If the failure of blacks on welfare warns Americans in general how they should not behave, the triumph of Asian Americans affirms the deeply rooted values of the Protestant ethic and self-reliance. Our society needs an Asian American "model minority" in an era anxious about a growing black underclass. If Asian Americans can make it on their own, why can't other groups? . . .

Betraying a certain nervousness over the seeming end of the American dream's boundlessness, praise for this "super minority" has become society's most recent jeremiad—a call for a renewed commitment to the traditional values of hard work, thrift, and industry. After all, it has been argued, the war on poverty and affirmative action were not really necessary. Look at the Asian Americans! They did it by pulling themselves up by their bootstraps. For blacks shut out of the labor market, the Asian American model provides the standards for acceptable behavior: Blacks should not depend on welfare or affirmative action. While congratulating Asian Americans for their family values, hard work, and high incomes, President Ronald Reagan chastised blacks for their dependency on the "spider's web of welfare" and their failure to recognize that the "only barrier" to success was "within" them.

SOURCE: Takaki, Ronald. 1993. *A Different Mirror: A History of Multicultural America.* Boston: Little, Brown. Pp. 414-417.

## Debate Questions to Consider

1. If Kitano's analysis is correct, what could other minority groups learn from the Japanese experience? If Portes and Zhou are correct, what could other minority groups learn from the Chinese experience? Do Portes and Zhou use cultural factors as part of their explanation? How? Are Portes and Zhou advocating segregation? Pluralism? Assimilation?

2. Why would the United States "need" a "model minority"? How would you answer Takaki's question: "For whom are Asian Americans supposed to be a model?" Whose interests are being served by these comparisons? Do Asian Americans gain anything from these labels and comparisons? Do they lose anything?

3. Which of these views are consistent with traditional assimilation theory? How? Which are consistent with human capital theory? How? Which views are consistent with the thinking of Noel and Blauner? How?

## MAIN POINTS

- Asian Americans and Pacific Islanders are diverse and have brought many different cultural and linguistic traditions to the United States. These groups are growing rapidly but are still only a tiny fraction of the total population.

- Chinese immigrants were the victims of a massive campaign of discrimination and exclusion and responded by constructing enclaves. Chinatowns became highly organized communities, largely run by the local CCBAs and other associations. The second generation faced many barriers to employment in the dominant society, although opportunities increased after World War II.

- Japanese immigration began in the 1890s and stimulated a campaign that attempted to oust the group from agriculture and curtail immigration from Japan. The Issei formed an enclave, but during World War II, Japanese Americans were forced into relocation camps, and this experience devastated the group economically and psychologically.

- Overall levels of anti-Asian prejudice and discrimination have probably declined in recent years but remain widespread. Levels of acculturation and secondary structural assimilation are variable. Members of these groups whose families have been in the United States longer tend to be highly acculturated and integrated. Recent immigrants from China, however, are "bipolar." Many are highly educated and skilled, but a sizeable number are "immigrant laborers" who bring modest educational credentials and are likely to be living in poverty.

- The notion that Asian Americans are a "model minority" is exaggerated, but comparisons with European immigrants and colonized minority groups suggest some of the reasons for the relative "success" of these groups.

- Public Sociology Assignment 2 on pages 220-221 focuses on racial and ethnic inequalities in health in your area. Can you document any differences in health between Asian groups and whites? Are there differences between specific Asian groups? Do these differences parallel the patterns of inequality documented in this chapter?

### Study Site on the Web

Don't forget the interactive quizzes and other resources and learning aids at www.www.pineforge.com/healeystudy4.

## For Further Reading

Espiritu, Yen. 1997. *Asian American Women and Men.* Thousand Oaks, CA: Sage. *(Analyzes the intersections of race, class, and gender among Asian Americans.)*

Kitano, Harry H. 1976. *Japanese Americans.* Englewood Cliffs, NJ: Prentice Hall.

Lyman, Stanford. 1974. *Chinese Americans.* New York: Random House. *(Two comprehensive case studies of the Asian American groups with the longest histories in the United States.)*

Kitano, Harry H. L., & Daniels, Roger. 1995. *Asian Americans: Emerging Minorities* (2nd ed.). Englewood Cliffs, NJ: Prentice Hall.

Min, Pyong Gap. 1995. *Asian Americans: Contemporary Trends and Issues.* Thousand Oaks, CA: Sage. *(Two good overviews of all the Asian American groups covered in this chapter.)*

Kwong, Peter. 1987. *The New Chinatown.* New York: Hill and Wang.

Zhou, Min. 1992. *Chinatown.* Philadelphia: Temple University Press. *(Two excellent analyses of Chinatowns, with a behind-the-scenes look at the realities often hidden from outsiders.)*

## Questions for Review and Study

1. Describe the cultural characteristics of Asian American groups. How did these characteristics shape relationships with the larger society? Did they contribute to the perception of Asian Americans as "successful"? How?

2. Compare and contrast the contact situation for Chinese Americans, Japanese Americans, and Cuban Americans. What common characteristics led to the construction of ethnic enclaves for all three groups? How and why did these enclaves vary from each other?

3. In what sense was the second generation of Chinese Americans "delayed?" How did this affect the relationship of the group with the larger society?

4. Compare and contrast the campaigns that arose in opposition to the immigration of Chinese and Japanese. Do the concepts of the Noel hypothesis help to explain the differences? Do you see any similarities with the changing federal policy toward Mexican immigrants across the 20th century? Explain.

5. Compare and contrast the Japanese relocation camps with Indian reservations in terms of paternalism and coerced acculturation. What impact did this experience have on the Japanese Americans economically? How were Japanese Americans compensated for their losses? Does the compensation paid to Japanese Americans provide a precedent for similar payments (reparations) to African Americans for their losses under slavery? Why or why not?

6. How do the Baruku in Japan illustrate "visibility" as a defining characteristic of minority group status? How is the minority status of this group maintained?

7. What gender differences characterize Asian American groups? What are some of the important ways in which the experiences of women and men vary?

8. Describe the situation of the Chinese and Japanese Americans in terms of prejudice and discrimination, acculturation and integration. Are these groups truly "success stories?" How? What factors or experiences might account for this "success?" Are all Asian American groups equally successful? Describe the important variations from group to group. Compare the integration and level of equality of these groups with other American racial minorities. How would you explain the differences? Are the concepts of the Noel and Blauner hypotheses helpful? Why or why not?

## Internet Research Project

Additional information and a list of relevant Web sites are included in the Appendix (Internet Resources).

### A. Updating the Chapter

The *Asian-Nation* Web site at http://www.asian-nation.org/index.html provides comprehensive coverage on a number of issues raised in this chapter. Update and expand the chapter by selecting one or two topics (e.g., the "model minority" image) and searching the Web site. Be sure to follow some of the links provided to see what additional information and perspectives you can uncover.

### B. Learning More About Asian and Pacific Islander Americans

Select one of the Asian or Pacific Islander groups discussed in this chapter other than Japanese Americans and Chinese Americans and conduct an Internet search using the name of the group. Follow the links and see what information you can add to the profile provided in the chapter. You might focus your search by seeking answers to basic questions such as these: How large is the group? Where do the members live in the United States (region of the country, rural vs. urban)? How acculturated is the group in terms of language? How does the group compare with national norms in terms of education, occupational profile, and income? What are the major issues from the perspective of the group?

CHAPTER

# New Americans

## Immigration and Assimilation

BETWEEN 1820 AND 1920, SOME 40 MILLION PEOPLE IMMIGRATED TO THE UNITED STATES. THIS wave of newcomers, mostly from Europe, transformed American society on almost every level: its neighborhoods and parishes and cities, its popular culture, its accent and dialect, its religion and its cuisine.

The United States is now experiencing a second wave of mass immigration, this one beginning in the 1960s and including people not just from Europe but from all over the world. Over the past four decades, well over 20 million newcomers have arrived (not counting undocumented immigrants), a rate that exceeds the pace of the first mass immigration. Since the 1960s, the United States has averaged about a half million newcomers each year, but this number has frequently risen above 750,000 and has been over 1 million on several occasions (U.S. Department of Homeland Security, 2003, p. 11). The record for most immigrants in a year was set in 1907, when almost 1.3 million people arrived on these shores. If undocumented immigrants were added to the recent totals, this century-old record might well have been eclipsed several times since the 1960s.

Will this new wave of immigrants transform the United States once again? How? Who are these new Americans? Where do they come from and what are they seeking? What do they contribute? What do they cost? Will they assimilate and adopt the ways of the dominant society? What are the implications if assimilation fails?

We have been asking questions like this throughout this text, and in this chapter, we will apply them to a variety of immigrant groups that are both newcomers and growing rapidly. We have already covered several large groups that have recently increased in size because of immigration: Mexican Americans in Chapter 9 and Chinese Americans in Chapter 10. In this chapter, we'll look at some smaller groups, dealing first with some Hispanic and Caribbean groups, then with some groups from Asia and the Pacific Islands, followed by Arab Americans and, finally, recent immigrants from Africa. In the last section of the chapter, we will examine some of the issues that have arisen as the United States confronts the challenges of absorbing these millions of newcomers.

Each of the groups covered in this chapter has had some members in the United States for decades, some for more than a century. However, in all cases, the groups were quite small until the latter third of the 20th century. Although they are growing rapidly now (and, all together, account for as much as 50%-60% of all immigrants in any one year), all remain relatively small, and none are larger than 1% of the population. Nonetheless, some will have a greater impact on American culture and society in the future, and one group—Arab Americans—has already become a focus of concern and controversy because of the events of 9-11 and the ensuing war on terrorism.

## RECENT IMMIGRATION FROM LATIN AMERICA, SOUTH AMERICA, AND THE CARIBBEAN

Immigration from Latin America, the Caribbean, and South America has been considerable, even excluding Mexico. Exhibit 11.1 shows a rapid increase, beginning in the 1960s and continuing to the turn of the century, with an average of about 200,000 immigrants each year. Generally, immigrants from these regions (minus Mexico) have been about 10% of all immigrants since the 1960s.

The sending nations for these immigrants are economically less developed, and most have long-standing relations with the United States. We have already discussed (see Chapter 9) the role that Mexico and Puerto Rico have historically played as sources of cheap labor and the ties that led Cubans to immigrate to the United States. Each of the other sending nations has been similarly linked to the United States, the dominant economic and political power in the region (Portes, 1990, p. 162).

Although the majority of these immigrants brings educational and occupational qualifications that are modest by U.S. standards, they tend to be more educated, more urbanized, and

**EXHIBIT 11.1** Immigration to the United States From Central America, South America, and the Caribbean, 1941-2003

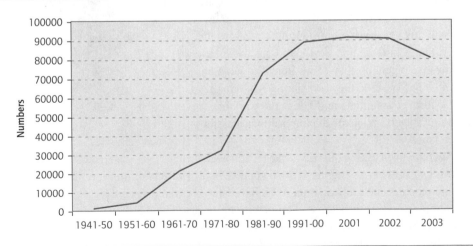

SOURCE: U.S. Department of Homeland Security (2003).

more skilled than the average citizens of the nations from which they come. Contrary to widely held beliefs, these immigrants do not represent the poorest of the poor, the "wretched refuse" of their homelands. They tend to be rather ambitious, as evidenced by their willingness to attempt to succeed in a society that has not been notably hospitable to Latinos or people of color in the past. Most of these immigrants are not so much fleeing poverty or joblessness as they are attempting to pursue their ambitions and seek opportunities for advancement that are simply not available in their country of origin (Portes & Rumbaut, 1996, p. 10-11).

This characterization applies to legal and unauthorized immigrants alike. In fact, the latter may illustrate the point more dramatically, because the cost of illegally entering the United States can be considerable, much higher than the cost of a legal entry. The venture may require years of saving money or the combined resources of a large kinship group. Forged papers and other costs of being smuggled into the country can easily amount to thousands of dollars, a considerable sum in nations in which the usual wage is a tiny fraction of the U.S. average (Orreniou, 2001, p. 7). Also, the passage can be extremely dangerous and can require a level of courage (or desperation) not often associated with the undocumented and illegal. Many Mexican would-be immigrants have died along the border, and many other immigrants have been lost at sea (for example, see "Dominicans Saved From Sea," 2004).

We should also note that this immigrant stream is quite diverse and includes French, British, and Portuguese traditions as well as Spanish. These immigrants come from more than a score of nations, including Jamaica, Grenada, Belize, Guatemala, Peru, and Brazil. Some are highly educated professionals, whereas others are farmhands, political refugees, skilled technicians, or the wives and children of U.S. citizens.

Rather than attempting to cover all of these groups, we will select four to serve as "case studies" and consider immigrants from the Dominican Republic, Haiti, El Salvador, and Colombia. Together, these four groups comprise a little less than 10% of all immigrants in recent years and about 20% of the immigrants from Central and South America and the Caribbean. These four groups had few members in the United States before the 1960s, and all have had high rates of immigration over the past four decades. However, the motivation of the immigrants and the immigration experience has varied from group to group, as we shall see later.

## Four Case Studies

Exhibit 11.3 displays some of the salient characteristics of three of our "case studies," using data from the 2000 Census. These data reflect the "newness" of these groups: Each has a high percentage of foreign-born members, and, predictably with so many members in the first generation, proficiency in English is an important issue. Although Colombians approach national norms in education, the other two groups have relatively low levels of human capital (education), and all are well above national norms in terms of poverty.

National information on Haitians is not available from the U.S. Census, but independent studies and other sources of information indicate that they are roughly comparable to Dominicans and Salvadorans and have a high percentage of foreign born, low English proficiency, low levels of education, and high levels of poverty. For example, one study of the Haitian community in Florida found that only 30% to 40% of parents had completed high school, and more than 80% of families had incomes lower than $25,000 per year (Rumbaut & Portes, 2001).

Exhibit 11.4 presents information on occupational distribution for the males and females of the three groups for which there is national information. Consistent with their low levels of

EXHIBIT 11.2

Map of Central and South America and the Caribbean showing the Dominican Republic, Haiti, El Salvador, and Columbia

---

**EXHIBIT 11.3** Characteristics of Four Groups

| Nation | Present Population | % of Total Population | % Foreign Born | % "Poor" English[a] | % HS[b] | % BA[c] | % Poor[d] |
|---|---|---|---|---|---|---|---|
| United States | 281,421,906 | NA | 11.1 | 8.1 | 80.4 | 24.4 | 9.2 |
| Dominican Republic | 799,768 | 0.28 | 68.2 | 53.7 | 51.1 | 10.9 | 27.6 |
| El Salvador | 708,741 | 0.25 | 75.6 | 61.5 | 36.1 | 5.5 | 18.6 |
| Columbia | 496,748 | 0.18 | 23.9 | 50.7 | 74.5 | 23.7 | 14.3 |
| Haiti | 548,199[e] | 0.19 | NA | NA | NA | NA | NA |

SOURCE: U.S. Bureau of the Census (n.d.), Summary File 4.

a. Percentage of group with "ability to speak English less than 'very well.'"

b. Percentage of high school graduates.

c. Percentage of college graduates.

d. Percentage of families below the poverty line.

e. From U.S. Census (n.d.), Summary File 3, Table QT-P13.

EXHIBIT 11.4a    Occupational Profile, Men

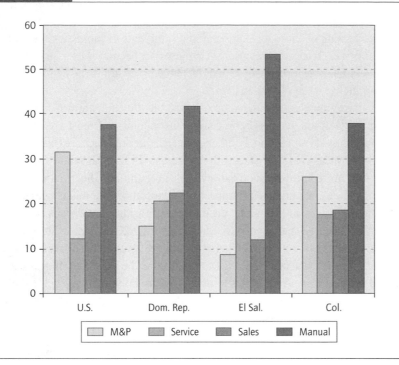

EXHIBIT 11.4b    Occupational Profile, Women

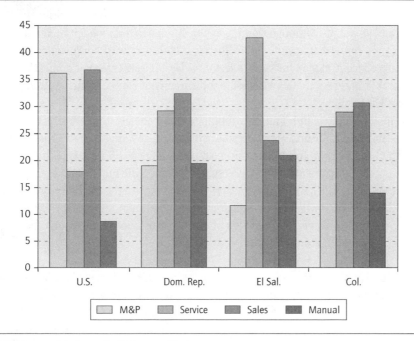

SOURCE: U.S. Bureau of the Census (n.d.) Summary File 4.

education, the men of all three groups (particularly Salvadorans) are underrepresented at the management and professional level (the jobs with the highest levels of prestige and rewards) and are overrepresented in service jobs and manual labor jobs, usually in the least desirable, secure, and rewarding of these jobs. Roughly the same pattern holds for the females, with Salvadoran women especially overrepresented in the service sector (often as poorly paid domestics and nannies). Of these three groups, Colombians come closest to the national norms, again reflecting their higher levels of human capital.

Although these groups share some common characteristics, they are also quite different from each other. The biggest difference is between Haitians, who come from a French tradition and speak Creole (a dialect of French) and the other groups, all three of which are Hispanic. The groups also differ in their "racial" characteristics, with Haitians and Dominicans more African in appearance, Colombians more European, and Salvadorans more Indian. The groups tend to settle in different places. Three of the groups (Dominicans, Haitians, and Colombians) are clustered along the East Coast, particularly in New York, New Jersey, and Florida; Salvadorans are more concentrated on the West Coast (Department of Homeland Security, 2003). Finally, the groups differ in the conditions of their entry or their "contact situation," a difference that, as we have seen, is quite consequential. Haitians and Salvadorans are more likely to be political refugees fleeing brutal civil wars and political repression; Dominicans and Colombians are more likely to be motivated by economics and the employment possibilities offered in the United States. We will consider each of these groups briefly and explore some of these differences further.

**Dominicans.** The Dominican Republic shares the Caribbean island of Hispaniola with Haiti. The island economy is still largely agricultural, although the tourist industry has grown in recent years. Unemployment and poverty are major problems, and Dominicans average less than 5 years of education (NationMaster.com, 2005b).

Dominican immigrants are motivated largely by economics, and they compete for jobs with Puerto Ricans, other immigrant groups, and native-born workers with lower levels of education and jobs skills. Although Dominicans are limited in their job options by the language barrier, they are somewhat advantaged by their willingness to work for lower wages, and they are especially concentrated in the service sector, as day laborers (men) or domestics (women). Dominicans maintain strong ties with home and are a major source of income and support for the families left behind.

In terms of acculturation and integration, Dominicans are roughly similar to Mexican Americans and Puerto Ricans, although some studies suggest that they are possibly the most impoverished immigrant group (see, for example, Camarota, 2002). A high percentage of Dominicans are undocumented, and many spend considerable money and take considerable risks to get to the United States. If these less visible members of the community were included in the official, government-generated statistics used in Exhibits 11.3 and 11.4, it is very likely that the portrait of poverty and low levels of education and jobs skills would be even more dramatic.

**Haitians.** Haiti is the poorest country in Western Hemisphere, and most of the population relies on small-scale subsistence agriculture for survival. Estimates are that 80% of the population lives below the poverty line and fewer than one third of adults hold formal jobs. Only about half the population is literate, and Haitians average less than 3 years of formal education (NationMaster.com, 2005d).

Haitian immigration was virtually nonexistent until the 1970s and 1980s, when thousands began to flee the brutal political repression of the Duvalier dictatorship, which—counting both father ("Papa Doc") and son ("Baby Doc")—lasted until the mid-1980s. In stark contrast to the treatment of Cuban immigrants (see Chapter 9), however, the United States government defined Haitians as economic refugees ineligible for asylum, and an intense campaign has been conducted to keep Haitians out of the United States. Thousands have been returned to Haiti, some to face political persecution, prison, and even death. Others have been incarcerated in the United States, and in the view of some, "During the 1970s and 1980s, no other immigrant group suffered more U.S. government prejudice and discrimination than Haitians" (Stepick, Stepick, Eugene, Teed, & Labissiere, 2001, p. 236).

What accounts for this cold, negative reception? Some reasons are not hard to identify. Haitians bring low levels of human capital and education. This creates concerns about their ability to support themselves in the United States and also means that they have relatively few resources with which to defend their self-interest. In addition, Haitians speak a language (Creole) that is spoken by almost no one else. This sharply limits the networks and alliances available to the group. Perhaps the most important reason for the rejection, however, is that Haitians are black and must cope with the centuries-old traditions of rejection, racism, and prejudice that are such an intimate part of American culture (Stepick et al., 2001).

One important study of Haitians in South Florida found that this combination of factors— their hostile reception, their poverty and lack of education, and their racial background— combined to lead the Haitian second generation (the children of the immigrants) to a relatively low level of academic achievement and a tendency to identify with the African American community. "Haitians are becoming American but in a specifically black ethnic fashion" (Stepick et al., 2001, p. 261). The ultimate path of Haitian assimilation will unfold in the future, but these tendencies—particularly their low levels of academic achievement—suggest that few of the second generation are likely to move into the middle class and that their assimilation will be segmented (Stepick et al., 2001, p. 261).

**Salvadorans.** El Salvador, like Haiti and the Dominican Republic, is a relatively poor nation, with a high percentage of the population relying on subsistence agriculture for survival. It is estimated that about 50% of the population is below poverty level, and there are major problems with unemployment and underemployment. About 80% of the population is literate, and the average number of years of school completed is a little more than five (NationMaster.com, 2005c).

El Salvador, like many sending nations, has a difficult time providing sufficient employment opportunities for its population, and much of the pressure to immigrate is economic. However, El Salvador also suffered through a brutal civil war in the 1980s, and many of the Salvadorans in the United States today are actually political refugees. The United States, under the administration of President Reagan, refused to grant political refugee status to Salvadorans, and many were returned to El Salvador. This federal policy resulted in high numbers of undocumented immigrants and also stimulated a sanctuary movement, led by American clergy, which aided Salvadoran immigrants, both undocumented and legal, to stay in United States. As was the case with Dominicans, if the undocumented immigrants from El Salvador were included in official government statistics, the picture of poverty would become even more extreme.

**Colombians.** Colombia is somewhat more developed then most other Central and South American nations but has suffered from more than 40 years of internal turmoil, civil war, and government corruption. The nation is a major center for the production and distribution of drugs to the world in general and the United States in particular, and the drug industry and profits are complexly intertwined with domestic strife. As reflected in Exhibit 11.3, Colombian Americans are closer to national norms of education and income than other Latino groups, and recent immigrants are a mixture of less skilled laborers and well-educated professionals seeking to further their career. Colombians are residentially concentrated in urban areas, especially in Florida and the Northeast, and often settle in areas close to other Latino neighborhoods. Of course, the huge majority of Colombian Americans are law abiding and not connected with the drug trade, but still they must deal with the pervasive stereotype that pictures Colombians as gangsters and drug smugglers (not unlike the Mafia stereotype encountered by Italian Americans).

## CONTEMPORARY IMMIGRATION FROM ASIA AND THE PACIFIC ISLANDS

Immigration from Asia and the Pacific Islands has been considerable since the 1960s, averaging close to 300,000 per year and running about 30% to 35% of all immigrants. As was the case with Hispanic and Caribbean immigrants, the sending nations are considerably less developed than the United States, and the primary motivation for most of these immigrants is economic. However, the Asian and Pacific Island immigrant stream also includes a large contingent of highly educated professionals seeking opportunities to practice their careers and expand their skills. While these more elite immigrants contribute to the image of "Asian success" (see Chapter 10), other Asian and Pacific Island immigrants are low skilled, less educated, and undocumented. Thus, this stream of immigrants, like Chinese Americans, is "bipolar" and includes a healthy representation of people from both the top and the bottom of the occupational and educational hierarchies.

Of course, other factors besides mere economics attract these immigrants to the United States. The United States has maintained military bases throughout the region (including South Korea and the Philippines) since the end of World War II, and many Asian and Pacific Islander immigrants are the spouses of American military personnel. Also, U.S. involvement in the war in Southeast Asia in the 1960s and 1970s created interpersonal ties and governmental programs that drew refugees from Vietnam, Cambodia, and Laos.

As before, rather than attempting to cover all the separate groups in this category, we will concentrate on four case studies and consider immigrant groups from India, Vietnam, Korea, and the Philippines. Together, these four groups comprise about half of all immigrants from Asia and the Pacific Islands, and Exhibit 11.5 displays their volume of immigration.

## Four Case Studies

Exhibit 11.7 repeats Exhibit 11.3 for the four Asian and Pacific Islander groups, again using data from the 2000 census. Note that all four groups are small and that they include a high percentage of foreign-born members. In contrast with Hispanic and Caribbean immigrants, however, note that two of the groups have dramatically lower percentages of members not fluent in English and that three groups actually exceed national norms for education (e.g., Indians have 2½ times the national norm for college-educated members) and two are well below national norms for poverty. Although Vietnamese Americans rank lower on measures of education and poverty, the picture presented by this table underscores the idea that many of the immigrants from these four groups are well prepared to compete in the American job market.

**EXHIBIT 11.5** Immigration to the United States From India, Vietnam, the Philippines, and Korea, 1941-2003

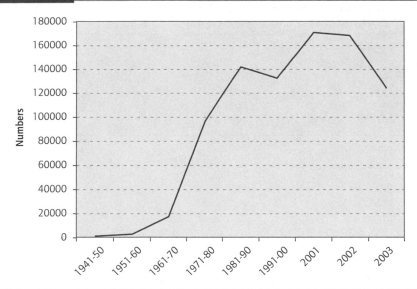

**EXHIBIT 11.6** Map of Asia, Showing India, Vietnam, Korea, and the Philippines

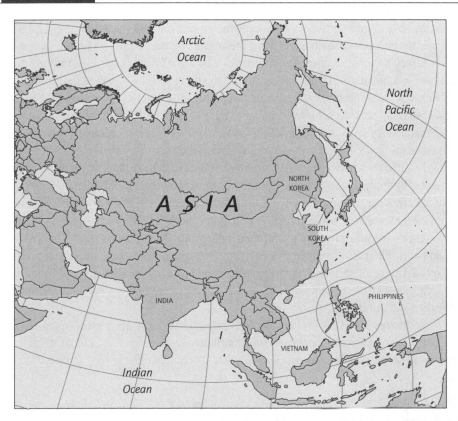

## EXHIBIT 11.7 Characteristics of Four Groups

| Nation of Origin | Number | % of Total Population | % Foreign Born | % "Poor" English[a] | % HS[b] | % BA[c] | % Poor[d] |
|---|---|---|---|---|---|---|---|
| United States | 281,421,906 | NA | 11.1 | 8.1 | 80.4 | 24.4 | 9.2 |
| Indian | 1,855,590 | 0.66 | 27.1 | 23.0 | 85.4 | 60.9 | 7.5 |
| Filipino | 2,385,216 | 0.85 | 55.8 | 20.5 | 87.4 | 41.7 | 5.4 |
| Korean | 1,226,825 | 0.44 | 69.9 | 46.0 | 86.4 | 43.1 | 13.0 |
| Vietnamese | 1,212,465 | 0.43 | 73.5 | 60.5 | 62.0 | 19.5 | 14.3 |

SOURCE: U.S. Bureau of the Census (n.d.), Summary File 4.

a. Percentage of group with "ability to speak English less than 'very well.'"

b. Percentage of high school graduates.

c. Percentage of college graduates.

d. Percentage of families below the poverty line.

Exhibit 11.8 reinforces the impression that many Asian and Pacific Islander groups bring high levels of human capital. Indian and Korean males are overrepresented in the highest occupational group and underrepresented among manual laborers. Indian and Filipino women are also overrepresented in the highest occupational grouping, but Vietnamese women are overrepresented in the lowest. Otherwise, the occupational distribution of both genders is roughly similar to national norms.

As we have done so often, we must note the diversity across these four groups. First, we can repeat the point made in Chapter 10 that the category "Asian and Pacific Islander Americans" is an arbitrary designation imposed on peoples who actually have little in common and who come from nations that vary in language, culture, religion, "racial" characteristics, and scores of other ways. More specifically, these four groups are quite different from each other. Perhaps the most striking contrast is between Indians, many of whom are highly educated and skilled, and Vietnamese Americans, who have a socioeconomic profile that more closely resembles non-Asian racial minorities in the United States and who challenge the stereotype of Asian success. Part of the difference between these two groups relates to their contact situations and can be illuminated by applying the Blauner hypothesis. Immigrants from India are at the "immigrant" end of Blauner's continuum. They bring strong educational credentials and are well equipped to compete for favorable positions in the occupational hierarchy. The Vietnamese, in sharp contrast, began their American experience as a refugee group fleeing the turmoil of war. Although they do not fit Bluaner's "conquered or colonized" category, most Vietnamese Americans had to adapt to American society with few resources and few contacts with an established immigrant community. The consequences of these vastly different contact situations are suggested by the data in Exhibit 11.8.

These groups also very in their settlement patterns. Most are concentrated along the West Coast, but Indians are roughly equally distributed on both the East and West Coasts, and Vietnamese have a sizeable presence in Texas, in part related to the fishing industry along the Gulf Coast.

**Indians.** India is the second most populous nation in the world, and its huge population of more than a billion people incorporates a wide variety of different languages (India has 19

**EXHIBIT 11.8a** Occupational Profile, Men

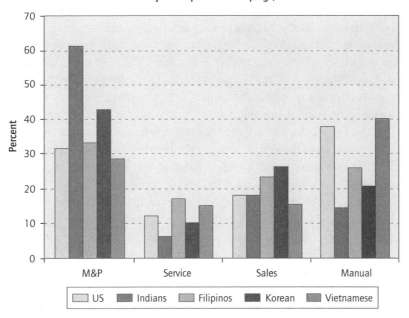

Major Occupational Groupings, Males

**EXHIBIT 11.8b** Occupational Profile, Women

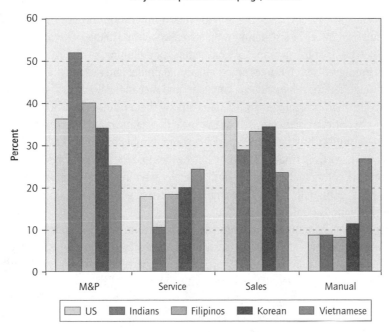

Major Occupational Groupings, Females

SOURCE: U.S. Bureau of the Census (n.d.). Summary File 4.

official languages, including English), religions, and ethnic groups. Overall, the level of education is fairly low. The population averages about 5 years of formal schooling, and only about 50% of females and 70% of males are literate. However, about 10% of the population does reach the postsecondary level of education, which means that there are roughly 100 million (10% of a billion) well-educated Indians looking for careers commensurate with their credentials. Because of the relative lack of development in the Indian economy, many members of this educated elite must search for career opportunities abroad, and not just in the United States.

It is also important to note that, as a legacy of India's long colonization by the British, English is the language of the educated. Thus Indian immigrants tend to be not only well educated but also English speaking (hence, the low percentage of members with "poor English" in Exhibit 11.7).

Immigration from India was low until the mid-1960s, and the group was quite small at that time. The group more than quadrupled in size between 1980 and 2000, and Indians are now the third-largest Asian American group today (behind Chinese and Filipinos).

As is reflected in Exhibits 11.7 and 11.8, Indian immigrants tend to be a select, highly educated and skilled group. According to the 2000 census, Indians are very overrepresented in some of the most prestigious occupations, including computer engineering, physicians, and college faculty (U.S. Bureau of the Census, n.d., Summary File 4). Immigrants from India are part of a worldwide movement of educated peoples from less developed countries to more developed countries. One need not ponder the differences in career opportunities, technology, and compensation for long to get some insight into the reasons for this movement. Other immigrants from India are more oriented to commerce and small business, and there is a sizable Indian ethnic enclave in many cities (Kitano & Daniels, 1995, pp. 96-111; Sheth, 1995).

**Koreans.** Immigration from Korea to the United States began at the turn of the century, when laborers were recruited to help fill the void in the job market left by the 1882 Chinese Exclusion Act. This group was extremely small until the 1950s, when the rate of immigration rose because of refugees and "war brides" after the Korean War. Immigration did not become substantial, however, until the 1960s. The size of the group increased fivefold in the 1970s and tripled between 1980 and 2000 but is still less than 0.5% of the total population.

Recent immigrants from Korea consist mostly of families and include many highly educated people. Although differences in culture, language, and race make Koreans visible targets of discrimination, the high percentage of Christians among them (almost half of South Koreans are Christian—see NationMaster.com, 2005a) may help them appear more "acceptable" to the dominant group. Certainly, Christian church parishes play a number of important roles for the Korean American community, offering assistance to newcomers and the less fortunate, serving as a focal point for networks of mutual assistance, and generally assisting in the completion of the myriad chores to which immigrant communities must attend (e.g., government paperwork, registering to vote, etc.) (Kitano & Daniels, 2001, p. 123).

Korean American immigrants have formed an enclave, and the group is heavily involved in small businesses and retail stores, particularly fruit and vegetable retail stores, or greengroceries. According to one study, Koreans had the second highest percentage of self-employment among immigrant groups (Greeks were the highest), with about 24% of the group in this occupational category (Kritz & Girak, 2004, p. 36). Another data source, also based on the 2000 census, shows that Koreans have the highest rate of business ownership among 11 different minority groups (U.S. Bureau of the Census, 2002), including other enclave minorities. Japanese Americans had the second highest rate (108 businesses per 1000 population), Chinese Americans were third (104 per

1000 population), and Cuban Americans were fourth (101 per 1000 population). In contrast, racial minority groups with strong histories of colonization and exclusion were at the bottom of the rankings: African Americans (24 businesses per 1000) and Puerto Ricans (21 per 1000) (see also Pollard & O'Hare, 1999, p. 39; Kim, Hurh, & Fernandez, 1989; Logan et al., 1994; Min, 1995, pp. 208-212.)

As is the case for other groups that have pursued this course, the enclave allows Korean Americans to avoid the discrimination and racism of the larger society yet survive in an economic niche in which lack of English fluency is not a particular problem. However, the enclave has its perils and its costs. For one thing, the success of Korean enterprises depends heavily on the mutual assistance and financial support of other Koreans and the willingness of family members to work long hours for little or no pay (recall the story of Kim Park from Chapter 1). These resources would be weakened or destroyed by acculturation, integration, and the resultant decline in ethnic solidarity. Only by maintaining a distance from the dominant culture and its pervasive appeal can the infrastructure survive.

Furthermore, the economic niches in which Mom-and-Pop greengroceries and other small businesses can survive are often in deteriorated neighborhoods populated largely by other minority groups. There has been a good deal of hostility and resentment expressed against Korean shop owners by African Americans, Puerto Ricans, and other urbanized minority groups. For example, anti-Korean sentiments were widely expressed in the 1992 Los Angeles riots that followed the acquittal of the policemen who had been charged in the beating of Rodney King. Korean-owned businesses were some of the first to be looted and burned, and when asked why, one participant in the looting said simply: "Because we hate 'em. Everybody hates them" (Cho, 1993, p. 199). Thus, part of the price of survival for many Korean merchants is to place themselves in positions in which antagonism and conflict with other minority groups is common (Kitano & Daniels, 1995, pp. 112-129; Light & Bonacich, 1988; Min, 1995, pp. 199-231; see also Hurh, 1998).

**Filipino Americans.** Ties between the United States and the Philippines were established in 1898 when Spain ceded the territory after its defeat in the Spanish-American war. The Philippines achieved independence following World War II, but the United States has maintained a strong military presence there for much of the past 50 years. The nation has been heavily influenced by American culture, and English remains one of two official languages. Thus, as reflected in Exhibit 11.7, Filipino immigrants are often conversant in English, at least as a second language.

Today, Filipinos are the second largest Asian American group, but their numbers became sizable only in the last few decades. There were fewer than 1000 Filipinos in the United States in 1910, and by 1960, the group still numbered fewer than 200,000. Most of the recent growth has come from increased post-1965 immigration. The group more than doubled in size between 1980 and 2000.

Many of the earliest immigrants were agricultural workers recruited for the sugar plantations of Hawaii and the fields of the West Coast. Because the Philippines was a U.S. territory, Filipinos could enter without regard to immigration quotas until 1935, when the nation became a self-governing commonwealth.

The most recent wave of immigrants is diversified, and like Chinese Americans, Filipino Americans are "bipolar" in their educational and occupational profiles. Many recent immigrants have entered under the family preference provisions of the U.S. immigration policy. These immigrants are often poor and compete for jobs in the low-wage secondary labor market (Kitano & Daniels, 1995, p. 94). More than half of all Filipino immigrants since 1965, however, have been professionals, many of them in the health and medical fields. Many female immigrants from the Philippines were nurses actively recruited by U.S. hospitals to fill gaps in the labor force (Amott & Matthaei, 1991, p. 245). Thus the Filipino American community includes some members in the higher wage primary labor market and others who are competing for work in the low-wage secondary sector (Agbayani-Siewart & Revilla, 1995; Espiritu, 1996; Kitano & Daniels, 1995, pp. 83-94; Mangiafico, 1988; Posadas, 1999).

**Vietnamese.** A flow of refugees from Vietnam began in the 1960s as a direct result of the war in Southeast Asia. The war began in Vietnam but expanded when the United States attacked communist forces in Cambodia and Laos. Social life was disrupted, and people were displaced throughout the region. In 1975, when Saigon (the South Vietnamese capital) fell and the U.S. military withdrew, many Vietnamese and other Southeast Asians who had collaborated with the United States and its allies fled in fear for their lives. This group included high-ranking officials and members of the region's educational and occupation elite. Later groups of refugees tended to be less well educated and more impoverished. Many Vietnamese waited in refugee camps for months or years before being admitted to the United States, and they often arrived with few resources or social networks to ease their transition to the new society (Kitano & Daniels, 1995, pp. 151-152). The Vietnamese are the largest of the Asian refugee groups, and contrary to Asian American success stories and notions of model minorities, they have incomes and educational levels comparable to colonized minority groups (see Exhibits 11.7 and 11.8).

# ARAB AMERICANS

Immigration from the Middle East and the Arab world began in the 19th century but has never been particularly large. The earliest immigrants tended to be merchants and traders, and the Arab American community has always been constructed around an ethnic small-business enclave.

The Arab American community has grown rapidly over the past several decades but still remains a tiny percentage of the total population. Exhibit 11.9 displays information on group size and growth rates, broken down by ancestry group. These data are from the U.S. Census and may very well underestimate the actual size of the group. For example, one source estimates total group size at over 3 million (see El-Badry, 2004).

As displayed in Exhibits 11.10 and 11.11, the Arab American community ranks relatively high in English ability, income, and occupation. In the 2000 census, 81% of Arab Americans reported that they were fluent in English, and Arab Americans exceeded national norms in terms of high school and college graduates. In fact, every subgroup within the Arab American community exceeded national norms in terms of percentage of college graduates by a considerable margin. Similarly, the group as a whole and most of the subgroups compares favorably to national norms in terms of poverty.

Data on occupational patterns in Exhibit 11.11 show an overrepresentation in the highest occupational group for men and women. Consistent with their enclave orientation, Arab American men are overrepresented in sales and underrepresented in occupations involving manual labor. Arab American women are also heavily involved in sales but in proportion to U.S. women in general. One study, using 1990 census data and a survey mailed to a national sample of Arab American women in 2000, found that immigrant Arab American women have a very low rate of employment, the lowest of any immigrant group. The author's analysis of this data strongly suggests that this pattern is due to traditional gender roles and family norms regarding the proper role of women (Read, 2004).

Arab Americans are diverse and vary along a number of dimensions. They bring different national traditions and cultures and also vary in religion. Although Islam is the dominant religion, many Arab immigrant groups are Christian.

## EXHIBIT 11.9    Arab Americans, 1990 and 2000: Totals and Largest Ancestry Groups

| Group | 1990 | | 2000 | | % Growth, 1990-2000 |
| --- | --- | --- | --- | --- | --- |
| | Number | % of all Arab Americans | Number | % of all Arab Americans | |
| Arab Americans | 860,354 | NA | 1,189,731 | NA | 38 |
| Largest ancestry groups | | | | | |
| Lebanese | 394,180 | 45.8 | 440,279 | 37.0 | 12 |
| Syrian | 129,606 | 15.1 | 142,897 | 12.0 | 10 |
| Egyptian | 78,574 | 9.1 | 142,832 | 12.0 | 82 |
| Palestinian | 48,019 | 5.6 | 72,112 | 6.1 | 50 |
| Jordanian | 20,656 | 2.4 | 39,734 | 3.3 | 92 |
| Moroccan | 19,089 | 2.2 | 38,923 | 3.3 | 104 |
| Iraqi | 23,212 | 2.7 | 37,714 | 3.2 | 63 |

SOURCE: de la Cruz and Brittingham (2003).

## EXHIBIT 11.10    Characteristics of Arab Americans and Eight Subgroups

| Nation of Origin | % of U.S. Population | % Foreign Born | % "Poor" English[a] | % HS[b] | % BA[c] | % Poor[d] |
| --- | --- | --- | --- | --- | --- | --- |
| United States | NA | 11.1 | 8.1 | 80.4 | 24.4 | 9.2 |
| Arab | 0.40 | 40.9 | 18.8 | 86.2 | 42.0 | 10.9 |
| Lebanese | 0.16 | 22.4 | 9.0 | 89.0 | 41.3 | 6.4 |
| Arabic | 0.07 | 49.8 | 27.3 | 78.5 | 33.7 | 18.9 |
| Syrian | 0.05 | 23.7 | 11.8 | 86.7 | 37.7 | 6.5 |
| Egyptian | 0.05 | 64.5 | 26.2 | 93.8 | 63.3 | 11.6 |
| Palestinian | 0.03 | 49.7 | 21.7 | 83.0 | 40.2 | 13.1 |
| Jordanian | 0.01 | 63.7 | 27.9 | 84.2 | 37.3 | 13.4 |
| Moroccan | 0.01 | 57.5 | 24.8 | 85.9 | 33.0 | 12.6 |
| Iraqi | 0.01 | 71.9 | 39.2 | 71.8 | 35.9 | 19.9 |

SOURCE: U.S. Bureau of the Census (n.d.), Summary File 4.

a. Percentage of group with "ability to speak English less than 'very well.'"

b. Percentage of high school graduates.

c. Percentage of college graduates.

d. Percentage of families below the poverty line.

## The Arab American Community in Detroit, Michigan by *Steve Gold*

The events of September 11, 2001, focused attention on Arab American communities. The Detroit area is home to more than 300,000 Arab Americans, one of the largest ethnic enclaves in the United States. Nineteenth-century immigrants from Syria and Lebanon were the first to arrive. With the increased demand for automobiles and the steel to make them at the beginning of the 20th century, more immigrants from the Middle East came to work in Detroit's many factories. By 1916, the Ford motor company counted 555 Arab men among its workforce. The first Islamic mosque in America was established in Highland Park in 1919. The relationship between Arab immigrants and auto manufacturing endures. Next to Ford's famous River Rouge plant is Dearborn's "Arab village."

Immigrants continue to arrive in Detroit, reuniting families that have been divided across borders and continents. Whether from Iraq, Yemen, or Palestine, they seek economic advancement and escape from the Middle East's chronic violence. In 1990, more than one-third of Michigan residents of Arab origin had been born outside of the United States; about 40 percent had immigrated after 1980. Although all are Arab, their religious affiliations are diverse: Lebanese Christians; Sunni and Shiite Muslims; Palestinians and Jordanians who are Catholic, Protestant, Greek Orthodox, and Sunni Muslims; Eastern rite Catholic Chaldeans and Yemenis of different Muslim sects.

The Arab community is also socioeconomically diverse, but the 1990 Census showed them to be generally well off as a group. College graduation rates are high, and comparatively few are unemployed or struggling on below-poverty incomes. Besides careers in the auto industry, Arab Americans also become professionals, and many are self-employed.

With their new visibility since September 2001, Arab Americans have experienced renewed negative attention. But this, too, has deep roots. Metropolitan Detroit has a long history of racial and ethnic violence, and Arab American residents have become well acquainted with discrimination and stereotyping—from ethnic slurs like being called "camel jockeys" to the more pernicious dominance of European traditions and standards in schools. Neither is this the first conflict in the Middle East for which Arabs were demonized. With a rich community life, Arab Americans have developed a range of organizational supports that provide succor in the face of the episodic but persistent hostilities they face in America.

### Recommended Resources:

Abraham, Sameer Y. 1983. "Detroit's Arab-American Community" pp. 84-108 in *Arabs in the New World* ed. Sameer Y. Abraham and Nabeel Abraham. Detroit: Wayne State University Center for Urban Studies.

Abraham, Nabeel and Andrew Shryock eds. 2000. *Arab Detroit: From Margins to Mainstream*. Detroit: Wayne State University Press.

Johnson, Nan E. 1995. *Health Profiles of Michigan Populations of Color*. Lansing: Michigan Department of Public Health.

## Two Stories of Immigration

*The following accounts illustrate some of the variety in Asian American experiences. The first recounts the experiences of Ho Yang, who immigrated to San Francisco's Chinatown as a young boy in 1920. He describes some of the dynamics of the enclave community he grew to be a part of. At the time of the interview (1980), he was an officer in one of the family associations that helped to organize and structure the Chinese American community.*

*The second account is from Vo Thi Tam, a Vietnamese refugee whose husband had been an officer in the South Vietnamese Air Force. She describes a harrowing passage to America, during which she became separated from her husband, was attacked by pirates, and gave birth in a refugee camp. These two Asian immigrants arrived in the United States under vastly different circumstances. What consequences will their different modes of incorporation have?*

### HO YANG

My village in Kwantung Province is very small, only about a hundred people, and it was really poor. . . . We used cows for plows, you know, because buffaloes were expensive. A whole life would depend on a cow. In fact, when a cow died there, I think the family wept more than when a relative died. . . .

My father went to Canton and worked there, and after a while, he saved up enough money and he came to the United States. And when I was 13, he came back to China and got me. He couldn't bring my mother for some legal reason, and my sister wanted to stay with her, so I was the only one he brought back. . . .

Later, I went back to China to get married. I had a friend over here who said, "You want to get married? Maybe I'll write a letter to my niece in China." And I said, "Well, all right, you can try. It won't hurt." And it turned out to be all right with her. . . . and we've been together for more than 40 years now. . . .

There's really two reasons people like to live in Chinatown. One is the language. Some Chinese have been here for thirty years and they've never been out of Chinatown and they can't speak English. The other reason is the work here. People own little shops. There must be over 200 shops in Chinatown. Little butcher shops, little curio shops, noodle shops, all those kinds of shops. It's usually just a husband and wife, and the kids work in there. And the small restaurants are family style. Everybody helps; washing dishes, waiters and waitresses, and all that. The money isn't too good but it's all in the family.

Many of the Chinese ladies, they go to the garment factory. . . . My wife did that. . . . [The] main reason ladies go in them is this: If you don't understand English, you can't go to work in an American place. Also, Americans pay you by the hour and you can't go too slow. Too slow and they fire you, you know. But in Chinatown, they go by piecework—so much a dozen. . . . And ladies with children, it's good for them, too, because they can bring their little kids with them and can run around there. And if the ladies need to leave, they're free to go to take their kids to school, because by the piece, the less time you spend there, the less money you get. Sometimes they call those companies sweatshops, because the pay is so low, but they're better now than they were before.

## VO THI TAM

[To escape] we got together with some other families and bought a big fishing boat. . . . Altogether there were about 37 of us that were to leave. I was five months pregnant.

[On the day of the escape, they were to rendezvous with her husband and another man outside the harbor] but there was no one there. [A patrol boat was approaching] and there was a discussion aboard the boat and the end of it was the people on our boat decided to leave without my husband and the other man. (Long pause)

When we reached the high seas, we discovered that the water container was leaking and only a little was left. So we had to ration the water from then on. We had brought some rice and some other food. . . . but the sea was so wavy that we could not cook anything at all. So all we had was raw rice and a few lemons and very little water. After seven days we ran out of water, so all we had to drink was the sea water. . . . Everyone was sick and, at one point, my mother and my little boy, four years old, were in agony, about to die. And the other people on the boat said that if they were agonizing like that, it would be better to throw them overboard so as to save them pain. . . .

[While we] were discussing throwing my mother and son overboard, we could see [a] ship coming and we were very happy. . . . When the boats came together, the people came on board . . . and made all of us go aboard the bigger boat. They began to search us—cutting off our blouses, our bras, searching everywhere. . . . Finally, they pried up the planks of our boat, trying to see if there was any gold or jewelry hidden there. And when they had taken everything, they put us back on our boat and pushed us away.

[The group was attacked twice more by pirates before finally reaching land in Malaysia. Once ashore, yet another group attacked them and one of the women was raped. They were finally rescued by Malaysian police and taken to a refugee camp on Bidong Island.] Perhaps in the beginning it was all right there, maybe for ten thousand people or so, but when we arrived, there were already fifteen to seventeen thousand crowded onto thirty acres. There was no facilities, no housing, nothing. . . .

The Malaysian authorities did what they could but . . . there were no sanitary installations, and many people had diarrhea. It was very hard to stop sickness under those conditions. . . . When the monsoons came, the floor of our shelter was all mud. We had one blanket and a board to lie on, and that was all. . . . After four months, it was time for my baby to come. Fortunately, we had many doctors among us, because many . . . had escaped from Vietnam, so we had medical care but no equipment. There was no bed, no hospital, no nothing, just a wooden plank to lie down on and let the baby be born. . . . After the delivery I had to get up and . . . make room for the next one to be born.

[After seven months in the camp, they finally came to the United States.] It was like waking up after a bad nightmare. Like coming out of hell into paradise. [Shortly after her arrival, Vo Thi Tam learned that her husband had been recaptured and was a prisoner in Vietnam.]

SOURCE: Morrison, Joan, & Zabusky, Charlotte Fox. 1980. *American Mosaic: The Immigrant Experience in the Words of Those Who Lived It*. New York: Dutton. Pp. 79-80 and 446-450.

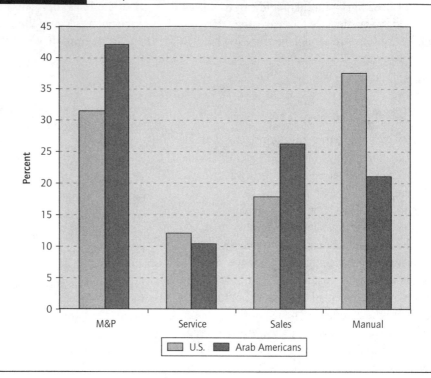

**EXHIBIT 11.11a** Occupational Profile, Men

**EXHIBIT 11.11b** Occupational Profile, Women

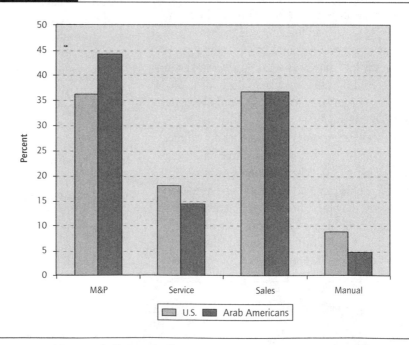

SOURCE: U.S. Bureau of the Census (n.d.). Summary File 4.

UNDERSTANDING U.S. DOMINANT-MINORITY RELATIONS

Residentially, Arab Americans are highly urbanized, and almost 50% live in just five states (California, New Jersey, New York, Florida, and Michigan). This settlement pattern is not too different from the other recent immigrant groups except for the heavy concentration in Michigan, especially in the Detroit area. Arab Americans account for 1.2% of the total population of Michigan, a far higher representation than in any other state. Arab Americans make up 30% of the population of Dearborn, Michigan, making it the most Arab city in the nation. (On the other hand, the greatest single concentration is in New York City, which has a population of about 70,000 Arab Americans.) These settlement patterns reflect chains of migration, some set up decades ago. Exhibit 11.12 shows the regional distribution of the group and clearly displays the clusters in Michigan, Florida, and Southern California.

**9-11 and Arab Americans.** There has always been at least a faint strain of prejudice directed at Middle Easterners in American culture (e.g., see the low position of Turks in the earliest social distance scales; most Americans probably are not aware of the fact that Turks and Arabs are different groups). These vague feelings have intensified in recent decades as relations with various Middle Eastern nations and groups worsened. For example, in 1979, the U.S. embassy

**EXHIBIT 11.12**   Regional Distribution of Arab Americans, 2000

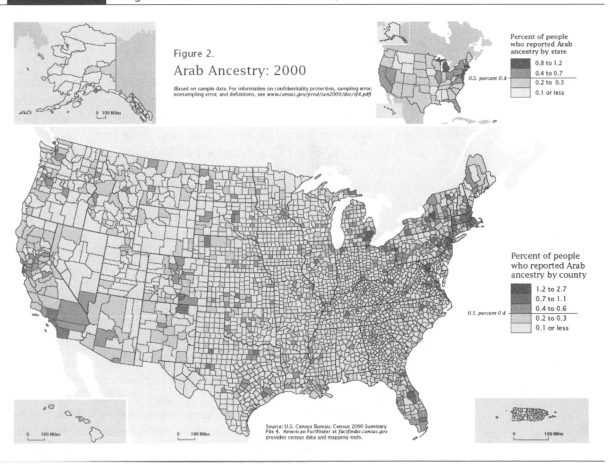

SOURCE: U.S. Bureau of the Census (n.d.).

in Tehran, Iran, was attacked and occupied and more than 50 Americans were held hostage for more than a year. The attack stimulated a massive reaction in the United States, in which anti-Arab feelings figured prominently. Continuing anti-American activities across the Middle East have been countered with a backlash of resentment and growing intolerance.

These earlier events pale in comparison, of course, to the events of September 11, 2001. Americans responded to the attacks on the World Trade Center and the Pentagon by Arab terrorists with an array of emotions that included bewilderment, shock, anger, patriotism, deep sorrow for the victims and their families, and—perhaps predictably in the intensity of the moment—intensified prejudicial rejection of Middle Easterners, Arabs, Muslims, and any group that seemed even vaguely associated with the perpetrators of the attacks. In the 9 weeks following September 11, more than 700 violent attacks were reported to the Arab-American Anti-Discrimination Committee, followed by another 165 violent incidents in the first 9 months of 2002. In this same time period, there were more than 80 incidents in which Arab Americans were removed from aircraft after boarding because of their ethnicity, more than 800 cases of employment discrimination, and "numerous instances of denial of service, discriminatory service, and housing discrimination" (Ibish, 2003, p. 7).

Anti-Arab passions may have cooled somewhat since the multiple traumas of 9-11, but the Arab American community faces a number of issues and problems, including profiling at airport security checks and greater restrictions on entering the country. Also, the USA Patriot Act, passed in 2001 to enhance the tools available to law enforcement to combat terrorism, allows for long-term detention of suspects, a wider scope for searches and surveillance, and other policies that many (not just Arab Americans) are concerned will encourage violations of due process and suspension of basic civil liberties.

Thus although the Arab American community is small in size, it has assumed a prominent place in the attention of the nation. The huge majority of the members of the community denounce and reject terrorism and violence, but, like Colombians and Italians, they are victimized by a strong stereotype that is, at least occasionally, applied uncritically and without qualification. Relations between Arab Americans and the larger society are certainly among the tensest and most problematic of any minority group, and, given the continuing occupations of Iraq and Afghanistan and the threat of further, even more damaging terrorist attacks by Al-Qaeda or other groups, they will not abate any time soon.

## IMMIGRANTS FROM AFRICA

Our final group of New Americans consists of immigrants from Africa. As displayed in Exhibit 11.13, immigration from Africa has been quite low over the past 50 years. However, there was the usual increase after the 1960s, and Africans have comprised about 5% of all immigrants in the past few years.

Exhibit 11.14 shows the total number of sub-Saharan Africans in the U.S. in 1990 and 2000, along with four of the largest subgroups. The number of Africans more than doubled over the decade, and this rapid growth suggests that these groups may have a greater impact on U.S. society in the future.

Exhibit 11.15 provides an overall view of all African immigrants, along with the four largest subgroups. The category "African" is extremely broad and encompasses destitute black refugees from African civil wars and relatively affluent white South Africans. In the remainder of this section, we will focus on the four subgroups rather than this very broad category.

EXHIBIT 11.13  Immigration to the United States From Africa, 1941-2003

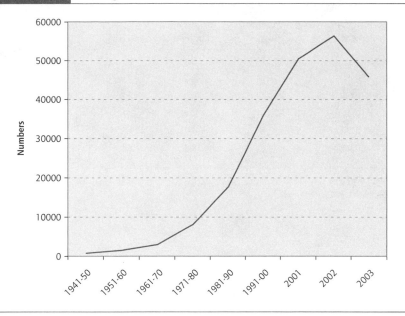

SOURCE: U.S.Department of Homeland Security (2003), p.13.

**EXHIBIT 11.14**  African Immigrant Groups

| | |
|---|---:|
| Sub-Saharan Africans, 1990 | 506,188 |
| Sub-Saharan Africans, 2000 | 1,183,316 |
|    Nigerians | 164,691 |
|    Ethiopians | 86,918 |
|    Cape Verdeans | 77,103 |
|    Ghanians | 49,944 |

SOURCE: U.S. Bureau of the Census (n.d.). Summary File 4.

Clearly, although they may be growing, these four groups are tiny minorities, with no one nationality group reaching as much as .1 of 1% of the total population. Three of the four groups (the exception being Cape Verdeans) have a high representation of first generation members, and all report relatively high levels of English fluency. Also, three of the four (again excepting Cape Verdeans) compare favorably with national norms in terms of education and poverty levels. These characteristics mark these groups as relatively elite and affluent immigrants, more like Arabs and Indians, not refugees or laborers like Haitians and Vietnamese.

The relatively high status of these groups of immigrants from Africa is reinforced in Exhibit 11.16. The men of two of the groups (Ghanians and Nigerians) tend to be overrepresented at the highest occupational levels; Ethiopian men are proportionally represented in all four occupational classes. Only Cape Verdeans occupy relatively low positions in the work force. They are underrepresented in the professions and management and overrepresented among service workers and manual laborers.

EXHIBIT 11.15 Characteristics of Africans and Four Subgroups

| Nation of Origin | Number | % of Total Population | % Foreign Born | % "Poor" English[a] | % HS[b] | % BA[c] | % Poor[d] |
|---|---|---|---|---|---|---|---|
| United States | 281,421,906 | NA | 11.1 | 8.1 | 80.4 | 24.4 | 9.2 |
| Africans[e] | 1,183,316 | 0.42 | 15.7 | 5.7 | 75.8 | 18.7 | 21.2 |
| Nigerian | 164,691 | 0.08 | 63.2 | 10.0 | 93.3 | 59.4 | 10.5 |
| Ethiopian | 86,918 | 0.04 | 77.0 | 34.8 | 81.8 | 27.7 | 14.7 |
| Cape Verdean | 77,103 | 0.04 | 32.4 | 23.2 | 65.2 | 13.9 | 16.2 |
| Ghanian | 49,944 | 0.02 | 79.1 | 18.2 | 88.1 | 32.8 | 7.7 |

SOURCE: U.S. Bureau of the Census (n.d.), Summary File 4.

a. Percentage of group with "ability to speak English less than 'very well.'"

b. Percentage of high school graduates.

c. Percentage of college graduates.

d. Percentage of families below the poverty line.

e. Africans may be of any race.

The women of these groups are considerably more varied in their occupational profiles than the men. Among other patterns, we can see that Nigerian women, like the men, are overrepresented in the professions and management and quite underrepresented among manual laborers and that Cape Verdean women have an occupational profile very similar to the men of their group.

How can we explain these patterns? First of all, Nigeria and Ghana are former British colonies, so the high level of English fluency in these groups is not surprising. All four nations suffer from economic underdevelopment, and most African immigrants are motivated by a search for work and sustenance, with immigrants from Nigeria, Ghana, and Ethiopia competing for positions in the higher reaches of the job structure.

Cape Verde is the exception to the pattern of English-speaking African immigrants with relatively high levels of human capital. Cape Verde is a tiny island nation off the west coast of Africa. It was colonized by the Portuguese in the 15th century and has been an important port for commercial shipping since that time. This maritime link to the larger world is part of what connected Cape Verde to the United States. Although the nation is politically stable, droughts and other economic difficulties have motivated many to seek their fortunes elsewhere, and there are now more Cape Verdeans living abroad than on the islands (NationMaster.com, 2005f). These immigrants bring relatively low levels of human capital and are more likely to find employment in service industries or in manual labor.

## SUMMARY: MODES OF INCORPORATION

As the case studies included in this chapter (as well as those in Chapters 9 and 10) demonstrate, recent immigrant groups can occupy very different positions in U.S. society. One way to address this diversity of relationships is to look at the contact situation, especially the characteristics the groups bring with them (their race and religion, the human capital with which they arrive) and the reaction of the larger society. There seem to be three main modes of incorporation for immigrants in the United States: entrance through the primary or secondary labor markets (see Chapter 6) or the ethnic enclave. We will consider each pathway separately and relate them to the groups discussed in this chapter.

EXHIBIT 11.16a Occupational Profiles, Men

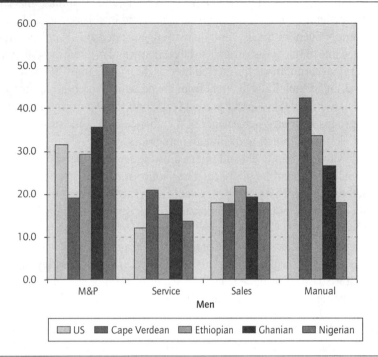

EXHIBIT 11.16b Occupational Profiles, Women

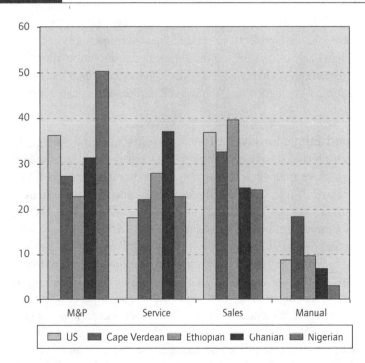

**Immigrants and the Primary Labor Market.** The primary labor market consists of more desirable jobs with greater security, higher pay, and benefits, and the immigrants entering this sector tend to be highly educated, skilled professionals and businesspeople. Members of this group are generally fluent in English, and many were educated at U.S. universities. They are highly integrated into the global urban-industrial economy, and in many cases, they are employees of multinational corporations transferred here by their companies. These immigrants are affluent, urbane, and dramatically different from the peasant laborers so common in the past (e.g., from Ireland and Italy) and in the present (e.g., from the Dominican Republic and from Mexico). The groups with high percentages of members entering the primary labor market include Arab, Colombian, Indian, and Filipino immigrants.

Because they tend to be affluent and enter a growing sector of the labor force, immigrants with professional backgrounds tend to attract less notice and fewer racist reactions than their more unskilled counterparts. Although they come closer to Blauner's pure immigrant group than most other minority groups we have considered, racism can still complicate their assimilation. Anecdotal evidence of discrimination for these high-status immigrants is common. In a *New York Times* article about anti-Asian prejudice, for example, Tun-Hsu McCoy, who immigrated more than 30 years ago and holds a Ph.D. in physics, is quoted as saying: "Every Asian can tell you that we have all encountered subconscious discrimination. People don't equate an Asian face with being an American" (Polner, 1993, p. 1).

**Immigrants and the Secondary Labor Market.** This mode of incorporation is more typical for immigrants with lower levels of education and fewer job skills. Jobs in this sector are less desirable and command lower pay, little security, and few benefits and are often seasonal or in the underground or informal economy. This labor market includes jobs in construction or the garment industry, in which workers are paid "off the books" and in which working conditions are unregulated by government authorities or labor unions; domestic work; and some forms of criminal or deviant activity, such as drugs and prostitution. The employers who control these jobs often prefer to hire undocumented immigrants because they are easier to control and less likely to complain to the authorities about abuse and mistreatment. The groups with high percentages of members in the secondary labor market include Dominicans, Haitians, Salvadorans, Vietnamese, and the less skilled and less educated kinfolk of the higher status immigrants.

**Immigrants and Ethnic Enclaves.** As we have seen, some immigrant groups—especially those that can bring financial capital and business experience—have established ethnic enclaves. Some members of these groups enter U.S. society as entrepreneurs, owners of small retail shops, and other businesses; their less skilled and educated coethnics serve as a source of cheap labor to staff the ethnic enterprises. The enclave provides contacts, financial and other services, and social support for the new immigrants of all social classes. Of the groups covered in this chapter, Arabs, Koreans, and Asian Indians have been particularly likely to follow this path.

This classification suggests some of the variety of relationships between the new Americans and the larger society. The stream of immigrants entering the United States is extremely diverse and includes people ranging from the most sophisticated and urbane to the most desperate and despairing. The variety is suggested by considering a list of occupations in which recent immigrants are overrepresented. For men, the list includes biologists and other natural scientists, taxi drivers, farm laborers, and waiters. For women, the list includes chemists, statisticians, produce packers, laundry workers, and domestics (Kritz & Girak, 2004).

# IMMIGRATION: ISSUES AND CONTROVERSIES
## How Welcoming Are Americans?

One factor that affects the fate of immigrant groups is the attitude of the larger society and, particularly, the groups in the larger society that have the most influence with governmental policy makers. Overall, we can say that native-born Americans (even those with immigrant parents) have never been particularly open to newcomers. The history of this nation is replete with movements to drastically reduce immigration or even eliminate it completely. We have already mentioned some of the anti-immigration movements directed against Mexicans (Chapter 9) and against the Chinese and Japanese (Chapter 10), and, in Chapter 12, we will cover the (ultimately successful) efforts to stop European immigration in the 19th and early 20th centuries. Here we will look at attitudes and reactions to contemporary immigrants.

First, although Americans have a lot of reservations about immigration, it seems that attitudes are somewhat more open now than in the past. Exhibit 11.17 shows some results of surveys administered to nationally representative samples for four different years between 1996 and 2004 (National Public Radio, 2004). The high point of resistance in this period was in 2001, when nearly 60% of the respondents agreed that immigration should be decreased. The most recent results show that support for decreasing immigration has dropped to about 40%, a particularly interesting decline given the reactions to the terrorist attacks of 9-11 summarized earlier.

What concerns do Americans have about immigration? One common set of concerns revolves around economics. About half of the respondents to the 2004 NPR survey were concerned that immigrants might take jobs from native-born workers, and almost two thirds (62%) were concerned that immigrants do not pay their fair share of taxes. These concerns were particularly strong among respondents who believed that the U.S. economy was performing only at a fair or poor level. Thus there seems to be a correlation between pessimism about the economy and perception of immigrants as threats, a relationship that recalls earlier material on competition and prejudice (e.g., the Noel hypothesis and the Robber's Cave experiment). Also, the survey found that attitudes were more positive for respondents who had had personal contacts with immigrants, a finding that recalls the contact hypothesis from Chapter 4. We will address the grounds for these concerns later.

## Views of the Immigrants

One interesting aspect of the survey mentioned earlier(National Public Radio, 2004) is that a sample of immigrants was also questioned, and the researchers found that their attitudes and views differed sharply from those of native-born respondents on a number of dimensions. For example, the immigrants were more likely to see immigration as a positive force for the larger society and more likely to say that immigrants work hard and pay their fair share of taxes.

More relevant for the ultimate impact of the contemporary wave of immigration, the survey found that only about 30% were sojourners (i.e., ultimately planning to return to their homeland), a finding that suggests that issues of assimilation and immigration will remain at the forefront of U.S. concerns for many decades.

The survey also showed that immigrants are very grateful for the economic opportunities available in the United States, with 84% agreeing that there are more opportunities to get ahead here than in their country of origin. On the other hand, the immigrants were ambivalent about U. S. culture and values. For example, nearly half (47%) said that the family was stronger in

EXHIBIT 11.17 Percentage Stating That Immigration Should Be Decreased

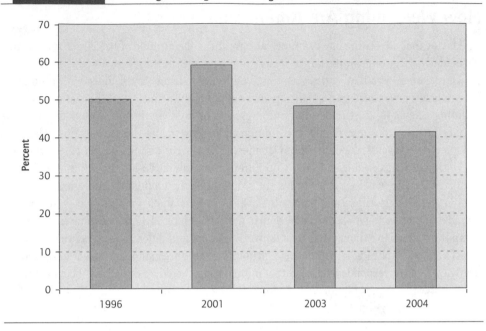

SOURCE: National Public Radio (2004).

their homeland than in the United States and only 28% saw U.S. society as having stronger moral values than their homeland.

## Costs and Benefits

Surveys show that Americans are especially concerned about the economic impact of immigration. Is this concern justified? Do immigrants take jobs, swell the welfare rolls, and claim more in benefits than they contribute in taxes?

These issues are complex, but many studies, especially those done at the national level, find that immigrants are not a burden. For example, a study conducted by the National Research Council (1997) found that immigrants are a positive addition to the economy. They add to the labor supply in areas as disparate as the garment industry, agriculture, domestic work, and college faculty (National Academy of Sciences, 1997).

Other researchers have found that low-skilled immigrants tend to find jobs in areas of the economy in which few U.S. citizens work or in the enclave economies of their own groups, taking jobs that would not have existed without the economic activity of their coethnics (Heer, 1996, pp. 190-194; Smith & Edmonston, 1997). One important recent study of the economic impact of recent immigrants concluded that there is a relatively small effect on the wages and employment of native workers, although there does seem to be a negative consequence for earlier immigrants and for African Americans (Bean & Stevens, 2003, p. 221-223).

Another concern is the strain that immigrants place on taxes and services such as schools and welfare programs. Again, these issues are complex, and they are far from settled, but some research projects suggest that immigrants cost less than they contribute. Taxes are automatically deducted from their paychecks (unless, of course, they are being paid "under the table"), and their use of such services as unemployment compensation, Medicare, food stamps, Aid to Families with Dependent Children, and Social Security is actually lower than their proportional contributions. This is particularly true for undocumented immigrants, whose use of services is sharply limited by their vulnerable legal status (Marcelli & Heer, 1998; Simon, 1989). Bean and Stevens (2003, pp. 66-93), in their recent study, find that immigrants are not overrepresented on the welfare rolls. Rather, the key determinant of welfare use is refugee status. Groups such as Haitians, Salvadorans, and Vietnamese—who arrive without resources and, by definition, are in need of assistance on all levels—are the most likely to be on the welfare rolls.

Final conclusions about the impact and costs of immigration must await further research. For now, we can say that the fears and concerns, although not unfounded, may be confounded with and exaggerated by prejudice and racism directed at newcomers and strangers. The current opposition to immigration may be a reaction to *who* as much as to *how many* or *how expensive*. The Current Debates section at the end of this chapter presents some of the common arguments for and against continued immigration.

Finally, we can repeat the finding of many studies (e.g., Bean & Stevens, 2003) that immigration is generally a positive force in the economy and that, as has been true for decades, immigrants, legal and illegal, continue to find work with Anglo employers and niches in American society in which they can survive. The networks that have delivered cheap immigrant labor for the low-wage secondary job market continue to operate and, frequently, the primary beneficiaries of this long-established system are not the immigrants (although they are grateful for the opportunities) but employers, who benefit from a cheaper, more easily exploited workforce, and American consumers, who benefit from lower prices in the marketplace.

## Is Contemporary Assimilation Segmented?

In Chapter 2, we reviewed some of the patterns of acculturation and integration that typified the adjustment of Europeans who immigrated to the United States before the 1930s. Although the process of adjustment was anything but smooth or simple, these groups eventually Americanized and achieved levels of education and affluence comparable to national norms (as we shall see in Chapter 12). Will contemporary immigrants from Latin America and the Caribbean experience similar success? Will their sons and daughters and grandsons and granddaughters rise in the occupational structure to a position of parity with the dominant group? Will the cultures and languages of these groups gradually fade and disappear?

Final answers to these questions must await future developments. In the meantime, there is considerable debate on these issues. Some analysts argue that assimilation will be segmented and that the success story of the white ethnic groups will not be repeated. Others find that the traditional perspective on assimilation—particularly the model of assimilation developed by Milton Gordon—continues to be a useful and accurate framework for understanding the experience of contemporary immigrants. We will review some of the most important and influential arguments from each side of this debate and, finally, attempt to come to some conclusions about the future of assimilation.

**The Case For Segmented Assimilation.** Sociologist Douglas Massey (1995) presents a particularly compelling argument in favor of the segmented assimilation perspective. He argues that there are three crucial differences between the European assimilation experience of the past and the contemporary period that call the traditional perspective into question. First, the flow of immigrants from Europe to the United States slowed to a mere trickle after the 1920s because of restrictive legislation, the worldwide depression of the 1930s, and World War II. Immigration in the 1930s, for example, was less than 10% of the flow of the early 1920s. Thus as the children and grandchildren of the immigrants from Europe Americanized and grew to adulthood in the 1930s and 1940s, few new immigrants fresh from the old country replaced them in the ethnic neighborhoods. European cultural traditions and languages weakened rapidly with the passing of the first generation and the Americanization of their descendents.

For contemporary immigration, in contrast, the networks and the demand for cheap labor are so strong that it is unlikely that there will be a similar hiatus in the flow of people. Immigration has become continuous, argues Massey, and as some contemporary immigrants (or their descendants) Americanize and rise to affluence and success, new arrivals will replace them and continuously revitalize the ethnic cultures and languages.

Second, the speed and ease of modern transportation and communication will help to maintain cultural and linguistic diversity. A century ago, immigrants from Europe could maintain contact with the old country only by mail, and most had no realistic expectation of ever returning. Most modern immigrants, in contrast, can return to their homes in a day or less and can use telephones, television, e-mail, and the Internet to stay in intimate contact with the families and friends they left behind. According to one recent survey (National Public Radio, 2004), a little more than 40% of immigrants return to their homeland at least every year or two, and some (6%) return every few months. Thus the cultures of modern immigrants can be kept vital and whole in ways that were not available (and not even imagined) 100 years ago.

Third, and perhaps most important, contemporary immigrants face an economy and a labor market that are vastly different from those faced by European immigrants of the 19th and early 20th century. The latter group generally rose in the class system as the economy shifted from manufacturing to service (see Exhibit 6.3). Today, rates of upward mobility have decreased, and just when the importance of education has increased, schools available to the children of immigrants have fallen into neglect (Massey, 1995, pp. 645-646).

For the immigrants from Europe a century ago, assimilation meant a gradual rise to middle-class respectability and suburban comfort, even if it took four or five generations to accomplish. Assimilation today, according to Massey, is segmented, and a large percentage of the descendants of contemporary immigrants—especially many of the Hispanic groups and Haitians—face permanent membership in a growing underclass population and continuing marginalization and powerlessness.

**The Case Against Segmented Assimilation.** Several recent studies have resurrected the somewhat tattered body of traditional assimilation theories. These studies argue that contemporary assimilation will ultimately follow the same course as European immigrant groups 100 years ago and as described in Gordon's theory (see Chapter 2). For example, two recent studies (Bean & Stevens, 2003, and Alba & Nee, 2003) find that most contemporary immigrant groups are acculturating and integrating at the "normal" three-generation pace. Those groups (notably Mexicans) that appear to be lagging behind this pace may take as many as four to five generations, but their descendants will eventually find their way onto the primary job market and the cultural mainstream.

Studies of language acculturation show that English language proficiency grows with time of residence and generation (Bean & Stevens, 2003, p. 168). We discussed these patterns in

Chapter 2 (see Exhibits 2.4 and 2.5). In terms of structural integration, contemporary immigrant groups are narrowing the income gap over time, although many groups (e.g., Dominicans, Mexicans, Haitians, and Vietnamese) are handicapped by very low levels of human capital at the start (Bean & Stevens, 2003, p. 142). Exhibits 11.18a and 11.18b illustrate this process with respect to wage differentials between Mexican and white males and females of various generations and levels of education. Looking first at "All workers," you can see that Mexican males who are recent immigrants earn a little less than half of what white males earn. The differential is lower for earlier immigrants, lower still for Mexicans males of the second and third generation, and lowest for the more educated members of those generations. For females, the wage differential also shrinks as the generations pass and level of education increases. However, note that for third generation, college-educated females, the wage differential shrinks virtually to zero, indicating complete integration on this variable.

Note how these patterns support the traditional perspective on assimilation. The wage gap shrinks by generation and level of education, and integration is substantial by the third generation (although complete only for one group). This pattern suggests that the movement of Mexican immigrants is toward the economic mainstream, even though they do not close the gap completely. Bean and Stevens conclude that this pattern is substantially consistent with the "three-generation model": The assimilation trajectory of Mexican Americans and other recent immigrant groups is not into the urban poor, the underclass, or the disenfranchised, disconnected, and marginalized. Assimilation is not segmented but is substantially repeating the experiences of the European groups on which Gordon based his theory.

How can we reconcile these opposed points of view? In large part, this debate concerns the nature of the evidence and judgments about how much weight to give to various facts and trends. On one hand, Massey's points about the importance of the postindustrial economy, declining opportunities for less educated workers, and the neglect that seems typical of inner-city schools are very well taken. On the other hand, it seems that even the least educated immigrant groups have been able to find economic niches in which they and their families can survive and eke out an existence long enough for their children and grandchildren to rise in the structure, a pattern that has been at the core of the American immigrant experience for almost two centuries.

Of course, this debate will continue and new evidence and interpretations will appear. Ultimately, however, until immigration stops (which, as Massey points out, is extremely unlikely) and the fate of the descendents of the last immigrant groups is measured, the debate cannot be resolved.

## Illegal Immigration

Americans are particularly concerned with undocumented immigrants, and many are frustrated with what they see as ineffective government efforts to curtail this flow of illegal aliens. For example, in a 2004 survey (National Public Radio, 2004), 72% of the respondents said they were "very or somewhat concerned" about the problem, and 66% agreed that the government was "not tough enough" on undocumented immigrants.

There is no question that the volume of illegal immigration is huge. In 2000, it was estimated that there were 8.5 million people living in United States illegally, more than double the number in 1992 (Martin & Widgren, 2002, p. 13). Some undocumented immigrants enter the country on tourist, temporary worker, or student visas and simply remain

**EXHIBIT 11.18a** Wage Differential of Mexican Workers Relative to Whites: Men

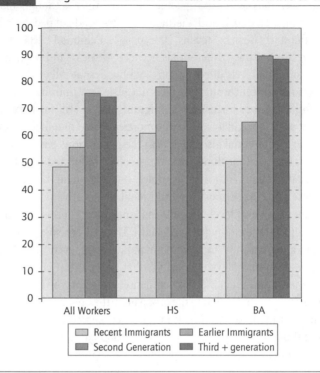

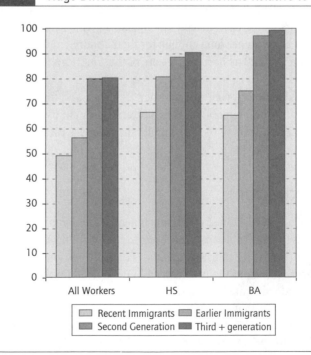

SOURCE: Bean and Stevens (2003), p. 139.

in the nation when their visa expires. In 2000 alone, more than 33 million tourists and more than a million more temporary workers and foreign students entered the United States, and these numbers suggest how difficult it would be to keep tabs on this source of illegal immigrants. Others cross the border illegally in the hopes of escaping the border police and finding their way into some niche in the American economy. The very fact that people keep coming suggests that most succeed.

A variety of efforts continues to be made to curtail and control the flow of illegal immigrants. Various states have attempted to lower the appeal of the United States by limiting benefits and opportunities. The best known of these attempts occurred in 1994 when California voters passed Proposition 187, which would have denied educational, health, and other services to illegal immigrants. The policy was declared unconstitutional, however, and never implemented. Federal efforts to decrease the flow of illegal immigration have included new legislation limiting welfare benefits for immigrants, increases in the size of the Border Patrol, and the construction of taller and wider walls along the border with Mexico. Following his reelection in 2004, President Bush proposed a "guest worker" program to try to control some of the flow of illegal immigrants. This program would allow immigrants (including those illegally in the country now) to apply for temporary work permits.

Although Americans will continue to be concerned about this problem, it seems unlikely that much can be done (within the framework of a democratic, humane society) to curtail the flow of people. The social networks that deliver immigrants—legal as well as illegal—are too well established, and the demand for cheap labor in the United States is simply insatiable. In fact, denying services, as envisioned in Proposition 187, may make illegal immigrants *more* attractive as a source of labor by reducing their ability to resist exploitation. For example, if the children of illegal immigrants were not permitted to attend school, they would become more likely to join the army of cheap labor on which some employers depend. Who would benefit from closing public schools to the children of illegal immigrants?

## RECENT IMMIGRATION IN HISTORICAL CONTEXT

The current wave of immigration to the United States is part of a centuries-old process that spans the globe. Underlying this immense and complex population movement is the powerful force of the continuing industrial revolution. The United States and other industrialized nations are the centers of growth in the global economy, and immigrants flow to the areas of greater opportunity. In the 19th century, population moved largely from Europe to the Western Hemisphere. Over the past 50 years, the movement has been from south to north. This pattern reflects the simple geography of industrialization and opportunity and the fact that the more developed nations are in the northern hemisphere.

The United States has been the world's dominant economic, political, and cultural power for much of the century and the preferred destination of most immigrants. Newcomers from around the globe continue the collective, social nature of past population movements (see Chapter 2). The direction of their travels reflects contemporary global inequalities: Labor continues to flow from the less developed nations to the more developed nations. The direction of this flow is not accidental or coincidental. It is determined by the differential rates of industrialization and modernization across the globe. Immigration contributes to the wealth and affluence of the more developed societies and particularly to the dominant groups and elite classes of those societies.

## Is Immigration Harmful or Helpful to the United States?

*The continuing debate over U.S. immigration has generated plenty of arguments but little consensus. Following are three positions in the debate. The first, a passionate argument against immigration, was presented by Peter Brimelow, a journalist and an immigrant himself, in his best seller* Alien Nation *(1995). The rejoinder is excerpted from sociologist Reynolds Farley's recent book* The New American Reality *(1996), an analysis of many issues and social problems besides immigration. Farley's analysis is generally proimmigration and is stated in more objective and scholarly terms—which does not, of course, mean that it is any more correct than Brimelow's argument. Third, George Borjas (1999) looks at the way in which immigration issues are typically raised in the United States and argues for a new approach.*

## Immigration Is Harmful

**PETER BRIMELOW**

Today, immigration . . . is not determined by economics; it is determined—or at least profoundly distorted—by public policy. . . . [The] effect of the 1965 reform [in immigration policy] has been to uncouple legal immigration from the needs of the U.S. economy. A low point was reached in 1986, when less than 8 percent of over 600,000 legal immigrants were admitted on the basis of skills. [Most of the remainder were admitted under family reunification provisions.] Of course, some of the family-reunification immigrants will have skills. But it is purely an accident whether their skills are wanted in the U.S. economy. The family-reunification policy inevitably contributes to two striking characteristics of the post-1965 flow:

Firstly: The post-1965 immigrants are, on average, less skilled than earlier immigrants. And getting even less so. As George Borjas [a leading immigration researcher] put it: "The skill level of successive immigrant waves admitted to the U.S. has declined precipitously in the last two or three decades."

Secondly: The post-1965 immigrants unmistakably display more mismatching between what they can do and what America needs. They seem not to be fitting as well into the economy as did earlier immigrants. Instead, they are showing a greater tendency to become what used to be called a "public charge."

[In] 1970 the average recent immigrant had 0.35 less years of schooling than native-born Americans. By 1990, the average recent immigrant had 1.32 years less schooling. . . . [Economists] view education as a proxy for skills. And the relative decline in immigrant education seems to be confirmed by the relative decline in their earnings that has occurred in the same period.

In 1970, immigrants on average actually earned some 3 percent more than native-born Americans. . . . But in 1990, the immigrant achievement had disappeared: Immigrants on average earned 16.2 percent less than native-born Americans.

The second striking characteristic of the post-1965 immigrant flow: increased mismatching with the U.S. labor market. This shows up in the immigrants' increasing tendency to go on welfare.

In the early 1980s, immigration researchers were generally pretty complacent about immigration's impact on the United States. It became an article of faith . . . that immigrants earned more, and went on welfare less, than native-born Americans.

The reason for this complacency, of course: The researchers were looking at old data. It still substantially reflected pre-1965 immigrants.

By the early 1990s, the scene had changed completely. It was becoming clear that, among the post-1965 immigrants, welfare participation rates were sharply higher. Immigrant welfare participation was, on average, higher than native-born Americans (9.1 vs. 7.4 percent). And what's more, immigrant households on welfare tended to consume more, and increasingly more, than native-born households on welfare. (In 1970, 6.7 percent of all welfare cash benefits went to immigrants; in 1990, 13.1 percent.)

(And note that "welfare" means just cash programs like Aid to Families with Dependent Children, Supplementary Security Income, and general assistance—not non-cash programs like Food Stamps and Medicaid, for which there are no good numbers.) . . .

Examining the group of immigrants arriving in the five years before 1970 reveals even more depressing news: Welfare participation actually increased the longer they stayed in the United States. Originally, their rate was 5.5 percent; the 1990 census reported it at 9.8 percent. All waves of immigrants show a similar drift. The conclusion is unavoidable: Immigrants are assimilating into the welfare system.

SOURCE: Brimelow, Peter. 1995. *Alien Nation* (pp. 141-149). New York: Random House.

## Immigration Is Not Harmful

**REYNOLDS FARLEY**

During the 1980s, the native-born labor force with a high school education or less fell from 55 million to 48 million, reflecting the shift toward greater educational attainment and the retirement of older workers who had less schooling. But 3 million immigrants who arrived in the 1980s had high school educations or less. Isn't it obvious that this high volume of immigration depresses employment opportunities and lowers wages for native-born Americans who lack college training? Wouldn't wages rise if we immediately terminated the flow of immigrants? Can't we blame the high level of immigration for the declining wages [of American workers]?

Because of the importance of immigration, this issue receives a great deal of attention. While there are still disagreements about the details, there is consensus that the effects of immigration on the employment prospects and wages of natives are modest. Summarizing several dozen studies based on the 1970 and 1980 census, Fix and Pascal (1994, p. 49) conclude that if immigrants as a share of the labor force in a metropolis went up from 10 percent . . . to 20 percent, the labor force participation rate of natives would drop only 1 percent, net of all other factors. . . .

This seems counterintuitive. How can the presence of many immigrants not depress employment opportunities and lower wages for natives? The economists who model these processes report that four factors explain this puzzle. First, immigration is concentrated in metropolises that are growing rapidly, most of them in the South and Southwest. Booming populations and economic growth in these places create thousands of jobs each year, and a fraction are filled by immigrants. Migrants, to a large degree, are fitting into occupational slots created by economic and demographic growth. Second, the presence of immigrants . . . may permit industries [that would otherwise move out of country] to thrive. . . . In recent years, the garment industry has prospered in New York, Los Angeles, and Miami largely because immigrants from China and the Caribbean are willing to work long hours for small paychecks, producing the costly dresses and suits that highly educated women need as they pursue careers. . . . And it is clear that quite a few new arrivals set up their own businesses, thereby hiring workers. . . .

Third, many immigrants fill jobs that native-born Americans are reluctant to accept—for example, the stoop labor traditionally needed in agriculture [or the jobs as nannies created] as women increasingly devote themselves to full-time jobs. . . .

There may be a fourth reason: employers may prefer illegals to citizens. Recent immigrants may, perhaps, be easily exploited and are unlikely to file suits about violations of minimum wage laws [or health] violations.

[Opposition to immigration will continue despite the evidence that immigration does little harm to the employment and wage prospects of natives.] Opposition . . . will come from those states and cities whose budgets are greatly impacted by the high volume of recent immigration. Several studies have investigated the financial consequences of undocumented immigration, especially in the seven states most affected. There were approximately three million illegals in those states in 1992 who paid an estimated $1.9 billion annually in state sales taxes, state and local property taxes, and state income taxes (Clark, Passel, Zimmerman, & Fix, 1994). The investigators considered the three most expensive state programs used by illegal aliens: the costs of emergency medical care, public schools, and prisons. These charges came to about $4 billion, implying that illegals imposed a burden of $2 billion upon taxpayers in these seven states. Although $2 billion is a very large sum and gives a clear indication of the substantial cost illegals place on local governments, the total expenditure of the governments in these seven states in 1992 was approximately $245 billion, so the termination of all undocumented immigrants would produce only a very modest reduction in state spending.

SOURCE: Farley, Reynolds. 1996. *The New American Reality* (pp. 199-207). New York: Russell Sage Foundation.

## We Need to Reframe the Immigration Debate

**GEORGE BORJAS**

As the 21st century begins, the United States is about to embark once again upon a historic debate about the type of immigration policy that the country should pursue. As in the past, the cost-benefit calculus frames the terms of the debate: Who loses from immigration, and by how much?

Who wins from immigration, and by how much? . . .

[These costs and benefits] are also symptoms of pursuing particular immigration policies. By arguing over . . . these symptoms—whether immigrants use a lot of welfare, whether consumer prices are lowered by immigration—the immigration debate is, in a sense, worrying about the height of trees in the forest, rather than the shape of the forest.

Typically, those who argue over . . . a particular social policy take sides by grasping onto a specific fact, and from that fact they immediately infer some policy reform that the country should pursue. In my view, this [approach] is just plain wrong.

To see why, single out a particular symptom of immigration over which there is little disagreement: Immigrant use of welfare is high. The policy implications of this fact depend crucially on what the U.S. is trying to accomplish. If the goal of immigration policy is to ensure that immigration did not place a fiscal burden on the native population, this symptom [implies] that the U.S. should take steps to restrict the entry of potential welfare recipients. If, in contrast, the goal of immigration policy is to help the poorest people in the world, this symptom has no relevance— it is the price that the country must pay to achieve a particular humanitarian objective.

In the end, a debate over the policy implications of . . . immigration cannot be based on the evidence alone. Any policy discussion requires explicitly stated assumptions about what constitutes the national interest. It is the combination of the evidence with an assumption about what Americans desire that permits an informed debate. . . . [First, the American people must] answer the bigger question: What should immigration policy accomplish?

Of course, answering this question is very difficult, even when the debate is restricted purely to . . . economic issues. To see why, divide the world into three distinct constituencies: the current population of the U.S., the immigrants themselves, and those who remain in the source countries. To draw policy implications . . . one has to know whose economic welfare the U.S. should try to improve. . . .

By framing the issue in this fashion, the tradeoffs . . . are made crystal clear. The native population probably benefits . . . when high-quality scientific workers [are admitted] but the people left behind in the source country probably lose a lot. Similarly, immigrants benefit when . . . policy favors the entry of their relatives, but natives may lose because the policy . . . might let in many persons who qualify for social services.

It is probably impossible to come up with an immigration policy where all relevant parties benefit. As a result, the U.S. will have to make difficult choices.

SOURCE: Borjas, George. 1999. *Heaven's Door: Immigration Policy and the American Economy*. Princeton, NJ: Princeton University Press. Pp. 4, 15-16.

## Debate Questions to Consider

1. Consider the nature of the arguments presented by Brimelow and Farley. To what extent do they appeal to emotion? To what extent do they base their arguments in evidence and logic? What specific disagreements over "facts" can you identify? What information would you need to resolve these disagreements?

2. What does Borjas add to the debate? Does his approach offer a way to resolve the disagreements between the other two authors? In Borjas's terms, what constituencies do Brimelow and Farley have in mind (native population, immigrants, or those left behind)? How might their arguments change if they considered a different constituency?

# MAIN POINTS

- Since the mid-1960s, immigrants have been coming to the United States at nearly record rates. Some of these immigrant groups have coethnics who have been in the United States for years (e.g., Mexicans or Chinese), but others are "New Americans," and we focus on these groups in this chapter. How will this new wave of immigration transform America? Will they assimilate? How?

- Immigrants from Central and South America and the Caribbean are diverse. Some are driven by economic needs; others are political refugees. They are an important source of cheap labor, and many are undocumented.

- Immigrants from Asia and the Pacific Islands are diverse and include many highly educated people along with the less skilled, "war brides," and refugees. Several of these groups have formed economic enclaves.

- Arab Americans, like other New Americans, have been growing rapidly in number, and their local communities tend to be centered in economic enclaves. The events of 9-11 make this group a special target for hate crimes and for security concerns.

- Immigrants from Africa remain a relatively small group, and many bring high levels of education and occupational skills, although others are concentrated in the lower levels of the occupational structure.

- Contemporary immigrants are generally experiencing three different modes of incorporation into U.S. society: the primary labor market, the secondary labor market, and the enclave. The pathway of each group is strongly influenced by the amount of human capital they bring, their race, the attitude of the larger society, and many other factors.

- Relations between immigrants and the larger society are animated by a number of issues, including the relative costs and benefits of immigration, concerns about undocumented immigrants, and the speed of assimilation. One important issue currently being debated by social scientists is whether assimilation for New Americans will be segmented or will ultimately follow the pathway established by immigrant groups from Europe in the 19th and 20th centuries.

- The public sociology assignments presented in the Introduction to Part I are very likely to bring you face to face with new Americans and the increasing diversity of the United States. It is also likely that you will encounter a variety of issues and problems that have been discussed in this and previous chapters including illegal immigration, costs and benefits of immigration, and bilingual education.

## Study Site on the Web

Don't forget the interactive quizzes and other resources and learning aids at www.www.pineforge.com/healeystudy4.

## For Further Reading

Portes, Alejandro, and Rumbaut, Ruebén. 2001. *Legacies: The Story of the Immigrant Second Generation.* New York: Russell Sage Foundation.

Portes, Alejandro, and Rumbaut, Ruebén. 2001. *Ethnicities: Children of Immigrants in America.* New York: Russell Sage Foundation. *(Two landmark studies of new American groups whose findings are generally consistent with the segmented assimilation hypothesis.)*

Bean, Frank, and Stevens, Gillian. 2003. *America's Newcomers and the Dynamics of Diversity.* New York: Russell Sage Foundation.

Alba, Richard, and Nee, Victor. 2003. *Remaking the American Mainstream: Assimilation and Contemporary Immigration.* Cambridge, MA: Harvard University Press. *(Two landmark studies of contemporary immigrants that find that assimilation is generally following a course consistent with the "traditional" model of assimilation.)*

## Questions for Review and Study

1. What differences exist between these New Americans in terms of their motivations for coming to the United States? What are the implications of these various "push" factors for their reception and adjustment to the United States?

2. Compare Asian and Pacific Islander immigrant groups with those from the Caribbean and Central and South America. Which group is more diverse? What differences exist in their patterns of adjustment and assimilation? Why do these patterns exist?

3. Compare and contrast the experiences of Arab Americans with those of Asian and Pacific Islander groups and Hispanic and Caribbean groups. How do they differ in terms of human capital and settlement patterns? Why do these differences exist? What are the implications of these differences for assimilation?

4. Compare and contrast African immigrants with the other groups. How do they differ? What are the implications of these differences for their adjustment to the larger society?

5. What, in your opinion, are the most important issues facing the United States in terms of immigration and assimilation? How are these issues playing out in your community? What are the implications of these issues for the future of the United States?

6. Will assimilation for contemporary immigrants be segmented? After examining the evidence and arguments presented by both sides, and using information from this and previous chapters, which side of the debate seems more credible? Why? What are the implications of this debate? What will the United States look like in the future if assimilation is segmented? How would the future change if assimilation is not segmented? Which of these scenarios is more desirable for

immigrant groups? For the society as a whole? For various segments of U.S. society (e.g., employers, labor unions, African Americans, consumers, the college educated, the urban underclass, etc.)?

## Internet Research Project

Additional information and a list of relevant Web sites are included in the Appendix (Internet Resources).

### A. Update and Expand This Chapter by an Internet Search

Many of the groups covered in this chapter have Web sites dedicated to them (e.g., Arab Americans are the subject of http://www.allied-media.com/Arab-American/default.htm). Select several of the groups covered in this chapter and conduct a search for relevant Web sites. See what you can learn about the concerns and situation of each group, and compare the information to what has been presented in this text. What information can you collect about their socioeconomic profile? What can you learn about their point of view regarding the United States and their treatment by the larger society? What issues are most important for them (e.g., learning English, job discrimination, hate crimes, availability of welfare services, etc.)?

### B. Update and Expand This Chapter With Census Data

The 2000 Census collected an array of information about most of the groups covered in this chapter, and the information is available online. Go to http://www.census.gov and click on "American Factfinder" on the left-hand panel of the home page. Next, click on "Data Sets" on the left-hand panel and select "Census 2000, Summary File 4" and "Quick Tables." On the next window, click "Add" to move the United States to the bottom window and click "Next." Choose a table from the list in the next window (e.g., QT-H9 Occupancy, Telephone Service, Housing Facilities, and Meals Included in Rent: 2000) and click "Add" and "Next" and choose a racial group or an ancestry group. The selected table will be displayed for the total population and for the subgroup(s) you selected. Extend the analysis in this chapter by comparing groups with each other and with the total population.

# 12

# White Ethnic Groups

## Assimilation and Identity—The Twilight of Ethnicity?

BETWEEN THE 1820S AND THE 1920S, THE FIRST GREAT WAVE OF IMMIGRATION ARRIVED IN THE United States. About 40 million people journeyed from Europe, and they came from every corner of the continent: Ireland, Greece, Germany, Italy, Poland, Portugal, Ukraine, Russia, and scores of other nations and provinces. They came as young men and women seeking jobs, as families fleeing religious persecution, as political radicals fleeing the police, as farmers seeking land and a fresh start, and as paupers barely able to scrape together the cost of the passage.

This first wave of immigrants shaped the United States in countless ways. When the wave started in the 1820s, the United States was not yet 50 years old, an agricultural nation clustered along the East Coast. The nation was just coming into contact with Mexicans in the Southwest, immigration from China had not begun, slavery was flourishing in the South, and American Indians had yet to be "removed" west of the Mississippi. When the immigration ended in the 1920s, the population of the United States had increased from fewer than 10 million to more than 100 million, and the society had industrialized, become a world power, and stretched from coast to coast, with colonies in the Pacific and the Caribbean.

It was no coincidence that European immigration, American industrialization, and the rise to global prominence occurred simultaneously. These changes were intimately interlinked, the mutual causes and effects of each other. Industrialization fueled the growth of U.S. military and political power, and the industrial machinery of the nation depended heavily on the flow of labor from Europe. By World War I, for example, 25% of the nation's total labor force was foreign born, and more than half of the workforce in New York, Detroit, and Chicago consisted of immigrant men. Immigrants were the majority of the workers in many important sectors of the economy, including coal mining, steel manufacturing, the garment industry, and meatpacking (Martin & Midgley, 1999, p. 15; Steinberg, 1981, p. 36).

# ASSIMILATION AND EQUALITY: SHOULD WHITE ETHNIC GROUPS BE CONSIDERED "MINORITY GROUPS"?

Perhaps the most important point about white ethnic groups (the descendants of the European immigrants) is that they are today on the verge of being completely assimilated. Even the groups that were the most despised and rejected in earlier years are acculturated, integrated, and thoroughly intermarried. To illustrate this point, we will consider matters of integration and equality at the start of this chapter.

To begin with secondary structural integration, Exhibits 12.1 through 12.3 display data collected during the 1990 census for 9 of the more than 60 white ethnic groups that people mentioned when asked to define their ancestries. The groups include the 2 largest white ethnic groups (German and Irish Americans) and 7 more chosen to represent a range of geographic regions of origin and times of immigration (U.S. Bureau of the Census, 2003b). The graphs show that, by 1990, all 9 of the groups selected were at or above national norms ("all persons") for all measures of equality. There is some variation among the groups, of course, but all exceeded the national averages for both high school and college education and for median income. Also, all 9 groups had dramatically lower poverty rates than the national average, and for most, the poverty rate was less than half the national average.

In other areas, the evidence for assimilation and equality is also persuasive. For example, the distinct ethnic neighborhoods that these groups created in American cities (Little Italy, Greektown, Little Warsaw, etc.) have faded away or been taken over by other groups, and the rate of intermarriage between members of different white ethnic groups is quite high. For example, based on data from the 1990 census, about 56% of all married whites have spouses whose ethnic backgrounds do not match their own (Alba, 1995, pp. 13-14).

The evidence that white ethnic groups have achieved equality is so compelling that it raises a question: Should they be included in this series of case studies of minority groups, or should they be treated as part of the dominant group? In fact, there are a number of reasons for including them.

First, although they no longer experience the systematic, widespread discrimination and inequality that is the major defining characteristic of a minority group, they have not completely vanished. Descendants of the European immigrants continue to identify themselves in ethnic terms and link themselves to the country from which their immigrant ancestors came. For example, when asked in a survey in the year 2002, "From what country or part of the world did your ancestors come?" over 80% of the white respondents named a European country, not the United States (National Opinion Research Council, 2002). Although this lingering ethnic identity is not very robust or deep (as we shall see at the end of the chapter), it is also not extinct (at least not yet). Furthermore, a few ethnic neighborhoods, such as Irish Catholic South Boston, have survived the pressures of assimilation, and the political, religious, and gastronomical traditions of the European immigrant groups continue to manifest themselves, especially in the industrial cities of the Northeast and the Midwest. Ancestry and ethnicity still matter to millions of European Americans, even though these factors are no longer at the center of their lives. We will consider the strength of white ethnic identity in contemporary America in more detail at the end of this chapter.

A second, related reason for treating white ethnic groups as minority groups is that the traditional prejudices against them persist, even though in weakened form. Stereotypes of the

EXHIBIT 12.1 Educational Attainment for Selected White Ethnic Groups, 1990

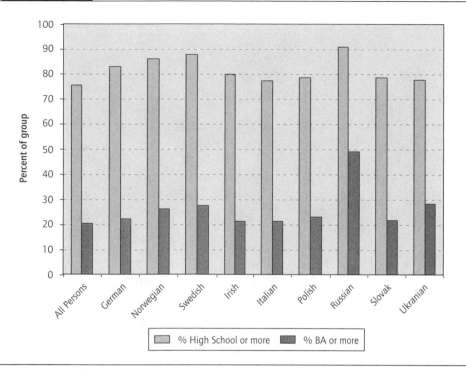

SOURCE: U.S. Bureau of the Census (1998).

EXHIBIT 12.2 Median Household Income for Selected White Ethnic Groups, 1990

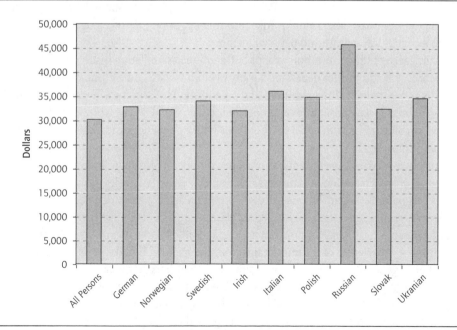

SOURCE: U.S. Bureau of the Census (1998).

EXHIBIT 12.3 Percentage of Families Living in Poverty for Selected White Ethnic Groups, 1990

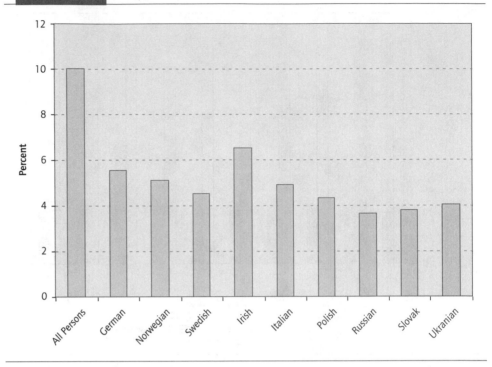

SOURCE: U.S. Bureau of the Census (1998).

various European groups (e.g., Jews as shrewd money handlers, Italians as quick-tempered and emotional, Irish as talkative drunks, Poles as not very bright, etc.), along with a repertoire of insulting names (Wop, Mick, Hunky, Kike, Kraut, Frog, Limey, Polack, and scores of others), remain a part of U.S. culture and national memory.

Third, each of the white ethnic groups had a unique assimilation history, and their varied experiences will add further depth and variety to our analysis. Some groups integrated by rising through the mainstream institutions and organizations of society, whereas others relied on separate ethnic enclave economies to propel their rise to equality. The white ethnic groups give us another comparison with and a sharper focus on the challenges and barriers facing today's racial and colonized minority groups.

Fourth, as we shall see, the actions of white ethnic groups also provide a partial explanation for the current situation of America's racial and colonized minority groups: The rise of the former was possible in part because of discrimination against the latter. European American immigrant groups protected their rising social class positions by helping to perpetuate the exclusion of African Americans, Hispanic Americans, and other minority groups of color.

Fifth, the experiences of the immigrants from Europe established a set of expectations and understandings about immigration and assimilation that shape our views of the progress of the post-1965 immigrants, the second great wave of humanity to strike these shores (see chapter 11). As we have seen, these perceptions and ideas are often useful for analyzing contemporary immigration, even when they have to be revised and updated to take account of the changing nature of the immigrant stream and the changing context of American society. An understanding of both the "baseline" experiences of European immigrants a century ago and the popular notions and sociological theories that developed from those experiences can provide a useful and more informed perspective on the experiences of immigrants today.

Finally, we can use the experience of the immigrants from Europe to further test the theories and concepts we have developed in previous chapters. We began this series of case studies by considering what Blauner (1972) calls "colonized minority groups" (African Americans and American Indians) and then moved to "mixed" types (Hispanic Americans, Asian Americans, contemporary immigrants). With European immigrants, we consider groups whose contact situation and conditions of entry most closely approximate "purely" immigrant groups, the endpoint of Blauner's typology. As we discussed in chapter 5, Blauner hypothesized that minority groups created by immigration will experience less intense prejudice and discrimination and that they will be disadvantaged for a shorter time than groups created by colonization. In this chapter, we investigate the dynamics and consequences of this more favored status.

We begin this final case study by examining the immigration experiences and histories of the white ethnic groups in the 19th and 20th centuries. We identify and consider the implications of the various modes of incorporation into U.S. society that they followed. We close the chapter by considering the meaning of white ethnicity and white ethnic identity at the dawn of the 21st century.

## INDUSTRIALIZATION AND IMMIGRATION

As you recall, one of the themes of this text is that dominant-minority relations reflect the economic and political characteristics of the larger society and change as those characteristics change (see chapter 6 and the introduction to Part IV). Thus it will come as no surprise to learn that the immigration from Europe that created so many minority groups in the United States was, at base, motivated by a revolution in subsistence technology. The Industrial Revolution began in England in the mid-1700s, and it replaced the traditional, labor-intensive forms of work and production with capital-intensive forms. The new technology transformed social relations first in Europe and then throughout the world, forever altering everyday life and relations between groups as it proceeded.

At the dawn of the industrial revolution, most people in Europe lived in small, rural villages and survived by labor-intensive farming. Industrialization destroyed this traditional way of life as it spread across the continent from England to Northern and Western Europe and then to Southern and Eastern Europe. Agriculture was modernized, machines replaced both people and draft animals in the fields, and the need for human labor in rural areas declined. Farmland was consolidated into larger and larger tracts for the sake of efficiency, further decreasing the need for human laborers. At the same time, the rural population began to grow even as survival in the rapidly changing rural economy became more difficult.

In response, peasants began to leave their home villages and move toward urban areas. Factories were being built in or near the cities, opening up opportunities for employment. The urban population tended to increase faster than the job supply, however, and many migrants had to move on. Many of these former peasants responded to opportunities available in the New World, especially in the United States. As industrialization took hold in Europe, the population movement to the cities and then to North America eventually grew to become the largest in human history (so far).

The timing of immigration followed the timing of industrialization. The first waves of immigrants, often called the "**Old Immigration**," came from Northern and Western Europe in the 1820s.

EXHIBIT 12.4   The Waves of Immigration

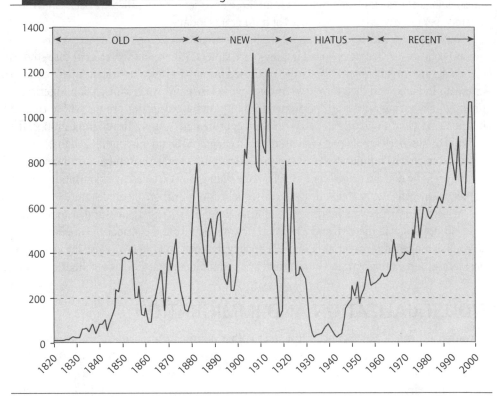

SOURCE: U.S. Immigration and Naturalization Service (2003).

NOTE: Does not include immigrants who legalized their status under the provisions of the Immigration Reform and Control Act.

A second wave, the "**New Immigration**," began arriving from Southern and Eastern Europe in the 1880s. Exhibit 12.4 shows both waves. Also note that immigration was higher in the latter period and decreased dramatically in the late 1920s, the "hiatus" we discussed in chapter 9.

## EUROPEAN ORIGINS, CONDITIONS OF ENTRY, AND THE CAMPAIGN AGAINST IMMIGRATION

Like the other immigrant groups we have discussed, the newcomers from Europe followed a variety of pathways into the United States, and their experiences were shaped by their cultural and class characteristics, their country of origin, and the timing of their arrival. Some groups encountered much more resistance than others, and different groups played different roles in the industrialization and urbanization of America. To discuss these diverse patterns systematically, we differentiate between three subgroups of European immigrants: Protestants from Northern and Western Europe, the largely Catholic immigrant laborers from Ireland and from Southern and Eastern Europe, and Jewish immigrants from Eastern Europe. We look at these subgroups in roughly the order of their arrival.

# Northern and Western Europeans

Northern and Western European immigrants included Germans, Norwegians, Swedes (the first three groups listed in Exhibits 11.1-11.3), Welsh, French, Dutch, and Danes. These groups were similar to the dominant group in their racial and religious characteristics and also shared many cultural values with the host society, including the Protestant Ethic—which stressed hard work, success, and individualism—and support for the principles of democratic government. These similarities eased their acceptance into a society that was highly intolerant of religious and racial differences until well into the 20th century, and these immigrant groups generally experienced a lower degree of ethnocentric rejection and racist disparagement than did the Irish and immigrants from Southern and Eastern Europe.

Northern and Western European immigrants came from nations that were just as developed as the United States. Thus these immigrants tended to be more skilled and educated than other immigrant groups, and they often brought money and other resources with which to secure a comfortable place for themselves in their new society. Many settled in the sparsely populated Midwest and in other frontier areas, where they farmed the fertile land that had become available after the conquest and removal of American Indians and Mexican Americans. By dispersing throughout the midsection of the country, they lowered their visibility and their degree of competition with dominant group members. Two brief case studies outline the experiences of these groups.

**Immigrants From Norway.** Norway had a small population base, and immigration from this Scandinavian nation was never sizable in absolute numbers. However, "America Fever" struck here as it did elsewhere in Europe, and on a per capita basis, Norway sent more immigrants to the United States before 1890 than any European nation except Ireland (Chan, 1990, p. 41).

The first Norwegian immigrants were moderately prosperous farmers searching for cheap land. They found abundant acreage in upper Midwest states such as Minnesota and Wisconsin and then found that the local labor supply was too small to effectively cultivate the available land. Many turned to their homeland for assistance and used their relatives and friends to create networks and recruit a labor force. Thus chains of communication and migration linking Norway to the northern plains were established, supplying immigrants to these areas for decades (Chan, 1990, p. 41). Today, a strong Scandinavian heritage is still evident in the farms, towns, and cities of the upper Midwest.

**Immigrants From Germany.** The stream of immigration from Germany was much larger than that from Norway, and German Americans left their mark on the economy, the political structure, and the cultural life of their new land. In the last half of the 19th century, at least 25% of the immigrants each year were German (Conzen, 1980, p. 406), and today more Americans (about 15%) trace their ancestry to Germany than to any other country except England (National Opinion Research Council, 1972-2000).

The German immigrants who arrived earlier in the 1800s moved into the newly opened farmland and the rapidly growing cities of the Midwest, as had many Scandinavians. By 1850, large German communities could be found in Milwaukee, St. Louis, and other Midwestern cities (Conzen, 1980, p. 413). Some German immigrants followed the transatlantic route of the cotton trade between Europe and the southern United States and entered through the port of New Orleans, moving from there to the Midwest and Southwest.

German immigrants arriving later in the century were more likely to settle in urban areas because fertile land was less available. Many of the city-bound German immigrants were skilled workers and artisans, and others found work as laborers in the rapidly expanding industrial sector. The double penetration of German immigrants into the rural economy and the higher sectors of the urban economy is reflected by the fact that by 1870, most employed German Americans were involved in skilled labor (37%) or farming (25%) (Conzen, 1980, p. 413).

German immigrants took relatively high occupational positions in the U.S. labor force, and their sons and daughters were able to translate that relative affluence into economic mobility. By the dawn of the 20th century, large numbers of second-generation German Americans were finding their way into white-collar and professional careers. Within a few generations, German Americans had achieved parity with national norms in education, income, and occupational prestige.

**A Successful Assimilation.** The process of acculturation and integration for Protestant immigrants from Northern and Western Europe was consistent with the traditional views of assimilation first stated in chapter 2 and reviewed in chapter 11. Although members of these groups felt the sting of rejection, prejudice, and discrimination, their movement to integration and equality was relatively smooth, especially when compared with the experiences of racial minority groups who were created by conquest and colonization. Their relative success and high degree of assimilation is suggested in Exhibits 12.1 through 12.3.

# Immigrant Laborers From Ireland and Southern and Eastern Europe

The relative ease of assimilation for Northern and Western Europeans contrasts sharply with the experiences of non-Protestant, less educated and skilled immigrants. These "immigrant laborers" came in two waves. The Irish were part of the Old Immigration that began in the 1820s, but the bulk of this group—Italians, Poles, Russians, Hungarians, Greeks, Serbs, Ukrainians, Slovaks, Bulgarians, and scores of other Southern and Eastern European nationalities—made up the New Immigration that began in the 1880s. Most of the immigrants in these nationality groups (like many of the "New Americans" reviewed in chapter 11) were peasants or unskilled laborers, with few resources other than their willingness to work. They came from rural, village-oriented cultures in which family and kin took precedence over individual needs or desires, similar to the traditional Asian cultures we discussed in chapter 10. Family life for them tended to be autocratic and male dominated, and children were expected to subordinate their personal desires and to work for the good of the family as a whole. Arranged marriages were common. This cultural background was less consistent with the industrializing, capitalistic, individualistic, Protestant, Anglo-American culture of the United States, and as a result, these immigrant laborers experienced greater levels of rejection and discrimination than the immigrants from Northern and Western Europe.

The immigrant laborers were much less likely to enter the rural economy than the Northern and Western European immigrants. Much of the better frontier land had already been claimed by the time most new immigrant groups began to arrive, and a large number of them had been permanently soured on farming by the oppressive and exploitative agrarian economies from which they were trying to escape. They settled in the cities of the industrializing Northeast and found work in plants, mills, mines, and factories. They supplied the armies of laborers needed to power the industrial revolution, although their view of this process was generally from the bottom looking up. They arrived during the decades in which the industrial and urban infrastructure of the United States was being constructed. They built roads, canals, and railroads, as well as the buildings that housed the machinery of industrialization. The first tunnels of the New York City subway system were dug, largely by hand, by laborers from Italy. Other immigrants found work in the coal fields of Pennsylvania and West Virginia and the steel mills of Pittsburgh, and they flocked by the millions to the factories of the Northeast.

Like other low-skill immigrant groups, these newcomers took jobs in which strength and stamina were more important than literacy or skilled craftsmanship. In fact, the minimum level of skills required for employment actually declined as industrialization proceeded through its early phases. To keep wages low and take advantage of what seemed like an inexhaustible supply of cheap labor, industrialists and factory owners developed technologies and machines that required few skills and little knowledge of English to operate. As mechanization proceeded, unskilled workers replaced skilled workers in the workforce. Not infrequently, women and children replaced men because they could be hired for lower wages (Steinberg, 1981, p. 35).

**Gender.** The gender of the immigrants shaped their experiences in countless ways. When immigrant women entered the workforce, they generally found jobs as domestics (e.g., maids, cooks, and nannies in affluent white middle-class homes) or in factories, where they were assigned to the most menial, lowest paid tasks. For example, many women from Bohemia had worked in cigar manufacturing in the old country and sought work in that industry in the United States. Although they were skilled and experienced, they were barred from the better, higher paying jobs, which were reserved for U.S.-born men. The immigrant women were assigned to the hardest, least desirable jobs in the factory, such as stripping tobacco in dank, airless basements (Amott & Matthaei, 1991, p. 111).

Immigrant women often were sent to work by their families at young ages, as were many U.S.-born women of the working class. Women of these groups were expected to work until they married, after which time it was expected that their husbands would support them and their children. In many cases, however, immigrant men could not earn enough to support their families, and their wives and children were required by necessity to contribute to the family budget. Immigrant wives sometimes continued to work outside the home, or they found other ways to make money. They took in boarders, did laundry or sewing, tended gardens, and were involved in myriad other activities that permitted them to contribute to the family budget and still stay home and attend to family and child-rearing responsibilities. A 1911 report on Southern and Eastern European households found that about half kept lodgers and that the income from this activity amounted to about 25% of the husbands' wages. Children also contributed to the family income by taking after-school and summertime jobs (Morawska, 1990, pp. 211-212).

For European immigrant males, entry-level, unskilled jobs in the industrial sector were plentiful, but most of these jobs offered no possibility of promotion and were insecure and often unsafe. Even salary raises were rare and grudgingly given, as there was a plentiful supply of immigrants "just off the boat" willing to work for less. Male immigrant laborers usually spent their entire working lives in jobs at the bottom of the occupational structure. The better paid, more secure, and skilled or supervisory positions were reserved for U.S.-born Anglo-Americans or for the descendants of Northern and Western European immigrants. The Irish and the Southern and Eastern European immigrants and most of their descendants remained a blue-collar, unskilled working class until well into the 20th century (Bodnar, 1985; Morawska, 1990).

**Ethnic and Religious Prejudice.** Today, it may be hard to conceive the bitterness and intensity of the prejudice that greeted the Irish, Italians, Poles, and other new immigrant groups. Even as they were becoming an indispensable segment of the American workforce, they were castigated, ridiculed, attacked, and disparaged. The Irish were the first immigrant laborers to arrive and thus the first to feel this intense prejudice and discrimination. Campaigns against immigrants were waged, Irish neighborhoods were attacked by mobs, and Roman Catholic churches and convents were burned. Some employers blatantly refused to hire the Irish, often advertising their ethnic preferences with signs that read "No Irish Need Apply." Until later arriving groups displaced them, the Irish were mired at the bottom of the job market. Indeed, at one time they were referred to as the "niggers of Boston" (Blessing, 1980; Potter, 1973; Shannon, 1964).

Other groups felt the same sting of rejection as they arrived. Italian immigrants were particularly likely to be the victims of violent attacks, one of the most vicious of which took place in New Orleans in 1891. The city's police chief was assassinated, and rumors of Italian involvement in the murder were rampant. Hundreds of Italians were arrested, and nine were brought to trial. All were acquitted. Anti-Italian sentiment was running so high, however, that a mob lynched 11 Italians while police and city officials did nothing (Higham, 1963).

Much of the prejudice against the Irish and the new immigrants was expressed as anti-Catholicism. Prior to the mid-19th century, Anglo-American society had been almost exclusively Protestant. Catholicism, with its celibate clergy, Latin masses, and cloistered nuns, seemed alien, exotic, and threatening. The growth of Catholicism, especially because it was associated with non-Anglo immigrants, raised fears that the Protestant religions would lose status. There were even rumors that the Pope was planning to move the Vatican to America and organize a takeover of the U.S. government.

Although Catholics were often stereotyped as single groups, they also varied along a number of dimensions. For example, the Catholic faith as practiced in Ireland differed significantly from that practiced in Italy, Poland, and other countries. Catholic immigrant groups often established their own parishes, with priests who could speak the old language. These cultural and national differences often separated Catholic groups, despite their common faith (Herberg, 1960). In chapter 2, we discussed the concept of the "triple melting pot" and how religion and ethnicity often became fused for European immigrants and their descendants.

**Upward Mobility.** Eventually, as the generations passed, the prejudice, systematic discrimination, and other barriers to upward mobility for the immigrant laborer groups weakened, and their descendants began to rise out of the working class. Although the first and second generations of these groups were largely limited to jobs at the unskilled or semiskilled level, the third and later generations rose in the American social class system. As Exhibits 12.1 through 12.3 show, the descendents of the immigrant laborers achieved parity with national norms by the latter half of the 20th century.

# Eastern European Jewish Immigrants and the Ethnic Enclave

Jewish immigrants from Russia and other parts of Eastern Europe followed a third pathway into U.S. society. These immigrants were a part of the New Immigration and began arriving in the 1880s. Unlike the immigrant laborer groups, who were generally economic refugees and included many young, single, male sojourners, Eastern European Jews were fleeing religious persecution and arrived as family units intending to settle permanently and become citizens. They settled in the urban areas of the Northeast and Midwest. New York City was the most common destination, and the Lower East Side became the best-known Jewish American neighborhood. By 1920, about 60% of all Jewish Americans lived in the urban areas between Boston and Philadelphia, with almost 50% living in New York City alone. Another 30% lived in the urban areas of the Midwest, particularly in Chicago (Goren, 1980, p. 581).

In Russia and other parts of Eastern Europe, Jews had been barred from agrarian occupations and had come to rely on the urban economy for their livelihoods. When they immigrated to the United States, they brought these urban skills and job experiences with them. For example, almost two thirds of the immigrant Jewish men had been tailors and other skilled laborers in eastern Europe (Goren, 1980, p. 581). In the rapidly industrializing U.S. economy of the early 20th century, they were able to use these skills to find work.

Other Jewish immigrants joined the urban working class and took manual labor and unskilled jobs in the industrial sector (Morawska, 1990, p. 202). The garment industry in particular became the lifeblood of the Jewish community and provided jobs to about one third of all Eastern European Jews residing in the major cities (Goren, 1980, p. 582). Women as well as men were involved in the garment industry. Jewish women, like the women of more recent immigrant laborer groups, found ways to combine their jobs and their domestic responsibilities. As young girls, they worked in factories and sweatshops, and after marriage, they did the same work at home, sewing precut garments together or doing other piecework such as wrapping cigars or making artificial flowers, often assisted by their children (Amott & Matthaei, 1991, p. 115).

**The Enclave and Upward Mobility.** Unlike most European immigrant groups, Jewish Americans became heavily involved in commerce and often found ways to start their own businesses and become self-employed. Drawing on their experience in the old country, many started businesses and small independent enterprises. The Jewish neighborhoods were densely populated and provided a ready market for services of all kinds. Some Jewish immigrants became street peddlers or started bakeries, butcher and candy shops, or any number of other retail enterprises. In a process that mirrored the activities of the Chinese and the Japanese on the West Coast at the same time, Eastern European Jews constructed an enclave economy on the East Coast.

Capitalizing on their residential concentration and close proximity, Jewish immigrants created dense networks of commercial, financial, and social cooperation. Like the other ethnic enclaves we have examined in previous chapters, the Jewish American enclave survived because of the cohesiveness of the group; the willingness of wives, children, and other relatives to work for little or no monetary compensation; and the commercial savvy of the early immigrants. Also, a large pool of cheap labor and sources of credit and other financial services were available within the community. The Jewish American enclave grew and provided a livelihood for many of the children and grandchildren of the immigrants (Portes & Manning, 1986, pp. 51-52). As was also the case with other enclave groups, economic advancement preceded extensive acculturation, and Jewish Americans made significant strides toward economic equality before they became fluent in English or were otherwise Americanized.

As we discussed in chapter 10, an obvious way in which an enclave immigrant group can improve its position is to develop an educated and acculturated second generation. The Americanized, English-speaking children of the immigrants used their greater familiarity with the dominant society and their language facility to help preserve and expand the family enterprise. Thus the same logic that led Chinese Americans and Japanese Americans to invest in education for the next generation also applied to Jewish immigrants. Furthermore, as the second generation appeared, the public school system was expanding, and education through the college level was free or very inexpensive in New York City and other cities (Steinberg, 1981, pp. 128-138).

There was also a strong push for the second and third generations to enter professions, and as Jewish Americans excelled in school, resistance to and discrimination against them increased. By the 1920s, many elite colleges and universities, such as Dartmouth, had established quotas that limited the number of Jewish students they would admit (Dinnerstein, 1977, p. 228). These quotas were not abolished until after World War II.

The enclave economy and the Jewish neighborhoods established by the immigrants proved to be an effective base from which to integrate into American society. The descendants of the Eastern European Jewish immigrants moved out of the ethnic neighborhoods years ago, and their positions in the economy—their pushcarts, stores, and jobs in the garment industry—have been taken over by more recent immigrants. When they left the enclave economy, many second- and third-generation Eastern European Jews did not enter the mainstream occupational structure at the bottom, as the immigrant laborer groups tended to do. They used the resources generated by the entrepreneurship of the early generations to gain access to prestigious and advantaged social class positions (Portes & Manning, 1986, p. 53). As a group, studies show that Jewish Americans today surpass national averages in income, levels of education, and occupational prestige (Sklare, 1971, pp. 60-69; see also Cohen, 1985; Massarik & Chenkin, 1973). The relatively higher status of Russian Americans shown in Exhibits 12.1 through 12.3 is due in part to the fact that many Jewish Americans are of Russian descent.

**Anti-Semitism.** One barrier that Jewish Americans were forced to overcome was prejudice and racism (or anti-Semitism). Biased sentiments and negative stereotypes of Jews have been a part of Western tradition for centuries and, in fact, have been stronger and more vicious in Europe than in the United States. For nearly two millennia, European Jews have been chastised and persecuted as the killers of Christ and stereotyped as materialistic moneylenders and crafty businessmen. The stereotype that links Jews and moneylending has its origins in the fact that in premodern Europe, Catholics were forbidden by the Church to engage in usury (charging interest for loans). Jews were under no such restriction, and they filled the gap thus created in the economy. The ultimate episode in the long history of European anti-Semitism was, of course, the Nazi Holocaust, in which 6 million Jews died. European anti-Semitism did not end with the demise of the Nazi regime, and it remains a prominent concern throughout Europe and Russia.

Before the mass immigration of Eastern European Jews began in the late 19th century, anti-Semitism in the United States was relatively mild, perhaps because the group was so small. As the immigration continued, anti-Jewish prejudice increased in intensity and viciousness, fostering the view of Jews as cunning but dishonest merchants. In the late 19th century, Jews began to be banned from social clubs and the boardrooms of businesses and other organizations. Summer resorts began posting notices, "We prefer not to entertain Hebrews" (Goren, 1980, p. 585).

By the 1920s and 1930s, anti-Semitism had become quite prominent among American prejudices and was being preached by the Ku Klux Klan and other extreme racist groups. Also, because many of the political radicals and labor leaders of the time were Jewish immigrants, anti-Semitism became fused with a fear of Communism and other anticapitalist doctrines. Some prominent Americans espoused anti-Semitic views, among them Henry Ford, the founder of Ford Motor Company; Charles Lindbergh, the aviator who was the first to fly solo across the Atlantic; and Father Charles Coughlin, a Catholic priest with a popular radio show (Selzer, 1972).

After reaching a peak before World War II, anti-Semitism has tapered off in recent decades, as illustrated in Exhibits 3.2 and 3.5 (see also Anti-Defamation League, 2000). Exhibit 3.2 shows a decline between 1933 and 1967 in the percentage of college students who characterized Jews as "shrewd, mercenary, and grasping," and Exhibit 3.5 shows declining social distance scores between 1926 and 1993. Note, however, that these exhibits also show that anti-Semitism persists, albeit in attenuated form. According to Exhibit 3.2, about one third of the respondents in 1967 still saw Jews as "shrewd and industrious"; and Exhibit 3.5 shows that, in 1993, Jews ranked at about the same level with respect to other groups as they had in 1926. The persistence of anti-Semitism suggested by these results may be due in part to the cultural nature of prejudice. Stereotypes and prejudicial sentiments can become embedded in the culture and are passed on from generation to generation through socialization (see chapter 3).

Anti-Semitism also has a prominent place in the ideologies of a variety of extremist groups that have emerged in recent years, including "skinheads" and various contemporary incarnations of the Ku Klux Klan. Some of this targeting of Jews seems to increase during economic recession and may be a type of scapegoating related to the stereotypical view of Jewish Americans as extremely prosperous and materialistic.

## The Campaign Against Immigration

In chapter 10, we discussed the campaign to end Chinese immigration that ended successfully with the passage of the Chinese Exclusion Act of 1882. Similar campaigns were waged against European immigration, the strength of which waxed and waned throughout the period of mass immigration from the 1820s to the 1920s. Organizations were formed to express opposition to immigration and to pressure the government to limit entry into the nation. Predictably, these organizations were particularly common during hard economic times and depressions. The anti-Catholic, anti-Semitic, and anti-immigration forces ultimately triumphed with the passage of the National Origins Act in 1924.

This act drastically reduced the overall number of immigrants that would be admitted each year. Furthermore, it established a quota system to determine the number of immigrants that would be accepted each year from each sending nation, a system that was openly racist.

# White Ethnics by *Eric Margolis*

"White Ethnics" is another odd conglomeration of peoples that testifies to our American obsession with race and ideology of assimilation. Italians and Greeks, Irish and Germans, Slavs, Hungarians, Croatians, Russians and Poles, Norwegians, Finns, and Swedes all came to be lumped together as white ethnics in the great "melting pot" of America.

Interestingly, some of these ethnic immigrants, Italians, Greeks, Irish, and Jews for instance, were not seen as "white" when they arrived. Even the Irish were seen as a different "race." Each group was stigmatized with ethnic slurs: Wop, Paddy, Kike, Bohunk. But unlike African Americans, Indians, and some Latinos, the "melting pot" process seemed to work for European Ethnics; as they gave up their native languages and customs they merged with the Anglo American population and became identified as "white."[1]

8. A GROUP OF GERMAN IMMIGRANTS AT ELLIS ISLAND - 1926

This is a typical German sampling of farmers, scholars, professional men and perhaps a butcher. The group is fairly prosperous as modern clothes and baggage indicate.

Photo-study by Lewis W. Hine

While some European immigrants came into the United States through ports such as Boston and New Orleans, New York City was far and away the busiest port of entry. The first sight of America for most newcomers was the Statue of Liberty with New York spreading out in the distance. The above photograph shows immigrants arriving at Ellis Island in the 1910s. Their first encounter with the laws of the new country took place in the great halls of Ellis Island where their papers were inspected and they were examined by doctors for signs of communicable diseases. Even such a small problem as "pink-eye" (conjunctivitis) was enough to cause one to be detained at the medical facilities at Ellis Island; more serious diseases could cause one to be sent back to the country of origin.

Some immigrants had been actively recruited by labor agents who may have even paid the passage way to bring workers needed by mines, or construction companies building canals and railroads. Others paid their own way and used labor agencies to find jobs. Many immigrant workers utilized kinship or ethnic networks to find work. In this way they became identified with particular occupations and locations, as our popular stereotypes would have it; the Irish built the railroads and later became policemen or firemen, Norwegians farmed the upper Midwest, Jews became tailors in New York's garment industry, and so on. In general, the first generation settled in ethnic enclaves where they could speak their home language, find the food and music they liked, and reproduce much of their culture. At the same time, their children attended American schools and experienced an intense process of Americanization. The first generation was hobbled by lack of English, the second generation became bilingual and often "translated" for their parents.

This photo of a rural one-room school looks for all the world like an episode of "Little House on the Prairie." But appearance is not reality. The photograph is from the Fred Hultstrand collection that was donated by a pioneer photographer to North Dakota State University. Whiteness in America has a peculiar transparency. In the case of white immigrants, nationality and linguistic proficiency are invisible, but according to text at the Hultstrand web site, many of these children were recent immigrants speaking Swedish, German, or Norwegian. While they were as much an immigrant as someone who crossed the Rio Grande at El Paso, these meanings disappear in the photographs as they disappeared in a society where white immigrants became invisible through assimilation in a couple of generations.

These girls were photographed wearing Slavic dress at a coal company town in Southern Colorado during the 1920s. Second generation, the first born in the U.S., they reflect an emerging pan-ethnic identity. Many Eastern Europeans worked in the coal mines: Serbs, Croats, Poles, Bulgarians, Hungarians, and Russians. But these girls' mixtures of clothing suggests that their specific origins no longer matter very much. The clothes are clean and unworn; the head scarfs not naturally tied; the shoes are all wrong. In other words traditional dress has become "costume," and Slavic identity a sort of pageant to be acted out in school.

The photograph of a Norwegian immigrant woman in front of her sod house suggests the hardships and rough living conditions that pioneers endured in settling the Great

Plains. Two generations later, Norwegian culture is enacted at a summer picnic. Except for adopting the trappings of culture in terms of folk dance, music, and ethnic food, these white ethnics have become indistinguishable from the general whiteness.

Immigration from Europe grew rapidly after the civil war and peaked in the years before World War I. The urban ethnic enclaves: Little Italy, Greek Town, Polish, Lithuanian, Irish, and Italian neighborhoods in back of the yards Chicago, South Boston's Irish community, and New York's Jewish lower east side thrived. The photo, upper right, from the Farmer Security Administration Files was made in 1938 by Arthur Rothstein. His notes read "Family from Italian section of Philadelphia

working in cranberry bog. Only families with many children are employed. Children are kept out of school for more than two months of the school year. Burlington County, New Jersey."

The central importance of ethnic identification in American consciousness is attested by the two photographs, bottom of the previous page, of the textile industry taken by the famous photographer, Lewis Hine, for the Works Progress Administration dating to the 1930s. Taken in Mt. Holyoke, Massachusetts, the first is titled "Putting skein on swift to wind on bobbin (Polish)" and the second "Rag sorting (Irish)."

After World War II, however, things changed. Car culture, suburbia, and a general prosperity combined

to create a highly mobile society. Third and fourth generation "white ethnics" became more and more assimilated to become simply "white Americans." They tended to intermarry and their identification with ethnic culture became more tenuous. Blue-collar factory workers held on to their identities longer than most, but during the last quarter of the 20th-century deindustrialization and the growth of the service economy further dispersed ethnically homogeneous communities. There are still a few urban communities, some "father and son" occupations or unions associated with the European ethnics, but by and large the concept of "white ethnics" is becoming an obsolete notion.

The old ethnic epithets lost some of their power and sting. With the exception of religion, which is more persistent, for many Americans their ethnic backgrounds faded and they raised their children in ethnically mixed suburbs. Ethnicity became less of a core identity than a form of social performance.

## Comparative Focus: Immigration and Assimilation in Canada

The United States was not the only destination for the immigrants who left Europe between the 1820s and the 1920s. Millions more went to Argentina and Brazil (mainly from Italy), Australia (mainly from Britain and Ireland), and to hundreds of other nations. The United States was the most popular destination, receiving about 60% of the immigrants (Daniels, 1990, p. 23), but the exodus out of Europe was a global phenomenon that deeply affected many other societies. Canada, for example, received more than 4 million immigrants during this time period. Did the immigrants to Canada follow patterns of settlement and adaptation similar to the groups that arrived in the United States?

Canada and the United States share history and culture along with their common border, and as you would expect, their immigration experiences are similar in many ways. The volume of immigration from Europe to both nations followed a similar rhythm, fluctuating according to social, economic, and political conditions in the Old and New Worlds. In both cases, rates of immigration peaked early in the 20th century, fell during World War I, rose again in the 1920s, and then plummeted during the Great Depression of the 1930s (a decline that in the United States was greatly abetted by the restrictive legislation passed in the 1920s).

On the other hand, the number of immigrants to Canada never approached the numbers coming to the United States. In fact, in many years prior to the 20th century, more people actually left Canada than arrived. For many European immigrants (particularly for the British and Irish), Canada was a cheaper or more convenient destination, but the greater economic opportunities available in the United States proved hard to resist. For example, during the famine years in Ireland, more than 2 million Irish left their homeland. Many went to Britain, Australia, and other places, but the bulk (nearly 1.5 million) came directly to the United States. The second-largest group, about a third of a million, went to Canada first and then drifted south, many reuniting with their countrymen in the urban Northeast (Daniels, 1990, p. 135).

Another important difference between the two nations is that Canadian immigrants have been much less diverse than those arriving in the United States. In the 18th and 19th centuries, immigrants to Canada were almost exclusively from the British Isles (including Ireland) and France, and in 1871 (the date of the first Canadian census), the Canadian population was more than 90% British or French. Other European groups did not begin to immigrate to Canada in substantial numbers until the completion of the national railroad system opened up the vast Canadian prairies in the late 1800s. Ukrainians were one such group, for example. Fleeing political unrest and overpopulation, they settled in the rich farming country of the western provinces of Canada, where the soil and climate were similar to their homeland. About 10,000 arrived by 1900, but this number swelled to more than 150,000 by the start of World War 1 in 1914 (Luciuk & Hryniuk, 1991).

The diversity of the Canadian immigrant stream continued to increase in the first half of the 20th century. The percentage of Canadians of European descent other than British and French rose from about 9% in 1901 to almost 20% in 1941. Parallel to the U.S. experience, the earlier immigrants were from Northern and Western Europe, and those arriving later were more likely to be of Eastern and Southern

European origin (Fong & Wilkes, 1999). However, although gradually declining, the numerical predominance of the British and French ancestral groups held up throughout the 20th century. In the most recent census (2001), the bulk of the population placed themselves in three "ancestral" groups: Canadian (39%), English (20%), and French (16%).

What happened to the European immigrants who arrived in Canada in the 19th and 20th centuries? Briefly stated, they settled in patterns not too different from the immigrants who came to the United States, and today, their descendants are at or above national norms in terms of income, schooling, unemployment, and other measures of integration and acculturation. For example, Fong and Wilkes (1999) found that European immigrants and their descendants in Canada seemed to follow the predictions of what we have called traditional assimilation theory: Each generation rose in status relative to their parents and became increasingly assimilated.

Another study (Sweetman & Dicks, 1999) found substantial differences between white and nonwhite Canadian groups in terms of education and income but comparatively minor differences within the white ethnic Canadian groups. Also, Stelcner (2000) found that most white ethnic groups were close to the national norms, with Spanish, Polish, and Italian men slightly below and German, British, and Ukrainian men a little above. In both studies, the major exception to the pattern of rough equality for white ethnic groups were Jewish Canadians, who were far above the norms, a difference that reflects enclave experiences and higher levels of human capital similar to Jewish Americans.

Today, the immigration experiences of the two nations continue to exhibit many parallels. Rates of immigration have risen in both cases, and recent immigrants are equally diverse, racially, culturally, and linguistically. The great majority of contemporary immigrants to both nations are coming from the same areas of Asia and Latin America, and Canada, like the United States, is becoming a more diverse and pluralistic society. For example, a half century ago, Canadians of Asian origins were less than 1% of the total population (Fong & Wilkes, 1999). Today, they are about 7% (Statistics Canada, 2004). Canadian immigration policy favors more skilled and educated applicants, and the government is officially committed to multiculturalism and a rejection of narrow Anglo-centered assimilation. Still, as in the past, Canada and the United States will share many challenges (permanent immigration and segmented assimilation, for example; see Chapters 2 and 9) in their immigration experiences

For example, the size of the quota for European nations was based on the proportional representation of each nationality in the United States as of 1890. This year was chosen because it predated the bulk of the New Immigration and gave the most generous quotas to Northern and Western European nations. Immigration from the Western Hemisphere was not directly affected by this legislation, but immigration from non-European nations (i.e., China, Japan, and other Asian nations) was banned altogether. This quota system allocated nearly 70% of the available immigration slots to the nations of Northern and Western Europe, despite the fact that immigration from those areas had largely ended by the 1920s. The act had a marked and immediate effect on the volume of immigration (see Exhibit 12.4). By the time the Great

Depression took hold of the American economy, immigration had dropped to the lowest levels in a century. The National Origins Act remained in effect until the mid-1960s.

## DEVELOPMENTS IN THE 20TH CENTURY: MOBILITY AND INTEGRATION

Apart from their initial mode of incorporation, the social class position and the rapidity of assimilation for white ethnic groups were affected by a number of other factors, including the following:

- The degree of similarity between the immigrant group and the dominant group
- The processes of **ethnic succession** and secondary structural assimilation
- The broad structural changes in the American economy caused by industrialization

### Degree of Similarity

When the European immigration began, the dominant group consisted largely of Protestants with ethnic origins in Northern and Western Europe and especially in England. The degree of resistance, prejudice, and discrimination encountered by the different European immigrant groups varied in part by the degree to which they differed from these dominant group characteristics. The most significant differences related to religion, language, cultural values, and, for some groups, physical characteristics. Thus Protestant immigrants from Northern and Western Europe experienced less resistance than the English-speaking Catholic Irish, who in turn were accepted more readily than the new immigrants, who were both non–English speaking and overwhelmingly non-Protestant.

These ethnocentric preferences of the dominant group correspond roughly to the arrival times of the immigrants. The most similar groups immigrated earliest, and the least similar tended to be the last to arrive. Because of this coincidence, resistance to any one group of immigrants tended to fade as new groups arrived. For example, anti-German prejudice and discrimination never became particularly vicious or widespread (except during the heat of the World Wars), because the Irish began arriving in large numbers at about the same time. Concerns about the German immigrants were swamped by the fear that the Catholic Irish could never be assimilated. Then, as the 19th century drew to a close, immigrants from Southern and Eastern Europe—even more different from the dominant group—began to arrive and made concerns about the Irish seem trivial.

In addition, the New Immigration was far more voluminous than the Old Immigration (see Exhibit 12.4). Southern and Eastern Europeans arrived in record numbers in the early 20th century, and the sheer volume of the immigration raised fears that American cities and institutions would be swamped by hordes of what were seen as racially inferior, unassimilable immigrants (a fear with strong echoes in the present).

Thus a preference hierarchy was formed among the European American ethnic groups by religion and region of origin. The hierarchy is illustrated by the social distance scale results presented in Exhibit 3.5. These rankings reflect more than the degree of dominant group ethnocentrism; they also reflect the ease with which the groups have been integrated. The sequence of mobility is captured by the concept of ethnic succession, the topic of the next section.

# Ethnic Succession

The process of ethnic succession refers to the myriad ways in which European ethnic groups unintentionally affected each other's position in the social class structure of the larger society. The overall pattern was that each European immigrant group tended to be pushed to higher social class levels and more favorable economic situations by the groups that arrived after them.

As more experienced groups became upwardly mobile and began to move out of the neighborhoods that served as their "ports of entry," they were often replaced by a new group of immigrants who would begin the process all over again. Some neighborhoods in the cities of the Northeast served as the ethnic neighborhood—the first safe haven in the new society—for a variety of successive groups. Some neighborhoods continue to fill this role today.

**Secondary Structural Assimilation.** This section traces the general pattern of ethnic succession and integration into the larger society. We focus on the Irish, the first immigrant laborers to arrive in large numbers, but the general patterns apply to all white ethnic groups.

The Irish tended to follow the Northern and Western Europeans in the job market and social class structure and were in turn followed by the wave of new immigrants. In many urban areas of the Northeast, the Irish moved into the neighborhoods and took jobs left behind by German laborers. After a period of adjustment, the Irish began to create their own connections with the mainstream society and improve their economic and social position. They were replaced in their neighborhoods and at the bottom of the occupational structure by Italians, Poles, and other immigrant groups arriving after them.

*Local Politics.* As the years passed and the Irish gained more experience, they began to forge links to the larger society through several institutions, with politics being perhaps the most important connection. The Irish allied themselves with the Democratic Party and helped to construct the political machines that came to dominate many city governments in the 19th and early 20th centuries.

Machine politicians were often corrupt and even criminal, regularly subverting the election process, bribing city and state officials, using city budgets to fill the pockets of the political bosses and their cronies, and passing out public jobs as payoffs for favors and faithful service. Although not exactly models of good government, the political machines performed a number of valuable social services for their constituents and loyal followers. Machine politicians, such as Boss Tweed of Tammany Hall in New York City, could find jobs, provide food and clothing for the destitute, aid victims of fires and other calamities, and intervene in the criminal and civil courts.

Much of the power of the urban political machines derived from their control of the city payroll. The leaders of the machines used municipal jobs and the city budget as part of a "spoils" system (as in "to the winner go the spoils") and as rewards for their supporters and allies. The faithful Irish party worker might be rewarded for service to the machine with a job in the police department (thus the stereotypical Irish cop) or some other agency. Private businessmen might be rewarded with lucrative contracts to supply services or perform other city business.

The political machines served as engines of economic opportunity and linked Irish Americans to a central and important institution of the dominant society. Using the resources controlled by local government as a power base, the Irish (and other immigrant groups after them) began to integrate themselves into the larger society and carve out a place in the mainstream structures of American society, as illustrated in the following Narrative Portrait.

# *Narrative Portrait*

## Ethnicity, Prejudice, and the Irish Political Machine

*David Gray grew up a Welsh Protestant in the city of Scranton, Pennsylvania, during the 1930s and 1940s. At that time, this coal-mining town was split along ethnic lines, and Gray (1991) recounts in this memoir his gradual socialization into the realities of in-groups and out-groups. He also describes how Scranton's Irish Catholic community responded to the Great Depression and how they used the local political machine to protect their own. Gray reflects on the consequences of these experiences for his own personal prejudices and sense of social distance.*

*Gray eventually left Scranton and earned a Ph.D. in sociology. He became a college professor and an accomplished and respected sociologist. Among his many admiring students was the author of this textbook, who grew up in Scranton's Irish Catholic community a generation after Gray.*

### SHADOW OF THE PAST

**David Gray**

C. Wright Mills (an American sociologist) [stressed] the intimate relationship of "history, social structure, and biography." . . . Though he did not say so directly, the logic of Mills' position would surely indicate that, for self-knowledge, no biography is more important than one's own. Born within a social context not of our own making, subject to social forces we did not create, in retrospect, we attempt to understand. . . .

Personally, then, I did not ask to be born Welsh Protestant in Scranton, Pennsylvania. No more than Eddie Gilroy, with whom I attended . . . school, asked to be born Irish Catholic. But there we both were in the heart of the anthracite coal region . . . during the years of the Great Depression. . . . We were friends, good friends. During recess and after 3:00 P.M., he played second base and I played shortstop in the

shrunken, dirt diamond in the schoolyard. . . . We thought we made a good double-play combination and, beyond the baseball field, we respected and liked each other as well.

But, there was something wrong with Eddie Gilroy. At age ten I didn't know exactly what it was. He didn't make many errors and we often shared whatever pennies we had . . . at the corner candy store. Still, there was something wrong with him—vague, general, apart from real experience, but true all the same.

His fundamental defect came into sharper focus at the age of twelve. Sunday movies had just arrived in Scranton and . . . I wanted to go with Eddie and Johnny Pesavento [but] I couldn't.

"Why?"

"Because Protestants don't go to the movies on Sunday—nor play cards, football, or baseball."

"How come Eddie and Johnny can go?"

"They're Catholic."

No one quite used the word "immoral" but . . . anyone who attended Sunday movies was certainly close to sinful. And the implication was clear: If Catholics did such bad things on Sunday, they surely did a lot of bad things on other days as well.

No matter, then, that Gilroy might sacrifice for even a Protestant runner to go to second, or let you borrow his glove, or share his candy. . . . His Catholicism permeated his being, . . . muting his individual qualities. Eddie wasn't the point, his Catholicism was.

[The] deeply held beliefs . . . of the adult world were visited upon the young. Most often subtly . . . but persistently and effectively, little Welsh Protestant boys and girls learned that Catholics were somehow the enemy. . . .

Unfortunately, from their vantage point, the Welsh of Scranton were not the only ones in town. While they had come to the coal regions in large numbers, others, in even larger numbers, had come also. Irish, Italian, Polish, German, many from eastern European countries, fewer who were Jewish—all constituted Scranton's ethnic portion of broader 19th century immigrant waves. With [some] obvious exceptions, most were Catholic.

In this communal setting—a very ethnically and religiously distinct one—the Great Depression arrived with particular force. [The region suffered from massive unemployment and began to lose population as people left in search of work elsewhere.] The coal industry, upon which the economy of Northeastern Pennsylvania essentially rested, was gone. The private sector, initially hard-hit, did not recover [until after the 1960s]. The public sector consequently became the primary possibility for often meager, by no means high-paying jobs.

And the Irish, their political talents augmented by the fact that they were the largest single ethnic group in town, controlled political power. Allied with others of Catholic faith, the Irish did their best to take care of their religiously affiliated, politically important, own.

In Scranton's political life, the intimate relationship of religion, politics, and economics was clear for all to see. The mayor was Jimmy Hanlon, . . . the political boss, Mickey Lawlor, . . . McNulty ran the post office, and Judge Hoban the courts. From the mayor's office to trash collectors, with policemen, foremen, school teachers, truant officers, and dog catchers in between, the public payroll included the names of O'Neill, Hennigan, Lydon, Kennedy, Walsh, Gerrity, and O'Hoolihan. As the depression persisted, Welsh Protestants came to know (with reason but also as an act of faith) that Lewis, Griffiths, and Williams need not apply.

Pale shades of contemporary Northern Ireland, but with political power reversed. No shots were fired, perhaps because American democratic traditions compel accommodation and compromise. Nonetheless, among the Welsh, the general feeling of resentment on more than one occasion was punctuated with: "Those goddam Irish Catholics."

Whatever may have been true in pre-depression years, however tolerant or intolerant individuals may have been, . . . that Welsh sentiment was not at all limited to individuals guilty of irrational prejudice. It was communally shared. Jobs, homes, and lives were at stake, and religious affiliation was relevant to them all. Irish Catholic political power was a fact from which Welsh Protestant resentment followed. Prejudice there certainly was—deeply felt, poignantly articulated, subjectively often going beyond what facts would justify and, unfortunately, communicated to the young. . . .

The public sector was vulnerable to Irish Catholic control. The Welsh knew that. The private sector (banks, small businesses) simultaneously retained a diminished but tightened, now more consciously Protestant, ownership and/or control. Though the musically inclined Welsh never composed it, their regional battle hymn surely was: If Irish politicians were using their political power to control what they could, it was essential for Protestants to protect what they privately had.

SOURCE: Gray, David J. 1991. "Shadow of the Past: The Rise and Fall of Prejudice in an American City." *American Journal of Economics and Sociology*, 50: 33-39.

*Labor Unions.* The labor movement provided a second link between the Irish, other European immigrant groups, and the larger society. Although virtually all white ethnic groups had a hand in the creation and eventual success of the movement, many of the founders and early leaders were Irish. For example, Terence Powderly, an Irish Catholic, founded one of the first U.S. labor unions, and in the early years of the 20th century, about one third of union leaders were Irish, and more than 50 national unions had Irish presidents (Bodnar, 1985, p. 111; Brody, 1980, p. 615).

As the labor movement grew in strength and gradually acquired legitimacy, the leaders of the movement also gained status, power, and other resources, while the rank-and-file membership gained job security, increased wages, and better fringe benefits. The labor movement provided another channel through which resources, power, status, and jobs flowed to the white ethnic groups.

Because of the way in which jobs were organized in industrializing America, union work typically required communication and cooperation across ethnic lines. The American workforce at the turn of the 20th century was multiethnic and multilingual, and union leaders had to coordinate and mobilize the efforts of many different language and cultural groups to represent the interest of the workers as a social class. Thus labor union leaders became important intermediaries between the larger society and European immigrant groups.

Women were also heavily involved in the labor movement. Immigrant women were among the most exploited segments of the labor force, and they were involved in some of the most significant events in American labor history. For example, one of the first victories of the union movement occurred in New York City in 1909. The Uprising of the 20,000 was a massive strike of mostly Jewish and Italian women (many in their teens) against the garment industry. The strike lasted 4 months despite attacks by thugs hired by the bosses and abuses by the police and the courts. The strikers eventually won recognition of the union from many employers, a reversal of a wage decrease, and a reduction in the 56- to 59-hour week they were expected to work (Goren, 1980, p. 584).

One of the great tragedies in the history of labor relations in the United States also involved European immigrant women. In 1911, a fire swept through the Triangle Shirtwaist Company, a garment industry shop located on the 10th floor of a building in New York City. The fire spread rapidly, and the few escape routes were quickly cut off. About 140 young immigrant girls died, and many chose to leap to their deaths rather than be consumed by the flames. The disaster outraged the public, and the funerals of the victims were attended by more than a quarter of a million people. The incident fueled a drive for reform and improvement of work conditions and safety regulations (Amott & Matthaei, 1991, pp. 114-116; see also Schoener, 1967).

European immigrant women also filled leadership roles in the labor movement and served as presidents and in other offices, although usually in female-dominated unions. One of the most colorful union activists was Mother Jones, an Irish immigrant who worked tirelessly to organize miners:

> Until she was nearly one hundred years old, Mother Jones was where the danger was greatest—crossing militia lines, spending weeks in damp prisons, incurring the wrath of governors, presidents, and coal operators—she helped to organize the United Mine Workers with the only tools she felt she needed: "convictions and a voice." (Forner, 1980, p. 281)

Women workers often faced opposition from men as well as from employers. The major unions were not only racially discriminatory but also hostile to organizing women. For example, women laundry workers in San Francisco at the start of the 20th century were required to live in dormitories and work from 6 AM until midnight. When they applied to the international laundry workers union for a charter, they were blocked by the male members. They eventually went on strike and won the right to an 8-hour workday in 1912 (Amott & Matthaei, 1991, p. 117).

*The Catholic Church.* A third avenue of mobility for the Irish and other white ethnic groups was provided by the religious institution. The Irish were the first large group of Catholic immigrants and were thus in a favorable position to eventually dominate the church's administrative structure. The Catholic priesthood became largely Irish, and as they were promoted through the hierarchy, these priests became bishops and cardinals.

The Catholic faith was practiced in different ways in different nations. As other Catholic immigrant groups began to arrive, conflict within the Irish-dominated church increased. Both Italian and Polish Catholic immigrants demanded their own parishes in which they could speak their own languages and celebrate their own customs and festivals. Dissatisfaction was so intense that some Polish Catholics broke with Rome and formed a separate Polish National Catholic Church (Lopata, 1976, p. 49).

The other Catholic immigrant groups eventually began to supply priests and other religious functionaries and to occupy leadership positions within the church. Although the Church continued to be disproportionately influenced by the Irish, other white ethnic groups also used the Catholic Church as part of their power bases for gaining acceptance and integration into the larger society.

*Other Pathways of Mobility.* Besides party politics, the union movement, and religion, European immigrant groups forged other not-so-legitimate pathways of upward mobility. One alternative to legitimate success was offered by crime, a pathway that has been used by every ethnic group to some extent. Crime became particularly lucrative and attractive when Prohibition, the attempt to eliminate all alcohol use in the United States, went into effect in the 1920s. The criminalization of liquor failed to lower the demand, and Prohibition created a golden economic opportunity for those willing to take the risks involved in manufacturing and supplying alcohol to the American public.

Italian Americans headed many of the criminal organizations that took advantage of Prohibition. Criminal leaders and organizations with roots in Sicily, a region with a long history of secret antiestablishment societies, were especially important (Alba, 1985, pp. 62-64). The connection between organized crime, Prohibition, and Italian Americans is well known, but it is not so widely recognized that ethnic succession operated in organized crime as it did in the legitimate opportunity structures. The Irish and Germans had been involved in organized crime for decades before the 1920s, and the Italians competed with these established gangsters and with Jewish crime syndicates for control of bootlegging and other criminal enterprises. The pattern of ethnic succession continued after the repeal of Prohibition, and members of groups newer to urban areas, including African Americans, Jamaicans, and Hispanic Americans, have recently challenged the Italian-dominated criminal "families."

Ethnic succession can also be observed in the institution of sports. Since the beginning of the 20th century, sports have offered a pathway to success and affluence that has attracted countless millions of young men. Success in many sports requires little in the way of formal credentials, education, or English fluency, and sports have been particularly appealing to the young men in minority groups that have few resources or opportunities.

For example, at the turn of the century, the Irish dominated the sport of boxing, but boxers from the Italian American community and other new immigrant groups eventually replaced them. Each successive wave of boxers reflected the concentration of a particular ethnic group at the bottom of the class structure. The succession of minority groups continues to this day, with boxing now dominated by African American and Latino fighters (Rader, 1983, pp. 87-106). A similar progression, or "layering," of ethnic and racial groups can be observed in other sports and in the entertainment industry.

The institutions of American society, legitimate and illegal alike, reflect the relative positions of minority groups at a particular moment in time. Just a few generations ago, European immigrant groups dominated both crime and sports because they were blocked from legitimate opportunities. Now, the colonized racial minority groups still excluded from the mainstream job market and mired in the urban underclass are supplying disproportionate numbers of young people to these alternative opportunity structures.

## Continuing Industrialization and Structural Mobility

Changes in the American economy and occupational structure also shaped the social class position and speed of integration of the European immigrants and their descendants. Industrialization is a continuous process, and as it proceeded, the nature of work in America evolved and changed and created opportunities for upward mobility for the white ethnic groups. One important form of upward mobility throughout the 20th century, called **structural mobility**, resulted more from changes in the structure of the economy and the labor market than from any individual effort or desire to "get ahead."

Structural mobility is the result of the continuing mechanization and automation of the workplace. As machines replaced people in the workforce, the supply of manual, blue-collar jobs that had provided employment for so many first- and second-generation European immigrant laborers dwindled. At the same time, the supply of other types of jobs increased. We saw in chapter 6 (see Exhibit 6.2) that job growth in recent decades has been in the service sector and in white-collar jobs and that access to the better jobs in these areas depends heavily on educational credentials. For white ethnic groups, a high school education became much more available in the 1930s, and college and university programs began to expand rapidly in the late 1940s, spurred in large part by the educational benefits made available to World War II veterans. Each generation of white ethnics, especially those born after 1925, was significantly more educated than its parents, and many were able to translate that increased human capital into upward mobility in the mainstream job market (Morawska, 1990, pp. 212-213).

Thus the descendants of European immigrants became upwardly mobile not only because of their values or ambitions but also because of the changing location of jobs and the progressively greater opportunities for education available to them. Of course, the pace and timing of this upward movement was highly variable from group to group and place to place. Ethnic succession continued to operate, and the descendants of the more recent immigrants from Europe tended to be the last to benefit from the general upgrading in education and the job market. Still, structural mobility is one of the keys to the eventual successful integration of all white ethnic groups that is documented in Exhibits 12.1 through 12.3. At the same time, the racial and colonized minority groups, with the notable exceptions of the enclave-oriented Chinese Americans and Japanese Americans, were generally excluded from the dominant group's educational system and from the opportunity to compete for better jobs.

# COMPARING EUROPEAN IMMIGRANTS AND COLONIZED MINORITY GROUPS

Could other groups have followed the pathways to integration and mobility forged by European immigrants and their descendants? How relevant are these experiences for today's racial minority groups? Let's address this question by comparing the relative positions of the groups at the start of the 20th century.

A century ago, when European immigrants were forging their links to the larger society, most African Americans still resided in the South, where Jim Crow segregation excluded them from better jobs and from political power. Mexican Americans were also victimized by systematic segregation and exclusion, and American Indians were dealing with military defeat, threats to the integrity of their culture, and the isolation and enforced dependency of the reservation. The Chinese, and later the Japanese, had been banned from immigration and were responding to the campaigns of rejection and discrimination by leaving the mainstream economy and withdrawing to ethnic enclaves.

Clearly, compared with these groups, white ethnic groups were in the best position to pursue integration and equality. Their relative advantage was the result of many factors, not the least of which was that they entered the United States though the industrializing, urbanizing sectors of the economy, whereas other minority groups, especially the colonized racial minority groups, remained geographically and socially distant from opportunities for inclusion.

European immigrants were not immune from racism and rejection, as we have seen. In an urban industrial economy based on wage labor, however, there was no need to control the European immigrant groups in the same way that black sharecroppers in the South or Mexican farm workers in the Southwest were controlled. It was impractical and unnecessary to construct repressive systems of group relations like de jure segregation in the urban, industrial environment occupied by white ethnic groups, especially since no obvious physical or "racial" difference separated them from the dominant group. As pointed out in the Blauner hypothesis, if such attempts had been made to control and repress European immigrants, they could have selected a different destination or not immigrated at all.

Their status as (relatively) free immigrants gave white ethnic groups a control of their fate that, although minimal in many ways, was superior to the decision-making power available to members of the colonized minority groups. At a time when the racial minority groups faced nearly complete exclusion and massive discrimination, the European immigrants, their children, and their grandchildren were finding pathways into the dominant society.

Why didn't the racial minority groups follow the same pathways? While the European immigrant groups were "pushing" one another up in the mainstream economy during the first half of the 20th century, the racial and colonized minority groups, particularly African Americans in the rural South, began to move to the cities and seek places in the industrial workforce (see chapter 6). Often, African American migrants moved into the very neighborhoods abandoned by the upwardly mobile European American ethnic groups and began to compete with them and with elements of the dominant group for jobs and other resources.

In their efforts to penetrate the urban industrial labor market, members of racial minority groups often found themselves caught between the labor unions, which excluded them, and the factory owners, employers, and other capitalists, who wanted to exploit them as a source of cheap labor. African Americans and other racial minorities were often used as strikebreakers or scabs. Because they were barred from membership by the unions, the racial minority groups had little to lose by crossing the picket lines (Brody, 1980, p. 615).

As the labor movement gradually succeeded, more and more workplaces became closed shops in which all workers were required to become members of a certain union. When that union practiced racial discrimination, all the jobs they controlled were closed to nonunion members (i.e., nonwhites). Thus the discriminatory labor unions made it more difficult for minority groups of color to follow the path that European American ethnic groups had carved out.

In addition, discrimination against African and Hispanic Americans by employers was widespread and, when combined with the discrimination by the unions, resulted in the general exclusion of racial minority groups from the better paying, more secure jobs. These forces made it extremely difficult for these groups to emulate white ethnic groups and penetrate the mainstream industrial occupational structure (Geschwender, 1978, p. 184). As the white ethnic groups rose in the social class structure, they tended to close the doors behind them.

The job prospects of the colonized minority groups were further limited by the continuing mechanization of the economy, the same process that tended to benefit white ethnic groups. By the time the nonwhite groups arrived in the manufacturing and industrial sectors of the economy, the unskilled, manual labor jobs that had sustained generations of white ethnic groups were already disappearing. The escalator to comfortable middle-class prosperity ceased to function just as minority groups of color began arriving in the industrial urban areas. The process of ethnic succession—one group pushing up earlier arrivals—tended to grind to a halt as the urban working class became non-Anglo.

As European American ethnic groups have integrated and attained equality, the opportunities for upward mobility in the mainstream economy for racial minorities have dwindled. Thus, instead of following the white ethnic groups out of the old ethnic neighborhoods, ghettos, and slums, racial minority groups, including African Americans, American Indians, Hispanic Americans, Asian Americans, and many of the new immigrant groups have disproportionately become part of an impoverished, powerless, urban underclass.

## WILL WHITE ETHNICITY SURVIVE?

By the 1950s and 1960s, the assimilation documented in Exhibits 12.1 through 12.3 was well underway. The great majority of the descendants of the European immigrants had left the old ethnic neighborhoods for better housing more in keeping with their relative prosperity. These grandchildren and great-grandchildren of immigrants grew up in a nonethnic world, and as adults, they were virtually indistinguishable in their values, voting patterns, and personal lives from others of their social class and educational background. As the groups dispersed into middle-class suburbia, the white ethnic community networks—political, religious, and economic—lost strength and performed fewer and fewer functions. Inevitably, as the old ethnic community infrastructure faded away, the personal sense of ethnicity and common peoplehood faded as well. The descendants of European immigrants might continue to think of themselves in ethnic, "hyphenated" terms (as Irish-American, Italian-American, Polish-American, etc.), but the label has become increasingly tangential to their self-images and increasingly minor in its effects on their everyday lives.

# Ethnic Revivals

Absorption into the American mainstream was neither linear nor continuous, however. White ethnic identity sporadically reasserted itself in many ways, two of which are especially notable. First, there was a tendency for later generations to be more interested in their ancestry and ethnicity than were earlier generations. Marcus Hansen (1952) captured this phenomenon in his **principle of third-generation interest**: "What the second generation tries to forget, the third generation tries to remember" (pp. 495). Hansen observed that the children of immigrants tended to minimize or deemphasize ("forget") their ethnicity to avoid the prejudice and intolerance of the larger society and compete on more favorable terms for jobs and other opportunities. As they became adults and started families of their own, the second generation tended to raise their children in nonethnic settings, with English as their first and only language.

By the time the third generation reached adulthood, especially the "new" immigrant groups that arrived last, the larger society had become more tolerant of ethnicity and diversity, and having little to risk, the third generation tried to reconnect with its grandparents and roots. These descendants wanted to remember their ethnic heritage and understand it as part of their personal identities, their sense of who they were and where they belonged in the larger society. Thus interest in the "old ways" and the strength of the identification with the ancestral group was often stronger in the more Americanized third generation than in the more ethnic second. Ironically, of course, the grandchildren of the immigrants could not recover much of the richness and detail of their heritage because their parents had spent their lives trying to forget it. Nonetheless, the desire of the third generation to reconnect with its ancestry and recover its ethnicity shows, once again, that assimilation is not a simple, unidimensional, or linear process.

In addition to this generational pattern, the strength of white ethnic identity also responded to the changing context of American society and the activities of other groups. For example, in the late 1960s and early 1970s, there was a notable increase in the visibility of and interest in white ethnic heritage, an upsurge often referred to as the **ethnic revival**. The revival manifested itself in a variety of ways. Some people became more interested in their families' genealogical roots, and others increased their participation in ethnic festivals, traditions, and organizations. The "white ethnic vote" became a factor in local, state, and national politics, and appearances at the churches, meeting halls, and neighborhoods associated with white ethnic groups became almost mandatory for candidates for office. Demonstrations and festivals celebrating white ethnic heritages were organized, and buttons and bumper stickers proclaiming the ancestry of everyone from Irish to Italians were widely displayed. The revival was also endorsed by politicians, editorialists, and intellectuals (e.g., see Novak, 1973), reinforcing the movement and giving it additional legitimacy.

The ethnic revival may have been partly fueled, à la Hansen's principle, by the desire to reconnect with ancestral roots, even though most groups were well beyond their third generation by the 1960s. More likely, the revival was a reaction to the increase in pluralistic sentiment in the society in general and by the pluralistic, even separatist assertions of other groups that marked the decade. Virtually every minority group generated a protest movement (Black Power, Red Power, Chicanismo, etc.) and proclaimed a recommitment to its own heritage and to the authenticity of its own culture and experience. The visibility of these movements for cultural pluralism among racial minority groups helped make it more acceptable for European Americans to express their own ethnicity and heritage.

Besides the general tenor of the times, the resurgence of white ethnicity had some political and economic dimensions that bring us back to issues of inequality, competition, and control of resources. In the 1960s, a white ethnic urban working class made up largely of Irish and Southern and Eastern Europe groups, still remained in the neighborhoods of the industrial Northeast and Midwest and still continued to breathe life into the old networks and traditions. At the same time cultural pluralism was coming to be seen as more legitimate, this ethnic working class was feeling increasingly threatened by minority groups of color. In the industrial cities, it was not unusual for white ethnic neighborhoods to adjoin black and Hispanic neighborhoods, putting these groups in direct competition for housing, jobs, and other resources. Many members of the white ethnic working class saw racial minority groups as inferior and perceived the advances being made by these groups as unfair, unjust, and threatening. They also reacted to what they saw as special treatment and attention being accorded on the basis of race, such as school busing and affirmative action. They had problems of their own (the declining number of good, unionized jobs; inadequate schooling; and deteriorating city services) and felt that their problems were being given lower priority and less legitimacy because they were white. The revived sense of ethnicity in the urban working class neighborhoods was in large part a way of resisting racial reform and expressing resentment for the racial minority groups. Thus, among its many other causes and forms, the revival of white ethnicity that began in the 1960s was fueled by competition for resources and opportunities. As we have seen throughout our analysis, such competition commonly leads to increased prejudice and a heightened sense of cohesion among group members.

## White Ethnicity in the 21st Century

As the conflicts of the 1960s faded and white ethnic groups continued to leave the old neighborhoods and rise in the class structure, the strength of white ethnic identity resumed its slow demise. Today, several more generations removed from the tumultuous 1960s, white ethnic identity has become increasingly nebulous and largely voluntary. Today, white ethnic identity is often described as symbolic ethnicity. The descendants of the European immigrants feel vaguely connected to their ancestors and to the "old country," but this part of their identity does not affect their lifestyles, circles of friends and neighbors, job prospects, eating habits, or other everyday routines (Gans, 1979; Lieberson & Waters, 1988). For the descendants of the European immigrants today, ethnicity is an increasingly minor part of their identities that is expressed only occasionally or sporadically. For example, they might join in ethnic or religious festivals (e.g., St. Patrick's Day for Irish Americans, Columbus Day for Italian Americans), but these activities are seasonal or otherwise peripheral to their lives and self-images. The descendants of the European immigrants have choices, in stark contrast with their ancestors and with members of racial minority groups: They can stress their ethnicity, ignore it completely, or maintain any degree of ethnic identity they choose. Many people have ancestors in more than one ethnic group and may change their sense of affiliation over time, sometimes emphasizing one group's traditions and sometimes another's (Waters, 1990).

In fact, white ethnic identity has become so ephemeral that it may be on the verge of disappearing altogether. For example, based on a series of in-depth interviews with white Americans from various regions of the nation, Gallagher (2001) found a sense of ethnicity so weak that it did not even rise to the level of "symbolic." His respondents were the products of ancestral lines so thoroughly intermixed and intermarried that any trace of a unique heritage from a particular group was completely lost. They had virtually no knowledge of the experiences of their immigrant ancestors or of the life and culture of the ethnic communities they had inhabited, and for many, their ethnic ancestry was no more meaningful to them than their state of birth. Their lack of interest in and information about their ethnic heritage was so complete that it led Gallagher to propose an addendum to Hansen's principle: "What the grandson wished to remember, the great-granddaughter has never been told."

At the same time that more specific white ethnic identities are disappearing, they are also evolving into new shapes and forms. In the view of many analysts, a new identity is developing that merges the various "hyphenated" ethnic identities (German-American, Polish-American, etc.) into a single, generalized "European American" identity based on race and a common history of immigration and assimilation. This new identity reinforces the racial lines of separation that run through contemporary society, but it does more than simply mark group boundaries. Embedded in this emerging identity is an understanding, often deeply flawed, of how the white immigrant groups succeeded and assimilated in the past and a view, often deeply ideological, of how the racial minority groups should behave in the present. These understandings are encapsulated in "immigrant tales": legends that stress heroic individual effort and grim determination as key ingredients leading to success in the old days. These tales feature impoverished, victimized immigrant ancestors who survived and made a place for themselves and their children by working hard, saving their money, and otherwise exemplifying the virtues of the Protestant Ethic and American individualism. They stress the idea that past generations became successful despite the brutal hostility of the dominant group and with no government intervention, and they equate the historical difficulties faced by immigrants from Europe with those suffered by colonized minority groups (slavery, segregation, attempted genocide, etc.). They strongly imply—and sometimes blatantly assert—that the latter groups could succeed in America by simply following the example set by the former (Alba, 1990; Gallagher, 2001).

These accounts echo some of the debate over Asian Americans as "model minorities" and mix versions of human capital theory and traditional views of assimilation with modern racism. Without denying or trivializing the resolve and fortitude of European immigrants, equating their experiences and levels of disadvantage with those of African Americans, American Indians, and Mexican Americans is a comparison so far off the mark that it should not require further comment at this point in the text. These views support an attitude of disdain and lack of sympathy for the multiple dilemmas faced today by the racial minority groups and by many contemporary immigrants. They permit the subtle expression of prejudice and racism and allow whites to use these highly distorted views of their immigrant ancestors as a rhetorical device to express a host of race-based grievances without appearing racist (Gallagher, 2001). As Alba (1990) concludes:

> The thrust of the [emerging] European American identity is to defend the individualistic view of the American system, because it portrays the system as open to those who are willing to work hard and pull themselves out of poverty and discrimination. Recent research suggests that it is precisely this individualism that prevents many whites from sympathizing with the need for African Americans and other minorities to receive affirmative action in order to overcome institutional barriers to their advancement. (p. 317)

## COMPARING MINORITY GROUPS: IMMIGRATION VERSUS COLONIZATION

Among all the groups covered in this text, white ethnic groups are the closest to achieving assimilation and equality, an outcome that is quite consistent with the Blauner hypothesis. These groups succeeded because they entered U.S. society through the dynamic, urban industrial sector (often at the bottom, in the most miserable and least desirable jobs). Their rise to success took generations and was made possible not only by their own efforts but also by structural mobility and the expanding educational opportunities provided by the larger society. Not least among the ingredients in their recipe for success were their race and their consequent ability to blend into the mainstream and, when necessary, lose their ethnic identity completely.

Can their experiences serve as a model for today's racial minority groups or for the immigrants who have arrived since the mid-1960s? How relevant are the "immigrant tales" of determination and hard work? As we have seen repeatedly, the United States today no longer bears much resemblance to the society in which the white immigrant ancestors lived, worked, and died. The postindustrial economy provides few opportunities for less-educated manual laborers, and the promise of mobility for future generations has a distinctly hollow ring in the impoverished, inner-city neighborhoods inhabited by so many American minority groups.

## The Racial Identities of Whites and Blacks

*Earlier, we referred to the merging of the separate white ethnic identities (Irish American, Polish American, Italian American, etc.) into a single, all-encompassing, generalized, "European American" identity. In the selections that follow, we go beyond this assimilative process to consider some broader issues of racial identity in the United States today. A growing number of scholars have been exploring contemporary white racial identity, examining its nature and analyzing how it differs from the racial identity of nonwhites. In the first selection, Dyer (2002) argues that whites see themselves in nonracial terms, as the norm against which all other groups are compared. The perception of whiteness as "normal" distances all other groups and reinforces the power relationships that have dominated American society virtually since its inception.*

*Waters (1996) points out that "symbolic ethnicity," the ability to choose the extent to which one identifies with one's ancestral groups, is a luxury available only to whites. Members of racial and colonized groups are not free to excuse themselves from their groups, and those memberships continue to shape and limit their lives. Furthermore, argues Waters, the way whites think about their own ethnicity limits their ability to understand the situation and reactions of nonwhites, even when they are motivated by genuine acceptance of and interest in members of other groups.*

*Unlike other Current Debates, these selections are not opposed to each other. Rather, both challenge some "taken for granted" assumptions that are deeply embedded in the consciousness of white Americans, including, increasingly, the descendents of the white ethnic groups.*

### The Need to Understand Whiteness

RICHARD DYER

Racial imagery is central to the organization of the modern world. . . . Whose voices are listened to at international gatherings, who bombs and who is bombed, who gets what jobs, housing, access to health care and education . . . these are all largely inextricable from racial imagery. . . . Race is not the only factor governing these things . . . but it is never not a factor, never not in play. . . .

There has been an enormous amount of analysis of racial imagery in the past decades. . . . Yet, until recently, a notable absence from such work has been the study of images of white people. Indeed, to say that one is interested in race has come to mean that one is interested in any racial imagery other than that of white people.

This essay is about the racial imagery of white people. . . . This is not done merely to fill a gap in the analytical literature, but because there is something at stake in looking at . . . white racial imagery. As long as race is something only applied to non-white peoples, as long as white people are not racially seen and named, they/we function as a human norm. Other people are raced, we are just people. . . . There is no more powerful position than that of being "just" human. The claim to power is the claim to speak for the commonality of humanity. Raced people can't do that—they only speak for their own race.

The sense of white as non-raced is most evident in the absence of reference to whiteness in the habitual speech and writing of white people. . . . Whites will speak of, say, the blackness or Chineseness of friends, neighbors, colleagues . . . and it may be in the most genuinely friendly and accepting manner, but we don't mention the whiteness of white people we know. An old style white comedian will often start a joke: "There's this bloke walking down the street and he meets a black geezer," never thinking to race the bloke as well as the geezer. . . .

The assumption that white people are just people, which is not far off from saying that whites are people whereas other colors are something else, is endemic to white culture. . . . The invisibility of whiteness as a racial position in white (which is to say dominant) discourse is of a piece with its ubiquity. . . . Whites are everywhere in representation. Yet precisely because of this and their placing as the norm they seem not to be represented to themselves as whites but as people who are variously gendered, classed, sexualized, and abled. At the level of racial representation, in other words, whites are not of a certain race, they're just the human race. . . .

This is why it is important to come to see whiteness. . . . [As] long as whiteness is felt to be the human condition, then it alone defines normality. . . . [The] equation of being white with being human secures a position of power. White people have power and believe that they think, feel, and act like and for all people; white people, unable to see their particularity, cannot take account of other people's [particularity]. . . . White power . . . reproduces itself . . . overwhelmingly because it is not seen as whiteness but as normal. White people need to learn to see themselves as white, to see their particularity. In other words, whiteness needs to be made strange.

SOURCE: Dyer, Richard. 2002. "The Matter of Whiteness." In Paula Rothenberg (Ed.), *White Privilege* (pp. 9-12). New York: Worth.

## Symbolic and Involuntary Ethnicity

**MARY WATERS**

[Symbolic ethnicity is] confined to White Americans of European origin. Black Americans, Hispanic Americans, Asian Americans, and American Indians do not have the option of a symbolic ethnicity at present. . . . For all of the ways in which ethnicity does not matter for White Americans, it does matter for non-Whites. Who your ancestors are does affect your choice of spouse, where you live, what job you have, who your friends are, and what your chances are for success in American society, if those ancestors happen not to be from Europe. The reality is that White ethnics have a lot more choice and

room to maneuver than they themselves think they do. The situation is very different for members of racial minorities, whose lives are strongly influenced by their race or national origin regardless of how much they choose to identify themselves in terms of their ancestries.

When white Americans learn the stories of how their [ancestors] triumphed . . . over adversity, they are usually told in terms of their individual efforts. . . . The important role of labor unions and other organized political and economic factors in their social and economic success are left out of the story in favor of a story of individual Americans rising up against . . . Old World intolerance and New World resistance. As a result, the "individualized" voluntary, cultural view of ethnicity for Whites is what is remembered. . . .

The symbolic ethnic tends to think that all groups are equal: Everyone has a background that is their right to celebrate and pass on to their children. This leads to the conclusion that all identities are equal. . . . The important thing is to treat people as individuals and all equally. However, this assumption ignores the very big difference between an individualistic symbolic identity and a socially enforced and imposed racial identity. . . . When White Americans equate their own symbolic ethnicities with the socially enforced identities of non-White Americans, they obscure the fact that the experiences of Whites and non-Whites have been qualitatively different . . . and that the current identities of individuals partly reflect their unequal history. . . .

An example of the kind of misunderstanding that can arise because of the different understandings of the meaning and implications of symbolic versus [involuntary] identities concerns questions [college] students ask one another . . . in the dorms about personal appearance and customs. A very common type of interaction in the dorms concerns questions Whites ask Blacks about their hair. . . . Whites are generally quite curious about Black students' hair [and] wonder to themselves whether they should ask . . . questions. One thought experiment Whites perform is to ask themselves whether a particular question would upset them. Adopting a "do unto others" rule, they ask themselves, "If a Black person was curious about my hair would I get upset?" The answer is usually "No, I would be happy to tell them." [So, assuming that everyone would be equally open, they proceed to ask their questions and are surprised when their] innocent questions . . . lead to resentment. The . . . stereotypes about Black Americans and the assumption that all Blacks are alike . . . has . . . power to hurt and offend a Black person.

The innocent questions about Black hair also bring up the asymmetries between Black and White experience. Because Blacks tend to have more knowledge about Whites than vice versa, there is not an even exchange going on. . . . Because of the [historical] differences [between the groups], there are some connotations to Black hair that don't exist about White hair. (For instance, is straightening your hair a form of assimilation. . . . How is this related to looking "White"?) Finally, even a Black student who cheerfully disregards . . . these asymmetries will soon slam into another asymmetry if she willingly answers every innocent question asked of her. In a situation where Blacks make up only 10 percent of the student body, if every non-Black needs to be educated about hair, she will have to explain it to nine other students. As one Black student explained

to me, after you've been asked a couple of times about something so personal you begin to feel like you are an attraction in a zoo, that you are at the university for the education of White students.

SOURCE: Waters, Mary. 1996. "Optional Ethnicities: For Whites Only?" In S. Pedraza & R. Rumbaut (Eds.), *Origins and Destinies* (pp. 449-452). Belmont, CA: Wadsworth.

## Debate Questions to Consider

1. Is Dyer right about the tendency to "race" only nonwhites? Can you detect this pattern in the everyday conversations of people around you? What are the implications of this tendency for people's perceptions of each other and the possibilities for honest, clear communication across group lines? What does he mean when he says that we need to make whiteness strange?

2. Can you extend Dyer's point to gender relations? Do only females have gender? How?

3. Is Waters saying that it is wrong to treat people equally and as individuals? How can it be wrong to be "color blind"? What does she mean by the distinction she makes between an "individualistic symbolic identity" and an "imposed racial identity"? Can you find examples in your experience of how these realities have hampered communication across group lines?

- Mass immigration from Europe to the United States lasted for a century and supplied much of the labor force needed to fuel the American industrial revolution. In turn, the economic strength of the United States helped it become a world power.

- The descendants of the immigrants are assimilated today, but there are many reasons to include them in a review of American minority groups.

- European immigrant groups were highly diversified. Immigrants from Northern and Western Europe entered the United States largely through higher status positions in the urban economy and as independent farmers. Their descendants tended to be acculturated and integrated by the early 20th century. Immigrants from Ireland and Southern and Eastern Europe became the labor force that powered the industrial revolution, and their descendants remained largely an unskilled labor force until well into the 20th century. Jews from Eastern Europe entered the urban working class but also formed an ethnic enclave. Their descendants tended to enter the primary economy at more prestigious and professional levels. Religion was a particularly important criterion that separated Jews and Catholics from the dominant group.

- Social class position and the speed of assimilation were affected by the degree of similarity between European immigrants and white Anglo-Saxon Protestants. In the process of ethnic succession, European immigrant groups pushed one another up in the social class structure of the dominant society. The public institutions of U.S. society were integrated through local politics, labor unions, the Catholic Church, and other, less legitimate channels. The upward mobility of European American ethnic groups was abetted by structural mobility, the changing nature of the occupational structure, and the increasing availability of education.

- The pathways to integration followed by the European American ethnic groups in the past are generally not available to racial minority groups today.

- European American ethnicity has generally faded away as part of the process of assimilation. However, white ethnic identity tended to reassert itself in the third generation and especially in the 1960s. Today, white ethnic identity is largely symbolic and in the process of fading away. It may be replaced by a new, race-based identity that incorporates an ideology of modern racism.

## Study Site on the Web

Don't forget the interactive quizzes and other resources and learning aids at www.www.pineforge.com/healeystudy4.

## For Further Reading

Alba, Richard. 1985. *Italian Americans: Into the Twilight of Ethnicity.* Englewood Cliffs, NJ: Prentice Hall.

Fallows, Marjorie R. 1979. *Irish Americans: Identity and Assimilation.* Englewood Cliffs, NJ: Prentice Hall.

Goldstein, Sidney, & Goldscheider, Calvin. 1968. *Jewish Americans: Three Generations in a Jewish Community.* Englewood Cliffs, NJ: Prentice Hall.

Lopata, Helena Znaniecki. 1976. *Polish Americans.* Englewood Cliffs, NJ: Prentice Hall.

Sklare, Marshall. 1971. *America's Jews.* New York: Random House. *(Five concise, readable accounts of some of the most prominent European American ethnic groups.)*

Higham, John. 1963. *Strangers in the Land: Patterns of American Nativism, 1860-1925.* New York: Atheneum. *(The classic historical account of the efforts to restrict immigration and other movements of opposition to immigrants.)*

Schoener, Allon. 1967. *Portal to America: The Lower East Side, 1870-1925.* New York: Holt, Rinehart & Winston. *(An outstanding collection of photographs of a famous New York City ethnic neighborhood at the turn of the century. Moving, revealing, humorous, and informative. Includes a narrative regarding the nature of everyday life.)*

Cohen, Adam, & Taylor, Elizabeth. 2000. *American Pharaoh. Mayor Richard J. Daley: His Battle for Chicago and the Nation.* New York: Little, Brown. *(An impressive analysis of one of the most powerful urban political machines and its connections with ethnicity, religion, and race.)*

## Questions for Review and Study

1. Compared to the colonized and conquered groups we have considered in previous chapters, how does the history of white ethnic groups illustrate the Blauner hypothesis? Are these groups acculturated and integrated? How? Have they completed the stages of assimilation as described by Gordon? Provide evidence from the chapter for your answer.

2. Review the definition of "minority group" presented in chapter 1. Do contemporary white ethnic groups meet the criteria stated in the definition? Why or why not? How would your answer to this question change if you were considering the ancestors of today's groups that lived in the early decades of the 20th century?

3. In arguing that white ethnic groups can still be considered minorities, the text states that traditional prejudices and stereotypes against these groups persist. Is this convincing in terms of your own personal experience? Are you personally familiar with these attitudes and images? If you are, how do you think you acquired these ideas? If not, was there something about your socialization experience that might have insulated you from this type of prejudice?

4. Explain the importance of the industrial revolution both in motivating the immigration from Europe that led to the creation of white ethnic minority groups and in shaping the assimilation of the descendants of the immigrants.

5. Describe the immigration from Europe in terms of timing and the national origins of groups. What were the important social, cultural, and economic differences between the Old and New Immigration?

6. How did gender, religion, and social class shape the experiences of the immigrants and their descendants?

7. Compare the experiences of Jewish immigrants with Chinese, Japanese, and Cuban immigrants. What differences and similarities can you cite in their enclave experiences? What kept other European immigrant groups from also forming enclaves?

8. What effect did the National Origins Act of 1924 have on immigration from Europe? In what ways was that legislation based on racism and prejudice? What effects did the act have on the assimilation of white ethnic groups (see Massey's argument in chapter 11)?

9. Compare and contrast immigration and assimilation in Canada and the United States. What important similarities and differences can you identify in the two national experiences?

10. What factors shaped the assimilation of white ethnic groups? What is "ethnic succession," and how did it affect white ethnic groups? How did it affect the racial minority groups that followed white ethnic groups? What institutions and organizations of the larger society were involved in this assimilation process? How? What is "structural mobility," and why is the concept important for understanding the experiences of these groups?

11. Will white ethnicity survive? In what form? What is "symbolic ethnicity"? Is white ethnic identity becoming increasingly racial? Why?

## Internet Research Project

Additional information and a list of relevant Web sites are included in the Appendix (Internet Resources).

### A. Comparing Anti-Immigration Movements

The text describes the campaign against immigration that began in the 19th century and culminated in the passage of the National Origins Act in 1924. Keeping in mind relevant information from chapters 9 through 11, compare and contrast the campaign against immigration then with the contemporary movement. To get started, here are the addresses of two anti-immigrant sites:
The Federation for Immigration Reform (FAIR): http://www.fairus.org/.
Vdare (affiliated with Peter Brimelow's views on immigration; see Current Debate in chapter 10): http://www.vdare.com/.

What specific arguments against immigration are cited in the contemporary campaign? To what extent are the arguments based on data, objective sources, and logical reasoning? To what extent does the argument rely on emotional appeals and subtle prejudice? To develop a more balanced picture, search for counterarguments on the Internet and summarize and analyze these arguments as well.

## B. Immigration From Europe

Expand the information in the chapter about the experience of immigration from Europe between the 1820s and the 1920s by picking a group and doing an Internet search with the group's name (e.g., "Italian American" or "Polish American") and the keyword "immigration." Sort through the list of sites and links to find information and stories to supplement the material in the chapter. For the group you select, you might focus on such questions as: When did immigration begin and end? What were the primary motives for leaving? What resources did the immigrants typically bring with them? Where did they go in the United States? How did the dominant group (or other groups) respond to their arrival? What kind of work did they do? Other questions will occur to you from your reading of the chapter or during the process of your Internet search, but it is unlikely that you will find answers to all your questions online.

# PART V

## A Global View, a Summary, Some Conclusions, and a Look to the Future

**Chapter 13**
Dominant-Minority Relations
in Cross-National Perspective

**Chapter 14**
Minority Groups and U.S. Society:
Themes, Patterns, and the Future

In this section, the analytical framework developed in this text is applied to a variety of dominant-minority relations around the globe. The objective is to test the universality of these ideas and to identify the common dynamics that shape intergroup relations everywhere. Issues of assimilation and pluralism are not peculiar to the United States, and colonization and conquest are common causes of the most explosive and longest lasting group conflicts. Racism, prejudice, discrimination, and inequality are also common and important aspects of group relations. However, not all societies that incorporate more than one group are characterized by conflict and rancor, and we will take a look at some societies that are widely regarded as having relatively harmonious group relations.

Chapter 13 summarizes the major themes of this text, brings the analysis to a close, and speculates about the future of American race and ethnic relations.

## ABOUT THE PUBLIC SOCIOLOGY ASSIGNMENTS

The two assignments in this part are global in scope. The first focuses on natural and man-made disasters, public policy, emergency relief efforts, and the most vulnerable and exploitable segments of society. As we have seen throughout this text, minority groups (especially colonized groups) and women frequently have the fewest resources and the least ability to protect their self-interest. When disaster strikes, they are often the most exposed and victimized segment of the society. What policies, if any, do your community and state have to protect these most vulnerable populations? How can these policies be improved?

The second assignment connects to one of the most distressing and horrifying acts of which people are capable: genocide. Chapter 13 covers the genocide that occurred in Rwanda in 1994, and there have been several more genocides since, including one in the Darfur region of Somalia. What is known about the causes of these horrors? What can be done to prevent them? This exercise allows you to develop and present information about a particular genocide. Unfortunately, there are many from which to choose.

## Assignment 1
### Social Justice and Disaster Preparedness Planning

Each year the world experiences a plethora of natural and man-made disasters. Hurricanes, typhoons, earthquakes, tsunamis, flooding, drought, and heavy snowfall are a few of the natural disasters. Oil-tanker spills and terrorist and war-based attacks are prominent man-made disasters. These events have devastating effects on local populations. For example, the December 29, 2004 tsunami that impacted eastern Africa, South Asia, and parts of Southeast Asia killed in excess of 120,000 people. Many died due to water contamination, vulnerability to dengue fever and malaria, and other communicable diseases promoted by numerous unburied corpses. The September 11, 2001 terrorist attack on the World Trade Center killed 2752 people and caused billions of dollars in damages. The human suffering caused by incidents such as these is inestimable and is on a scale difficult even to comprehend.

We learned in this text that societies experience a range of social inequalities. Many times, especially vulnerable segments of the population are, for all practical purposes, invisible. During natural and man-made disasters, women, children, the aged, the underprivileged, and ethnic minorities may experience more severe trauma due to their "invisibility" or to lack of awareness on the part of disaster relief agencies and the policies they follow. For example, women and children in the December 29 tsunami experienced not simply loss of life, injuries, separation from loved ones, and basic needs but also rape and sexual exploitation. Disaster plans do not always include explicit gender perspective in all responses to humanitarian and recovery needs. This assignment is designed for you to explore local, state, and federal disaster preparedness and response policy, to discern whether particular populations are invisible and likely to inadvertently experience unequal treatment and unmitigated trauma. Responding rapidly and effectively to a disaster is extremely complex, and officials and personnel involved often put their lives at risk to help others get out of harm's way and recover. Your state department of emergency management may be able to use your research to examine its policy and response in an effort to serve the citizenry best.

### Step 1

You will first need to gain a basic understanding of disaster preparedness and how agencies cooperate with each other to serve the populace during times of crisis. Start with the Federal Emergency Management Agency (FEMA) Web site at http://www.fema.gov and conduct a literature review of their resources (which are quite good). If you want to focus on man-made disasters or terrorist attacks, you may want to explore the State Department of Homeland Security (to which FEMA reports) at http://www.dhs.gov/. Next, go to your state department of emergency management's Web site and conduct a similar literature review.

Three resources are listed at the end of this assignment to help you get started. The first is a United Nations report on environmental management and mitigation of natural disasters from a gender perspective. Other variables, such as age, ethnicity, and socioeconomic status, may be used instead of gender, as you prefer: The issues of inequality are similar from a policy point of view. The second resource is the Commonwealth of Virginia's Disaster Preparedness Plan, which will give you exposure to how one state approaches the problem. Your particular state will have its own plan and should be searched. The final resource is the U.S. National Response Plan, from the Department of Homeland Security. This gives you a global perspective useful to looking at how local county, state, and federal agencies in the United States must coordinate activities and prioritize relief efforts.

### Step 2

Choose a particular variable (e.g., gender, age, or race) on which to focus your policy and procedure review. Return to your literature review and reexamine the material to glean information on your variable from global, federal, state, and local points of view.

### Step 3

Using the information you obtained from your literature and resource reviews, draft a set of questions to refer to when speaking with agency and government officials. Your goal is to come up with information and material that the agency will find useful and helpful in carrying out its duties.

### Step 4

Contact your state director of emergency management. Discuss with her or him your interest in exploring the disaster preparedness plan and contributing information that may be used to ensure that especially vulnerable populations are not inadvertently overlooked in relief efforts. You will probably be directed to speak with a number of other agency contacts and should keep a log of conversations. Be open to suggestions they provide to you to customize your efforts in light of the needs they agree exist. In short, if an agency does not agree there is a need for such information, what you give them in the end will not be used, and so you must adjust realistically to their interest.

### Step 5

Using the resources you uncovered in steps one and two plus the resources you obtained from the agencies, begin a policy analysis on the relative invisibility of the group or groups on which you are focused. If the group you have chosen is indeed invisible or is only tangentially addressed, you must explore other disaster preparedness plans from other states, countries, and transnational agencies (i.e., International Federation of Red Cross and Red Crescent Societies, http://www.ifrc.org/; United Nations, http://www.un.org/; Doctors without Borders, http://www.doctorswithoutborders.org). You need to find relief protocols that already exist that your agency can consider adopting, along with the reasoning behind the protocols.

### Step 6

Examine the structure of your state's disaster preparedness plan and decide how to insert the content you obtained from your research. Your wording and language use must be consistent and conform to the existing document. Once you have worked this out, submit your finished content to your agency contacts and ask them to keep you informed of any adoption of the material you put together and revision of the disaster plan. Thank them for their assistance and commitment and for their providing you with the opportunity to contribute!

**Step 7**

Congratulate yourself for hard work well done! Do not be surprised if you have worked yourself into an agency internship!

**Resources**

http://daccessdds.un.org/doc/UNDOC/GEN/N01/722/05/PDF/N0172205.pdf?fOpenElement
Commonwealth of Virginia's Disaster Preparedness Plan:
http://www.vdem.state.va.us/library/ eopvol2/eopvolume2.pdf

U.S. National Response Plan: http://www.dhs.gov/dhspublic/display?theme=15& content=4269; if your computer can handle all 426 pages (4 MB) of the full text version, go straight to http://www.dhs.gov/interweb/assetlibrary/NRP_FullText.pdf

# Assignment 2
## Global Genocide Awareness and Education

Most students are familiar with the genocide during World War II perpetrated by Adolf Hitler and the German Nazi soldiers under his command against Jews, Romany, and other ethnic groups. There have been many other genocides since World War II. In fact, they seem to occur with alarming frequency. As inequalities increase among people not just in the United States but worldwide, the incidence of genocide seems to increase as well. Therefore, understanding genocide as an international war crime as well as a crime against humanity is paramount. In this assignment, you will create educational and informational materials for a local school, your college or university community, or a broader audience on a genocide of your choosing.

### Step 1

Review the different genocides. You will do this by reviewing the published literature on past and present genocides in your school library as well as online databases and Web sites. When using online resources, you must be careful to exercise good information literacy skills, because there is little editorial control over the content of sites, and there exist people who argue that certain genocides, such as the Jewish Holocaust during World War II, never happened. When in doubt, consult your university or college librarians for assistance, as they are experts in information literacy. A few online resources are suggested at the end of this assignment to get you started.

### Step 2

Choose a genocide to study in detail. These may be genocides in Cambodia in the late 1970s, the former Yugoslavia in the 1990s, Darfur Sudan in 2004, or another genocide. As a general rule, however, you might consider focusing on an event that has not already been covered in depth in history textbooks so that that your audience will be informed of the scope of the problem and its continuing prevalence.

### Step 3

Once your background research is completed, assess what audience and presentation format you feel best targets and promotes the knowledge you have synthesized. You may wish to compile learning aids for your alma mater high school or a grade school with which you are connected. You may wish to share your knowledge with your fellow university or college classmates and faculty through a poster or presentation kiosk exhibition in the local student center or union. If you are computer savvy and graphically inclined, you may wish to construct a Web site hosted on your college or university account or by a third-party account such as Geocities.

### Step 4

After deciding the final product format and audience, compile your resources and construct your learning materials. Be careful to cite your sources correctly and appropriately. If you are using Internet site links or relying on a Web site's resources, e-mail the site managers for each link to inform them of your link and purpose.

### Step 5

With a draft of your materials completed, share it with an impartial reviewer, such as a professor, teacher (especially if providing learning resources to a school), or community advocate or authority.

### Step 6

Consider the revisions your reviewer suggests and make appropriate changes to your materials. Polish your presentation, Web site, poster series, or learning resources into a final draft that makes an impact on the viewer.

### Step 7

Exhibit your materials and make yourself available to answer questions from your audience.

### Step 8

Send a thank-you message to those advocates who helped you with your materials and provide them with a copy, if appropriate, of your final product for them to make available to others. Do not forget to congratulate yourself for emotionally difficult yet rewarding work well done!

### Suggested Resources

Prevent Genocide International: http://www.preventgenocide.org/
The United Nations Human Rights Web site: http://www.un.org/rights/
The Australian Institute for Holocaust and Genocide Studies: http://www.aihgs.com/

# 13

# Dominant-Minority Relations In Cross-National Perspective

EARLY IN THIS TEXT, A SET OF CONCEPTS AND HYPOTHESES WERE DEVELOPED TO HELP US ANALYZE and understand dominant-minority relations. In chapters 7 through 12, our analytical framework was further elaborated and applied to the creation and evolution of minority group status across U.S. history. Although our concepts have proven their usefulness, it is important to recognize that they have been tested against the experiences of just a single nation. Just as you would not accept an interview with a single person as an adequate test of a psychological theory, you should not accept the experiences of a single nation as proof for the sociological perspective developed in this text. If our ideas apply to dominant-minority situations in other societies, we will have some assurance that the dynamics of intergroup relations in the United States are not unique and that our conclusions have some general applicability.

In this chapter, we will first briefly review the ideas that have guided our analysis and then apply them to various societies from around the globe. It is not possible to investigate every society in the world, and I will focus on "trouble spots," or societies with dominant-minority group conflicts that have been widely publicized and are therefore familiar to most people. For purposes of comparison, I have also included several societies in which group relations are thought to be generally peaceful.

You should be very clear about the limits of this "test." The sample of societies is small and is not representative of human societies in general, and therefore it will not permit a final or definitive test of theory. Before final conclusions can be reached, we need much more research on a broad array of societies drawn from a variety of time periods, regions, levels of development, and cultural backgrounds. Just as important, information about many of our most crucial concepts (for example, the degree and nature of prejudice or discrimination) is simply not available for many societies. Without precise, trustworthy information, our tests will necessarily be informal and impressionistic. At any rate, you may rest assured that the conclusions reached in this chapter will not be the final word on the subject.

## A BRIEF REVIEW OF MAJOR ANALYTICAL THEMES

Before commencing our cross-national tour, it will be useful to review the major analytical themes developed in this text. These ideas were summarized as seven themes in the introduction to Part IV and have been used extensively throughout the text. Thus a brief review will be sufficient.

One theme that has been constantly stressed is the importance of the initial contact situation between groups. The characteristics of the initial meeting (particularly the nature and intensity of the competition and the balance of power between the groups) can shape relations for centuries. We have also found that the fates of minority groups created by colonization and conquest are very different from those created by immigration. As we have seen repeatedly in U.S. history, colonized or conquered minority groups are subjected to greater rejection, discrimination, and inequality and become more completely mired in their minority status. Positive change is more difficult to accomplish for conquered or colonized groups, especially when the group is racially or physically different from the dominant group.

As we examine the most difficult and explosive group conflicts from around the globe in this chapter, you will notice that their origins are often in contact situations in which the colonizers were white Europeans and the eventual minority groups were peoples of color. This pattern of dominance and subordination reflects the conditions under which the present world system of societies was created. By the 1400s, the nations of Europe were the most technologically advanced in the world, and they used their superiority to explore, conquer, and sometimes destroy much of the rest of the world. The scores of conflicts between whites and nonwhites—and many of the conflicts between peoples of color—strewn around the globe today are one legacy of this enormous burst of European power and energy.

Of course, the pattern of white dominance is also in part an accident of history. Nations have been conquering, enslaving, persecuting, and oppressing their neighbors for millennia. When the neighbors differed in some visible way, prejudice, racism, and systems of inequality based on group membership often followed the military conquests. The unique contribution of Europeans to this ancient pattern was that their era of conquest and colonization coincided with breakthroughs in shipbuilding, navigation, and other technologies that enabled them to spread their influence far wider and more permanently than colonizers of the past. The nations of Europe (and the British in particular) were able to rule much of the world until very recent decades, and many of the present ethnic and racial conflicts were born during the era of European colonialism (see Wallace, 1997).

A second important theme is that dominant-minority relationships tend to change most rapidly and dramatically when the level of development or the basic subsistence technology of the larger society changes. For example, industrialization revolutionized not only technology and modes of production, it transformed group relationships in Europe, in the United States, and eventually, around the globe. In Europe, the new subsistence technology stimulated massive waves of immigration, beginning in the 1820s, and the new technology helped European nations to dominate the world system of societies in the 19th century and much of the 20th. In the United States, the industrial revolution led to a transition from paternalistic to rigid competitive group relations starting in the 19th century, and in the latter half of the 20th century, continuing modernization resulted in the emergence of fluid competitive relations between groups. The blatant racism and overt discrimination of the past have become more moderate, taking on milder, more ambiguous forms that are more difficult to identify and measure, and this evolution to less repressive forms of group relations has been propelled by the protest activities of minority group members and their allies.

Thus contact situations, assimilation and pluralism, prejudice, racism, and institutional discrimination are all central to understanding the past and present situations of U.S. minority groups. To what extent, however, are these themes and concepts applicable to group relations around the world? We begin our tour with Canada, our neighbor to the north, and then continue to the east, spanning the globe and returning to the Western Hemisphere with Brazil.

# A GLOBAL TOUR
## Canada

Citizens of the United States often see Canada as simply a colder version of their home society, a perception that is sustained by the enormous impact the United States has had on everyday social, economic, and political life in Canada. In fact, dominant-minority situations in the two societies share many similarities, both historically and at present. The two societies are, however, quite different. For example, although black Africans were enslaved in colonial Canada, the institution never took on the economic, political, or social significance it assumed in the United States.

Perhaps the most obvious difference between the two nations is that at present, the major minority issue in Canada is cultural and linguistic, not racial. For more than two centuries, Canadian society has been divided into two major language groups, French speaking and English speaking. French speakers (or Francophones) are the minority group and are concentrated in the province of Québec. Nationally, French speakers are about 25% of the population, but in Québec they constitute about 80% of the population.

In our terms, issues of assimilation and pluralism separate the two linguistic and cultural groups. French Canadians have preserved their language and culture in the face of domination by English speakers for more than 200 years, and they continue to maintain their traditions today. Although French Canadians are largely pluralistic, they are not unanimous about the type of relationship that they would like to have with the larger society. At one extreme, some Francophones want complete separation between Québec and English-speaking Canada: Their goal is to make Québec an independent nation. Others would be satisfied with guarantees of more autonomy for Québec and national recognition of the right of the French-speaking residents of Québec to maintain their language and culture.

English-speaking Canadians have shown little support for separation or pluralism. In a series of referenda over the past several decades, the national electorate has defeated several different proposals to grant more autonomy to Québec. In 1992, for example, Canadians voted down a proposal to grant special status and more self-governance to Québec. Interestingly, the proposal was also defeated in Québec but for different reasons. Whereas Canadians outside Québec felt the 1992 proposal went too far in granting special status to Québec, residents of Québec rejected the proposal because it did not go far enough. Nationalist sentiment remains strong in Québec, and the intertwined issues of bilingualism, cultural separation, and political autonomy remain unresolved as Canada, like the United States, searches for ways to deal with its diversity.

**EXHIBIT 13.1** Map of Canada, Showing Provinces

What caused the conflict between French- and English-speaking Canadians? It will not surprise you that the answer begins with the contact situation between the English and the French in Canada. Throughout the 1600s and 1700s, France and England (and other European nations) fought for control of North America. The French were eliminated as a colonial power when in 1759 and 1760, the British captured Québec City and Montreal and ended the French and Indian War (as it is called in the United States). The French who remained after the war were largely concentrated in what is now Québec, and they became the ancestral community to today's pluralistic movement. The French community was organized around farming, and the victorious British took control of the economic and political institutions of the region.

The present pluralistic movement began in the 1960s. At that time, about 200 years after France ceased to be a colonial power in North America, French-speaking residents of Québec were still a minority group. English-speaking Canadians remained in control of the central institutions of Québec, and there were marked differences in wealth, education, occupational profile, and political power between French and English speakers in the province. Since the 1960s, the status of Québec's French-speaking residents has risen, and they have gained more economic and political power, but issues of control of resources and wealth continue to animate the struggle.

Québec continues to attempt to work out its relationship with the rest of the nation as Canada faces a number of other minority group issues, most of which will be familiar to citizens of the United States. For example, after years of maintaining a restrictive immigration policy that favored whites, Canada reformed its laws in the 1960s. Since that time, there has been a steady and large influx of newcomers from the same areas that supply immigrants to the United States: Latin America, the Caribbean, and Asia. Also, the native peoples of Canada share many problems and inequities with American Indians in the United States. Many live on remote reservations (called "reserves") that have high levels of poverty and unemployment and low levels of health care and educational opportunities.

In conclusion, Canada's problems of group relations can be analyzed in familiar terms. Some Canadian minority groups (French speakers and Canadian Indians) originated in conquest and colonization and have been victimized by discrimination and rejection for centuries. Especially since the 1960s, members of these groups have actively protested their situations, and some reforms and improvements have been made. Other groups consist of recent immigrants who share much in common with similar groups in the United States. In fact, despite the clear and important differences that exist between the nations, Canada faces many of the same issues that confront U.S. society: questions of unity and diversity, fairness and equality, assimilation and pluralism.

## Northern Ireland

Other nations face issues similar to those faced by Canada but with different levels of intensity, urgency, and lethality. In Northern Ireland, the bitter, violent conflict between Protestants and Catholics has some parallels with Canadian and U.S. group relations and has been closely watched and widely reported. Thousands of people have lost their lives during the struggles, many of them victims of terrorist attacks.

The roots of this conflict lie in armed hostilities between England and Ireland that began centuries ago. By the 1600s, England had colonized much of Ireland and had encouraged Protestants from Scotland and England to move to what is now Northern Ireland to help pacify and control the Catholic Irish. The newcomers, assisted by the English invaders, came to own much of the land and control the economy and the governing structure of the northern regions of the island.

Over the centuries, the Protestants in Northern Ireland have consolidated their position and power and separated themselves from the native Catholic population in the school system, in residential areas, and in most other areas of society. Law and strong custom reinforced the subordinate position of Catholics, and the system, at its height, came to resemble Jim Crow segregation. That is, it was a system of rigid competitive relations in which the Protestants sought to limit the ability of Catholics to compete for jobs, political power, housing, wealth, and other resources.

The British never succeeded in completely subordinating the Irish, who periodically attempted to achieve their independence through violent rebellions. These efforts came to partial fruition in the 1920s when an uprising that began with the Easter Rebellion in 1916 led to the creation of an independent Republic of Ireland. The new nation encompassed most of the island, but the largely Protestant northern counties, traditionally known as the province of Ulster, remained part of Great Britain.

The partition of the island into an overwhelmingly Catholic Republic and a Protestant Northern Ireland set the stage for the troubles that continue to the present. The Catholics of Northern Ireland began a civil rights movement in the late 1960s, seeking amelioration for their

**EXHIBIT 13.2**  Map of Great Britain and Ireland, Showing Northern Ireland

minority status. Protestants, fearing loss of privilege and control, resisted attempts at reform, and the confrontation escalated into terrorism and violence. In 1998, lengthy and difficult negotiations—made possible in large part by the involvement and support of Great Britain, the Republic of Ireland, and the United States—resulted in the "Good Friday Agreement." This accord established a new power-sharing arrangement for the governance of Northern Ireland in which both Protestant and Catholic parties will participate. The new governmental arrangement has not gone smoothly but has survived several difficult crises, including a terrorist attack on a shopping area in Omagh, Northern Ireland, in August 1998 that left nearly 30 people dead. Although fragile and tenuous, the Good Friday Agreement is overwhelmingly supported by the electorate and may eventually lead to a peaceful resolution to this ancient rivalry.

Note that in this case, as in the case of relations between Québec and the rest of Canada, both the dominant and the minority group are of the same race. The deep divisions that separate groups are mainly ethnic (English vs. non-English) and religious (Protestant vs. Catholic). In both nations, these divisions are highly correlated with social class position, access to education and jobs, and political power. That is, Catholics in Northern Ireland—like the French-speaking residents of Québec—are a minority group that has been victimized by intense, systematic, and persistent discrimination and prejudice. What is at stake is not simply a question of cultural survival or religion. These clashes are so bitter, so deadly, and so intractable because they also concern the distribution of real resources and questions about who gets what and how much.

# Germany

In the annals of intergroup relations, Germany is infamous as the site of the greatest minority group atrocities in history. In the 1930s and 1940s, the Nazi leadership of the nation attempted to eradicate the Jewish community (and several other groups) and nearly succeeded. Six million Jews died in the concentration camps.

Since the end of World War II, modern Germany has broken from its racist past, democratized, industrialized, and modernized. It is a global leader politically and economically and has one of the world's best-trained and educated workforces. Germany has worked hard to atone for its Nazi past, but it now faces new dominant-minority group challenges. Like the United States, Canada, and other nations of Western Europe, Germany has become a highly desirable destination for immigrants who come to satisfy the demand for both unskilled, cheap labor and "high-tech" professionals. Besides the demand in various parts of the job market, immigrants are also pulled to Germany (and many other European nations) by the low rate of population growth. Birth rates are low throughout Western Europe, and Germany's birth rate (about 8 births per 1000 population) is actually lower than its death rate (about 10 deaths per 1000 population) (NationMaster.com, 2005e). Thus, if this trend continues, Germany will actually begin to lose population. Germany has responded to the threat of population decline by instituting a new immigration policy that recognizes that the society needs immigrant workers to fill the gaps in the labor force and to continue to prosper. At any rate, the experience of Germany (along with that of Canada and the United States) confirms the idea that immigration is in large measure a flow of labor from areas of lower opportunity (less developed nations) to areas of higher opportunity.

Based on the patterns we have documented in the United States, we would predict that high rates of immigration would be accompanied by episodes of racist violence. Unfortunately, it is easy to find hate crimes and violent attacks against immigrants and other minority group members in Germany (and other European nations) in recent years. These attacks include bombings, killings, and beatings, and myriad other forms of violence and brutality. Also, skinheads, neo-Nazis, and other hate groups are active and well-publicized elements of German life. For example, on February 13, 2005, several thousand neo-Nazis marched through Dresden, Germany to protest the fire bombing and near total destruction of the city by Allied bombers in World War II (Whitlock, 2005).

These phenomena are, of course, a part of everyday life in other European nations and the United States and seem to have similar causes: high rates of immigration combined with economic uncertainty for working-class, less-educated males and strong traditions of racism and intolerance. Still, the memory of the Holocaust gives special resonance to attacks on minority groups in Germany.

## Switzerland

Although our focus is on the ethnic and racial trouble spots around the globe, it is also important to consider societies in which group relations are generally peaceful and conflict is comparatively minimal. One such society is Switzerland. Swiss society incorporates three major and distinct language and cultural groups: French speakers, German speakers, and Italian speakers. Each language group resides in a particular region of the country and enjoys considerable control of its local affairs. In our terms, Switzerland is a pluralistic society in which the groups are separate both culturally and structurally. That is, at the local level, the groups have neither acculturated nor integrated. Each group maintains its unique cultural and linguistic heritage and its separate institutional and organizational structures.

At the national level, political power and economic resources are shared in proportion to the size of each group. The leaders of the different groups are careful to cooperate in national affairs and maintain the sense of proportional sharing and fundamental fairness. With the combination of cooperation at the national level and autonomy at the local level, Switzerland is able to function effectively as a multicultural, multilingual society.

Perhaps the key to the success of the Swiss in combining diversity and unity is that none of the three major groups were forced to join the nation by military conquest or coercion. The groups joined together voluntarily and created this pluralistic nation for mutual advantage. Thus, for the three major groups that make up Swiss society, there is no history of conquest or subordination and no patterns of structured inequality, prejudice, and resentment.

## Former Yugoslavia

The case of Switzerland indicates that peaceful and prosperous pluralistic societies can be created, but it is not typical of multigroup societies. Conquest and coercion are more common than voluntary cooperation, and the potential for rancor, conflict, and violence are high. The case of the former nation of Yugoslavia is an example.

Eastern Europe is a region of immense ethnic, linguistic, and religious diversity. Travel, trade, and warfare have mixed and scattered groups, and over the centuries, nations and empires have come and gone. The former nation of Yugoslavia exemplifies both the diversity of the region and the complexities of intergroup conflict and cooperation.

The history of the modern nation of Yugoslavia is both short and complex. When it was created in 1918, at the end of World War I, the nation encompassed a variety of ethnic groups, each with its own language, religion, history, and memories of grievances against other groups. The larger groups include Croats (who are mainly Roman Catholic), Serbs (primarily Eastern Orthodox), and Bosnians (roughly half Muslim, half Christian). Each of these groups had a home territory in which it was the numerical majority. For example, in 1992, Croatia was 78% Croatian, and Serbia was 85% Serbian. Bosnia was the most diverse of the former Republics of Yugoslavia. In 1992, about 44% of the population of Bosnia was Muslim, 39% was Serb, and 17% was Croat (Remington, 1997, p. 275).

During World War II, Yugoslavia was one of the bloody battlegrounds, and each of these groups took sides. German forces invaded the region and created a puppet government in Croatia. The Croatian allies of the Nazis participated not only in the persecution of Jews but also in a campaign against the Serbs residing within their reach. Concentration camps were constructed and mass executions carried out. By the end of war, the fascist Croatian government had murdered hundreds of thousands of Serbs. However, the Croats were not alone in their atrocities. Their campaign against Serbs provoked anti-Croatian violence in Serbia; hostility and resentment between the two groups had grown to new heights by the end of the war.

World War II also saw the emergence of Josip Broz Tito as a leader of anti-Nazi guerrilla forces. After the war, Tito became the chief architect of the modern nation of Yugoslavia. Tito's design incorporated many of the same elements that make Switzerland a successful pluralistic society. Postwar Yugoslavia comprised several different subnations, or republics, each of which was associated with a particular ethnic group. Power at the national level was allocated proportionately, and each region had considerable autonomy in the conduct of its affairs.

A major difference between Yugoslavia and Switzerland, however, lies in the contact situation. Whereas the latter nation was formed on a voluntary basis, Yugoslavia was first created by post–World War I diplomatic negotiations and then recreated at the end of World War II by the authoritarian regime of Tito. The nation was held together largely by the forcefulness of Tito's leadership. After his death in 1980, little remained to preserve the integrity of the Yugoslavian experiment in nation building. The memories of past hostilities and World War II atrocities were strong, and the separate republics began to secede from the Yugoslav federation in the 1990s.

Self-serving political and military leaders in Serbia and in the other former Yugoslavian states inflamed prejudices and antipathies. Vicious conflicts broke out throughout the region, with the worst violence occurring in Bosnia. Bosnia's attempt to establish its independence was opposed by Serbia and by the Serbian and Croatian residents of Bosnia, both of whom formed armed militias. Bosnia became a killing field as these different contingents confronted each other. The Serbs began a campaign of "ethnic cleansing" in Bosnia in 1992 and committed the worst excesses. In the areas of Bosnia where they could establish control, Serbs mounted a campaign to eliminate non-Serbs by forced relocation or, if necessary, by wholesale massacre. Concentration camps appeared, houses were torched, former neighbors became blood enemies, women were raped, and children were killed along with their parents.

The Serbs were not alone in their resort to tactics of mass terror and murder. Croats used the same tactics against Bosnian Muslims, and Bosnians have retaliated in kind against Serbs. By the time relative peace was established in Bosnia in 1995, more than 200,000 people had died in the murderous ethnic conflict. Many of the patterns of vicious brutality reappeared in the conflict between Serbia and Kosovo that began in 1999 and was ended by the armed intervention of the United States and its NATO allies.

The disintegration of the former Yugoslavia into savage ethnic violence is one of the nightmarish episodes of the 20th century. Unfortunately, it is not unique.

## Rwanda

In the spring of 1994, the tiny African nation of Rwanda sprang into international headlines. Rwanda's two ethnic groups, Hutus and Tutsis, had a long history of mutual enmity and hatred, but the attacks that began in 1994 reached new heights of brutality. Perhaps 800,000 people—perhaps many more—were murdered, and millions fled to neighboring nations (Gourevitch, 1999, p. 133). Accounts by witnesses and survivors told of massacres with rifles, machetes, rocks, and fists. No one was spared in the killing frenzy. Old people, pregnant women, and small children were executed along with the men in what became one of the most horrific, unimaginable episodes of intergroup violence in world history.

What caused this outburst? As seems to be the case whenever intense ethnic violence is found, colonization and conquest are part of the explanation for the brutal confrontation between the Hutus and Tutsis. European nations began colonizing Africa in the 1400s, and the area that became Rwanda did not escape domination. Germany established control over the region in the late 1800s. Following its defeat in World War I, Germany lost its overseas possessions, and Belgium became the dominant power in the region. Both European powers valued Rwanda for its mild climate and fertile soil. The native population was harnessed to the task of producing agricultural products, especially tea and coffee, for export.

The European colonizers attempted to ease the difficulty of administering and controlling Rwanda by capitalizing on the long-standing enmity between Tutsis and Hutus. In a classic case of divide and rule, Germany placed the Tutsis in position to govern the Hutus, a move that perpetuated and intensified hostilities between the tribes. The Belgians continued the tradition and maintained the political and economic differentials between the tribes.

Throughout the colonial era, mutual tribal hostilities were punctuated by periodic armed clashes, some of which rose to the level of massacre. In the early 1960s, the era of direct European

**EXHIBIT 13.4**  Map of Africa, Showing Rwanda and South Africa

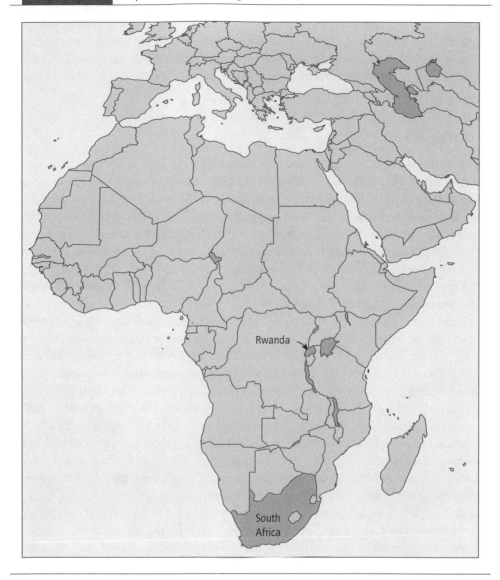

political colonialism ended, and two nations were created in the region: Rwanda was dominated by the Hutus and neighboring Burundi by the Tutsis. Hostilities did not stop at this point, however, and the short histories of these two new nations are filled with conflicts with each other. What portion of these conflicts are international and what portion are domestic is difficult to determine, because a substantial number of Tutsis continued to reside in Rwanda, and many residents of Burundi were Hutu. In other words, the borders between the two nations were drawn arbitrarily and do not reflect local traditions or tribal realities.

In the early 1990s, a rebel force led by exiled Tutsis invaded Rwanda with the intention of overthrowing the Hutu-dominated government. The conflict continued until the spring of 1994, when the plane carrying the Hutu president of Rwanda was shot down, killing all aboard. It was this incident that set off the massacres, with Hutus seeking revenge for the death of their president and attempting to eliminate their Tutsi rivals. In another of the great nightmarish episodes of the 20th century, perhaps as many as half of the Tutsis in Rwanda died in the confrontation, and millions more fled for their lives. Although surely not a complete explanation for these horrors, the history of intertribal enmity and competition for power and control enhanced and magnified by European colonialism is part of the background for understanding these horrors—if such a thing is possible.

## South Africa

Not all stories are nightmares, and the dreary litany of hatred, conflict, and violence occasionally takes a surprising twist. As recently as the late 1980s, the Republic of South Africa was one of the most racist and discriminatory societies in the world. A small minority of whites (about 30%) dominated the black African population and enjoyed a level of race-based privilege rarely equaled in the history of the world. Today, although enormous problems of inequality and racism remain, South Africa has officially dismantled the machinery of racial oppression, has enfranchised nonwhites, and has elected two black presidents. Even in a world in which change is rapid and unpredictable, the end of state-supported racism and race privilege in South Africa is one of the more stunning surprises of recent times.

Some background will illuminate the magnitude of the change. Europeans first came into contact with the area that became the nation of South Africa in the 1600s, at about the time the British were establishing colonies in North America. First to arrive were the Dutch, who established ports on the coast to resupply merchant ships for the journey between Asia and Europe. Some of the Dutch began moving into the interior to establish farms and sheep and cattle ranches. The "trekkers," as they were called, regularly fought with indigenous black Africans and with tribes moving into the area from the North. These interracial conflicts were extremely bloody and resulted in enslavement for some black Africans, genocide for others, and a gradual push of the remaining black Africans into the interior. In some ways, this contact period resembled that between European Americans and Native Americans, and in other ways, it resembled the early days of the establishment of black slavery in North America.

In the 1800s, South Africa became a British colony, and the new governing group attempted to grant more privileges to blacks. These efforts stopped far short of equality, however, and South Africa continued to evolve as a racially divided, white-dominated society into the 20th century. The white community continued to be split along ethnic lines, and hostilities erupted into violence on a number of occasions. In 1899, British and Dutch factions fought each other in the Boer War, a bitter and intense struggle that widened and solidified the divisions between the two white communities. Generally, the descendants of the Dutch have been more opposed to racial change than have the descendants of the British.

In 1948, the National Party, the primary political vehicle of the Afrikaans, or Dutch, segment of the white community, came into control of the state. As the society modernized and industrialized, there was growing concern about controlling the majority black population. Under the leadership of the National Party, the system of apartheid was constructed to firmly establish white superiority. In Afrikaans, apartheid means "separate" or "apart"; the basic logic of the system was to separate whites and blacks in every area of life: schools, neighborhoods, jobs, buses, churches, and so forth. Apartheid resembled the Jim Crow system of segregation in the United States except it was even more repressive, elaborate, and unequal.

Although the official government propaganda claimed that apartheid would permit blacks and whites to develop separately and equally, the system was clearly intended to solidify white privilege and black powerlessness. By keeping blacks poor and powerless, white South Africans created a pool of workers who were both cheap and docile. Whites of even modest means could afford the luxuries of personal servants, and employers could minimize their payrolls and their overhead. Of the dominant-minority situations considered in this text, perhaps only American slavery rivals apartheid for its naked, unabashed subjugation of one group for the benefit of another.

Note that the coming of apartheid reverses the relationship between modernization and control of minority groups we observed in the United States. As the United States industrialized and modernized, group relations evolved from paternalistic to rigid competitive to fluid competitive forms, each stage representing a looser form of control over the minority group. In South Africa after 1948, group relations became more rigid and the structures of control became stronger and more oppressive. Why the difference?

Just as U.S. Southerners attempted to defend their privileged status and resist the end of de jure segregation in the 1950s and 1960s, white South Africans were committed to retaining their status and the benefits it created. Although South Africans of British descent tended to be more liberal in matters of race than those of Dutch descent, both groups were firmly committed to white supremacy. Thus, unlike the situation in the United States at the end of Jim Crow segregation, in which white liberals and non-Southerners put considerable pressure on the racist South, there was little internal opposition among South African whites to the creation of apartheid.

Furthermore, South African blacks in the late 1940s were comparatively more powerless than blacks in the United States in the 1950s and 1960s. Although South African black protest organizations existed, they were illegal and had to operate underground or from exile and under conditions of extreme repression. In the United States, in contrast, blacks living outside the South were able to organize and pool their resources to assist in the campaign against Jim Crow, and these activities were protected (more or less) by the national commitment to civil liberties and political freedom.

A final difference between the two situations has to do with numbers. Whereas in the United States blacks are a numerical minority, they were the great majority of the population in South Africa. Part of the impetus for establishing the rigid system of apartheid was the fear of whites that they would be "swamped" by the numerical majority unless black powerlessness was perpetuated. The difference in group size helped to contribute to what has been described as a "fortress" mentality among some white South Africans: the feeling that they were defending a small (but luxurious) outpost surrounded and besieged by savage hordes who threatened their immediate and total destruction. This strong sense of threat among whites and the need to be vigilant and constantly resist the least hint of racial change is part of what made the events of the 1990s so remarkable and unexpected.

The system of racial privilege called apartheid lasted about 40 years. Through the 1970s and 1980s, changes within South Africa and in the world in general built up pressure against the system. Internally, protests against apartheid by blacks began in the 1960s and continued to build in intensity. The South African government responded to these protests with violent repression, and thousands died in the confrontations with police and the army. Nonetheless, anti-apartheid activism continued to attack the system from below.

Apartheid also suffered from internal weaknesses and contradictions. For example, jobs were strictly segregated, along with all other aspects of South African society. In a modern, industrial economy, however, new types of jobs are continually being created, and old jobs are continually lost to mechanization and automation, making it difficult to maintain simple, caste-like rules about who can do what kinds of work. Also, many of the newer jobs required higher levels of education and special skills, and the number of white South Africans was too small to fill the demand. Thus, some black South Africans were slowly rising to positions of greater affluence and personal freedom even as the system attempted to coerce and repress the group as a whole.

Internationally, pressure on South Africa to end apartheid was significant. Other nations established trade embargoes and organized boycotts of South African goods. South Africa was officially banned from the Olympics and other international competitions. Although many of these efforts were more symbolic than real and had only minor impact on everyday social life, they sustained an outcast status for South Africa and helped create an atmosphere of uncertainty among its economic and political elite.

In the late 1980s, these various pressures made it impossible to ignore the need for reform any longer. In 1990, F. W. de Klerk, the leader of the National Party and the prime minister of the nation, began a series of changes that eventually ended apartheid. He lifted the ban on many outlawed black African protest organizations, and perhaps most significantly, he released Nelson Mandela from prison. Mandela was the leader of the African National Congress, one of the oldest and most important black organizations, and he had served a 27-year prison term for actively protesting apartheid. Together, de Klerk and Mandela helped to ease South Africa through a period of rapid racial change that saw the franchise being extended to blacks, the first open election in South African history, and in 1994, Mandela's election to a 5-year term as president. In 1999, Mandela was replaced by Thabo M. Mbeke, another black South African.

The future of South Africa remains unclear. Although the majority black population now has considerable political power, much of the wealth of the nation remains in white hands. Furthermore, the school system did little to prepare blacks for positions of leadership and for jobs demanding specialized skills or technical expertise. Thus most of the crucial jobs in business and government continue to be held by whites. Tribal affiliations, language differences, and political loyalties split black South Africans, and unified action is often problematical for the minority group. This experiment in racial reform might still fail, and South Africa could still become the site of a devastating race war, but this dramatic transition away from massive racism and institutionalized discrimination could also provide a model of change for other racially divided societies.

## The Middle East

The tense, often violent relations between Israel and its Arab neighbors are yet another of the complex, long-lasting conflicts that seem to defy the most concerted, best intentioned efforts at conciliation. Hatred, terrorism, and pledges to fight to the death are as common in the Middle East as they are in other situations around the globe. The conflict has roots deep in history but took on its modern form with the founding of the nation of Israel in 1948.

As with many of the situations considered in this chapter, the present-day Middle East conflict between Jews and Arabs has its origins in military conquest. Following World War II and the horrors of the Holocaust, European Jews began to push for the establishment of a Jewish state in their traditional homeland. This cause was strongly supported by the United Nations and by the United States, and the modern state of Israel was founded in 1948. Unfortunately, the Jewish homeland was established by taking land that was occupied by Arabs (Palestinians) who also regarded it as their rightful homeland. Thus began the dominant (Israelis)–minority (Palestinians) situation that continues today (see Exhibit 13.5).

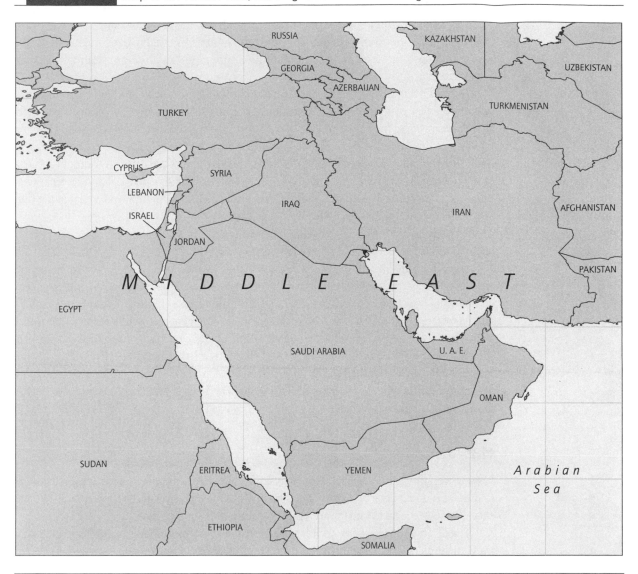

A major difference between this and other intergroup struggles is the scale of time involved. Although the modern state of Israel encompasses the traditional Jewish homeland, few Jews have lived in this area for the past 2000 years. Jews were exiled from the region and resettled in parts of Europe, Africa, and Asia. The Middle East has been Arab land for most of the past thousand years. When Jews began to immigrate to the area after World War II, they found a well-entrenched Arab society and more than one million Palestinian Arabs on what they considered to be "their" land.

After its establishment, Israel found itself surrounded by hostile Arab nations. Warfare began almost immediately, and violent confrontations of one sort or another have been nearly continuous. Full-scale wars were fought in 1948, 1967 (the famous Six-Day War), and again in 1973. Israel was victorious in all three instances, and it claimed additional territory from its Arab neighbors to reduce the threat and provide a buffer zone. The wars also created a large group of refugees in the Arab countries neighboring Israel. The Arabs who remained in Israel tended to be a subordinate group, although some eventually became Israeli citizens.

Today, the number of Palestinian Arabs exceeds six million, many of whom continue to live as displaced people in refugee camps, longing for a return to their former homes or, increasingly as time wears on, to the homes of their parents or grandparents. Part of the complexity and the intensity of this situation stems from the fact that the groups involved are separated along so many different lines: religion, language, ethnicity, history, and social class. In addition, because of the huge oil reserves in the region, the Israeli-Arab conflict has political and international dimensions that directly involve the rest of the world. The United States involvement in the Gulf War of 1991, the war against terror following the September 11, 2001, attacks on the United States, and the wars in Afghanistan and Iraq have certainly added a level of complexity to the already tense relationships between Israel and its Arab neighbors.

There are some indications that a solution to the enmities in the Middle East is not impossible. In 1979, Egypt, formerly committed to the destruction of the Jewish state, signed a peace accord with Israel. More recently, Israel and the Palestinians, represented by the Palestine Liberation Organization, have been negotiating a peace settlement that would permit a Palestinian state. These negotiations have been extremely difficult and constantly threatened by violence, suicide bombings, attacks, and counterattacks. Yassir Arafat, the militant leader of the Palestine Liberation Organization, died in 2004. His successor, Mahmoud Abbas, may be a more moderate figure, more open to negotiation with the Israelis, and this change in leadership may lay the groundwork for an eventual solution.

## Hawaii

Like Switzerland, Hawaii is often identified as a society that maintains peaceful group relations in the face of great diversity. This reputation justifies the inclusion of the islands in this global survey despite the fact that Hawaii is not a separate, autonomous nation.

The diversity of Hawaiian society is suggested by its racial and ethnic makeup. First of all, the population of Hawaii is much more racially mixed than the general population of the United States. In the 2000 census, for example, 21.4% of Hawaiians chose more than one category to describe their race, compared with less than 3% of the U.S. population as a whole (U.S. Bureau of the Census, 2000n). The racial breakdown of the state, including both people who chose only one racial or ethnic category and people who chose more than one, is shown in Exhibit 13.6. Americans of Asian descent were the largest group, and within that group, Japanese Americans and Filipino Americans were the largest categories. Whites were a numerical minority, and only about 7% of the population identified themselves as "pure-bred" Native Hawaiians (that is, chose only "Native Hawaiian" as their race). The population also includes a large number of people of Chinese, Korean, and Samoan descent, along with Hispanic and African Americans. The cultures and traditions of all these groups are evident in the mix of Hawaiian society and the rhythm of everyday life. The relatively low levels of prejudice, discrimination, and group conflict in the midst of this diversity are the bases for the sometimes glowing (and many would argue, overstated) depictions of Hawaii as a racial paradise.

**EXHIBIT 13.6** Racial and Ethnic Makeup of Hawaii, 2000

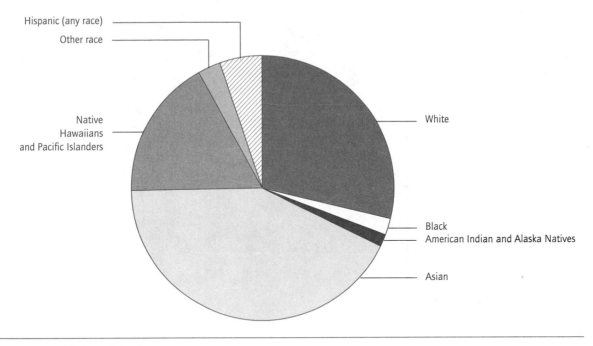

SOURCE: U.S. Bureau of the Census (2000n).

NOTE: The chart shows the percentages of people choosing one race alone or a combination of races. Numbers exceed the population of the state because people could choose more than one category.

The comparatively high levels of tolerance seem unusual in a world that often features just the opposite. A brief review of the history of the islands provides some insight into the development of these peaceful relations, as well as the suggestion that the peaceful facade hides a grimmer reality.

Hawaii first came into contact with Europeans in 1788, but conquest and colonization did not follow the initial contact. Early relations between the islanders and Europeans were organized around trade and commerce—not agriculture, as was the case in the United States, South Africa, Northern Ireland, Québec, and so many other places. Thus the contact situation did not lead immediately to competition over the control of land or labor. Also, Hawaiian society was highly developed and had sufficient military strength to protect itself from the relatively few Europeans who came to the islands in these early days.

Although initial contact with Europeans did not result in conquest or military dominance, it did bring other consequences, including smallpox and other diseases to which native Hawaiians had no immunity. Death rates began to rise, and the population of native Hawaiians, which numbered about 300,000 in 1788, fell to less than 60,000 a century later (Kitano & Daniels, 1995, p. 137).

As relations between the islands and Europeans developed, the land gradually began to be turned to commercial agriculture. By the mid-1800s, white planters had established sugar plantations, an enterprise that is extremely labor intensive and that has often been associated with systems of enforced labor and slavery (Curtin, 1990). By that time, however, there were not enough native Hawaiians to fill the demand for labor, and the planters began to recruit abroad,

**EXHIBIT 13.7** Map of the Hawaiian Islands

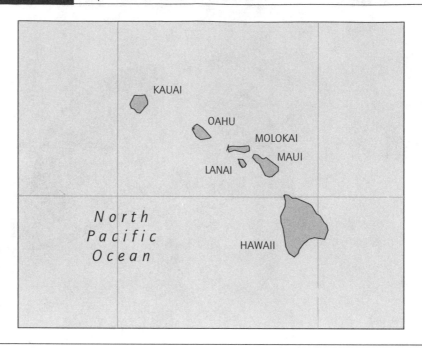

mostly in China, Portugal, Japan, Korea, Puerto Rico, and the Philippines. Thus the original immigrants of the Asian American groups we discussed in chapter 10 often came first to the Hawaiian Islands, not to the U.S. mainland.

The white plantation owners came to dominate the island economy and political structure. Other groups, however, were not excluded from secondary structural assimilation. Laws banning entire groups from public institutions or practices such as school segregation are unknown in Hawaiian history. Americans of Japanese ancestry, for example, are very powerful in politics and have produced many of the leading Hawaiian politicians. (In contrast to events on the mainland, Japanese Americans in Hawaii were not interned during World War II.) Most other groups have taken advantage of the relative openness of Hawaiian society and have carved out niches for themselves in the institutional structure.

In the area of primary structural assimilation, rates of intermarriage among the various groups are much higher than on the mainland, reflecting an openness to intimacy across group lines that has characterized Hawaii since first contact. In particular, Native Hawaiians have intermarried freely with other groups (Kitano & Daniels, 1995, pp. 138-139).

Hawaii has no history of the most blatant and oppressive forms of group domination, racism, and legalized discrimination. Still, all is not perfect in the reputed racial paradise, and there is evidence of ethnic and racial stratification, as well as prejudice and discrimination. In particular, Native Hawaiians tend to be the poorest of the various ethnic and racial groups, and recent immigrants from Asia, like their mainland counterparts, tend to be "bipolar" in their occupational and economic profiles. A protest movement of Native Hawaiians that stresses self-determination and the return of illegally taken land has been in existence since at least the 1960s.

# Brazil

Imagine a contact situation involving three racially distinct groups in which there is a struggle for land and labor. Imagine that the victorious (dominant) group is white and that harsh treatment and disease devastate one of the defeated groups. Imagine that the other defeated (minority) group is used for slave labor on plantations owned by the whites. What predictions would you make about the future of race relations in such a society? Would you expect the society to be highly stratified by race? Would you predict intense prejudice and widespread institutional discrimination? These predictions would be logical and well supported by the evidence we have reviewed in this text, at least for the case of the United States. In the case of Brazil, however, they would be overstated and, in some ways, wrong.

Brazil is the largest nation in South America. Its territory stretches from the Atlantic Ocean deep into the interior and almost across the continent (see Exhibit 13.8). Its population of 172 million, about 62% of the population of the United States, is racially and ethnically diverse. Several hundred thousand Indians survive, down from perhaps five million at first contact. Brazil was a colony of Portugal until 1822, and Portuguese remains its primary language. The colonial history of Brazil began almost a century before Jamestown was established. In fact, the African slave trade on which the British colonies became so dependent in the 1600s and 1700s was created to provide labor for colonial Brazil in the 1500s (Curtin, 1990).

The racial histories of Brazil and the United States run parallel in many ways, and racism, discrimination, and racial inequality are very much a part of Brazilian society, past and present. There are also some important differences in the experiences of the two nations, and today, race relations in Brazil are generally regarded as less problematical and confrontational than in the United States. A variety of theories has been advanced to explain the difference in group relations between the two nations (see Degler, 1971; Tannenbaum, 1947).

The issues cannot be fully explored in these few paragraphs, but we can make the point that the foundation for today's race relations may have been laid in the distant past, both before and during the contact situation. At the time Brazil was established, Portugal, unlike England, had had a long acquaintance with African cultures and peoples. In fact, Moors from North Africa ruled Portugal for a time. Thus, darker skin and other African "racial" features were familiar to the Portuguese and not, in and of themselves, regarded as a stigma or an indication of inferiority.

The relative absence of skin color prejudice also may be reflected in the high rates of intermarriage between Portuguese, Africans, and natives. The Brazilian colonists were mostly males, unlike their British counterparts, who were much more likely to immigrate in family groups, and they took brides from other groups. These intermarriages produced a large class of mulattos or people of mixed race. Today, whites are a bare majority of the Brazilian population (54%), and blacks are only a little more than 5%. The remainder of the population (almost 40%) consists of *pardos*, or people of mixed-race ancestry (Instituto Brasileiro do Geografica e Estatistica, 1999).

Brazilian slavery tended to be more open than the North American variety. Brazilian slaves were freed at a much higher rate than British American slaves were, and there was a large class of free blacks and mulattos filling virtually every job and position available in the society. Compared with the U.S. experience, slavery lasted longer in Brazil (until 1888) but ended more gradually and with less opposition.

In Brazil, slavery was not so thoroughly equated with race as it was in North America. Although slave status was certainly regarded as undesirable and unfortunate, it did not carry

**EXHIBIT 13.8** Map of South America, Showing Brazil

the presumption of racial inferiority. In North America, in contrast, antiblack prejudice and racism came into being as way of rationalizing and supporting the system (see chapter 5); slavery, blackness, and inferiority were tightly linked in the dominant ideology, an equation with powerful echoes in the present.

The results of the higher rates of racial intermarriage, large population of mulattos, and lower levels of racial prejudice in Brazil are manifold. First, they helped to sustain a way of thinking about race that is sharply different from North American practices. In Brazil and other parts of South and Central America, race is seen as a series of categories that have ambiguous, indeterminate boundaries. Black, white, and other colors shade into each other in an infinite variety of ways, and no hard or sharp borders mark the end of one group and the start of another.

In the United States, in contrast, race is seen as a set of sharply delineated categories with clear, definite boundaries. One's race is determined by the social group one belongs to, regardless of appearance or actual ancestry, and everyone belongs to one and only one race. Thus people who are raised in and identify with the black community—including people who "look white"—are black.

Second, after the end of slavery, Brazil did not go through a period of legalized racial segregation like the Jim Crow system or apartheid. Such a system would be difficult to construct or enforce when race is seen as a set of open-ended categories that gradually fade into one another. Racial segregation requires a simple racial classification system in which people are classified unambiguously into a single category. The more nuanced and subtle perception of race in Brazil is not conducive to a strict system of racial inequality.

It should be stressed that Brazil has not solved its dominant-minority problems. The legacy of slavery is still strong, and there is a very high correlation between skin color and social status. For example, mortality rates for black children are nearly double those for whites, and life expectancy is 6 years shorter. Black Brazilians have much higher illiteracy, unemployment, and poverty rates and are much less likely to have access to a university education (Kuperman, 2001, p. 25). Whites dominate the more prestigious and lucrative occupations and the leadership positions in the economy and in politics, whereas blacks are concentrated at the bottom of the class system, with mixed-race people in between.

Brazil is not a racial utopia, as is sometimes claimed. Racial discrimination and inequality are massive problems there, as they are in the United States. Still, the comparison between the two nations is instructive. Differences in the contact period and in the development of race relations over time have resulted in a notably different and somewhat milder form of group relations today.

## ANALYZING GROUP RELATIONS

Our tour of group relations around the globe has been brief and highly selective in the stops we made. Nonetheless, some conclusions are possible.

Problems of dominant-minority relations are extremely common. It seems that the only nations that lack such problems are the relatively few (such as Sweden) that are homogeneous in their racial, cultural, religious, and linguistic makeup.

Dominant-minority problems are highly variable in their form and their intensity. They range from genocide in former Yugoslavia and Rwanda to hate crimes motivated by race, religion, or ethnicity in Germany (and many other nations) to complaints of racism, unfairness, and injustice virtually everywhere. Some long-standing minority grievances remain unresolved (e.g., Catholics in Northern Ireland), and new problem areas appear on a regular basis. There is little indication that these various problems of group relations will be settled or otherwise fade away at any point in the near future.

As we have noted on a number of occasions, the most intense, violent, and seemingly intractable problems of group relations almost always have their origins in contact situations in which one group is conquered or colonized by another. Blauner's hypothesis seems well supported by this examination of dominant-minority relations around the globe.

The impact of modernization and industrialization on racial and ethnic relations is variable. Whereas these forces led to less rigid group relations in the United States, they had the opposite effect in South Africa until the 1990s. Furthermore, around the globe, ethnic and racial groups that were thought to have been submerged in the hustle and bustle of modern society have been reappearing with surprising regularity. The former Yugoslavia supplies some of the most dramatic examples of the seeming imperviousness of ethnicity to industrialization and modernization, but others can be found in Great Britain, Belgium, Spain, the former Soviet Union, Mexico, China, Nigeria, Iraq, and scores of other nations. In each of these cases, pluralistic or separatist movements based on ethnic and racial groups are present and, in some cases, thriving.

It seems unlikely that even the most sophisticated and modern of nations will outgrow the power of ethnic loyalties at any point in the near future. In virtually all the cases discussed, whatever tendencies modernization creates to reduce prejudice seem to be offset by memories of past injustices, unresolved grievances, a simple yearning for revenge, and continuing struggles over control of land, labor, and other resources. Ethnic and racial lines continue to reflect inequalities of wealth and power, and as long as minority group status is correlated with inequality, ethnic and racial loyalties will remain powerful motivations for conflict.

As we have noted, ethnic and racial group conflicts are especially intense when they coincide with class divisions and patterns of inequality. For example, minority group members in Canada, South Africa, and Northern Ireland command lower shares of wealth and political power, have worse jobs, poorer housing, and lower levels of education. When a conflict arises in these societies, whether the problem is one of economics, politics, or a dominant-minority issue, the same groups face each other across the lines of division. The greater the extent to which issues and lines of fracture coincide and reinforce each other, the greater the threat to society as a whole, and the more difficult it will be to manage the conflict and avoid escalation to the extremes.

With respect to the intensity and nature of dominant-minority problems, the United States is hardly in a unique or unusual position. Many nations are dealing with problems of assimilation and pluralism and diversity and unity, and some of these issues seem far more difficult and complex than those facing our society. Societies such as Switzerland and Hawaii help sustain the idea that peaceful, just, and equal group relations are possible even for very diverse nations. Our tour of the globe also shows that there are no racial paradises; even the multigroup societies with the most glowing reputations for tolerance are not immune from conflict, inequality, discrimination, and racism.

# MAIN POINTS

- This chapter applies the ideas developed in this text to a variety of societies around the globe. Although not a complete or definitive test of theory, confidence in our ideas will increase to the extent that they are found to be applicable to dominant-minority situations in other societies.

- Dominant-minority conflicts, inequality, and discrimination were found in Canada, Northern Ireland, Germany, the former Yugoslavia, Rwanda, South Africa, and the Middle East. With the exception of immigrant workers in Germany, these conflicts are decades or centuries old and began in a contact period that featured competition and conquest. The exact issues at the core of the conflicts are highly variable but commonly rotate around questions of assimilation and pluralism, inequality and access to resources and opportunities, prejudice and racism, and diversity and unity.

- Hawaii, Switzerland, and Brazil have reputations for relatively peaceful intergroup relations and high levels of tolerance. Although none (particularly Brazil) are racial paradises, two of these three societies lack the histories of colonization and conquest that characterize those societies with more hostile group relations.

- Depending on the choices you make, either public sociology assignment described in the Introduction to Part V can connect you to minority-dominant relations around the globe. It is likely that some new disaster will have struck some corner of the globe by the time you read these words and this might be your focus for assignment #1 on pp. 467–469. Hopefully, you will not have a current case of genocide to study for the assignment on pp. 469-470 and this project can be completely historical.

## Study Site on the Web

Don't forget the interactive quizzes and other resources and learning aids at www.www.pineforge.com/healeystudy4.

## For Further Reading

*The first four sources deal with more than one society. All others are basically case studies.*

Curtin, Phillip. 1990. *The Rise and Fall of the Plantation Complex.* New York: Cambridge University Press.

Degler, Carl. 1971. *Neither Black nor White: Slavery and Race Relations in Brazil and the United States.* New York: Macmillan.

van den Berghe, Pierre. 1978. *Race and Racism: A Comparative Perspective.* New York: Wiley.

Wilson, William J. 1973. *Power, Racism, and Privilege.* New York: Free Press.

Beinart, William. 1994. Twentieth-Century South Africa. New York: Oxford University Press.

Fontaine, Pierre-Michel. 1986. *Race, Class, and Power in Brazil.* Los Angeles: UCLA Center for Afro-American Studies.

Fraser, Morris. 1973. *Children in Conflict: Growing Up in Northern Ireland.* New York: Basic Books.

Gourevitch, Philip. 1999. *We Wish to Inform You That Tomorrow We Will Be Killed With Our Families: Stories from Rwanda.* New York: Picador.

Li, Peter. 1990. *Race and Ethnic Relations in Canada.* Toronto: Oxford University Press.

McFarlane, Bruce. 1988. *Yugoslavia: Politics, Economics and Society.* London: Pinter.

McRoberts, Kenneth. 1988. *Quebec: Social Change and Political Crisis.* Toronto: McClelland and Stewart.

Smith, David, & Chambers, Gerald. 1991. *Inequality in Northern Ireland.* Oxford: Clarendon Press.

Temple-Raston, Dina. 2005. *Justice on the Grass: Three Rwandan Journalists, Their Trial for War Crimes and a Nation's Quest for Redemption.* New York: Free Press.

## Questions for Review and Study

1. Apply the major concepts of this text to the case studies examined in this chapter. How do the case studies illustrate the importance of the contact situation and subsistence technology? How do modernization and industrialization shape group relations?

2. For each case study in this chapter (except Switzerland and Hawaii), list the racial and cultural characteristics of the dominant and minority groups, the nature of the contact situation, and the type of competition that motivated the construction of minority status. Look for common patterns in your list and describe what you see in terms of the concepts presented in this text.

3. Switzerland and Hawaii are often cited as examples of multigroup societies that are relatively harmonious. What characteristics of their contact situations might help account for this?

4. Compare the development of dominant-minority relations in Brazil with that in the United States. What important differences and similarities can you identify? How do these historical differences affect contemporary group relations?

5. What does this chapter suggest about the prevalence and persistence of minority inequality, prejudice, and racism? Will there ever be a time when the nations of the world will be free of these problems?

## Internet Research Project

Additional information and a list of relevant Web sites are included in the Appendix (Internet Resources).

Select one or more of the dominant-minority situations covered in this chapter and update the information. What events have transpired since this text was published? You might search for information using the newspaper home pages listed in the Appendix or conduct an Internet search using the group or country names as keywords. Also, your search for information could cite the issue (e.g., language diversity in Canada) as a keyword. As always, a more refined search using multiple keywords is likely to produce the most relevant information.

# Minority Groups and U.S. Society

## Themes, Patterns, and the Future

Over the past 13 chapters, we have analyzed ideas and theories about dominant-minority relations, examined the historical and contemporary situations of minority groups in U.S. society, and surveyed group relations around the globe. Now it is time to reexamine our major themes and concepts and determine what conclusions can be derived from our analysis.

## SIX AMERICANS REVISITED

Let's begin with an exercise. Turn back to chapter 1 and reread the biographies of the six Americans at the beginning of the chapter. After reading this text, you should now see these people through different eyes.

You should recognize that Kim Park lives in an enclave economy and that Shirley Umphlett's life was profoundly affected by the migration of African Americans from the rural South to the urban North. Mary Ann O'Brien's family history exemplifies the slow rise to middle-class status characteristic of so many European American immigrants, whereas George Snyder seems trapped by the urban poverty and underclass marginality confronting so many racial minority groups today. Hector Gonzalez has a strong attachment to the culture of his Mexican ancestors even though he has been thoroughly integrated into the U.S. job market. In contrast, William Buford occupies an elite social and economic position but has no interest in his or anyone

else's ethnic origin. He often argues that anyone, regardless of social class or race, could duplicate his success with sufficient diligence and hard work, conveniently forgetting that his wealth was inherited.

You might think that Buford's conclusions are not particularly insightful or informed. However, his superficial analysis is shared by millions of other Americans. Americans traditionally see success or failure as a matter of individual choice and personal effort. Blaming the victims of racism for their situation can be comforting because it absolves the more fortunate of guilt or complicity in the perpetuation of minority group poverty and powerlessness. More accurate analyses and more compelling conclusions might be found in the thinking of people (like George Snyder) who are the victims of the system. Unlike the beneficiaries of the status quo, minority group members are sensitized to the dynamics of racism and discrimination by their efforts to avoid victimization. We should remember, however, that our understandings are always limited by who we are, where we come from, and what we have experienced. Our ability to imagine the realities faced by others is never perfect, and what we can see of the world depends very much on where we stand.

If we are to understand the forces that have created racial and ethnic minority groups in the United States and around the globe, we must find ways to surpass the limitations of our personal experiences and honestly confront the often ugly realities of the past and present. I believe that the information and the ideas developed in this text can help us liberate ourselves from the narrow confines of our own experiences and perspectives.

In this final chapter, I restate the general themes of this text and draw conclusions from the material we have covered. I also raise speculative questions about the future. As we look backward to the past and forward to the future, it seems appropriate to paraphrase the words of the historian Oscar Handlin (1951): "Once I thought to write a history of the minority groups in America. Then, I discovered that the minority groups were American history" (p. 3).

## THE IMPORTANCE OF SUBSISTENCE TECHNOLOGY

Perhaps the most important sociological idea we have developed is that dominant-minority relations are shaped by large social, political, and economic forces and change as these broad characteristics change. To understand the evolution of America's minority groups is to understand the history of the United States, from the earliest colonial settlement to the modern megalopolis. As we saw in chapter 13, these same broad forces have left their imprint on many societies around the globe.

Subsistence technology is the most basic force shaping a society and the relationships between dominant and minority groups in that society. In the colonial United States, minority relations were bent to the demands of a land-hungry, labor-intensive agrarian technology, and the early relationships between Africans, Europeans, and American Indians flowed from the colonists' desire to control both land and labor. By the mid-1800s, two centuries after Jamestown was founded, the same dynamics that had enslaved African Americans and nearly annihilated American Indians made a minority group out of Mexican Americans.

The agrarian era came to an end in the 19th century as the new technologies of the industrial revolution increased the productivity of the economy and eventually changed every aspect of life in the United States. The paternalistic, oppressive systems used to control the labor of minority groups in the agrarian system were abolished and replaced by competitive systems of group relations. These newer systems evolved from more rigid forms to more fluid forms as industrialization and urbanization progressed.

As the United States grew and developed, new minority groups were created, and old minority groups were transformed. Rapid industrialization combined with the opportunities available on the frontier made the United States an attractive destination for immigrants from Europe, Asia, Latin America, and other parts of the world. Immigrants helped to farm the Great

Plains, mine the riches of the West, and above all, supply the armies of labor required by industrialization.

The descendants of the immigrants from Europe benefited from the continuing industrialization of the economy, rising in the social class structure as the economy grew and matured. Immigrants from Asia and Latin America were not so fortunate. Chinese Americans and Japanese Americans survived in ethnic enclaves on the fringes of the mainstream society, and Mexican Americans and Puerto Ricans supplied low-paid manual labor for both the rural and the urban economy. Both Asian Americans and Hispanic Americans were barred from access to dominant group institutions and higher paid jobs.

The racial minority groups, particularly African Americans, Mexican Americans, and Puerto Ricans, began to enter the urban working class after European American ethnic groups had started to move up in the occupational structure, at a time when the supply of manual, unskilled jobs was dwindling. Thus the processes that allowed upward mobility for European Americans failed to work for the racial minority groups, who confronted urban poverty and bankrupt cities in addition to the continuing barriers of racial prejudice and institutional discrimination.

We can only speculate about what the future holds, but the emerging information-based, high-tech society is unlikely to offer many opportunities for people with lower educational backgrounds and occupational skills. It seems fairly certain that members of the racial and colonized minority groups and some of recent immigrant groups will be participating in the mainstream economy of the future at lower levels than the dominant group, the descendants of the European immigrants, and the more advantaged recent immigrant groups. Upgraded urban educational systems, job training programs, and other community development programs might alter the grim scenario of continuing exclusion. As discussed at the end of chapter 4, current public opinion about matters of race and discrimination makes it unlikely that such programs will be created.

Inaction and perpetuation of the status quo will bar a large percentage of the population from the emerging mainstream economy. Those segments of the African American, Hispanic American, and Asian American communities currently mired in the urban underclass will continue to compete with some of the newer immigrants for jobs in the low-wage, secondary labor market or in alternative opportunity structures, including crime.

## THE IMPORTANCE OF THE CONTACT SITUATION, GROUP COMPETITION, AND POWER

We have stressed the importance of the contact situation—the conditions under which the minority group and dominant group first come into contact with each other—throughout this text. Blauner's distinction between immigrant and colonized minority groups is fundamental, a distinction so basic that it helps to clarify minority group situations centuries after the initial contact period. In Part IV, we used Blauner's distinction as an organizing principle and covered American minority groups in approximate order from "most colonized" to "most immigrant." The groups covered first (African Americans and American Indians) are clearly at a greater disadvantage in contemporary society than the groups covered last (white ethnic groups). For example, prejudice, racism, and discrimination against African Americans remain formidable forces in contemporary America even though they may have softened into more subtle forms. In contrast, prejudice and discrimination against European American groups such as the Irish, Italians, and Polish Americans have nearly disappeared today even though they were quite formidable just a few generations ago. In the same way, contemporary immigrant groups that are nonwhite and bring few resources and low levels of human capital (e.g., Haitians) may experience segmented assimilation and find themselves in situations resembling those of colonized minority groups. Contemporary immigrant groups that are the opposite end of the continuum (e.g., Asian Indians) are more likely to approximate the experiences of white ethnics and find themselves in some version of middle-class suburbia.

Noel's hypothesis states that if three conditions are present in the contact situation—ethnocentrism, competition, and the differential in power—ethnic or racial stratification will result. The relevance of ethnocentrism is largely limited to the actual contact situation, but the other two concepts help to clarify the changes occurring after initial contact.

We have examined numerous instances in which group competition—or even the threat of competition—increased prejudice and led to greater discrimination and more repression. Recall, for example, the opposition of the labor movement (dominated by European American ethnic groups) to Chinese immigrants. The anti-Chinese campaign led to the Chinese Exclusion Act of 1882, the first significant restriction on immigration to the United States. There are parallels between campaigns for exclusion in the past and current ideas about ending or curtailing immigration. Clearly, some part of the current opposition to immigration is motivated by a sense of threat and the fear that immigrants are a danger not only to jobs and to the economy but also to the cultural integrity of U.S. society.

Noel's third variable, the differential in power, determines the outcome of the initial contact situation and which group becomes dominant and which becomes minority. Following the initial contact, the superior power of the dominant group helps it sustain the inferior position of the minority group. Minority groups by definition have fewer power resources, but they characteristically use what they have in an attempt to improve their situation. The improvements in the situations of American minority groups since the middle of the 20th century have been due in large part to the fact that they (especially African Americans, who typically led the way in protest and demands for change) finally acquired some power resources of their own. For example, one important source of power for the Civil Rights movement in the South during the 1950s and 1960s was the growth of African American voting strength in the North. After World War II, the African American electorate became too sizable to ignore, and its political power helped pressure the federal government to take action and pass the legislation that ended the Jim Crow era.

Minority status being what it is, however, each of the groups we have discussed (with the exception of the white ethnic groups) still controls relatively few power resources and is limited in its ability to pursue its own self-interest. Many of these limitations are economic and related to social class; many minority groups simply lack the monetary resources to finance campaigns for reform or to exert significant pressure on the political institution. Other limitations include small group size (e.g., Asian American groups), language barriers (e.g., many Hispanic groups), and divided loyalties within the group (e.g., American Indians separated by tribal allegiances).

At any rate, the relative powerlessness of minority groups today is a legacy of the contact situations that created the groups in the first place. In general, colonized groups are at a greater power disadvantage than immigrant groups. Contact situations set agendas for group relations that have impacts centuries after the initial meeting.

Given all that we have examined in this text, it is obvious that competition and differences in power resources will continue to shape intergroup relations (including relations between minority groups themselves) well into the future. Because they are so basic and consequential, jobs will continue to be primary objects of competition, but there will be plenty of other issues to divide the nation. Included on this divisive list will be debates about crime and the criminal justice system, welfare reform, national health-care policy, school busing, bilingual education, immigration policy, and multicultural curricula in schools.

These and other public issues will continue to separate us along ethnic and racial lines because those lines have become so deeply embedded in the economy, in politics, in our schools and neighborhoods, and in virtually every nook and cranny of U.S. society. These deep divisions reflect fundamental realities about who gets what in the United States, and they will continue to reflect the distribution of power and stimulate competition along group lines for generations to come.

## DIVERSITY WITHIN MINORITY GROUPS

All too often, and this text is probably no exception, minority groups are seen as unitary and undifferentiated. Although overgeneralizations are sometimes difficult to avoid, I want to stress again the diversity within each of the groups we have examined. Minority group members vary from each other by age, sex, region of residence, levels of education, urban versus rural residence, political ideology, and many other variables. The experience of one segment of the group (college-educated, fourth-generation, native-born Chinese American females) may bear little resemblance to the experience of another (illegal Chinese male immigrants with less than a high school education), and the problems of some members may not be the problems of others.

I have tried to highlight the importance of this diversity by exploring gender differentiation within each minority group. Study of minority groups by U.S. social scientists has focused predominantly on males, and the experiences of minority women have been described in much less depth. All the cultures examined in this text have strong patriarchal traditions. Women of the dominant group as well as minority women have had much less access to leadership roles and higher status positions and have generally occupied a subordinate status, even in their own groups. The experiences of minority group women and the extent of their differences from minority group males and dominant group women are only now being fully explored.

One clear conclusion we can make about gender is that minority group females are doubly oppressed and disempowered. Limited by both their minority and their gender roles, they are among the most vulnerable and exploited segments of the society. At one time or another, the women of every minority group have taken the least desirable, lowest status positions available in the economy, often while trying to raise children and attend to other family needs. They have been expected to provide support for other members of their families, kinship groups, and communities, often sacrificing their own self-interest to the welfare of others. Jade Snow Wong (1993), a Chinese American daughter of immigrant parents, describes the subordinate role and circumscribed world of minority group females in a remembrance of her mother:

> My mother dutifully followed my father's leadership. She was extremely thrifty, but the thrifty need pennies to manage, and the old world had denied her those. Upon arrival in the new world of San Francisco, she accepted the elements her mate had selected to shape her new life: domestic duties, seamstress work in the factory-home, mothering each child in turn, church once a week, and occasional movies. (p. 50)

In their roles outside the family, minority women have encountered discrimination based on their minority group membership, compounded with discrimination based on their gender. The result is, predictably, an economic and social status at the bottom of the social structure. For example, average incomes of African American females today are lower than those of white males, white females, and black males (see Exhibit 7.3). The same pattern holds for other groups, and the women of many minority groups are highly concentrated in the low-paid secondary labor market and employed in jobs that provide services to members of more privileged groups.

The inequality confronted by minority women extends beyond matters of economics and jobs: Women of color have higher rates of infant mortality and births out of wedlock and a host of other health-related, quality-of-life problems. In short, there is ample evidence to document a pervasive pattern of gender inequality within America's minority groups. Much of this gender inequality is complexly interconnected with rising rates of poverty and female-headed households, teenage pregnancy, and unemployment for minority males in the inner city.

Gender differentiation cuts through minority groups in a variety of ways. Specific issues might unite minority women with women of the dominant group (e.g., sexual harassment in schools and the workplace), and others might unite them with the men of their minority group (e.g., the enforcement of civil rights legislation). The problems and issues of minority women are complexly tied to the patterns of inequality and discrimination in the larger society and within their own groups. Solving the problems faced by minority groups will not resolve the problems faced by minority women and neither will resolving the problems of gender inequality alone. Women of color are embedded in structures of inequality and discrimination that limit them in two independent but simultaneous ways. Articulating and addressing these difficulties requires recognition of the complex interactions between gender and minority group status.

## ASSIMILATION AND PLURALISM

It seems fair to conclude that the diversity and complexity of minority group experiences in the United States are not well characterized by some of the traditional or "melting pot" views of assimilation. For example, the idea that assimilation is a linear, inevitable process has little support. Immigrants from Europe probably fit that model better than other groups, but as the ethnic revival of the 1960s demonstrated, assimilation and ethnic identity can take surprising turns.

Also without support is the notion that there is always a simple, ordered relationship between the various stages of assimilation: acculturation, integration into public institutions, integration into the private sector, and so forth. We have seen that some groups integrated before they acculturated, others have become *more* committed to their ethnic or racial identity over the generations, and still others have been acculturated for generations but are no closer to full integration. New expressions of ethnicity come and go, and minority groups emerge, combine, and recombine in unexpected and seemingly unpredictable ways. The 1960s saw a reassertion of ethnicity and loyalty to old identities among some groups, even as other groups developed new coalitions and invented new ethnic identities (for example, pantribalism among American Indians). No simple or linear view of assimilation can begin to make sense of the array of minority group experiences.

Indeed, the very desirability of assimilation has been subject to debate. Since the 1960s, many minority spokespersons have questioned the wisdom of becoming a part of a sociocultural structure that was constructed by the systematic exploitation of minority groups. Pluralistic themes increased in prominence as the commitment of the larger society to racial equality faltered. Virtually every minority group proclaimed the authenticity of its own experiences, its own culture, and its own version of history, separate from but as valid as that of the dominant groups. From what might have seemed like a nation on the verge of integration in the 1950s, America evolved into what might have seemed like a Tower of Babel in the 1960s. The consensus that assimilation was the best solution and the most sensible goal for all of America's minority groups was shattered (if it ever really existed at all).

Let's review the state of acculturation and integration in the United States on a group-by-group basis, following the order of the case studies in Part IV. African Americans are highly acculturated. Despite the many unique cultural traits forged in America and those that survive from Africa, black Americans share language, values and beliefs, and most other aspects of culture with white Americans of similar class and educational background. In terms of integration, in contrast, African Americans present a mixed picture. For middle-class, more educated members of the group, American society offers more opportunities for upward mobility and success than ever before. Without denying the prejudice, discrimination, and racism that remain, this segment of the group is in a favorable position to achieve higher levels of affluence and power for their children and grandchildren. At the same time, a large percentage of African Americans remain mired in urban poverty, and for them, affluence, security, and power are just as distant (perhaps more so) than they were a generation ago. Considering the group as a whole, African Americans are still highly segregated in their residential and school attendance patterns, and their political power, although rising, is not proportional to their size. Unemployment, lower average incomes, and poverty in general remain serious problems and may be more serious than they were a generation ago.

American Indians are less acculturated than African Americans, and there is evidence that American Indian culture and language may be increasing in strength and vitality. On measures of integration, there is some indication of improvement, but by and large, American Indians remain one of the most isolated and impoverished minority groups in the United States. One possible bright spot for some reservations lies in the further development of the gambling industry and the investment of profits in the tribal infrastructure to upgrade schools, health clinics, job training centers, and so forth.

The largest Hispanic American groups are also generally less acculturated than African Americans. Hispanic traditions and the Spanish language have been sustained by the exclusion and isolation of these groups within the United States and have been continually renewed and revitalized by immigration. Cubans have moved closer to equality than the other two large Hispanic groups but did so by resisting assimilation and building an ethnic enclave economy. Mexican Americans and Puerto Ricans share many of the problems of urban poverty that confront African Americans, and they are below national norms on measures of equality and integration. The smaller Hispanic groups consist mostly of new immigrants who are just beginning the assimilation process. Many members of these groups, along with Mexican Americans and Puerto Ricans, are less educated and have few occupational skills, and they face the dangers of blending into a permanent urban underclass. Nonetheless, there is some evidence that these groups (or, more accurately, their descendants) may eventually find their way into the American mainstream (recall the debate over segmented assimilation in chapter 11).

As with Hispanic Americans, the extent of assimilation among Asian Americans is highly variable. Some groups (for example, third- and fourth-generation native-born Japanese

Americans and Chinese Americans) have virtually completed the assimilation process and are remarkably successful; others (the more elite immigrants from India and the Philippines) seem to be finding a place in the American mainstream. Other Asian American groups consist largely of newer immigrants with occupational and educational profiles that resemble colonized minority groups, and these groups face the same dangers of permanent marginalization and exclusion. Still other Asian American groups (e.g., Korean Americans) have used their cohesiveness and solidarity to construct ethnic enclaves in which they have achieved relative economic equality by resisting acculturation.

Only European American ethnic groups seem to approximate the traditional model of assimilation. The development even of these groups, however, has taken unexpected twists and turns, and the pluralism of the 1960s and 1970s suggests that ethnic traditions and ethnic identity, in some form, may withstand the pressures of assimilation for generations to come. Culturally and racially, these groups are the closest to the dominant group. If they still retain a sense of ethnicity, even if merely symbolic, after generations of acculturation and integration, what is the likelihood that the sense of group membership will fade in the racially stigmatized minority groups?

Assimilation is far from accomplished. The group divisions that remain are real and consequential; they cannot be willed away by pretending we are all "just American." Group membership continues to be important because it continues to be linked to fundamental patterns of exclusion and inequality. The realities of pluralism, inequality, and ethnic and racial identity continue to persist to the extent that the American promise of a truly open opportunity structure continues to fail. The group divisions forged in the past and perpetuated over the decades by racism and discrimination will remain to the extent that racial and ethnic group membership continues to be correlated with inequality and position in the social class structure.

Along with economic and political pressures, other forces help to sustain the pluralistic group divisions. Some argue that ethnicity is rooted in biology and can never be fully eradicated (see van den Berghe, 1981). Although this may be an extreme position, there is little doubt that many people find their own ancestry to be a matter of great interest. Some (perhaps most) of the impetus behind the preservation of ethnic and racial identity may be a result of the most vicious and destructive intergroup competition. In other ways, though, ethnicity can be a positive force that helps people locate themselves in time and space and understand their position in the contemporary world. Ethnicity remains an important aspect of self-identity and pride for many Americans from every group and tradition. It seems unlikely that this sense of a personal link to particular groups and heritages within U.S. society will soon fade.

Can we survive as a pluralistic, culturally and linguistically fragmented, racially and ethnically unequal society? What will save us from balkanization and fractionalization and nightmares such as those that occurred in the former Yugoslavia or Rwanda? Given our history of colonization and racism, can U.S. society move closer to the relatively harmonious models of race relations found in Switzerland and Hawaii? As we deal with these questions, we need to remember that in and of itself, diversity is no more "bad" than unity is "good." Our society has grown to a position of global preeminence despite, or perhaps because of, our diversity. In fact, many have argued that our diversity is a fundamental and essential characteristic of U.S. society and a great strength to be cherished and encouraged. Sociologist Ronald Takaki (1993) ended his history of multicultural America (*A Different Mirror*) with an eloquent endorsement of our diversity and pluralism:

As Americans, we originally came from many different shores and our diversity has been at the center of the making of America. While our stories contain the memories of different communities, together they inscribe a larger narrative. Filled with what Walt Whitman celebrated as the "varied carols" of America, our history generously gives all of us our "mystic chords of memory."

Throughout our past of oppressions and struggles for equality, Americans of different races and ethnicities have been "singing with open mouths their strong melodious songs" in the textile mills of Lowell, the cotton fields of Mississippi, on the Indian reservations of South Dakota, the railroad tracks high in the Sierras of California, in the garment factories of the Lower East Side, the canefields of Hawaii, and a thousand other places across the country. Our denied history "bursts with telling." As we hear America singing, we find ourselves invited to bring our cultural diversity [into the open], to accept ourselves. (p. 428)

The question for our future might not be so much "Unity or diversity?" as "What blend of pluralistic and assimilationist policies will serve us best in the 21st century?" Are there ways in which the society can prosper without repressing our diversity? How can we increase the degree of openness, fairness, and justice without threatening group loyalties? The one-way, Anglo-conformity mode of assimilation of the past is too narrow and destructive to be a blueprint for the future, but the more extreme forms of minority group pluralism and separatism might be equally dangerous.

How much unity do we need? How much diversity can we tolerate? These are questions you must answer for yourself, and they are questions you will face in a thousand different ways over the course of your life. Let me illustrate by citing some pertinent issues:

Is it desirable to separate college dormitories by racial or ethnic group? Is this destructive self-segregation or a positive strategy for group empowerment? Will such practices increase prejudice (remember the contact hypothesis from chapter 4), or will they work like ethnic enclaves and strengthen minority group cohesion and solidarity and permit the groups to deal with the larger society from a stronger position? For the campus as a whole, what good could come from residential separation? In what ways would minority students benefit? Is there a "correct" balance between separation and unity in this situation? Who gets to define what the balance is?

How much attention should be devoted to minority group experiences in elementary and high school texts and curricula? Who should write and control these curricula? What should they say? How candid and critical should they be about America's often dismal past? How should such topics as slavery, genocide, and the racist exclusion of certain immigrant groups be presented in elementary school texts? In high school texts? Will educating children about the experiences of U.S. minority groups be an effective antidote to prejudice? Is it proper to use classrooms to build respect for the traditions of other groups and an appreciation of their experiences? If the realities of the experiences of minority groups are *not* addressed in school, what message will children hear? In the absence of minority group voices, what's left?

What are the limits of free speech with respect to minority relations? When does an ethnic joke become offensive? When are racial and ethnic epithets protected by the First Amendment? As long as lines of ethnicity and race divide the nation and as long as people feel passionately about these lines, the language of dominant-minority relationships will continue to have harsh, crude, and intentionally insulting components. Under what conditions, if any, should a civil society tolerate disparagement of other groups? Should the racial and ethnic epithets uttered by minority group members be treated any differently from those of dominant group members?

What should the national policy on immigration be? How many immigrants should be admitted each year? How should immigrants be screened? What qualifications should be demanded? Should immigration policy continue to favor the family and close relatives of citizens and permanent residents? What should be done about illegal immigrants? Should illegal immigrants or their children receive health care and schooling? If so, who should pay for these services?

I do not pretend that the ideas presented in this text can fully resolve these issues or others that will arise in the future. As long as immigrants and minority groups are a part of the United States, as long as prejudice and discrimination persist, the debates will continue, and new issues will arise as old ones are resolved.

As U.S. society attempts to deal with new immigrants and unresolved minority grievances, we should recognize that it is not diversity per se that threatens stability but the realities of split labor markets, racial and ethnic stratification, urban poverty, and institutionalized discrimination. We need to focus on the issues that confront us with an honest recognition of the past and the economic, political, and social forces that have shaped us. As the United States continues to remake itself, an informed sense of where we have been will help us decide where we should go. Clearly, the simplistic, one-way, Anglo-conformity model of assimilation of the past does not provide a basis for dealing with these problems realistically and should not be the blueprint for the future of U.S. society.

## MINORITY GROUP PROGRESS AND THE IDEOLOGY OF AMERICAN INDIVIDUALISM

There is so much sadness, misery, and unfairness in the history of minority groups that evidence of progress sometimes goes unnoticed. Lest we be guilty of ignoring the good news in favor of the bad, let us note some ways in which the situations of American minority groups are better today than they were in the past. Evidence of progress is easy to find for some groups; we need look only to the relative economic, educational, and income equality of European American ethnic groups and some Asian American groups. The United States has become more tolerant and open, and minority group members can be found at the highest levels of success, affluence, and prestige.

One of the most obvious changes is the decline of traditional racism and prejudice. As we discussed in chapters 3 and 4, the strong racial and ethnic sentiments and stereotypes of the past are no longer the primary vocabulary for discussing race relations among dominant group members, at least not in public. Although the prejudices unquestionably still exist, Americans have become more circumspect and discreet in their public utterances.

The demise of blatant bigotry in polite company is, without doubt, a positive change. However, it seems that negative intergroup feelings and stereotypes have not so much disappeared as changed form. The old racist feelings are now being expressed in other guises, specifically in what has been called modern or symbolic racism: the view that holds that once Jim Crow–type segregation ended in the 1960s, the opportunity channels and routes of upward mobility of American society were opened to all. This individualistic view of social mobility is consistent with the human capital perspective and the traditional, melting-pot view of assimilation. Taken together, these ideologies present a powerful and widely shared perspective on the nature of minority group problems in modern American society. Proponents of these views tend to be unsympathetic to the plight of minorities and to programs such as school busing and affirmative action, which are intended to ameliorate these problems. The overt bigotry of the past has been replaced by blandness and an indifference more difficult to define and harder to measure than "old-fashioned" racism, yet still unsympathetic to racial change.

This text has argued that the most serious problems facing contemporary minority groups, however, are structural and institutional, not individual or personal. For example, the paucity of jobs and high rates of unemployment in the inner cities are the result of economic and political forces beyond the control not only of the minority communities but also of local and state governments. The marginalization of the minority group labor force is a reflection of the essence of modern American capitalism. The mainstream, higher paying, blue-collar jobs available to people with modest educational credentials are controlled by national and multinational corporations, which maximize profits by automating their production processes and moving the jobs that remain to areas, often outside the United States, with abundant supplies of cheaper labor.

We have also seen that some of the more effective strategies for pursuing equality require strong in-group cohesion and networks of cooperation, not heroic individual effort. Immigration to this country is (and always has been) a group process that involves extensive, long-lasting networks of communication and chains of population movement, usually built around family ties and larger kinship groups. Group networks continue to operate in America and assist individual immigrants with early adjustments and later opportunities for jobs and upward mobility. A variation on this theme is the ethnic enclave found among so many different groups.

Survival and success in America for all minority groups has had more to do with group processes than with individual will or motivation. The concerted, coordinated actions of the minority community provided support during hard times and, when possible, provided the means to climb higher in the social structure during good times. Far from being a hymn to individualism, the story of U.S. minority groups is profoundly sociological.

## A FINAL WORD

U.S. society and its minority groups are linked in fractious unity. They are part of the same structures but are separated by lines of color and culture and by long histories (and clear memories) of exploitation and unfairness. This society owes its prosperity and position of prominence in the world no less to the labor of minority groups than to that of the dominant group. By harnessing the labor and energy of these minority groups, the nation has grown prosperous and powerful, but the benefits have flowed disproportionately to the dominant group.

Since the middle of the 20th century, minority groups have demanded greater openness, fairness, equality, respect for their traditions, and justice. Increasingly, the demands have been made on the terms of the minority groups, not on those of the dominant group. Some of these demands have been met, at least verbally, and the society as a whole has rejected the oppressive racism of the past. Minority group progress has stalled well short of equality, however, and the patterns of poverty, discrimination, marginality, hopelessness, and despair continue to limit the lives of millions.

As we begin the 21st century, the dilemmas of America's minority groups remain perhaps the primary unresolved domestic issue facing the nation. The answers of the past—the simple faith in assimilation and the belief that success in America is open to all who simply try hard enough—have proved inadequate, even destructive and dangerous, because they help to sustain the belief that the barriers to equality no longer exist and that any remaining inequalities are the problems of the minority groups, not the larger society.

These problems of equality and access will not solve themselves or simply fade away. They will continue to manifest themselves in myriad ways; through protest activities, rancorous debates, diffused rage, and pervasive violence. The solutions and policies that will carry us through these coming travails are not clear. Only by asking the proper questions, realistically and honestly, can we hope to find the answers that will help our society fulfill its promises to the millions who are currently excluded from achieving the American Dream.

As we saw in chapter 13, the United States is one of many ethnically and racially diverse nations in the world today. As the globe continues to shrink and networks of communication, immigration, trade, and transportation continue to link all peoples into a single global entity, the problems of diversity will become more international in their scope and implications. Ties will grow between African Americans and the nations of Africa, agreements between the United States and the nations of Latin America will have direct impact on immigration patterns, Asian Americans will be affected by international developments on the Pacific Rim, and so forth. Domestic and international group relations will blend into a single reality. In many ways, the patterns of dominant-minority relations discussed in this text have already been reproduced on the global stage. The mostly Anglo industrialized nations of the Northern Hemisphere have continuously exploited the labor and resources of the mostly nonwhite, undeveloped nations of the Southern Hemisphere. Thus the tensions and resentments we have observed in U.S. society are mirrored in the global system of societies.

The United States is neither the most nor the least diverse country in the world. Likewise, our nation is neither the most nor the least successful in confronting the problems of prejudice, discrimination, and racism. However, the multigroup nature of our society, along with the present influx of immigrants from around the globe, do present an opportunity to improve on our record and make a lasting contribution. A society that finds a way to deal fairly and humanely with the problems of diversity and difference, prejudice and inequality, and racism and discrimination can provide a sorely needed model for other nations and, indeed, for the world.

# References

Aberson, Christopher, Shoemaker, Carl, & Tomolillo, Christina. 2004. "Implicit Bias and Contact: The Role of Interethnic Friendships." *Journal of Social Psychology,* 144: 335-347.

Abrahamson, Harold. 1980. "Assimilation and Pluralism." In S. Thernstrom (Ed.), *Harvard Encyclopedia of Ethnic Groups* (pp. 150-160). Cambridge, MA: Harvard University Press.

Acuna, Rodolfo. 1988. *Occupied America* (3rd ed.). New York: Harper & Row.

Acuna, Rodolfo. 1999. *Occupied America* (4th ed.). New York: Harper & Row.

Adarand Constructors Inc. v. Pena, 515 U.S. 200 (1995).

Adorno, T. W., Frenkel-Brunswick, E., Levinson, D., & Sanford, N. 1950. *The Authoritarian Personality.* New York: Harper & Row.

Agbayani-Siewert, Pauline, & Revilla, Linda. 1995. "Filipino Americans." In P. G. Min (Ed.), *Asian Americans: Contemporary Issues and Trends* (pp. 134-168). Thousands Oaks, CA: Sage.

Alba, Richard. 1985. *Italian Americans: Into the Twilight of Ethnicity.* Englewood Cliffs, NJ: Prentice Hall.

Alba, Richard. 1990. *Ethnic Identity: The Transformation of White America.* New Haven, CT: Yale University Press.

Alba, Richard. 1995. "Assimilation's Quiet Tide." *Public Interest,* 119: 3-19.

Alba, Richard, Logan, John, Lutz, Amy, & Stults, Brian. 2002. "Only English by the Third Generation? Loss and Preservation of the Mother Tongue Among the Grandchildren of Contemporary Immigrants." *Demography,* 39(3): 472.

Alba, Richard, & Nee, Victor. 1997. "Rethinking Assimilation Theory for a New Era of Immigration." *International Migration Review,* 31:826–875.

Alba, Richard, & Nee, Victor. 2003. *Remaking the American Mainstream: Assimilation and Contemporary Immigration.* Cambridge, MA: Harvard University Press.

Allport, Gordon. 1954. *The Nature of Prejudice.* Reading, MA: Addison-Wesley.

Almquist, Elizabeth M. 1979. "Black Women and the Pursuit of Equality." In J. Freeman (Ed.), *Women: A Feminist Perspective* (pp. 430-450). Palo Alto, CA: Mayfield.

Altemeyer, Bob. 2004. "Highly Domination, Highly Authoritarian Personalities." *Journal of Social Psychology,* 144: 421-448.

Alvarez, Rodolfo. 1973. "The Psycho-Historical and Socioeconomic Development of the Chicano Community in the United States." *Social Science Quarterly,* 53: 920-942.

American Indian Higher Education Consortium. 2001. *Building Strong Communities: Tribal Colleges as Engaged Institutions.* Retrieved December 12, 2004, from http://www.ihep.com/Pubs/PDF/ Communities.pdf

Amott, Teresa, & Matthaei, Julie. 1991. *Race, Gender, and Work: A Multicultural History of Women in the United States.* Boston: South End.

Andersen, Margaret L. 1993. *Thinking About Women: Sociological Perspectives on Sex and Gender* (3rd ed.). New York: Macmillan.

Anti-Defamation League. 2000. "Anti-Semitism in the United States." Retrieved July 12, 2002, from http://www.adl.org/backgrounders/Anti_Semitism_us.html

Arab-American Anti-Discrimination Committee. 2002. "ADC Fact Sheet: The Condition of Arab-Americans Post 9/11." Retrieved June 22, 2002, from http://www.adc.org/terror_attack/9–11aftermath.PDF

Aronson, Eliot, & Gonzalez, Alex. 1988. "Desegregation, Jigsaw, and the Mexican-American Experience." In P. Katz & D. Taylor (Eds.), *Eliminating Racism: Profiles in Controversy*. New York: Plenum.

Aronson, E., & Patnoe, S. 1997. The Jigsaw Classroom: Building Cooperation in the Classroom (2nd ed.). New York: Addison Wesley Longman.

Ashmore, Richard, & DelBoca, Frances. 1976. "Psychological Approaches to Understanding Group Conflict." In P. Katz (Ed.), *Towards the Elimination of Racism* (pp. 73-123). New York: Pergamon.

Australian Bureau of Statistics. 2002. "Australian Social Trends 2002, Population, National Summary Tables." Retrieved July 5, 2002, from http://www.abs.gov.au

Australian Human Rights and Equal Opportunity Commission. 1997. "Bringing Them Home: Report of the National Inquiry into the Separation of Aboriginal and Torres Strait Islander Children from Their Families." Retrieved July 5, 2002, from http://www.austlii.edu.au/au/special/rsjproject/rsjlibrary/hreoc/stolen/

Avery, Robert, & Rendall, Michael. 2002 "Lifetime Inheritances of Three Generations of Whites and Blacks." *American Journal of Sociology,* 107: 1300-1346.

Baca Zinn, Maxine, & Dill, Bonnie Thornton. 1994. *Women of Color in U.S. Society.* Philadelphia: Temple University Press.

Baca Zinn, Maxine, & Eitzen, D. Stanley. 1990. *Diversity in Families.* New York: HarperCollins.

Ball-Rokeach, Sandra, Grube, Joel, & Rokeach, Milton. 1981. "Roots: The Next Generation—Who Watched and With What Effect?" *Public Opinion Quarterly,* 45: 58-68.

Barringer, Herbert, Takeuchi, David, & Levin, Michael. 1995. *Asians and Pacific Islanders in the United States.* New York: Russell Sage.

Barringer, Herbert, Takeuchi, David, & Xenos, Peter. 1990. "Education, Occupational Prestige, and Income of Asian Americans." *Sociology of Education,* 63: 27-43.

Bass, Bernard. November, 1955. "Authoritarianism or Acquiescence?" *Journal of Abnormal and Social Psychology:* 616-623.

Bean, Frank, & Stevens, Gillian. 2003. *America's Newcomers and the Dynamics of Diversity.* New York: Russell Sage.

Beaton, Anne, Tougas, Francine, & Joly, Stephane. 1996. "Neosexism Among Male Managers: Is It a Matter of Numbers?" *Journal of Applied Social Psychology,* 26: 2189-2204.

Becerra, Rosina. 1988. "The Mexican American Family." In C. H. Mindel, R. W. Habenstein, & R. Wright (Eds.), *Ethnic Families in America: Patterns and Variations* (3rd ed., pp. 141-159). New York: Elsevier.

Beck, E. M., & Clark, Timothy. 2002. "Strangers, Community Miscreants, or Locals: Who Were the Black Victims of Mob Violence?" *Historical Methods,* 35(2): 77-84.

Beck, E. M., & Tolnay, Stewart. 1990. "The Killing Fields of the Deep South: The Market for Cotton and the Lynching of Blacks, 1882-1930." *American Sociological Review,* 55: 526-539.

Beinart, William. 1994. *Twentieth-Century South Africa.* New York: Oxford University Press.

Bell, Daniel. 1973. *The Coming of Post-Industrial Society.* New York: Basic Books.

Bell, Derrick. 1992. *Race, Racism, and American Law* (3rd ed.). Boston: Little, Brown.

Benedict, Ruth. 1946. *The Chrysanthemum and the Sword: Patterns of Japanese Culture.* Boston: Houghton Mifflin.

Berkowitz, Leonard. 1978. "Whatever Happened to the Frustration-Aggression Hypothesis?" *American Behavioral Scientist,* 21: 691-708.

Berkowitz, Leonard, & Green, James. April, 1962. "The Stimulus Qualities of the Scapegoat." *Journal of Abnormal and Social Psychology:* 293-301.

Berthelson, Christian. February 19, 2000. "U.S. to Seek Death Penalty in Shooting of Los Angeles Mail Carrier." *New York Times:* A12.

Bird, Elizabeth. 1999. "Gendered Construction of the American Indian in Popular Media." *Journal of Communication,* 49: 60-83.

Biskupic, Joan. October 28, 1989. "House Approves Entitlement for Japanese-Americans." *Congressional Quarterly Weekly Report*: 2879.

Black-Gutman, D., & Hickson, F. 1996. "The Relationship Between Racial Attitudes and Social-Cognitive Development in Children: An Australian Study." *Developmental Psychology*, 32: 448-457.

Blassingame, John W. 1972. *The Slave Community: Plantation Life in the Antebellum South.* New York: Oxford University Press.

Blau, Peter M., & Duncan, Otis Dudley. 1967. *The American Occupational Structure.* New York: Wiley.

Blauner, Robert. 1972. *Racial Oppression in America.* New York: Harper & Row.

Blessing, Patrick. 1980. "Irish." In S. Thernstrom (Ed.), *Harvard Encyclopedia of Ethnic Groups* (pp. 524-545). Cambridge, MA: Harvard University Press.

Bluestone, Barry, & Harrison, Bennet. 1982. *The Deindustrialization of America.* New York: Basic Books.

Blumer, Herbert. 1965. "Industrialization and Race Relations." In G. Hunter (Ed.), *Industrialization and Race Relations: A Symposium* (pp. 200-253). London: Oxford University Press.

Bobo, Lawrence. 1988. "Group Conflict, Prejudice, and the Paradox of Contemporary Racial Attitudes." In P. Katz & D. Taylor (Eds.), *Eliminating Racism: Profiles in Controversy* (pp. 85-114). New York: Plenum.

Bobo, Lawrence. 2001. "Racial Attitudes and Relations at the Close of the Twentieth Century." In N. Smelser, W. Wilson, & F. Mitchell (Eds.), *America Becoming: Racial Trends and Their Consequences* (Vol. 1, pp. 264-301). Washington, DC: National Academy Press.

Bodnar, John. 1985. *The Transplanted.* Bloomington: Indiana University Press.

Bogardus, Emory. 1933. "A Social Distance Scale." *Sociology and Social Research*, 17: 265-271.

Bonacich, Edna. 1972. "A Theory of Ethnic Antagonism: The Split Labor Market." *American Sociological Review*, 37: 547-559.

Bonacich, Edna, & Modell, John. 1980. *The Economic Basis of Ethnic Solidarity: Small Business in the Japanese American Community.* Berkeley: University of California Press.

Bordewich, Fergus. 1996. *Killing the White Man's Indian.* New York: Doubleday.

Borjas, George. 1999. *Heaven's Door: Immigration Policy and the American Economy.* Princeton, NJ: Princeton University Press.

Boswell, Terry. 1986. "A Split Labor Market Analysis of Discrimination Against Chinese Immigrants, 1850-1882." *American Sociological Review*, 51: 352-371.

Bouvier, Leon F., & Gardner, Robert W. November 1986. "Immigration to the U.S.: The Unfinished Story." *Population Bulletin*: 13-15, 41.

Brace, Matthew. 2001. "A Nation Divided." *Geographical*, 73: 14-20.

Brimelow, Peter. 1995. *Alien Nation: Common Sense About America's Immigration Disaster.* New York: Random House.

Brody, David. 1980. "Labor." In S. Thernstrom (Ed.), *Harvard Encyclopedia of Ethnic Groups* (pp. 609-618). Cambridge, MA: Harvard University Press.

Brown, Dee. 1970. *Bury My Heart at Wounded Knee.* New York: Holt, Rinehart & Winston.

Brown, Rupert. 1995. *Prejudice: Its Social Psychology.* Cambridge, MA: Blackwell.

Brown v. Board of Education of Topeka, 247 U.S. 483 (1954).

Brown, Kendrick T., Brown, Tony N., Jackson, James S., Sellers, Robert M., & Manuel, Warde J. 2003. "Teammates on and off the Field? Contact With Black Teammates and the Racial Attitudes of White Student Athletes." *Journal of Applied Social Psychology*, 33: 1379-1404.

Browne, Irene (Ed.). 1999. *Latinas and African American Women at Work: Race, Gender, and Economic Inequality.* New York: Russell Sage.

Buraku Liberation League. 2001. Discrimination Against Buraku People. Retrieved July 10, 2002, from http://www.blhrri.org/index_e.htm

Buriel, Raymond. 1993. "Acculturation, Respect for Cultural Differences, and Biculturalism Among Three Generations of Mexican American and Euro-American School Children." *Journal of Genetic Psychology*, 154: 531-544.

Burns, Peter, & Gimpel, James. 2000. "Economic Insecurity, Prejudicial Stereotypes, and Public Opinion on Immigration Policy." *Political Science Quarterly*, 115: 201-205.

Camarillo, Albert, & Bonilla, Frank. 2001. "Hispanics in a Multicultural Society: A New American Dilemma?" In N. Smelser, W. Wilson, & F. Mitchell (Eds.), *America Becoming: Racial Trends and Their Consequences* (Vol. 2, pp. 103-134). Washington, DC: National Academy Press.

Cameron, James. 2001. "Social Identity, Modern Sexism, and Perceptions of Personal and Group Discrimination by Women and Men." *Sex Roles*, 45: 743-766.

Camarota, Steven. 2002. "Immigrants in the United States: 2002," *Center for Immigration Studies*. Retrieved February 15, 2005, from http://www.cis.org/articles/2002/back1302.html

Campbell, Bebe Moore. 1993. "To Be Black, Gifted, and Alone." In V. Cyrus (Ed.), *Experiencing Race, Class, and Gender in the United States*. Mountain View, CA: Mayfield.

Cancio, S., Evans, T., & Maume, D. 1996. "Reconsidering the Declining Significance of Race: Racial Differences in Early Career Wages." *American Sociological Review*, 61: 541-556.

Central Intelligence Agency. 2004. "The World Fact Book 2004." Retrieved March 18, 2005, from http://www.cia.gov/cia/publications/factbook/

Chan, Sucheng. 1990. "European and Asian Immigrants into the United States in Comparative Perspective, 1820s to 1920s." In V. Yans-McLaughlin (Ed.), *Immigration Reconsidered: History, Sociology, and Politics* (pp. 37-75). New York: Oxford University Press.

Charles, Camille. 2003. "The Dynamics of Racial Residential Segregation." *Annual Review of Sociology*, 29: 167-207.

Cheng, Susan M., & Ho, T. Linh. 2003. *A Portrait of Race and Ethnicity in Hawaii: An Analysis of Social and Economic Outcomes of Hawaii's People*. Honolulu: Pacific American Research Center. Retrieved April 19, 2005, from http://www.thepaf.org/Research/Portrait_I.pdf

Chirot, Daniel. 1994. *How Societies Change*. Thousand Oaks, CA: Pine Forge.

Cho, Sumi. 1993. "Korean Americans vs. African Americans: Conflict and Construction." In R. Gooding-Williams (Ed.), *Reading Rodney King, Reading Urban Uprising* (pp. 196-211). New York: Routledge and Kegan Paul.

Christie, R., & Yahoda, M. (Eds.). 1954. *Studies in the Scope and Method of the Authoritarian Personality*. Glencoe, IL: Free Press.

Churchill, Ward. December 1985. "Resisting Relocation: Dine and Hopis Fight to Keep Their Land." *Dollars and Sense:* 112-115.

Civil Rights Act of 1964, Pub. L. 88–352 § 42 U.S.C. 2000 (1964).

Clark, M. L., & Person, Willie. 1982. "Racial Stereotypes Revisited." *International Journal of Intercultural Relations*, 6: 381-392.

Clark, Rebecca, Passel, Jeffrey, Zimmerman, Wendy, & Fix, Michael. 1994. *Fiscal Impacts of Undocumented Aliens: Selected Estimates for Seven States*. Washington, DC: Urban Institute.

Cofer, Judith Ortiz. 1995. *The Latin Deli: Prose and Poetry*. Athens, GA: University of Georgia Press.

Cohen, Adam, & Taylor, Elizabeth. 2000. *American Pharaoh, Mayor Richard J. Daley: His Battle for Chicago and the Nation*. New York: Little, Brown.

Cohen, Steven M. 1985. *The 1984 National Survey of American Jews: Political and Social Outlooks*. New York: American Jewish Committee.

Coltrane, Scott, & Messineo, Melinda. 2000. "The Perpetuation of Subtle Prejudice: Race and Gender Imagery in 1990s Television Advertising." *Sex Roles: A Journal of Research*, 42: 363-389.

Conot, Robert. 1967. *Rivers of Blood, Years of Darkness*. New York: Bantam.

Conzen, Kathleen N. 1980. "Germans." In S. Thernstrom (Ed.), *Harvard Encyclopedia of Ethnic Groups* (pp. 405-425). Cambridge, MA: Harvard University Press.

Coover, Gail. 2001. "Television and Social Identity: Race Representation as 'White' Accomodation." *Journal of Broadcasting and Electronic Media*, 45: 413-431.

Cornell, Stephen. 1987. "American Indians, American Dreams, and the Meaning of Success." *American Indian Culture and Research Journal*, 11: 59-71.

Cornell, Stephen. 1988. *The Return of the Native: American Indian Political Resurgence.* New York: Oxford University Press.

Cornell, Stephen. 1990. "Land, Labor, and Group Formation: Blacks and Indians in the United States." *Ethnic and Racial Studies*, 13: 368-388.

Cornell, Stephen, & Kalt, Joseph. 2000. "Where's the Glue? Institutional and Cultural Foundations of American Indian Economic Development." *Journal of Socio-Economics*, 29: 443-470.

Cornell, Stephen, Kalt, Joseph, Krepps, Matthew, & Taylor, Johnathon. 1998. *American Indian Gaming Policy and Its Socio-Economic Effects: A Report to the National Impact Gambling Study Commission.* Cambridge, MA: Economics Resource Group.

Cortes, Carlos. 1980. "Mexicans." In S. Thernstrom (Ed.), *Harvard Encyclopedia of Ethnic Groups* (pp. 697-719). Cambridge, MA: Harvard University Press.

Cose, Ellis. 1993. *The Rage of a Privileged Class.* New York: HarperCollins.

Cox, Oliver. 1948. *Caste, Class, and Race: A Study in Social Dynamics.* New York: Modern Reader Paperbacks.

Crow Dog, Mary. 1990. *Lakota Woman.* New York: HarperCollins.

Curtin, Philip. 1990. *The Rise and Fall of the Plantation Complex.* New York: Cambridge University Press.

D'Alessio, Stewart, Stolzenberg, Lisa, & Eitle, David. 2002. "The Effect of Racial Threat on Interracial and Intraracial Crimes. *Social Science Research,* 31(3): 392-408.

Damico, Sandra, & Sparks, Christopher. 1986. "Cross-Group Contact Opportunities: Impact on Interpersonal Relationships in Desegregated Middle Schools." *Sociology of Education*, 59: 113-123.

D'Angelo, Raymond. 2001. *The American Civil Rights Movement: Readings and Interpretations.* New York: McGraw-Hill.

Daniels, Roger. 1990. *Coming to America.* New York: HarperCollins.

Debo, Angie. 1970. *A History of the Indians of the United States.* Norman: University of Oklahoma Press.

DeBose, Brian. November 8, 2004. "Bush Share of Hispanic Vote Rose to 44 Percent." *Washington Times.* Retrieved December 27, 2004, from http://www.washintontimes.com

Degler, Carl. 1971. *Neither Black nor White: Slavery and Race Relations in Brazil and the United States.* New York: Macmillan.

de la Cruz, G. Patricia, & Brittingham, Angela. December 2003. *The Arab Population: 2000* (Census 2000 Brief). Retrieved April 5, 2005, from http://www.census.gov/prod/2003pubs/c2kbr-23.pdf

de la Garza, Rodolfo O., DeSipio, L., Garcia, F. C., Garcia, J., & Falcon, A. 1992. *Latino Voices: Mexican, Puerto Rican, and Cuban Perspectives on American Politics.* Boulder, CO: Westview.

de la Garza, Rodolfo O., Falcon, Angelo, & Garcia, F. Chris. 1996. "Will the Real Americans Please Stand Up: Anglo and Mexican-American Support of Core American Political Values." *American Journal of Political Science*, 40: 335-351.

Deloria, Vine. 1969. *Custer Died for Your Sins.* New York: Macmillan.

Deloria, Vine. 1970. *We Talk, You Listen.* New York: Macmillan.

Deloria, Vine. 1995. *Red Earth, White Lies.* New York: Scribner's.

Del Pinal, Jorge, & Singer, Audrey. 1997. "Generations of Diversity: Latinos in the United States." *Population Bulletin*, 52(3).

De Navas, Carmen, Proctor, Bernadette, & Mills, Robert. 2004. *Income, Poverty, and Health Insurance Coverage in the United States: 2003.* Washington, DC: U.S. Government Printing Office.

Deutsch, Morton, & Collins, Mary Ann. 1951. *Interracial Housing: A Psychological Evaluation of a Social Experiment.* Minneapolis: University of Minnesota Press.

Devine, Patricia, & Elliot, Andrew. 1995. "Are Racial Stereotypes Really Fading? The Princeton Trilogy Revisited." *Personality and Social Psychology Bulletin*, 21: 1139-1150.

Dinnerstein, Leonard. 1977. "The East European Jewish Immigration." In L. Dinnerstein & F. C. Jaher (Eds.), *Uncertain Americans* (pp. 216-231). New York: Oxford University Press.

Dollard, John, Miller, Neal E., Doob, Leonard W., Mowrer, O. H., & Sears, Robert R. (with Ford, Clellan S., Hovland, Carl Iver, & Sollenberger, Richard T.). 1939. *Frustration and Aggression.* New Haven, CT: Yale University Press.

"Dominicans Saved From Sea Tell of Attacks and Deaths of Thirst." August 12, 2004. *New York Times:* p A13.

D'Orso, Michael. 1996. *Like Judgment Day: The Ruin and Redemption of a Town Called Rosewood.* New York: Putnam.

Doyle, Anna Beth, & Aboud, Frances E. 1995. "A Longitudinal Study of White Children's Racial Prejudice as a Socio-Cognitive Development." *Merrill-Palmer Quarterly*, 41: 209-228.

Du Bois, W.E.B. 1961. *The Souls of Black Folk.* Greenwich, CT: Fawcett.

Duleep, Harriet O. 1988. *Economic Status of Americans of Asian Descent.* Washington, DC: U.S. Commission on Civil Rights.

Dyer, Richard. 2002. "The Matter of Whiteness." In P. Rothenberg (Ed.), *White Privilege* (pp. 9-12). New York: Worth.

Eichenwald, Kurt. November 16, 1996. "Texaco to Make Record Payment in Bias Lawsuit." *New York Times:* 1.

El-Badry, Samia. 2004. "Arab American Demographics," *Allied Media Corp.* Retrieved April 5, 2005, from http://www.allied-media.com/Arab-American/Arab%20american%20Demographics.htm

Elkins, Stanley. 1959. *Slavery: A Problem in American Institutional and Intellectual Life.* New York: Universal Library.

Ellison, Christopher, & Powers, Daniel. 1994. "The Contact Hypothesis and Racial Attitudes Among Black Americans." *Social Science Quarterly*, 75: 385-400.

Ellsworth, Scott. 1982. *Death in a Promised Land: The Tulsa Race Riot of 1921.* Baton Rouge: Louisiana State University Press.

Entine, Jon. 2000. *Taboo: Why Black Athletes Dominate Sports and Why We're Afraid to Talk About It.* New York: Public Affairs.

Espinosa, Kristin, & Massey, Douglas. 1997. "Determinants of English Proficiency Among Mexican Migrants to the United States." *International Migration Review*, 31: 28-51.

Espiritu, Yen. 1996. "Colonial Oppression, Labour Importation, and Group Formation: Filipinos in the United States." *Ethnic and Racial Studies*, 19: 29-49.

Espiritu, Yen. 1997. *Asian American Women and Men.* Thousand Oaks, CA: Sage.

Essien-Udom, E. U. 1962. *Black Nationalism.* Chicago: University of Chicago Press.

Evans, Sara M. 1989. *Born for Liberty: A History of Women in America.* New York: Free Press.

Evans, William, & Topoleski, Julie. 2002. *The Social and Economic Impact of Native American Casinos.* Retrieved December 5, 2004, from http://www.bsos.umd.edu/econ/evans/wpapers/evans_topoleski_casinos.pdf

Evans, Sara M. 1979. *Personal Politics.* New York: Knopf.

Fallows, Marjorie R. 1979. *Irish Americans: Identity and Assimilation.* Englewood Cliffs, NJ: Prentice Hall.

Fanning, Bryan, 2003. *Racism and Social Change in the Republic of Ireland.* Manchester, UK: Manchester University Press

Farley, John. 1988. *Majority-Minority Relations* (2nd ed.). Englewood Cliffs, NJ: Prentice-Hall.

Farley, John. 2000. *Majority-Minority Relations* (4th ed.). Englewood Cliffs, NJ: Prentice Hall.

Farley, Reynolds. 1996. *The New American Reality.* New York: Russell Sage.

Feagin, Joe. 2001. *Racist America: Roots, Current Realities, and Future Reparations.* New York: Routledge.

Feagin, Joe R., & Feagin, Clairece Booher. 1986. *Discrimination American Style: Institutional Racism and Sexism.* Malabar, FL: Robert E. Krieger.

Feagin, Joe R., & Vera, Hernan. 1995. *White Racism: The Basics.* New York: Routledge.

Federal Bureau of Investigation. 2004. "Hate Crime Statistics." Retrieved October 24, 2004, from http://www.fbi.gov/ucr/hatecrime202.pdf

Fernandez-Kelly, M. Patricia, & Schauffler, Richard. 1994. "Divided Fates: Immigrant Children in a Restructured U.S. Economy." *International Immigration Review*, 28: 662-689.

Feshbeck, Seymour, & Singer, Robert. May 1957. "The Effects of Personal and Shared Threats upon Social Prejudice." *Journal of Abnormal and Social Psychology:* 411-416.

Firefighters Local Union No. 1784 v. Stotts, 467 U.S. 561 (1984).

Fitzpatrick, Joseph P. 1976. "The Puerto Rican Family." In C. H. Mindel & R. W. Habenstein (Eds.), *Ethnic Families in America* (pp. 173-195). New York: Elsevier.

Fitzpatrick, Joseph P. 1980. "Puerto Ricans." In S. Thernstrom (Ed.), *Harvard Encyclopedia of Ethnic Groups* (pp. 858-867). Cambridge, MA: Harvard University Press.

Fitzpatrick, Joseph P. 1987. *Puerto Rican Americans: The Meaning of Migration to the Mainland* (2nd ed.). Englewood Cliffs, NJ: Prentice Hall.

Fix, Michael, & Pascal, Jeffrey. 1994. *Immigration and Immigrants: Setting the Record Straight.* Washington, DC: Urban Institute.

Fong, Eric, & Markham, William. 1991. "Immigration, Ethnicity, and Conflict: The California Chinese, 1849-1882." *Sociological Inquiry*, 61: 471-490.

Fong, Eric, & Wilkes, Rima. 1999. "The Spatial Assimilation Model Reexamined: An Assessment by Canadian Data." *International Migration Review*, 33: 594-615.

Fong, Timothy. 2002. *The Contemporary Asian American Experience* (2nd ed.). Upper Saddle River, NJ: Prentice Hall.

Fontaine, Pierre-Michel. 1986. *Race, Class, and Power in Brazil.* Los Angeles: UCLA Center for Afro-American Studies.

Fonte John. 2004. "How to Make an American." *The American Enterprise:* 15, 4-5.

Forbes, H. D. 1997. *Ethnic Conflict: Commerce, Culture and the Contact Hypothesis.* New Haven, CT: Yale University Press.

Forner, Philip S. 1980. *Women and the American Labor Movement: From World War I to the Present.* New York: Free Press.

Franklin, John Hope. 1967. *From Slavery to Freedom* (3rd ed.). New York: Knopf.

Franklin, John Hope, & Moss, Alfred. 1994. *From Slavery to Freedom* (7th ed.). New York: McGraw-Hill.

Fraser, Morris. 1973. *Children in Conflict: Growing up in Northern Ireland.* New York: Basic Books.

Frazier, E. Franklin. 1957. *Black Bourgeoisie: The Rise of a New Middle Class.* New York: Free Press.

Fukuyama, Francis. June 4, 2004. "Identity Crisis: Why We Shouldn't Worry About Mexican Immigration." *Slate.* Retrieved April 2, 2005, from http://slate.msn.com/id/2101756/#continuearticle

Gallagher, Charles. April 4-7, 2001. "Playing the Ethnic Card: How Ethnic Narratives Maintain Racial Privilege." Paper presented at the Annual Meetings of the Southern Sociological Society, Atlanta, GA.

Gallup Organization. 2001. "Black White Relations in the United States, 2001 Update." Retrieved December 23, 2004, from http://www.gallup.com/poll/specialReports/

Gans, Herbert. 1979. "Symbolic Ethnicity: The Future of Ethnic Groups and Cultures in America." *Ethnic and Racial Studies*, 2: 1-20.

Garcia, Maria Cristina. 1996. *Havana US: Cuban Exiles and Cuban Americans in South Florida, 1959-1994.* Berkeley: University of California Press.

Garvey, Marcus. 1969. *Philosophy and Opinions of Marcus Garvey* (Vols. 1-2; A. J. Garvey, Ed.). New York: Atheneum.

Garvey, Marcus. 1977. *Philosophy and Opinions of Marcus Garvey* (Vol. 3; A. J. Garvey & E. U. Essien-Udom, Eds.). London: Frank Cass.

Genovese, Eugene D. 1974. *Roll, Jordan, Roll: The World the Slaves Made.* New York: Pantheon.

Gerth, Hans, & Mills, C. Wright (Eds.). 1946. *From Max Weber: Essays in Sociology.* New York: Oxford University Press.

Geschwender, James A. 1978. *Racial Stratification in America.* Dubuque, IA: William C. Brown.

Giago, T. January 27, 1992. "I Hope the Redskins Lose." *Newsweek:* 8.

Glaeser, Edward, & Vigdor, Jacob. 2001. *Racial Segregation in the 2000 Census: Promising News.* Washington, DC: Brookings Institution.

Glazer, Nathan, & Moynihan, Daniel. 1970. *Beyond the Melting Pot* (2nd ed.). Cambridge: MIT Press.

Gleason, Philip. 1980. "American Identity and Americanization." In S. Thernstrom (Ed.), *Harvard Encyclopedia of Ethnic Groups* (pp. 31-57). Cambridge, MA: Harvard University Press.

Glick, Peter, & Fiske, Susan. 1996. "The Ambivalent Sexism Inventory: Differentiating Hostile and Benevolent Sexism." *Journal of Personality and Social Psychology*, 70: 491-512.

Glick, Peter, Fiske, Susan, Mladinic, Saiz, Antonio, Jose L., Abrams, Dominic, Masser, Barbara, et al. 2000. "Beyond Prejudice as Simple Antipathy: Hostile and Benevolent Sexism Across Cultures." *Journal of Personality and Social Psychology*, 79: 763-775.

Godstein, Amy, & Suro, Robert. January 16, 2000. "A Journey in Stages: Assimilation's Pull Is Still Strong but Its Pace Varies." *Washington Post*: A1.

Goldberg, S. 1999. The Logic of Patriarchy. *Gender Issues*, 17: 53-62.

Goldstein, Sidney, & Goldscheider, Calvin. 1968. *Jewish Americans: Three Generations in a Jewish Community.* Englewood Cliffs, NJ: Prentice Hall.

Gooding-Williams, Robert. 1993. *Reading Rodney King, Reading Urban Uprising.* New York: Routledge and Kegan Paul.

Gordon, Milton. 1964. *Assimilation in American Life.* New York: Oxford University Press.

Goren, Arthur. 1980. "Jews." In S. Thernstrom (Ed.), *Harvard Encyclopedia of Ethnic Groups* (pp. 571-598). Cambridge, MA: Harvard University Press.

Gourevitch, Philip. 1999. *We Wish to Inform You That Tomorrow We Will Be Killed With Our Families: Stories from Rwanda.* New York: Picador.

Graves, Sherryl Browne. 1999. "Television and Prejudice Reduction: When Does Television as a Vicarious Experience Make a Difference?" *Journal of Social Issues*, 55: 707-723.

Gray, David J. 1991. "Shadow of the Past: The Rise and Fall of Prejudice in an American City." *American Journal of Economics and Sociology*, 50: 33-39.

Grebler, Leo, Moore, Joan W., & Guzman, Ralph C. 1970. *The Mexican American People.* New York: Free Press.

Greeley, Andrew M. 1974. *Ethnicity in the United States: A Preliminary Reconnaissance.* New York: Wiley.

Green, Donald. 1999. "Native Americans." In A. Dworkin & R. Dworkin (Eds.), *The Minority Report* (pp. 255-277). Orlando, FL: Harcourt-Brace.

Greenfield, Thomas. April 1975. "Race and Passive Voice at Monticello." *Crisis.*

Guilbault, Rose Del Castillo. 1993. "Americanization Is Tough on 'Macho.'" In D. La Guardia & H. Guth (Eds.), *American Voices* (pp. 163-165). Mountain View, CA: Mayfield.

Gutman, Herbert. 1976. *The Black Family in Slavery and Freedom, 1750-1925.* New York: Vintage.

Hacker, Andrew. 1992. *Two Nations: Black and White, Separate, Hostile, Unequal.* New York: Scribner's.

Hamer, Fannie Lou. 1967. *To Praise Our Bridges: An Autobiography of Fannie Lou Hamer.* Jackson, MS: KIPCO.

Handlin, Oscar. 1951. *The Uprooted.* New York: Grosset & Dunlap.

Hansen, Marcus Lee. 1952. "The Third Generation in America." *Commentary*, 14: 493-500.

Hanson, Jeffery, & Rouse, Linda. 1987. "Dimensions of Native American Stereotyping." *American Indian Culture and Research Journal*, 11: 33-58.

Harjo, Suzan. 1996. "Now and Then: Native Peoples in the United States." *Dissent*, 43: 58-60.

Harris, Marvin. 1988. *Culture, People, Nature.* New York: Harper & Row.

Hartley, E. L. 1946. *Problems in Prejudice.* New York: Kings Crown.

Hawkins, Hugh. 1962. *Booker T. Washington and His Critics: The Problem of Negro Leadership.* Boston: D. C. Heath.

Heaton, Tim, Chadwick, Bruce, & Jacobson, Cardell. 2000. *Statistical Handbook on Racial Groups in the United States.* Phoenix, AZ: Oryx.

Heer, David M. 1996. *Immigration in America's Future.* Boulder, CO: Westview.

Herberg, Will. 1960. *Protestant-Catholic-Jew: An Essay in American Religious Sociology.* New York: Anchor.

Herrnstein, Richard, & Murray, Charles. 1994. *The Bell Curve.* New York: Free Press.

Higham, John. 1963. *Strangers in the Land: Patterns of American Nativism, 1860-1925.* New York: Atheneum.

Hill, Lawrence. 2001. "Black + White ... Equals Black." *Maclean's*, 114: 16-21.

Hill-Collins, Patricia. 1991. *Black Feminist Thought.* New York: Routledge.

Hirschman, Charles. 1983. "America's Melting Pot Reconsidered." *Annual Review of Sociology,* 9: 397-423.

Hirschman, Charles, & Wong, Morrison. 1984. "Socioeconomic Gains of Asian Americans, Blacks, and Hispanics: 1960-1976." *American Journal of Sociology,* 90: 584 607.

Hirschman, Charles, & Wong, Morrison. 1986. "The Extraordinary Educational Attainment of Asian-Americans: A Search for Historical Evidence and Explanations." *Social Forces,* 65: 1-27.

Hostetler, John. 1980. *Amish Society.* Baltimore, MD: Johns Hopkins University Press.

Hovland, Carl I., & Sears, Robert R. 1940. "Minor Studies of Aggression: Correlation of Lynchings and Economic Indices." *Journal of Psychology,* 9: 301-310.

"How to Tell Your Friends from the Japs." October-December 1941. *Time:* 33.

Hoxie, Frederick. 1984. *A Final Promise: The Campaign to Assimilate the Indian, 1880-1920.* Lincoln: University of Nebraska Press.

Hraba, Joseph. 1979. *American Ethnicity.* Itasca, IL: F. E. Peacock.

Hughes, Michael, & Thomas, Melvin. 1998. "The Continuing Significance of Race Revisited: A Study of Race, Class and Quality of Life in America, 1972 to 1996." *American Sociological Review,* 63: 785-803.

Hur, Kenneth K., & Robinson, John P. 1978. "The Social Impact of Roots." *Journalism Quarterly,* 55: 19-21, 83.

Hurh, Won Moo. 1998. *The Korean Americans.* Westport, CT: Greenwood.

Hurtado, Aida, & Vega, Luis A. 2004. "Shift happens: Spanish and English Transmission between Parents and their Children." *Journal of Social Issues,* 60: 137-155.

Hyman, Herbert, & Sheatsley, Paul. 1964. "Attitudes Toward Desegregation." *Scientific American,* 211: 16-23.

Ibish, Hussein. Ed. 2003. "Report on Hate Crimes and Discrimination Against Arab Americans: The Post September 11 Backlash." *American-Arab Anti-Discrimination Committee.* Retrieved February 14, 2005, from http://www.adc.org/hatecrimes/pdf/2003_report_web.pdf

Institute for Social Research. 1996. *World Values Survey.* Ann Arbor, MI: Inter-university Consortium for Political and Social Research.

Instituto Brasileiro do Geografica e Estatistica. 1999. "Distribution of the Resident Population, by Major Regions, Urban or Rural Situation, Sex, Skin Color or Race." Retrieved July 17, 2002, from http://www.ibge.gov.br/english/estatistica/populacao/trabalhoerendimento/pnad99/sintese/tab1_2_b_1999.shtm.

Jackman, Mary. 1973. "Education and Prejudice or Education and Response Set." *American Sociological Review,* 40: 327-339.

Jackman, Mary. 1978. "General and Applied Tolerance: Does Education Increase Commitment to Racial Integration?" *American Journal of Political Science,* 22: 302-324.

Jackman, Mary. 1981. "Education and Policy Commitment to Racial Integration." *American Journal of Political Science,* 25: 256-259.

Jackman, Mary, & Muha, M. 1984. "Education and Intergroup Attitudes: Moral Enlightenment, Superficial Democratic Commitment, or Ideological Refinement?" *American Sociological Review,* 49: 751-769.

Jackson, Beverly. 2000. *Splendid Slippers: A Thousand Years of an Erotic Tradition.* Berkeley, CA: Ten Speed.

Jacobs, David, & Wood, Katherine. 1999. "Interracial Conflict and Interracial Homicide: Do Political and Economic Rivalries Explain White Killings of Blacks or Black Killings of Whites?" *American Journal of Sociology,* 105: 157-180.

Jacobs, Harriet. 1987. *Incidents in the Life of a Slave Girl, Written by Herself* (J. Yellin, Ed.). Cambridge, MA: Harvard University Press.

Jacoby, Russell, & Glauberman, Naomi. 1995. *The Bell Curve Debate.* New York: Random House.

Jarvis, Brian. May 13, 1993. "Against the Great Divide." *Newsweek:* 14.

Jibou, Robert M. 1988. "Ethnic Hegemony and the Japanese of California." *American Sociological Review,* 53: 353-367.

Joe, Jennie, & Miller, Dorothy. 1994. "Cultural Survival and Contemporary American Indian Women in the City." In M. Zinn & B. T. Dill (Eds.), *Women of Color in U.S. Society.* Philadelphia: Temple University Press.

Jones, James. 1997. *Prejudice and Racism* (2nd ed.). New York: McGraw-Hill.

Jones, Jeffrey. 2001. "Racial or Ethnic Labels Make Little Difference to Blacks, Hispanics." Retrieved July 5, 2002, from http://www.gallup.com/ poll/releases/pr010911.asp

Jones, Melinda. 2002. *Social Psychology of Prejudice.* Upper Saddle River, NJ: Prentice-Hall.

Jordan, Winthrop. 1968. *White Over Black: American Attitudes Towards the Negro: 1550-1812.* Chapel Hill: University of North Carolina Press.

Josephy, Alvin M. 1968. *The Indian Heritage of America.* New York: Knopf.

Kahlenberg, Richard. 1997. *The Remedy: Class, Race, and Affirmative Action.* New York: Basic Books.

Kallen, Horace M. February 18, 1915a. "Democracy Versus the Melting Pot." *The Nation:* 190-194.

Kallen, Horace M. February 25, 1915b. "Democracy Versus the Melting Pot." *The Nation:* 217-222.

Karlins, Marvin, Coffman, Thomas, & Walters, Gary. 1969. "On the Fading of Social Stereotypes: Studies in Three Generations of College Students." *Journal of Personality and Social Psychology*, 13: 1-16.

Kasarda, John D. 1989. "Urban Industrial Transition and the Underclass." *Annals of the American Academy*, 501: 26-47.

Katz, Phyllis. 1976. "The Acquisition of Racial Attitudes in Children." In P. Katz (Ed.), *Towards the Elimination of Racism* (pp. 125-154). New York: Pergamon.

Katz, Phyllis, & Taylor, Dalmas. Eds. 1988. *Eliminating Racism: Profiles in Controversy.* New York: Plenum.

Kennedy, Randall. 2001. "Racial Trends in the Administration of Criminal Justice." In N. Smelser, W. Wilson, & F. Mitchell (Eds.), *America Becoming: Racial Trends and Their Consequences* (Vol. II, pp. 1-20). Washington, DC: National Academy Press.

Kennedy, Ruby Jo. 1944. "Single or Triple Melting Pot: Intermarriage Trends in New Haven, 1870-1940." *American Journal of Sociology*, 49: 331-339.

Kennedy, Ruby Jo. 1952. "Single or Triple Melting Pot: Intermarriage Trends in New Haven, 1870-1950." *American Journal of Sociology*, 58: 56-59.

Kephart, William, & Zellner, William. 1994. *Extraordinary Groups.* New York: St. Martin's.

Killian, Lewis. 1975. *The Impossible Revolution, Phase 2: Black Power and the American Dream.* New York: Random House.

Kim, Kwang Chung, Hurh, Won Moo, & Fernandez, Marilyn. 1989. "Intra-group Differences in Business Participation: Three Asian Immigrant Groups." *International Migration Review*, 23: 73-95.

Kinder, Donald R., & Sears, David O. 1981. "Prejudice and Politics: Symbolic Racism Versus Racial Threats to the Good Life." *Journal of Personality and Social Psychology*, 40: 414-431.

King, C. Richard, Staurowsky, Ellen J., Baca, Lawrence, Davis, R., & Pewewardy, Cornel. 2002. "Of Polls and Race Prejudice: Sports Illustrated's Errant "Indian Wars." *Journal of Sport and Social Issues,* 26: 381-403.

King, Martin Luther, Jr. 1958. *Stride Toward Freedom: The Montgomery Story.* New York: Harper & Row.

King, Martin Luther, Jr. 1963. *Why We Can't Wait.* New York: Mentor.

King, Martin Luther, Jr. 1968. *Where Do We Go from Here: Chaos or Community?* New York: Harper & Row.

Kitano, Harry H. L. 1976. *Japanese Americans.* Englewood Cliffs, NJ: Prentice Hall.

Kitano, Harry H. L. 1980. "Japanese." In S. Thernstrom (Ed.), *Harvard Encyclopedia of Ethnic Groups* (pp. 561-571). Cambridge, MA: Harvard University Press.

Kitano, Harry, & Daniels, Roger. 1988. *Asian Americans: Emerging Minorities.* Englewood Cliffs, NJ: Prentice Hall.

Kitano, Harry, & Daniels, Roger. 1995. *Asian Americans: Emerging Minorities* (2nd ed.). Englewood Cliffs, NJ: Prentice Hall.

Kitano, Harry, & Daniels, Roger. 2001. *Asian Americans: Emerging Minorities* (3rd ed.). Upper Saddle River, NJ: Prentice Hall.

Kleg, M., & Yamamoto, K. 1998. "As the World Turns: Ethno-Racial Distances After 70 Years." *Social Science Journal*, 35: 183-191.

Kluegel, James R., & Smith, Eliot R. 1982. "Whites' Beliefs About Blacks' Opportunities." *American Sociological Review*, 47: 518-532.

Kochhar, Rakesh. 2004. "The Wealth of Hispanic Households," *Pew Hispanic Center*. Retrieved February 15, 2004, from http://www.pewhispanic.org/site/docs/pdf/The%20Wealth%20of%20Hispanic%20Households.pdf

Kraybill, Donald B., & Bowman, Carl F. 2001. *On the Backroad to Heaven: Old Order Hutterites, Mennonites, Amish, and Brethren.* Baltimore, MD: Johns Hopkins University Press.

Krikorian, Mark. 1997. "Will Americanization Work in America?" *Freedom Review,* 28: 48-49.

Kritz, Mary, & Girak, Douglas. 2004. *The American People: Immigration and a Changing America.* New York: Russell Sage Foundation.

Krysan, Maria, & Farley, Reynolds. 2002. "The Residential Preferences of Blacks: Do They Explain Persistent Segregation?" *Social Forces,* 80: 937-981.

Kuperman, Diane. September 2001. "Stuck at the Gates of Paradise." *Unesco Courier:* 24-26.

Kwong, Peter. 1987. *The New Chinatown.* New York: Hill and Wang.

Lach, Jennifer. January 2000. "Interracial Friendships." *American Demographics.*

Lacy, Dan. 1972. *The White Use of Blacks in America.* New York: McGraw-Hill.

Lai, H. M. 1980. "Chinese." In S. Thernstrom (Ed.), *Harvard Encyclopedia of Ethnic Groups* (pp. 217-234). Cambridge, MA: Harvard University Press.

Lame Deer, John (Fire), & Erdoes, Richard. 1972. *Lame Deer: Seeker of Visions.* New York: Simon & Schuster.

Lamont-Brown, Raymond. 1993. "The Burakumin: Japan's Underclass." *Contemporary Review,* 263: 136-140.

LaPiere, Robert. 1934. "Attitudes vs. Actions." *Social Forces,* 13: 230-237.

Lee, Chungmei. 2004. "Is Resegregation Real?" Retrieved April 8, 2005, from http://www.civilrights project.harvard.edu/

Lee, Sharon. 1998. "Asian Americans: Diverse and Growing." *Population Bulletin,* 53(2).

Lee, Sharon, & Fernandez, Marilyn. 1998. "Trends in Asian American Racial/Ethnic Intermarriage: A Comparison of 1980 and 1990 Census Data." *Sociological Perspectives,* 41: 323-343.

Lee, Sharon M., & Yamanaka, Keiko. 1990. "Patterns of Asian American Intermarriage and Marital Assimilation." *Journal of Comparative Family Studies,* 21: 287-305.

Lenski, Gerhard, Nolan, Patrick, & Lenski, Jean. 1995. *Human Societies: An Introduction to Macrosociology* (7th ed.). New York: McGraw-Hill.

Levin, Jack, & Levin, William. 1982. *The Functions of Discrimination and Prejudice.* New York: Harper & Row.

Levin, Jack, & McDevitt, Jack. 1993. *Hate Crimes: The Rising Tide of Bigotry and Bloodshed.* New York: Plenum.

Levine, Lawrence. 1977. *Black Culture and Black Consciousness.* New York: Oxford University Press.

Levy, Jacques. 1975. *Cesar Chavez: Autobiography of La Causa.* New York: Norton.

Lewis Mumford Center. 2001. "Ethnic Diversity Grows, Neighborhood Integration Lags Behind." Retrieved July 2, 2002, from http://mumford1.dyndns.org/cen2000/report.html

Lewis, Oscar. 1959. *Five Families: Mexican Case Studies in the Culture of Poverty.* New York: Basic Books.

Lewis, Oscar. 1965. *La Vida: A Puerto Rican Family in the Culture of Poverty.* New York: Random House.

Lewis, Oscar. October 1966. "The Culture of Poverty." *Scientific American:* 19-25.

Li, Peter. 1990. *Race and Ethnic Relations in Canada.* Toronto: Oxford University Press.

Lieberson, Stanley. 1980. *A Piece of the Pie: Blacks and White Immigrants Since 1880.* Berkeley: University of California Press.

Lieberson, Stanley, & Waters, Mary C. 1988. *From Many Strands.* New York: Russell Sage.

Light, Ivan, & Bonacich, Edna. 1988. *Immigrant Entrepreneurs: Koreans in Los Angeles, 1965-1982.* Berkeley: University of California Press.

Lincoln, C. Eric. 1961. *The Black Muslims in America.* Boston: Beacon.

Ling, Huping. 2000. "Family and Marriage of Late-Nineteenth and Early-Twentieth Century Chinese Immigrant Women." *Journal of American Ethnic History,* 9: 43-65.

Locust, Carol. 1990. "Wounding the Spirit: Discrimination and Traditional American Indian Belief Systems." In G. Thomas (Ed.), *U.S. Race Relations in the 1980s and 1990s: Challenges and Alternatives* (pp. 219-232). New York: Hemisphere.

Logan, John, Alba, Richard, & McNulty, Thomas. 1994. "Ethnic Economies in Metropolitan Regions: Miami and Beyond." *Social Forces*, 72: 691-724.

Lopata, Helena Znaniecki. 1976. *Polish Americans.* Englewood Cliffs, NJ: Prentice Hall.

Luciuk, Lubomyr, & Hryniuk, Stelkla. Eds. 1991. *Canada's Ukrainians Negotiating an Identity.* Toronto, ON: University of Toronto Press.

Lurie, Nancy Oestrich. 1982. "The American Indian: Historical Background." In N. Yetman & C. H. Steele (Eds.), *Majority and Minority* (3rd ed., pp. 131-144). Boston: Allyn & Bacon.

Lyman, Stanford. 1974. *Chinese Americans.* New York: Random House.

Malik, Kenan. September 18, 2000. "Yes, Nature Does Help to Explain African Sporting Success. If You Think That's Racist, Your Idea of Race is Wrong." *New Statesman*, 129: 13-18.

Mangiafico, Luciano. 1988. *Contemporary American Immigrants.* New York: Praeger.

Mannix, Daniel P. 1962. *Black Cargoes: A History of the Atlantic Slave Trade.* New York: Viking.

Marable, Manning. August 27, 2001. "An Idea Whose Time Has Come. . . . Whites Have an Obligation to Recognize Slavery's Legacy." *Newsweek:* 22.

Marcelli, Enrico, & Heer, David. 1998. "The Unauthorized Mexican Immigrant Population and Welfare in Los Angeles County: A Comparative Statistical Analysis." *Sociological Perspectives*, 41: 279-303.

Margolis, Richard. 1989. "If We Won, Why Aren't We Smiling?" In C. Willie (Ed.), *Round Two of the Willie/Wilson Debate* (2nd ed., pp. 95-100). Dix Hills, NY: General Hall.

Martin, Philip, & Midgley, Elizabeth. 1999. "Immigration to the United States." *Population Bulletin*, 54(2): 15.

Martin, Philip, & Widgren, Jonas. 2002. *International Migration: Facing the Challenge.* Washington, DC: Population Reference Bureau.

Marx, Karl, & Engels, Friedrich. 1967. *The Communist Manifesto.* Baltimore, MD: Penguin. (Original work published 1848)

Massarik, Fred, & Chenkin, Alvin. 1973. "United States National Jewish Population Study: A First Report." In American Jewish Committee (Ed.), *American Jewish Year Book, 1973* (pp. 264-306). New York: American Jewish Committee.

Massey, Douglas. 1995. "The New Immigration and Ethnicity in the United States." *Population and Development Review*, 21: 631-652.

Massey, Douglas. 2000. "Housing Discrimination 101." *Population Today*, 28: 1, 4.

Massey, Douglas, & Denton, Nancy. 1993. *American Apartheid.* Cambridge, MA: Harvard University Press.

Massey, Douglas, & Singer, Audrey. 1995. "New Estimates of Undocumented Mexican Migration to the United States and the Probability of Apprehension." *Demography*, 32: 203-213.

Mathabane, Mark. 1986. *Kaffir Boy.* New York: Plume Books.

Mauer, Marc, & Huling, Tracy. 2000. "Young Black Americans and the Criminal Justice System." In J. Skolnick & E. Currie (Eds.), *Crisis in American Institutions* (11th ed., pp. 417-424). New York: Allyn & Bacon.

Mazzuca, Josephine. 2004. "For Most Americans, Friendship is Colorblind." Retrieved September 17, 2004, from http://www.gallup.com

McConahy, John B. 1986. "Modern Racism, Ambivalence, and the Modern Racism Scale." In J. F. Dovidio & S. Gartner (Eds.), *Prejudice, Discrimination and Racism* (pp. 91-125). Orlando, FL: Academic Press.

McDowell, Amber. September 10, 2004. "Cracker Barrel Settles Lawsuit: Black Customers, Workers Reported Discrimination." *Washington Post:* E1.

McFarlane, Bruce. 1988. *Yugoslavia: Politics, Economics and Society.* London: Pinter.

McLaren, Lauren. 2003. "Anti-Immigrant Prejudice in Europe: Contact, Threat Perception, and Preferences for the Exclusion of Migrants." *Social Forces*, 81: 909-936.

McLemore, S. Dale. 1973. "The Origins of Mexican American Subordination in Texas." *Social Science Quarterly*, 53: 656-679.

McNickle, D'Arcy. 1973. *Native American Tribalism: Indian Survivals and Renewals.* New York: Oxford University Press.

McRoberts, Kenneth. 1988. *Quebec: Social Change and Political Crisis.* Toronto, ON: McClelland and Stewart.

McWhorter, John. 2001. "Blood Money: An Analysis of Slavery Reparations." *American Enterprise,* 12: 18.

McWilliams, Carey. 1961. *North from Mexico: The Spanish Speaking People of the United States.* New York: Monthly Review Press.

Medoff, Marshall. 1999. "Allocation of Time and Hateful Behavior: A Theoretical and Positive Analysis Of Hate and Hate Crimes." *American Journal of Economics and Sociology,* 58: 959-973.

Merton, Robert. 1968. Social Theory and Social Structure. New York: Free Press.

Miller, Neal, & Bugleski, R. 1948. "Minor Studies of Aggression: The Influence of Frustrations Imposed by the Ingroup on Attitudes Expressed Towards Outgroups." *Journal of Psychology,* 25: 437-442.

Miller, Norman, & Brewer, Marilyn. Eds. 1984. *Groups in Contact: The Psychology of Desegregation.* Orlando, FL: Academic Press.

Min, Pyong Gap. 1995. *Asian Americans: Contemporary Trends and Issues.* Thousand Oaks, CA: Sage.

Mirandé, Alfredo. 1985. *The Chicano Experience: An Alternative Perspective.* Notre Dame, IN: University of Notre Dame Press.

Mirandé, Alfredo, & Enriquez, Evangelica. 1979. *La Chicana: The Mexican-American Women.* Chicago: University of Chicago Press.

Moore, Joan W. 1970. *Mexican Americans.* Englewood Cliffs, NJ: Prentice Hall.

Moore, Joan W., & Pachon, Harry. 1985. *Hispanics in the United States.* Englewood Cliffs, NJ: Prentice Hall.

Moore, Joan, & Pinderhughes, Raquel. 1993. *In the Barrios: Latinos and the Underclass Debate.* New York: Sage.

Moquin, Wayne, & Van Doren, Charles. Eds. 1971. *A Documentary History of Mexican Americans.* New York: Bantam.

Morawska, Ewa. 1990. "The Sociology and Historiography of Immigration." In V. Yans-McLaughlin (Ed.), *Immigration Reconsidered: History, Sociology, and Politics.* New York: Oxford University Press.

Morgan, Edmund. 1975. *American Slavery, American Freedom.* New York: Norton.

Morin, Richard, & Cottman, Michael. June 22, 2001. "Discrimination's Lingering Sting." *Washington Post:* A1.

Morris, Aldon D. 1984. *The Origins of the Civil Rights Movement.* New York: Free Press.

Morrison, Joan, & Zabusky, Charlotte Fox. 1980. *American Mosaic: The Immigrant Experience in the Words of Those Who Lived It.* New York: Dutton.

Moynihan, Daniel. 1965. *The Negro Family: The Case for National Action.* Washington, DC: U.S. Department of Labor.

Mujica, Mauro, 2003. "Official English Legislation: Myths and Realities." *Human Events,* 59: 24.

Myrdal, Gunnar. 1962. *An American Dilemma: The Negro Problem and Modern Democracy.* New York: Harper & Row.

Nabakov, Peter. Ed. 1999. *Native American Testimony* (Rev. ed.). New York: Penguin.

National Academy of Sciences, 1997. "The New Americans: Economic, Demographic, and Fiscal Effects of Immigration." Retrieved January 23, 2005, from http://books.nap.edu/execsumm_pdf/5779.pdf

National Advisory Commission. 1968. *Report of the National Advisory Commission on Civil Disorders.* New York: *New York Times.*

National Indian Gaming Commission. n.d.a. "Gaming Tribes." Retrieved March 31, 2005, from http://www.nigc.gov/nigc/nigcControl?option=GAMING_TRIBES&REGIONID=0

National Indian Gaming Commission. n.d.b. [Home page]. Retrieved March 31, 2005, from http://www.nigc.gov/nigc/nigcControl?option=HOME

National Opinion Research Council. 1972-2000. *General Social Survey.* Chicago: Author.

National Opinion Research Council. 2002. *General Social Survey.* Chicago: Author.

National Origins Act, Pub. L. 139, Chapter 190, § 43 Stat. 153 (1924).

National Public Radio. 2004. "Immigration Survey." Retrieved February 15, 2005, from http://www.npr.org/templates/story/story.php?storyId=4062605

NationMaster.com. (2005a). "Asia: Korea, South: Religion." Retrieved April 6, 2005, from http://www.nationmaster.com/country/ks/Religion

NationMaster.com. (2005b). "Central America and the Caribbean: Dominican Republic: Economy." Retrieved April 5, 2005, from http://www.nationmaster.com/country/dr/Economy

NationMaster.com. (2005c). "Central America and the Caribbean: El Salvador." Retrieved April 5, 2005, from http://www.nationmaster.com/country/es/

NationMaster.com. (2005d). "Central America and the Caribbean: Haiti: Economy." Retrieved April 5, 2005, from http://www.nationmaster.com/country/ha/Economy

NationMaster.com. (2005e). "Europe: Germany: People." Retrieved April 8, 2005, from http://www.nationmaster.com/country/gm/People

NationMaster.com. (2005f). "Other: Cape Verde." Retrieved April 6, 2005, from http://www.nationmaster.com/country/cv

Nelli, Humbert S. 1980. "Italians." In S. Thernstrom (Ed.), *Harvard Encyclopedia of Ethnic Groups* (pp. 545-560). Cambridge, MA: Harvard University Press.

Nishi, Setsuko. 1995. "Japanese Americans." In P. G. Min (Ed.), *Asian Americans: Contemporary Trends and Issues.* Thousand Oaks, CA: Sage.

Noel, Donald. 1968. "A Theory of the Origin of Ethnic Stratification." *Social Problems*, 16: 157-172.

Nolan, Patrick, & Lenski, Gerhard. 2004 *Human Societies.* Boulder, CO: Paradigm.

Novak, Michael. 1973. *The Rise of the Unmeltable Ethnics: Politics and Culture in the 1970s.* New York: Collier.

Ogunwole, Stella. 2002. *The American Indian and Alaska Native Population: 2000* (U.S. Census Brief). Washington, DC: U.S. Bureau of the Census.

O'Hare, William P. 1992. "America's Minorities: The Demographics of Diversity." *Population Bulletin*, 47(4).

O'Hare, William, Pollard, Kelvin, Mann, Taynia, & Kent, Mary. 1991. *African Americans in the 1990s.* Washington, DC: Population Reference Bureau.

O'Hare, William P., & Usdansky, Margaret. 1992. "What the 1990 Census Tells Us About Segregation in 25 Large Metros." *Population Today*, 20(9): 34.

Oliver, Melvin, & Shapiro, Thomas. 1995. *Black Wealth, White Wealth.* New York: Routledge.

Oliver, Melvin, & Shapiro, Thomas. 2001. "Wealth and Racial Stratification." In N. Smelser, W. Wilson, & F. Mitchell (Eds.), *America Becoming: Racial Trends and Their Consequences* (Vol. 1, pp. 222-251). Washington, DC: National Academy Press.

Olson, James, & Wilson, R. 1984. *Native Americans in the Twentieth Century.* Provo, UT: Brigham Young University Press.

Omi, Michael, & Winant, Howard. 1986. *Racial Formation in the United States From the 1960s to the 1980s.* New York: Routledge and Kegan Paul.

Orfield, Gary. 2001. *Schools More Separate: Consequences of a Decade of Resegregation.* Cambridge, MA: Harvard University. Retrieved June 28, 2002, from http://www.law.harvard.edu/civilrights

Orreniou, Pia. 2001. "Illegal Immigration and Enforcement Along the U.S.-Mexico Border: An Overview." *Economic & Financial Review:* 2-11.

Osofsky, Gilbert. 1969. *Puttin' on Ole Massa.* New York: Harper & Row.

Oswalt, Wendell, & Neely, Sharlotte. 1996. *This Land Was Theirs.* Mountain View, CA: Mayfield.

Parish, Peter J. 1989. *Slavery: History and Historians.* New York: Harper & Row.

Park, Robert E., & Burgess, Ernest W. 1924. *Introduction to the Science of Society.* Chicago: University of Chicago Press.

Parke, Ross, & Buriel, Raymond. 2002. "Socialization Concerns in African American, American Indian, Asian American, and Latino Families." In N. Benokraitis (Ed.), *Contemporary Ethnic Families in the United States.* Upper Saddle Brook, NJ: Prentice Hall.

Parrado, Emilio, & Zenteno, Rene. 2001. "Economic Restructuring, Financial Crises, and Women's Work in Mexico." *Social Problems*, 48: 456-477.

Parrillo, Vince. 2003. *Strangers to These Shores* (7th ed.). Boston: Allyn and Bacon.

Patterson, Orlando. 1997. *The Ordeal of Integration*. Washington, DC: Civitas.

Pego, David. 1998. "To Educate a Nation: Native American Tribe Hopes to Bring Higher Education to an Arizona Reservation." *Black Issues in Higher Education*, 15: 60-63.

Perez, Lisandro. 1980. "Cubans." In S. Thernstrom (Ed.), *Harvard Encyclopedia of Ethnic Groups* (pp. 256-261). Cambridge, MA: Harvard University Press.

Petersen, Williams. 1971. *Japanese Americans*. New York: Random House.

Peterson, Mark. 1995. "Leading Cuban-American Entrepreneurs: The Process of Developing Motives, Abilities, and Resources." *Human Relations,* 48: 1193-1216.

Pettigrew, Thomas. 1958. "Personality and Sociocultural Factors in Intergroup Attitudes: A Cross-National Comparison." *Journal of Conflict Resolution,* 2: 29-42.

Pettigrew, Thomas. 1971. *Racially Separate or Together?* New York: McGraw-Hill.

Pettigrew, Thomas. 1980. "Prejudice." In S Thernstrom (Ed.), *Harvard Encyclopedia of Ethnic Groups* (pp. 820-829). Cambridge, MA: Harvard University Press.

Pettigrew, Thomas. 1997. "Generalized Intergroup Contact Effects on Prejudice." *Personality and Social Psychology Bulletin,* 23: 175-185.

Pettigrew, Thomas. 1998. "Intergroup Contact Theory." *Annual Review of Psychology,* 49: 65-85.

Pettit, Becky, & Western, Bruce. 2004. "Mass Imprisonment and the Life Course: Race and Class Inequality in U.S. Incarceration." *American Sociological Review,* 69: 151-169.

Phillips, Ulrich B. 1918. *American Negro Slavery*. New York: Appleton.

Piersen, William D. 1996. *From Africa to America: African American History From the Colonial Era to the Early Republic, 1526-1790*. New York: Twayne.

Pilger, John. 2000. "Australia Is the Only Developed Country Whose Government Has Been Condemned as Racist by the United Nations." *New Statesman*, 129: 17.

Pitt, Leonard. 1970. *The Decline of the Californios: A Social History of the Spanish-Speaking Californians, 1846-1890*. Berkeley: University of California Press.

Plessy v. Ferguson, 163 U.S. 537 (1896).

Pollard, Kelvin, & O'Hare, William. 1999. "America's Racial and Ethnic Minorities." *Population Bulletin*, 54(3): 29-39.

Polner, Murray. March 7, 1993. "Asian Americans Say They Are Treated Like Foreigners." *New York Times:* 1.

Population Reference Bureau. 2000. "Occupational Segregation." Retrieved June 18, 2002, from http://www.prb.org/Content/NavigationMenu/Ameristat/Topics1/RaceandEthnicity/U_S_Occupational_Segregation.htm

Popp, Danielle, Donavan, Roxanne, Crawford, Mary, Marsh, Kerry, & Peele, Melanie. 2003. "Gender, Race, and Speech Style Stereotypes." *Sex Roles,* 48(7/8): 317-325.

Portes, Alejandro. 1990. "From South of the Border: Hispanic Minorities in the United States." In V. Yans-McLaughlin (Ed.), *Immigration Reconsidered* (pp. 160-184). New York: Oxford University Press.

Portes, Alejandro, & Bach, Robert L. 1985. *Latin Journey: Cuban and Mexican Immigrants in the United States*. Berkeley: University of California Press.

Portes, Alejandro, & Manning, Robert. 1986. "The Immigrant Enclave: Theory and Empirical Examples." In S. Olzak & J. Nagel (Eds.), *Competitive Ethnic Relations*. New York: Academic Press.

Portes, A., & Rumbaut, R. 1996. *Immigrant America: A Portrait* (2nd ed.). Berkeley: University of California Press.

Portes, A., & Rumbaut, R. 2001. *Legacies: The Story of the Immigrant Second Generation*. Berkeley: University of California Press.

Portes, Alejandro, & Zhou, Min. 1992. "Gaining the Upper Hand: Economic Mobility Among Immigrant and Domestic Minorities." *Ethnic and Racial Studies*, 15: 491-518.

Portes, Alejandro, & Zhou, Min. November 1993. "The New Second Generation: Segmented Assimilation and Its Variants." *Annals of American Academy of Political and Social Sciences:* 74-96.

Posadas, Barbara. 1999. *The Filipino Americans*. Westport, CT: Greenwood.

Potter, George. 1973. *To the Golden Door: The Story of the Irish in Ireland and America.* Westport, CT: Greenwood.

Poulan, Richard. 2003. "Globalization and the Sex Trade: Trafficking and the Commodification of Women and Children." *Canadian Woman Studies,* 22: 38-43.

Powers, Daniel, & Ellison, Christopher. 1995. "Interracial Contact and Black Racial Attitudes: The Contact Hypothesis and Selectivity Bias." *Social Forces,* 74: 205-226.

Powlishta, K., Serbin, L., Doyle, A., & White, D. 1994. "Gender, Ethnic, and Body-Type Biases: The Generality of Prejudice in Childhood." *Developmental Psychology,* 30: 526-537.

Price, S. L. & Woo, Andrea. March 4, 2002. "The Indian Wars." *Sports Illustrated,* 96: 66-73.

Prosise, Theodore O., & Johnson, Ann. 2004. "Law Enforcement and Crime on *Cops* and *World's Wildest Police Videos:* Anecdotal Form and the Justification of Racial Profiling." *Western Journal of Communication,* 68: 72-92.

Puzo, Mario. 1993. "Choosing a Dream: Italians in Hell's Kitchen." In W. Brown & A. Ling (Eds.), *Visions of America* (pp. 56-57). New York: Persea Books.

Quillian, Lincoln, & Campbell, Mary. 2003. "Beyond Black and White: The Present and Future of Multiracial Friendship Segregation." *American Sociological Review,* 68: 540-567.

Rader, Benjamin G. 1983. *American Sports: From the Age of Folk Games to the Age of Spectators.* Englewood Cliffs, NJ: Prentice Hall.

Rawick, George P. 1972. *From Sundown to Sunup: The Making of the Black Community.* Westport, CT: Greenwood.

Raymer, Patricia. August 1974. "Wisconsin's Menominees: Indians on a Seesaw." *National Geographic:* 228-251.

Read, Jen'nan Ghazal. 2004. "Cultural Influences on Immigrant Women's Labor Force Participation: The Arab-American Case." *International Migration Review,* 38: 52-77.

Reich, Michael. 1986. "The Political-Economic Effects of Racism." In R. Edwards, M. Reich, & T. Weisskopf (Eds.), *The Capitalist System: A Radical Analysis of American Society* (3rd ed., pp. 381-388). Englewood Cliffs, NJ: Prentice Hall.

Remington, Robin. 1997. "Ethnonationalism and the Disintegration of Yugoslavia." In Winston Van Horne (Ed.), *Global Convulsions.* Albany, NY: SUNY.

Rifkin, Jeremy. 1996. *The End of Work: The Decline of the Global Labor Force and the Dawn of the Post-Market Era.* New York: Putnam.

Robertson, Claire. 1996. "Africa and the Americas? Slavery and Women, the Family, and the Gender Division of Labor." In D. Gaspar & D. Hine (Eds.), *More Than Chattel: Black Women and Slavery in the Americas* (pp. 4-40). Bloomington: Indiana University Press.

Robinson, Randall. 2001. *The Debt: What America Owes to Blacks.* New York: Plume.

Rodriguez, Clara. 1989. *Puerto Ricans: Born in the USA.* Boston: Unwin Hyman.

Rodriguez, Clara, & Cordero-Guzman, Hector. 1992. "Placing Race in Context." *Ethnic and Racial Studies,* 15: 523-542.

Rodriguez, Luis. 1993. Always Running: La Vida Loca. New York: Touchstone Books.

Rosenfield, Michael. 2002. "Measures of Assimilation in the Marriage Market: Mexican Americans 1970-1990." *Journal of Marriage and the Family,* 64: 152-163.

Rouse, Linda, & Hanson, Jeffery. 1991. "American Indian Stereotyping, Resource Competition, and Status-Based Prejudice." *American Indian Culture and Research Journal,* 15: 1-17.

Rowatt, Wade, & Franklin, Lewis. 2004. "Christian Orthodoxy, Religious Fundamentalism, and Right-Wing Authoritarianism as Predictors of Implicit Racial Prejudice." *International Journal of Psychology of Religion,* 14(2): 125-138.

Rumbaut, Rubén G. 1991. "Passage to America: Perspectives on the New Immigration." In A. Wolfe (Ed.), *America at Century's End* (pp. 208-245). Berkeley: University of California Press.

Rumbaut, Rubén, & Portes, Alejandro. 2001. *Ethnicities: Children of Immigrants in America.* New York: Russell Sage Foundation.

Russell, James W. 1994. *After the Fifth Sun: Class and Race in North America.* Englewood Cliffs, NJ: Prentice Hall.

Saenz, Rogelio. 1999. "Mexican Americans." In A. Dworkin & R. Dworkin (Eds.), *The Minority Report* (pp. 209-229). Orlando, FL: Harcourt Brace.

Sanchirico, Andrew. 1991. "The Importance of Small Business Ownership in Chinese American Educational Achievement." *Sociology of Education,* 64:293-304.

Schafer, John, & Navarro, Joe. 2004. "The Seven Stage Hate Model: The Psychopathology of Hate Groups. *The FBI Law Enforcement Bulletin, 72:* 1-9.

Schlesinger, Arthur M., Jr. 1992. *The Disuniting of America: Reflections on a Multicultural Society.* New York: Norton.

Schoener, Allon. 1967. *Portal to America: The Lower East Side, 1870-1925.* New York: Holt, Rinehart & Winston.

Schumann, Howard, Steeh, Charlotte, & Bobo, Lawrence. 1997. *Racial Attitudes in America: Trends and Interpretations.* Cambridge, MA: Harvard University Press.

Sears, David. 1988. "Symbolic Racism." In P. Katz & D. Taylor (Eds.), *Eliminating Racism: Profiles in Controversy* (pp. 53-84). New York: Plenum.

Sears, David, & Henry, P. J. 2003. "The Origins of Modern Racism." *Journal of Personality and Social Psychology, 85:* 259-275.

See, Katherine O'Sullivan, & Wilson, William J. 1988. "Race and Ethnicity." In N. Smelser (Ed.), *Handbook of Sociology* (pp. 223-242). Newbury Park, CA: Sage.

Seller, Maxine S. 1987. "Beyond the Stereotype: A New Look at the Immigrant Woman." In R. Takaki (Ed.), *From Different Shores: Perspectives on Race and Ethnicity in America* (pp. 197-203). New York: Oxford University Press.

Selzer, Michael. 1972. *"Kike": Anti-Semitism in America.* New York: Meridian.

Selznik, G. J., & Steinberg, S. 1969. *The Tenacity of Prejudice.* New York: Harper & Row.

Shannon, William V. 1964. *The American Irish.* New York: Macmillan.

Sheet Metal Workers v. EEOC, 478 U.S. 421 (1986).

Shelton, B. A., & John, D. 1996. "The Division of Household Labor." *Annual Review of Sociology,* 22: 299-322.

Sherif, Muzafer, Harvey, O. J., White, B. Jack, Hood, William, & Sherif, Carolyn. 1961. *Intergroup Conflict and Cooperation: The Robber's Cave Experiment.* Norman, OK: University Book Exchange.

Sheth, Manju. 1995. "Asian Indian Americans." In P. G. Min (Ed.), *Asian American: Contemporary Issues and Trends* (pp. 169-198). Thousand Oaks, CA: Sage.

Shils, E. A. 1954. "Authoritarianism: Right and Left." In R. Christie & M. Yahoda (Eds.), *Studies in the Scope and Method of the Authoritarian Personality* (pp. 123-147). Glencoe, IL: Free Press.

Shim, Doobo. 1998. "From Yellow Peril Through Model Minority to Renewed Yellow Peril (Asians in Popular Media)." *Journal of Communication Inquiry,* 22: 385-410.

Shinagawa, Larry, & Pang, Gin Yong. 1996. "Asian American Panethnicity and Intermarriage." *Amerasia Journal,* 22: 127-153.

Sigelman, Lee, & Welch, Susan. 1993. "The Contact Hypothesis Revisited: Black-White Interaction and Positive Racial Attitudes." *Social Forces,* 71: 781-795.

Simon, Julian. 1989. *The Economic Consequences of Immigration.* Cambridge, MA: Blackwell.

Simpson, George, & Yinger, Milton. 1985. *Racial and Cultural Minorities: An Analysis of Prejudice and Discrimination.* New York: Plenum.

Sklare, Marshall. 1971. *America's Jews.* New York: Random House.

Smedley, Audrey. 1999. *Race in North America: Origins and Evolution of Worldview* (2nd ed.). Boulder, CO: Westview.

Smelser, N., Wilson, W., & Mitchell, F. (Eds.) 2001. *America Becoming: Racial Trends and Their Consequences* (Vol. 1). Washington, DC: National Academy Press.

Smith, Christopher B. 1994. "Back to the Future: The Intergroup Contact Hypothesis Revisited." *Sociological Inquiry,* 64: 438-455.

Smith, David, & Chambers, Gerald. 1991. *Inequality in Northern Ireland.* Oxford: Clarendon.

Smith, James, & Edmonston, Barry. (Eds.). 1997. *The New Americans: Economic, Demographic, and Fiscal Effects of Immigration.* Washington, DC: National Academy Press.

Smith, Kevin, & Seelbach, Wayne. 1987. "Education and Intergroup Attitudes: More on the Jackman and Muha Thesis." *Sociological Spectrum,* 7: 157-170.

Smith, Tom, & Dempsey, Glenn. 1983. "The Polls: Ethnic Social Distance and Prejudice." *Public Opinion Quarterly,* 47: 584-600.

Smith, Vern. August 27, 2001. "Debating the Wages of Slavery." *Newsweek:* 20-25.

Snipp, C. Matthew. 1989. *American Indians: The First of This Land.* New York: Russell Sage Foundation.

Snipp, C. Matthew. 1992. "Sociological Perspectives on American Indians." *Annual Review of Sociology,* 18: 351-371.

Snipp, C. Matthew. 1996. "The First Americans: American Indians." In S. Pedraza & R. G. Rumbaut (Eds.), *Origins and Destinies: Immigration, Race, and Ethnicity in America* (pp. 390-403). Belmont, CA: Wadsworth.

"A Sorry Tale." 2000. *The Economist,* 356: 12.

Southern Poverty Law Center. 2005. "Intelligence Project: Active U.S. Hate Groups in 2003." Retrieved March 23, 2005, from http://www.splcenter.org/intel/map/hate.jsp

Sowell, Thomas. October 6, 1997. "How 'Affirmative Action' Hurts Blacks." *Forbes,* 160: 64.

Spicer, Edward H. 1980. "American Indians." In S. Thernstrom (Ed.), *Harvard Encyclopedia of Ethnic Groups* (pp. 58-122). Cambridge, MA: Harvard University Press.

Spickard, Paul. 1996. *Japanese Americans: The Formation and Transformations of an Ethnic Group.* New York: Twayne.

Spilde, Kate. 2001. "The Economic Development Journey of Indian Nations." Retrieved July 5, 2002, from http://indiangaming.org/library/ newsletters/index.html

Stampp, Kenneth. 1956. *The Peculiar Institution: Slavery in the Ante-Bellum South.* New York: Random House.

Staples, Robert. 1988. "The Black American Family." In C. Mindel, R. Habenstein, & R. Wright (Eds.), *Ethnic Families in America* (3rd ed., pp. 303-324). New York: Elsevier.

Starling, Kelly. 1999. "New TV Season: National Uproar Forces Schedule Change." *Ebony,* 55: 82-88.

Statistics Canada. 2004. "1996 Census." Retrieved April 14, 2005, from http://www12.statcan.ca/english/census01/info/census96.cfm

Staub, Ervin. 1996. "Cultural-Societal Roots of Violence: The Examples of Genocidal Violence and Contemporary Youth Violence in the United States." *American Psychologist,* 51: 117-132.

Steinberg, Stephen. 1981. *The Ethnic Myth: Race, Ethnicity, and Class in America.* New York: Atheneum.

Stelcner, Morton. 2000. "Earnings Differentials Among Ethnic Groups in Canada: A Review of the Research." *Review of Social Economy,* 58: 295-422.

Stember, C. H. 1961. *Education and Attitude Change.* New York: Institute of Human Relations Press.

Stepick, Alex, Stepick, Carol D., Eugene, Emmanuel, Teed, Deborah, & Labissiere, Yves. 2001. "Shifting Identities and Intergenerational Conflict: Growing Up Haitian in Miami." In R. Rumbaut & A. Portes (Eds.), *Ethnicities: Children of Immigrants in America* (pp. 229-266). Berkeley: University of California Press.

Stoddard, Ellwyn. 1973. *Mexican Americans.* New York: Random House.

Stoll, Michael. 2004. *African Americans and the Color Line.* New York: Russell Sage Foundation.

Stuckey, Sterling. 1987. *Slave Culture: Nationalist Theory and the Foundations of Black America.* New York: Harper & Row.

Sung, Betty Lee. 1990. "Chinese American Intermarriage." *Journal of Comparative Family Studies,* 21: 337-352.

Swaine, Thomas, & Nishimoto, Richard S. 1946. *The Spoilage.* Berkeley: University of California Press. Retrieved February 11, 2005, from http://www.geocities.com/Athens/8420/kurihara.html

Sweetman, Arthur, & Dicks, Gordon. 1999. "Education and Ethnicity in Canada." *Journal of Human Resources,* 34: 668-690.

Swim, Janet, & Cohen, Laurie. 1997. "Overt, Covert, and Subtle Sexism: A Comparison Between the Attitudes Toward Women and Modern Sexism Scales." *Psychology of Women Quarterly,* 21: 103-119.

Swim, Janet, Mallett, Robyn, & Stangor, Charles. 2004. "Understanding Subtle Sexism: Detection and Use of Sexist Language." *Sex Roles,* 51: 117-128.

Takaki, Ronald. 1993. *A Different Mirror: A History of Multicultural America.* Boston: Little, Brown.

Tannenbaum, Frank. 1947. *Slave and Citizen: The Negro in the Americas.* New York: Knopf.

Taylor, Jared, & Whitney, Glayde. 1999. "Crime and Racial Profiling by U.S. Police: Is There an Empirical Basis?" *Journal of Social, Political and Economic Studies,* 24: 485-516.

Taylor, Jared, & Whitney, Glade. 2002. "Racial Profiling: Is There an Empirical Basis?" *Mankind Quarterly,* 42: 285-313.

Terkel, Studs. 1992. *Race.* New York: New Press.

Thernstrom, Stephan, & Thernstrom, Abigail. 1997. *America in Black and White.* New York: Simon & Schuster.

Thomas, Melvin. 1993. "Race, Class, and Personal Income: An Empirical Test of the Declining Significance of Race Thesis, 1968-1988." *Social Problems,* 40: 328-342.

Thornton, Russell. 2001. "Trends Among American Indians in the United States." In N. Smelser, W. Wilson, & F. Mitchell (Eds.), *America Becoming: Racial Trends and Their Consequences* (Vol. 1, pp. 135-169). Washington, DC: National Academy Press.

Tilly, Charles. 1990. "Transplanted Networks." In V. Yans-McLaughlin (Ed.), *Immigration Reconsidered: History, Sociology, and Politics* (pp. 79-95). New York: Oxford University Press.

Tougas, Francine, Rupert, Ann, & Joly, Stephane. 1995. "Neosexism: Plus Ça Change, Plus C'est Pareil." *Personality & Social Psychology Bulletin,* 21: 842-850.

Tsai, Shih-Shan Henry. 1986. *The Chinese Experience in America.* Bloomington: Indiana University Press.

Udry, Richard. 2000. "Biological Limits of Gender Construction." *American Sociological Review,* 65: 443-457.

United Nations. 2000. "U.N. Releases Most Recent Statistics on World's Women." Retrieved June 27, 2002, from http://unstats.un.org/ unsd/demographic/ww2000/ww2000pr.htm

U.S. Bureau of the Census. 1977. *Statistical Abstract of the United States: 1977* (98th ed.). Washington, DC: U.S. Government Printing Office.

U.S. Bureau of the Census. 1996. *Statistical Abstract of the United States: 1996* (116th ed.). Washington, DC: U.S. Government Printing Office.

U.S. Bureau of the Census. 2000a. "Mapping Census 2000: The Geography of U.S. Diversity." Retrieved April 2, 2005, from http://www.census.gov/population/cen2000/atlas/censr01-111.pdf and http://www.census.gov/population/cen2000/atlas/censr01–108.pdf

U.S. Bureau of the Census. 2000b. "Number of People, 2000. One Race: Black or African American." Retrieved July 2, 2002, from http://www.census.gov/population/cen2000/atlas/censr01–106.pdf

U.S. Bureau of the Census. 2000c. "Population by Region, Sex, Hispanic Origin, and Race, With Percentage Distribution by Hispanic Origin and Race: March 2000." Retrieved July 8, 2002, from http://www.census.gov/population/socdemo/hispanic/p20-535/tab19-1.txt

U.S. Bureau of the Census. 2000d. "Population, Race, Hispanic or Latino. Hawaii." Retrieved July 12, 2002, from http://factfinder.census.gov/bf/_lang=en_vt_name=DEC_2000_PL_U_QTPL_geo_id=04000US15.html

U.S. Bureau of the Census. 2000e. "Poverty Status of Families in 1999 by Family Type, and by Hispanic Origin and Race of Householder." Retrieved July 8, 2002, from http://www.census.gov/population/socdemo/hispanic/p20-535/tab15-1.txt

U.S. Bureau of the Census. 2000f. "Profiles of General Demographic Characteristics, 2000 Census of Population and Housing." Retrieved July 8, 2002, from http://www2.census.gov/census_2000/datasets/demographic_profile/Florida/2kh12.pdf

U.S. Bureau of the Census. 2000g. "Projections of the Resident Population by Race, Hispanic Origin, and Nativity." Retrieved March 15, 2005, from http://www.census.gov/population/www/projections/natsum.html

U.S. Bureau of the Census. 2001. "Profiles of General Demographic Characteristics, 2000." Retrieved July 5, 2002, from http://www.census.gov/prod/cen2000/dp1/2kh00.pdf

U.S. Bureau of the Census. 2002. *Statistical Abstract of the United States, 2001* (121st ed.). Washington, DC: U.S. Government Printing Office.

U.S. Bureau of the Census. 2003a. "Hispanic Population Reaches All-Time High." Retrieved September 2, 2004, from http://www.census.gov/Press-Releases/www/2003

U.S. Bureau of the Census. 2003b. "Index of /population/socdemo/ancestry." Retrieved April 14, 2005, from http://www.census.gov/population/socdemo/ancestry/

U.S. Bureau of the Census. 2003c. *Statistical Abstract of the United States, 2002* (122nd ed.). Washington, DC: U.S. Government Printing Office.

U.S. Bureau of the Census. 2004. "Historical Income Tables—People." Retrieved March 29, 2005, from http://www.census.gov/hhes/income/histinc/incperdet.html

U.S. Bureau of the Census. 2005. *Statistical Abstract of the United States, 2004-2005* (124th ed.). Washington, DC: U.S. Government Printing Office.

U.S. Bureau of the Census. n.d. "Data Sets," *American FactFinder.* Retrieved March 31, 2005, from http://factfinder.census.gov/servlet/DatasetMainPageServlet?_program=DEC&_lang=en

U.S. Bureau of Indian Affairs. 1997. "1997 Labor Market Information on the Indian Labor Force." Retrieved May 17, 2002, from http://www.doi.gov/bia/Labor/97LFRCovFinal.pdf

U.S. Commission on Civil Rights. 1976. *Puerto Ricans in the Continental United States: An Uncertain Future.* Washington, DC: U.S. Government Printing Office.

U.S. Commission on Civil Rights. 1992. *Civil Rights Issues Facing Asian Americans in the 1990s.* Washington, DC: U.S. Government Printing Office.

U.S. Department of Homeland Security. 2003. *Yearbook of Immigration Statistics, 2002.* Washington, DC: U.S. Government Printing Office.

U.S. Department of Homeland Security. 2004. *Yearbook of Immigration Statistics: 2003.* Washington, DC: U.S. Government Printing Office.

U.S. Immigration and Naturalization Service. 1993. *Statistical Yearbook of the Immigration and Naturalization Service, 1992.* Washington, DC: U.S. Government Printing Office.

U.S. Immigration and Naturalization Service. 1997. Statistical Yearbook of the Immigration and Naturalization Service, 1995. Washington, DC: U.S. Government Printing Office.

United Steelworkers of America, AFL-CIO-CLC v. Weber, 443 U.S. 193 (1979).

"Utah Supreme Court Rules That Non-Indian Members of Native American Church Can Use Peyote in Church Ceremonies." June 23, 2004. *New York Times:* A20.

Valentine, Sean, & Mosley, Gordon. 2000. "Acculturation and Sex-Role Attitudes Among Mexican Americans: A Longitudinal Analysis." *Hispanic Journal of Behavioral Sciences*, 22: 104-204.

van den Berghe, Pierre L. 1967. *Race and Racism: A Comparative Perspective.* New York: Wiley.

van den Berghe, Pierre L. 1978. *Man in Society.* New York: Elsevier.

van den Berghe, Pierre L. 1981. *The Ethnic Phenomenon.* New York: Elsevier.

Vander Waerdt, Lois. 1997. *Affirmative Action in Higher Education: A Source Book* (3rd ed.). St. Louis, MO: Employment Partnership.

Vidmar, Neil, & Rokeach, Milton. 1974. "Archie Bunker's Bigotry." *Journal of Communication*, 24: 36-47.

Vigilant, Linda. 1997. "Race and Biology." In W. Van Horne (Ed.), *Global Convulsions: Race, Ethnicity, and Nationalism at the End of the Twentieth Century* (pp. 49-62). Albany, NY: SUNY.

Vincent, Theodore G. 1976. *Black Power and the Garvey Movement.* San Francisco: Ramparts.

Vinje, David. 1996. "Native American Economic Development on Selected Reservations: A Comparative Analysis." *American Journal of Economics and Sociology*, 55: 427-442.

Voting Rights Act, 42 U.S.C. § 1971 (1965).

Vrij, A., van Schie, E., & Cherryman, J. 1996. "Reducing Ethnic Prejudice Through Public Communication Programs: A Social-Psychological Perspective." *Journal of Psychology*, 130: 413-421.

Wagley, Charles, & Harris, Marvin. 1958. *Minorities in the New World: Six Case Studies.* New York: Columbia University Press.

Wallace, Walter. 1997. *The Future of Ethnicity, Race, and Nationality.* Westport, CT: Praeger.

Washington, Booker T. 1965. *Up from Slavery.* New York: Dell.

Waters, Mary. 1990. *Ethnic Options.* Berkeley: University of California Press.

Waters, Mary. 1996. "Optional Ethnicities: For Whites Only?" In S. Pedraza & R. Rumbaut (Eds.), *Origins and Destinies: Immigration, Race, and Ethnicity in America* (pp. 449-452). Belmont, CA: Wadsworth.

Wax, Murray. 1971. *Indian Americans: Unity and Diversity.* Englewood Cliffs, NJ: Prentice Hall.

Weeks, Philip. 1988. *The American Indian Experience.* Arlington Heights, IL: Forum Press.

Weil, Frederick. 1985. "The Variable Effects of Education on Liberal Attitudes: A Comparative-Historical Analysis of Anti-Semitism Using Public Opinion Survey Data." *American Sociological Review,* 50: 458-474.

Weitz, Rose, & Gordon, Leonard. 1993. "Images of Black Women Among Anglo College Students." *Sex Roles,* 28: 19-34.

Wertheimer, Barbara M. 1979. "'Union Is Power': Sketches From Women's Labor History." In J. Freeman (Ed.), *Women: A Feminist Perspective* (pp. 339-358). Palo Alto, CA: Mayfield.

West, Patrick. June 17, 2002. "The New Ireland Kicks Ass." *New Statesman London,* 15(711): 20-22.

White, Deborah Gray. 1985. *Ar'n't I a Woman? Female Slaves in the Plantation South.* New York: Norton.

Whiting, Robert. 1990. *You Gotta Have Wa.* New York: Macmillan.

Whitlock, Craig, February 14, 2005. "As Dresden Recalls Days of Ruin, Neo-Nazis Issue a Rallying Cry." *Washington Post:* A1.

Wilkens, Roger. May 3, 1992. "L.A.: Images in the Flames—Looking Back in Anger: 27 Years After Watts, Our Nation Remains Divided by Racism." *Washington Post:* C1.

Wilkerson, Isabel. 2002. "The Most Powerful Woman in the World." *Essence,* 32: 114-118, 144, 152-158, 160-162.

Williams, Juan. 1987. *Eyes on the Prize: America's Civil Rights Years, 1954-1965.* New York: Penguin.

Williams, R. 1964. *Strangers Next Door.* Englewood Cliffs, NJ: Prentice Hall.

Willie, Charles (Ed.). 1989. *Round Two of the Willie/Wilson Debate* (2nd ed.). Dix Hills, NY: General Hall.

Wilson, George. 1997. "Payoffs to Power Among Males in the Middle Class: Has Race Declined in Its Significance?" *Sociological Quarterly,* 38: 607-623.

Wilson, William J. 1973. *Power, Racism, and Privilege: Race Relations in Theoretical and Sociohistorical Perspectives.* New York: Free Press.

Wilson, William J. 1980. *The Declining Significance of Race* (2nd ed.). Chicago: University of Chicago Press.

Wilson, William J. 1987. *The Truly Disadvantaged: The Inner City, the Underclass, and Public Policy.* Chicago: University of Chicago Press.

Wilson, William J. 1996. *When Work Disappears.* New York: Knopf.

Wirth, Louis. 1945. "The Problem of Minority Groups." In R. Linton (Ed.), *The Science of Man in the World* (pp. 347-372). New York: Columbia University Press.

Wittig, M., & Grant-Thompson, S. 1998. "The Utility of Allport's Conditions of Intergroup Contact for Predicting Perceptions of Improved Racial Attitudes and Beliefs." *Journal of Social Issues,* 54: 795-812.

Wolfenstein, Eugene V. 1993. *The Victims of Democracy: Malcolm X.* New York: Guilford.

Wong, Jade Snow. 1993. "Fifth Chinese Daughter." In D. LaGuardia & H. Guth (Eds.), *American Voices.* Palo Alto, CA: Mayfield.

Wong, Morrison. 1995. "Chinese Americans." In P. G. Min (Ed.), *Asian Americans: Contemporary Trends and Issues.* Thousand Oaks, CA: Sage.

Wood, Peter, & Chesser, Michele. 1994. "Black Stereotyping in a University Population." *Sociological Focus,* 27: 17-34.

Woodrum, Eric. April 1979. "Japanese Americans: A Test of the Assimilation Success Story." Paper presented at the Southern Sociological Society, Atlanta, GA.

Woodward, C. Vann. 1974. *The Strange Career of Jim Crow* (3rd ed.). New York: Oxford University Press.

Worsnop, Richard. May 8, 1992. "Native Americans." *CQ Researcher:* 387-407.

Wright, Richard. 1940. *Native Son.* New York: Harper & Brothers.

Wright, Richard. 1945. *Black Boy: A Record of Childhood and Youth.* New York: Harper & Brothers.

Wright, Richard. 1988. *12 Million Black Voices.* New York: Thunder's Mouth Press.

Wyman, Mark. 1993. *Round Trip to America.* Ithaca, NY: Cornell University Press.

X, Malcolm. 1964. *The Autobiography of Malcolm X.* New York: Grove.

Xie, Yu, & Goyette, Kimberly. 2004. *A Demographic Portrait of Asian Americans.* New York: Russell Sage Foundation.

Yamato, Alexander. 1994. "Racial Antagonism and the Formation of Segmented Labor Markets: Japanese Americans and Their Exclusion from the Work Force." *Humboldt Journal of Social Relations*, 20: 31-63.

Yancey, George. 1999. "An Examination of the Effects of Residential and Church Integration on Racial Attitudes of Whites." *Sociological Perspectives*, 42: 279-294.

Yinger, J. Milton. 1985. "Ethnicity." *Annual Review of Sociology*, 11: 151-180.

Zhou, Min. 1992. *Chinatown.* Philadelphia: Temple University Press.

Zhou, Min, & Bankston, Carl. 1998. *Growing up American: How Vietnamese Children Adapt to Life in the United States.* New York: Russell Sage.

Zhou, Min, & Logan, John R. 1989. "Returns on Human Capital in Ethnic Enclaves: New York City's Chinatown." *American Sociological Review,* 54: 809-820.

Zuriff, G. E. 2002. "Inventing Racism." *Public Interest,* 146: 114-130.

# ADDITIONAL SOURCES

Anton, Mike. September 22, 2001. "After the Attack: The Psychic Toll." *Los Angeles Times:* A26.

Central Statistics Office, Ireland. 2002. "Annual Migration Estimates." Retrieved June 20, 2002, from http://eirestat.cso.ie/PECAvarlist.html

Chin, Ko-lin. 2000. *Smuggled Chinese: Clandestine Immigration to the United States.* Philadelphia, PA: Temple University Press.

Cohn, D'Vera. October 25, 2001. "Illegal Immigrant Total is Raised." *Washington Post:* A24.

Davis, F. 1979. *Yearning for Yesterday.* New York: Free Press.

Eaves, L. J., & Eysenck, H. J. 1974. "Genetics and the Development of Social Attitudes." *Nature*, 249: 288-289.

Gallup Organization. 2000. "What Americans Think: Black or White?" *Spectrum,* 73(7).

Gladwell, Malcolm. October 8, 1995. "Personal Experience, The Primary Gauge." *Washington Post:* A26.

Gordon, Milton. 1978. *Human Nature, Class, and Ethnicity.* New York: Oxford University Press.

Halbswach, Maurice. 1950. *The Collective Memory.* New York: Harper & Row.

Houston, Jeanne Wakatsuki. 1994. "Manzanar, U.S.A." In L. Kirszner & S. Mandell (Eds.), *Common Ground: Reading and Writing About America's Cultures* (pp. 98-103). New York: St. Martin's.

Hraba, Joseph. 1994. *American Ethnicity* (2nd ed.). Itasca, IL: F. E. Peacock.

Huntington, Samuel P. 2004. "The Hispanic Challenge." *Foreign Policy,* 141: 30-46.

Johnson, M, & Marini, M. 1998. "Bridging the Racial Divide in the United States: The Effect of Gender." *Social Psychology Quarterly*, 61: 247-259.

Kamen, Al. November 16, 1992. "After Immigration, an Unexpected Fear: New Jersey's Indian Community Is Terrorized by Racial Violence." *Washington Post:* A1.

Kinder, Donald, & Winter, Nicholas. 2001. "Exploring the Racial Divide: Blacks, Whites, and Opinion on National Policy." *American Journal of Political Science*, 45: 439-453.

King, Robert D. 1997. "Should English Be the Law?" *Atlantic Monthly*, 279: 55-62.

Labaton, Stephen. May 25, 1994. "Denny's Restaurants to Pay $54 Million in Race Bias Suits." *New York Times:* A1.

Lamm, Richard D., & Imhoff, Gary. 1985. *The Immigration Time Bomb: The Fragmenting of America.* New York: E. P. Dutton.

Lenski, Gerhard. 1984. *Power and Privilege: A Theory of Stratification.* Chapel Hill, NC: University of North Carolina Press.

Marger, Martin N. 1994. *Race and Ethnic Relations: American and Global Perspectives* (3rd ed.). Belmont, CA: Wadsworth.

Marks, Jonathan. 2000. "Review of *Taboo: Why Black Athletes Dominate Sports and Why We're Afraid to Talk About It." Human Biology*, 72: 1074.

Martin, W., Eaves, L. J., Heath, A. C., Jardine, R., Feingold, L. M., & Eysenck, H. J. 1986. "Transmission of Social Attitudes." *Proceedings of National Academy of Science*, 83: 4364-4368.

Massey, Douglas, & Denton, Nancy. 1992. "Residential Segregation of Asian-Origin Groups in U.S. Metropolitan Areas." *Sociology and Social Research*, 76: 170-177.

McKay, James. 1982. "An Exploratory Synthesis of Primordial and Mobilizationist Approaches to Ethnic Phenomena." *Ethnic and Racial Studies*, 5: 395-420.

Momaday, Scott. 1999. "Confronting Columbus Again." In P. Nabakov (Ed.), *Native American Testimony* (Rev. ed., pp. 437-440). New York: Penguin.

Moore, Robert B. 1988. "Racial Stereotyping in the English Language." In P. S. Rothenberg (Ed.), *Racism and Sexism: An Integrated Study* (pp. 269-279). New York: St. Martin's.

Murray, C., Kaiser, R., & Taylor, S. 1997. "The O.J. Simpson Verdict: Predictors of Beliefs About Innocence or Guilt." *Journal of Social Issues*, 53: 455-476.

O'Sullivan, Eoin. 2003. "Migration and Housing in Ireland: Report to the European Observatory on Homelessness." Retrieved February 14, 2005, from http://www.feantsa.org/files/national_reports/ireland/ireland_migration_2002.pdf

"Poisoning the Web: Hatred Online." 1999. *Corrections Today*, 61: 102-108.

Rinaldi, Alfred. 1999. "No Turks, Please, We're German." *New Statesman*, 128: 23-25.

Roberts, Johnnie. January 28, 2002. "The Race to the Top." *Newsweek:* 44-49.

Rumbaut, Rubén. 1995. "Vietnamese, Laotian, and Cambodian Americans." In P. G. Min (Ed.), *Asian Americans: Contemporary Issues and Trends.* Thousand Oaks, CA: Sage.

Schmitt, Eric. March 8, 2001. "New Census Shows Hispanics Are Even With Blacks in U.S." *New York Times:* A1.

Staples, Robert (Ed.). 1994. *The Black Family.* Belmont, CA: Wadsworth.

Steele, Shelby. 1990. *The Content of Our Character.* New York: St. Martin's.

Turner, Ralph, & Killian, Lewis. 1987. *Collective Behavior* (3rd ed.). Englewood Cliffs, NJ: Prentice Hall.

U.S. Bureau of the Census. 1979. *Current Population Survey.* Washington, DC: U.S. Government Printing Office.

U.S. Bureau of the Census. 1988. *Statistical Abstract of the United States: 1988* (108th ed.). Washington, DC: U.S. Government Printing Office.

U.S. Bureau of the Census. 1990. *Summary Population and Housing Characteristics: United States.* Washington, DC: U.S. Government Printing Office.

U.S. Bureau of the Census. 1992. *Statistical Abstract of the United States: 1992* (112th ed.). Washington, DC: U.S. Government Printing Office.

U.S. Bureau of the Census. 1993. *Statistical Abstract of the United States: 1993* (113th ed.). Washington, DC: U.S. Government Printing Office.

U.S. Bureau of the Census. 1995. "Selected Social and Economic Characteristics for the 25 Largest American Indian Tribes: 1990." Retrieved July 5, 2002, from http://www.census.gov/population/socdemo/race/indian/ailang2.txt

U.S. Bureau of the Census. 1998. "Educational Attainment for Selected Ancestry Groups." Retrieved July 11, 2002, from http://www.census.gov/population/ socdemo/ancestry/table_01.txt

U.S. Bureau of the Census. 1998. "Income and Poverty for Selected Ancestry Groups." Retrieved July 11, 2002, from http://www.census.gov/population/ socdemo/ancestry/table_04.txt

U.S. Bureau of the Census. 1999. *Statistical Abstract of the United States, 1999* (199th ed.). Washington, DC: U.S. Government Printing Office.

U.S. Bureau of the Census. 2000. "Earnings of Full-Time, Year-Round Workers 15 Years and Over in 1999 by Sex, Hispanic Origin, and Race." Retrieved July 8, 2002, from http://www.census.gov/ population/socdemo/hispanic/p20–535/tab11–2.txt and http://www.census.gov/population/ socdemo/hispanic/p20–535/tab11–3.txt

U.S. Bureau of the Census. 2000. "Educational Attainment of the Population 25 Years and Over by Sex, Hispanic Origin, and Race." Retrieved July 8, 2002, from http://www.cen-sus.gov/population/ socdemo/hispanic/p20–535/tab07–2/txt

U.S. Bureau of the Census. 2000. "Educational Attainment of the Population 25 Years and Over by Sex, and Race and Hispanic Origin." Retrieved July 11, 2002, from http://www.census.gov/ population/socdemo/race/api/ppl-146/tab07.txt

U.S. Bureau of the Census. 2000. "Historical Income Tables—Families." Retrieved July 2, 2002, from http://www.census.gov/hhes/income/histinc/f05.html

U.S. Bureau of the Census. 2000. "Major Occupation Groups of the Employed Civilian Population 16 Years and Over by Sex, and Race and Hispanic Origin." Retrieved July 11, 2002, from http://www.census.gov/population/socdemo/race/api/ppl-146/tab11.txt

U.S. Bureau of the Census. 2000. "Number of People, 2000. One Race: American Indian and Alaska Native." Retrieved July 2, 2002, from http://www.census.gov/population/cen2000/atlas/censr01–107.pdf

U.S. Bureau of the Census. 2000. "Number of People, 2000. One Race: Asian." Retrieved July 10, 2002, from http://www.census.gov/population/cen2000/atlas/censr01–108.pdf

U.S. Bureau of the Census. 2000. "Number of People, 2000. Hispanic or Latino Origin, All Races." Retrieved July 8, 2002, from http://www.census.gov/population/ cen2000/atlas/censr01-111.pdf

U.S. Bureau of the Census. 2000. "Occupation of the Employed Civilian Population 16 Years and Over by Sex, Hispanic Origin, and Race." Retrieved July 8, 2002, from http://www.census.gov/population/ socdemo/hispanic/p20-535/tab10-2.txt

U.S. Bureau of the Census. 2000. "Population by Metropolitan and Nonmetropolitan Residence, Sex, Hispanic Origin, and Race." Retrieved July 8, 2002, from http://www.census.gov/population/ socdemo/hispanic/p20-535/tab21-1.txt

U.S. Bureau of the Census. 2000. "Population by Metropolitan and Nonmetropolitan Residence, Sex, Race, and Hispanic Origin." Retrieved July 11, 2002, from http://www.census.gov/population/socdemo/ race/api/ppl-146/tab21.pdf

U.S. Bureau of the Census. 2000. "Poverty Status of Families in 1999 by Type and Race and Hispanic Origin of the Householder." Retrieved July 11, 2002, from http://www.census.gov/population/socdemo/ race/api/ppl-146/tab17.txt

U.S. Bureau of the Census. 2000. "Profiles of General Demographic Characteristics." Retrieved July 2, 2002, from http://www.census.gov/prod/cen2000/dp1/2khus.pdf

U.S. Bureau of the Census. 2000. "Profiles of General Demographic Characteristics, 2000" (Table DP-1). Retrieved July 5, 2002, from http://www.census.gov/prod/cen2000/dp1/2khus.pdf

U.S. Bureau of the Census. 2000. "Quarterly Estimates of the United States Foreign-Born and Native Resident Populations." Retrieved July 8, 2002, from http://eire.census.gov/popest/archives/national/ us_nativity/fbtab001.txt

U.S. Bureau of the Census. 2000. "Race and Hispanic Origin of People by Median Income and Sex: 1947 to 2000." Retrieved July 2, 2002, from http://www.census.gov/hhes/income/histinc/p02.html

U.S. Bureau of the Census. 2000. *Statistical Abstract of the United States* (120th ed.). Washington, DC: U.S. Government Printing Office.

U.S. Bureau of the Census. 2000. "Total Money Income in 1999 of Families by Type, and Race and Hispanic Origin of the Householder." Retrieved July 11, 2002, from http://www.census.gov/population/socdemo/race/api/ppl-146/tab15.txt

U.S. Bureau of the Census. 2001. "Overview of Race and Hispanic Origin." Retrieved June 17, 2002, from http://blue.census.gov/prod/2001pubs/c2kbr01-1.pdf

U.S. Bureau of Indian Affairs. 1991. *American Indians Today: Answers to Your Questions.* Washington, DC: U.S. Department of the Interior.

U.S. Immigration and Naturalization Service. 1992. *Statistical Yearbook of the Immigration and Naturalization Service, 1991.* Washington, DC: U.S. Government Printing Office.

Vander Zanden, James. 1965. *Race Relations in Transition.* New York: Random House.

Whitaker, M. October 16, 1995. "Whites v. Blacks." *Newsweek:* 28-35.

White, Jack. November 27, 2000. "The Real Winners: Black Voters." *Time:* 60.

Wickham, DeWayne. November 27, 2000. "Gore Topped Bush in Appeal to Broader Segment of Americans." *USA Today.*

Williams, Gregory. 1995. *Life on the Color Line.* New York: Dutton.

Wilson, William J. 1978. *The Declining Significance of Race* (1st ed.). Chicago: University of Chicago Press.

Women's International Network. 1998. "Philippines: Women Bearing the Cross of Globalization." *WIN News,* 24: 62-64.

# Glossary and Index

Numbers in brackets refer to the chapter in which the term is introduced.

Ethnic identity
  as rhetorical device against other
      groups, 53, 455
  hyphenated, 455
**Ethnic minority groups** [1] Minority
    groups identified primarily by cultural
    characteristics, such as language
    or religion:
  definition of, 13, 535
**Ethnic revival** [12] The movement toward
    increased salience for ethnic identity,
    which began for European Americans in
    the 1960s:
  definition of, 535
  white ethnicity survival and, 453–454
**Ethnic succession** [12] The process by which
    European ethnic groups affected each
    other's position in the social class
    structure:
  definition of, 535
  in housing/occupations, 319
  white ethnic group and, 445, 448–450
  *See also* Secondary structural assimilation
**Ethnocentrism** [5] Judging other groups,
    societies, or cultures by the standards
    of one's own, 150, 153
  definition of, 535
  Mexican Americans and, 170
  *See also* Noel Hypothesis
**Ethnogenesis** [2] A process by which new
    minority groups may be formed from a
    variety of traditions, 52–53, 535
Eugene, E., 391
European immigrant women, in labor force,
    448–449
European immigrants
  Blauner hypothesis and, 451
  colonized minority groups and, 152
  crime as pathway of mobility, 449
  first wave of, 36, 425
  numbers of, 425
  *See also specific European immigrant
      groups*
Evans, S. M., 46, 169, 195, 196, 232, 270
Evans, T., 238, 279
Executive Order 9066, 358
**Extractive (primary) occupations** [6] Jobs
    that involve the production of raw
    materials. Examples include farmer and
    miner, 198, 535

Fair Employment Practices Commission, 225
"Fair-weather liberal," 77
Falcon, A., 325
Fallows, M. R., 461
Family reunification policy, 418
Fanning, B., 62
Farley, J., 86e, 201e, 241, 247
Farley, R., 204, 419–420
Farm Security Administration (FSA), 186
**Fatalism** [7] The view that one's fate is beyond
    one's control, 238, 535
Feagin, C. B., 512
Feagin, J., 236, 238, 246, 252
Feagin, J. R., 132
Feingold, L. M.
Fernandez, M., 374, 397
Fernandez-Kelly, M. P., 326
Feshbeck, S., 87
15th Amendment, 189
Filipino Americans
  Catholic, 349
  diversity of, 397
  in Hawaii, 397, 486
  occupational profile, 394, 395e
  organized labor and, 314
  population figures, 348e
  violence against, 366
Filipino women, in international sex trade, 204
*Firefighters Local Union N. v. Stotts,* 206
First Reconstruction, 255
Fiske, S., 99, 100, 101
Fitzpatrick, J. P., 318, 333
Fix, M., 419, 420
**Fluid competitive system** [6] A system of
    group relations in which minority group
    members are freer to compete for jobs and
    other scarce resources. Associated with
    advanced industrialization, 201–202, 535
Fong, E., 376, 443
Fong, T., 364, 367, 370
Fonte, John, 340–341
Forbes, H. D., 118
Forner, P. S., 448
14th Amendment, 189
Franklin, J. H., 148–149, 154, 155, 165, 189, 194,
    225, 226, 249
Franklin, L., 86
Frazier, M., 234
Freedom Party, 232
French colonization, 173–174

French immigrants, 431
Frenkel-Brunswick, E., 85, 86e
Fukuyama, Francis, 342–343

Gallagher, C., 53, 115, 454, 455
Gallup Organization, 13
Gans, H., 454
Garcia, F. C., 325
Garcia, J., 325
Garcia, M. C., 345
Gardner, R. W., 311
Garvey, Marcus, 194, 229
Gays/lesbians
    as minorities, 14
    discrimination/prejudice against, 86, 186
Gender
    assimilation and, 45–46
    Chicano Protest Movement, 315
    minority group status and, 19, 23–26
    slavery and, 165–166
Gender inequality
    in China, 349
    in earnings, 127, 128e
    postindustrial U.S., occupational, 203e–204
**Gender roles** [1] Expectations about the proper
        behavior, attitudes, and personality traits
        for males and females, 19, 23–26
    as genetic, 25
    as genetic/learned, 25
    as learned, 24–25
    black protest and, 231–232
    definition of, 535
    in hunter-gatherer societies, 19, 23
Genetics
    gender roles and, 25
    superiority in sports and, 25–26
**Genocide** [1] The deliberate attempt to
        exterminate an entire group of people:
    definition of, 12, 535
    Holocaust as, 124, 478
    in Rwanda, 481–482
Genovese, E. D., 154, 155, 164
German immigrants, 431–432, 439
Germany
    dominant-minority relations in, 477–478
    hate crimes/groups in, 477
    in Rwanda, 480
    need for immigrant workers, 477
    new immigration policy, 477
    See also Holocaust

Gerth, H., 197
Geschwender, J. A., 37, 188, 191e, 224, 225, 452
Ghettos, 190, 193–194, 237
    vs. ethnic enclave, 323
Giago, T., 281
Gimpel, J., 97
Girak, D., 396, 410
Glaeser, E., 245
Glauberman, N., 29
Glazer, N., 52
Gleason, P., 50
Glick, P., 99
Globalization, 200–201, 202–207
Glossary, 533–539
Godstein, A., 57e, 325
Goldberg, Steven, 25
Gonzalez, A., 119
Gonzalez, Hector, 327
Gonzalez, Rodolfo, 314
Gonzalez, Sylvia, 315
Gooding-Williams, R., 233
Gordon, L., 82
Gordon, Milton, 37–39, 38e, 44, 51, 118, 172, 413
Goren, A., 435, 437, 448
Gourevitch, P., 480
Goyette, K., 348f, 352f, 370, 374
Grant-Thompson, S., 118
Graves, S. B., 112
Gray, David, 446–447
Great Migration, of African Americans,
        190–192, 191e
"Great Society," 273
Grebler, L., 310, 313, 333
Greek immigrants, 396, 432, 438
Greektowns, 43, 426, 440
Greeley, Andrew M., 39, 52–53
Green, D., 271
Green, J., 87
Group conflict, relationship with prejudice,
        95–96
Grube, J., 112
"Guest worker" program, in U.S., 417
Guibault, Rose Del Castillo, 308–309
Gulf War (1991), Israel situation and, 486
Gutierrez, José Angel, 314
Gutman, H., 155, 195
Guzman, R. C., 310, 313

Hacker, A., 154
Haitians, 390–391

States to be a direct result of individual efforts, personal values and skills, and education, 39–40
definition of, 535
modern racism and, 238, 241
Hunter-gatherer societies, gender roles in, 19, 23
Hur, K. K., 112
Hurh, W. M., 397
Hurtado, Aida, 64–66
Hutus *vs.* Tutsis, 480–482
Hyman, H., 110*e*

Ibish, H., 85, 406
**Ideological racism** [1] A belief system asserting that a particular group is inferior. Although individuals may subscribe to racist beliefs, the ideology itself is incorporated into the culture of the society and passed on from generation to generation, 26, 27, 163, 535
Ileto, Joseph, murder of, 366
Immigrant laborers
    ethnic/religious prejudice and, 434
    gender and, 433–434
    Irish/Southern European/Eastern European, 432–434
    upward mobility of, 434
    *See also specific immigrant groups*
**Immigrant minority groups** [5] Groups whose initial contact with the dominant group was through immigration:
    Blauner hypothesis and, 152
    definition of, 535
    *See also specific immigrant groups*
Immigrant tales, 455
Immigrants, contemporary
    ethnic enclaves and, 410
    factors shaping fate of, 8–9
    key factors shaping fate of, 55*e*
    percentage speaking only English at home, by generation, 56, 57*e*
    primary labor market and, 410
    secondary labor market and, 410
    segmented assimilation of, 54–56
    welfare rights of, 50
    *See also individual immigrants*
Immigration
    as collective experience, 417
    campaign against European, 437, 443–444
    chain, 42–43, 326

1820–1920 rates, 385
    motivation for, 61, 152, 224, 307, 319, 351, 387, 390, 392, 408, 429
    recent, in historical context, 417
    traditional perspective on, 35–36
    *See also* Chain immigration; Sojourners
Immigration, issues/controversies in, 411–417
    attitude of Americans toward immigration, 411, 412*e*
    attitude of immigrants toward U.S., 411, 412*e*
    case against segmented assimilation, 414–415
    case for segmented assimilation, 413–414
    economic impact, 412–413
    harmful/helpful, 418–421
    illegal immigration, 415, 417
Immigration policies, fluctuating labor demands and, 307, 309
Immigration Reform and Control Act (IRCA), 311
**Indentured servant** [5] A contract laborer who is obligated to serve a particular master for a specified length of time:
    black, 148–149, 153, 163
    definition of, 535
    Irish Catholic, 153
    white, 149
    white *vs.* black, 149, 153
Indian Americans, 51, 348
Indian Claims Commission, 273
Indian Relocation [Removal] Act of 1830, 167, 285
**Indian Reorganization Act (IRA)** [8] Federal legislation passed in 1934 that was intended to give Native American tribes more autonomy, 266, 269–279, 535
Indian schools, 265–266
Indian Self-Determination and Education Assistance Act, 173
Industrial Revolution
    as capital intensive, 181
    English beginnings, 182–183, 429
    innovations, 182
Industrialization, 196–201
    bureaucracy/rationality, 197–198
    changing workforce (1840–2002), 199*e*
    dual labor market and, 200
    globalization and, 200–201
    importance of education and, 199–200
    inequality and, 16–17

Jacobs, Harriet, 162
Jacobson, C., 191e
Jacoby, R., 29
Japan, "invisible minority" in, 365–366
Japanese American Citizens League, 357
Japanese American women, in Relocation
    Camps, 358
Japanese Americans
    acculturation and, 367
    Americanization of, 357
    anti-Japanese campaign, 355–356
    as "model minority," 363
    assimilation and, 502–503
    business ownership by, 396
    compared with other minority groups,
        363–364
    contact situation, 350, 355–358, 362–363
    discrimination against, 356
    education and, 368, 371e, 377
    enclave economy of, 357, 363
    ethnic enclaves of, 356–357
    European immigrants and, 451
    first generation (Issei), 356–357, 362
    fourth generation (Yonsei), 363, 539
    "Gentlemen's Agreement," 356
    GI Bill and, 363
    group harmony (wa) and, 349
    in Hawaii, 488
    "invisible minority" designation,
        365–366
    jobs/income, 356–357, 363, 370
    population figures, 348, 355
    population trends, 352
    post-World War II, 362–363
    poverty rate of, 369
    prejudice against, 84
    scapegoating, 84
    second generation (Nisei), 357, 362–363
    serving in World War II, 352
    stereotypes of, 357, 363
    third generation (Sansei), 363, 538
    vs. African Americans, 363
    vs. American Indians, 363
    vs. colonized minority groups
    vs. Mexican Americans, 363
Japanese immigrants
    as sojourners, 375
    vs. Jewish immigrants, 436
Japanese relocation/internment camps,
    357–358, 360
    effect on internees, 358
    effect on Japanese American community, 362
    Executive Order 9066, 358
    Japanese American protests against, 358
    Manzanar, 361–362
    reparations and, 358, 362
Jarvis, B., 118
Jewish Americans
    education of, 436
    occupational prestige of, 436
    prejudice against, 437
    stereotypes of, 81, 436, 437
Jewish Community Center shooting (CA)
Jewish immigrants, Eastern European
    business ownership by, 435
    education, 436
    employment, men/women, 45, 435
    ethnic enclaves/upward mobility of, 435–436
    exclusion policies and, 436
    vs. Chinese/Japanese immigrants, 436
    See also Anti-Semitism
Jews, as victims of genocide, 479
Jibou, R. M., 356, 357
**Jigsaw method** [4] A learning technique
    that requires cooperation among
    students, 119, 536
**Jim Crow system** [6] See de jure
    segregation.187–190, 197, 205, 243
    cultural domination under, 243
    end of, 224, 227, 244, 504
    housing discrimination, 228
    need for justification, 187
    rejection of, 228–229
    schools under, 228, 247
    weakening of, 226
    See also De jure segregation
John, D., 203
Johnson, Ann, 102–103
Johnson, Jack, 48
Johnson, Lyndon B., 227
Johnson-O'Malley Act, 267
Joly, S., 127, 128
Jones, James, 78
Jones, Jeffrey, 306
Jones, M., 86
Jones, Peter, 61
Jordan, Barbara, 223
Jordan, Michael, 223
Jordan, W., 154, 163
Josephy, A. M., 264, 270

Powlishta, K., 91

**Prejudice** [1] The tendency of individuals to think and feel negatively toward others:
affective, 26, 78
authoritarian personality theory and, 86
cognitive, 26, 78
culture-based theories of, 87–89, 91–95
    children and, 89–91
    limitations of, 95
    reduction strategy, 121
    situational influences, 94–95
    social distance, 91–94
    sources of prejudice, 90–91
    vicious cycle, 88e–89
declining, 110e–111
definition of, 26, 537
discrimination and, 77, 78e
    (*See also* Prejudice/discrimination, reduction efforts)
individual
    cognitive, 27e
    emotional, 87, 122
intergroup competition and, 121
intergroup contact as reducing, 116–117
learned, 98, 120, 121, 163
personality-centered theory of, 83–87, 120
power-conflict theory of
    limitations, 97
    Marxist analysis, 96–97
    Robber's Cave experiment, 95–96
    split labor market theory, 97
racial profiling and, 102–105, 234
role in group conflict, 95–96
sexism and, 98–101, 99e, 242–243
theories of, 83–97
types of, 97–98
*See also* Prejudice, individual; Prejudice/discrimination, reduction efforts; Stereotypes

Prejudice/discrimination, reduction efforts
causal relation model, prejudice/discrimination, 120e
contact/increased communication between groups, 115–119
education, 113e–115, 114e
future of, 119–121
limitations of, 121
persuasion through mass media, 11–113, 111–113

**Prestige** [1] The amount of honor or respect accorded a particular person or group, 16, 436, 537
Pretextual stops, racial profiling, 103
Price, S. L., 295–296
**Primary labor market** [6] The segment of the labor market that encompasses better paying, higher status, more secure jobs. Usually in large bureaucracies, 200, 410, 537
**Primary occupations** [6] *See* extractive (primary) occupations:
definition of, 537
**Primary sector of the social structure** [2] Relationships and groups that are intimate and personal. Groups in the primary sector are small, 38, 537
Primary social structure, 38, 538
Primary structural assimilation
    African American, 252–253
    Asian Americans/Pacific Islander, 373–374
    Hispanic American, 333e
**Principle of third-generation interest** [12] The notion that the grandchildren of immigrants will stress their ethnicity much more than the second generation will,, 453, 537
**projection** [3] Seeing in others characteristics or feelings we cannot admit we have in ourselves:
authoritarian personality, 83–84, 85–86e
definition of, 537
prejudice and, 84–85
**Proletariat** [1] In Marxist theory, the workers in an industrial society, 15, 537
Proposition 187, 417
Prosise, Theodore, 102–103
Protestant religion, 171, 434, 444
Protestant work ethic, 125, 133, 134, 381, 431, 455
Pseudopatriotism, 86e
Pseudotolerance, 154
Public sociology, description of, 1–2
Puerto Rican Americans
    acculturation of, 501
    African Americans and, 319
    assimilation and, 325–326, 334
    business ownership, 397
    enslavement of, 318

female-headed households, 331
in New York City, 317
in Northeastern United States,
317, 318–319
institutionalized racial barriers and, 319
Mexican Americans and, 319
migration/employment and, 200, 316–317
occupational profiles, 329–330
other minority groups and, 318–319
poverty rate for, 334e
pull/push factors for, 317
racial identification, 318
racial intermarriage by, 318
religious practice of, 318
residential patterns of, 326
socioeconomic profiles of, 330–331
stereotypes of, 321, 325
transitions, 318
*See also* Hispanic Americans
Puerto Rican women
as heads of households, 331
personal narrative of, 320–321
stereotypes of, 321
**pull** [9] Factors that cause population
movement out of an area, 537
*See also* push.
**push** [9] Factors that cause population
movement into an area, 537. *See also* pull.
definition of, 537
for Asians/Pacific Islanders, 392
for Chinese Americans, 351
for Mexicans, 339
for Puerto Ricans, 317
Puzo, Mario, 59–60

Quillian, L., 333

**Race** [1] Biologically, an isolated, inbreeding
population with a distinctive genetic
heritage. Socially, the term is used loosely
and reflects patterns of inequality and
power:
as biological triviality, 13, 198
biological dimension of, 18–19
definition of, 537
social dimension of, 19, 47
social *vs.* biological dimension, 19
*vs.* class, 237–238, 241e, 248e
*See also* Racial identity, social construction
of; Skin color

Race relations, post-Civil War South
Blauner hypothesis and, 187
de jure segregation and (*See* De jure
segregation)
Reconstruction, 183–187
sharecropping/tenant farming system,
188, 538
**race relations cycle** [2] A concept associated
with Robert Park, who believed that
relations between different groups would
go through predictable cycles, from
conflict to eventual assimilation, 37, 537
Race riots, 122, 129
Racial hatred, dynamics of, 131–132
Racial identity, social construction of, 22–23
Racial imagery, 457
**racial minority groups** [1] Minority groups
identified primarily by physical
characteristics such as skin color
(e.g., Asian Americans):
definition of, 13, 537
*See also* Skin color; *specific racial minority
groups*
Racial profiling, 102–105, 234
Racial progress, contemporary society,
253–254
Racial steering, realtor practice of, 246
Racial stratification, 79, 84, 88
**racism** [1] A belief system that asserts the
inferiority of a group:
by nation, 101e
Christianity and, 123
definition of, 26, 27, 535, 537
ideological, 26, 27, 163, 535
*See also* Modern racism
Racist extremist groups, 129
Rader, B. G., 450
Randolph, A. Phillip, 225
Raspberry, W., 380
Rawick, G. P., 176
Raymer, P., 271
Read, J. G., 398
Reagan, R., 381
**Reconstruction** [6] the period of Southern
race relations following the Civil War.
Reconstruction lasted from 1865 until the
1880s and witnessed many racial reforms,
all of which were reversed during de jure
segregation, or the Jim Crow era; 183–187,
255, 537

definition of, 537
end of, 187
First, 255
Second, 255
Red Power movement, 274–275, 291
Reich, M., 97
Religion
American Indians, 282
Arab Americans, 398, 400
Asian American/Pacific Islanders, 349
assimilation and, 43–44, 432
Catholic, 349, 426, 446–447
(*See also* Catholic Church;
Catholicism)
Mexican Americans, 306
Protestant, 171, 306, 342, 434, 444
White ethnic groups, 426, 446–447
**Relocation camps** [10] The camps in which
Japanese Americans were held during
World War II:
definition of, 538
*See also* Japanese relocation/internment
camps
Remington, R., 479
Rendall, M., 235
**repatriation** [9] A government campaign
begun during the Great Depression of the
1930s to deport illegal immigrants back to
Mexico. The campaign also caused legal
immigrants and native-born Mexican
Americans to leave the United States,
156–158, 194
definition of, 538
Mexican American, 310
Reservations
in Canada, 475
in U.S. (*See* American Indians,
reservation life)
Residential discrimination, 244–247, 246*e*
against African Americans, 244*e*–247,
245*e*, 246*e*, 326
against Asian Americans/Pacific Islanders,
367, 369*e*
against Buraku, 366
Response set, 87
Reverse discrimination, 208
Revilla, L., 398
**Revolution** [2] A minority group goal.
A revolutionary group wishes to change
places with the dominant group or

create a new social order, perhaps in
alliance with other groups:
as minority group goal, 57–58
definition of, 538
Rice, Condoleezza, 239–240
Rifkin, J., 198
**Rigid competitive group system** [6] A system
of group relations in which the dominant
group seeks to exclude minority groups or
limit their ability to compete for scarce
resources such as jobs.
relations, 182–183, 538
Robber's Cave experiment, 95–96
contact hypothesis and, 117
Robertson, C., 166
Robinson, J. P., 112
Robinson, R., 255
Rodriguez, C., 318, 333
Rodriguez, Luis, 60
Rokeach, M., 112
Roosevelt, Franklin D., 225, 269, 357, 358
Roosevelt, Theodore, 211
Rouse, L., 281, 282
Rowatt, W., 86
Rumbaut, R., 54, 55, 55*e*, 311, 325, 387
Rupert, A., 127, 128
Russell, J. W., 174
Rwanda, 480–482, 481*e*

Saenz, R., 325
Salavatorans, 390
Samoan Americans, in Hawaii, 486
Sanchirico, A., 377
Sanford, N., 85, 86*e*
**Sansei** [10] Third-generation Japanese
Americans, 362, 538
**Scapegoat hypothesis** [3] A theory of
prejudice that posits that under certain
conditions, people will express their
aggressions against substitute targets.
When other groups are chosen as
substitute targets, prejudice increases:
Anti-Semitism and, 85
definition of, 84, 538
Japanese Americans and, 84
limitations of, 86–87
Mexican Americans and, 84
Nazi Germany and, 85
Schauffler, R., 326
Schlesinger Jr., A. M., 36

Skin color, 13, 18, 19, 79
  in Brazil, 489, 491
Skinheads
  German, 477
  in U.S., 437
Sklare, M., 436
Slave owners, 154–155
Slave trade, 149–150
Slavery
  abolition of, 155, 157–158
  African American culture and, 175–177
  as caste system, 154
  creation of American, key concepts in
    assimilation, 164–165
    Blauner hypothesis and, 151–152
    competition, 150
    ethnocentrism, 150
    gender relations, 165–166
    inequality, 14–15, 163
    institutional discrimination, 163
    Noel hypothesis and, 150–151, 153e, 163
    paternalism and, 154–155
    power differential, 60, 96, 150–151,
      155, 163
    prejudice/racism, 163–164e
    pseudotolerance, 154
  enforced code of etiquette, 188
  in Brazil, 489–490, 491
  Nat Turner's Revolt, 155
  Noel hypothesis and, 153
  origins of, 148–155
    black indentured servants, 148–149,
      153, 163
    first slave laws, 149
    labor supply problem and, 149–150
    plantation system and, 149
  stereotypes and, 160
  women under, 166
Slaves
  as chattel, 154
  forms of resistance used by, 155
  individual history of, 161–162
  lack of research on female, 177
  runaway, 155, 161–162
Smedley, A., 19, 149, 163
Smelser, N., 134
Smith, C. B., 118
Smith, E. R., 125
Smith, J., 11, 412
Smith, K., 115

Smith, T., 93e, 282
Smith, Tommie, 122
Smith, V., 255
Snipp, C. M., 167, 272, 273, 277, 282, 285,
  288, 289
Social class [1] A group of people who
  command similar amounts of valued
  goods and services, such as income,
  property, and education:
  assimilation and, 44–45
  definition of, 15, 538
  hate crime and, 130
Social distance [3] The degree of intimacy
  to which a person is willing to admit
  members of other groups:
  as cultural component of prejudice, 91–94
  definition of, 538
  seven degrees of, 92
Social distance scale
  American Indian scores, 281–282
  anti-Semitism scores, 92–94, 93e
  Asian group scores, 94, 364
  Mexican American scores, 325
  rankings, 92, 93e
Social mobility [1] Movement from one
  social class to another, 17, 538
Social structure [2] The networks of social
  relationships, groups, organizations,
  communities, and institutions that
  organize the work of a society and connect
  individuals to each other and to the larger
  society, 38, 538
Socialization [3] The process of physical,
  psychological, and social development by
  which a person learns his or her culture:
  definition of, 538
  into race-conscious society, 79
Sojourners [6] Immigrants who intend to
  return to their country of origin:
  Chinese, 375
  definition of, 538
  Italian, 46
  Japanese, 375
  South Africa, 482–484
Southern Poverty Law Center (SPLC), 129
Sowell, T., 208–209
Spanish colonization, 173
  missions and, 336
Sparks, C., 118
Spicer, E. H., 264, 269, 279

Spickard, P., 363

Spilde, K., 279

Split labor market

Chinese immigrants and, 351

Mexican Americans and, 313

**Split labor market theory** [3] When the labor
force is divided into a higher paid segment
composed of members of the dominant
group and a lower paid segment composed
of minority group members, higher paid
labor uses prejudice and racism to limit
the ability of cheaper labor to compete for
jobs, 97, 331, 538

Stampp, K., 154

Stangor, C., 127

Staples, R., 196

Starling, K., 112

Statistics Canada, 443

Staub, E., 85

Staurowsky, Ellen J., 296–298

Steinberg, S., 45, 53, 115, 196, 250, 425, 433, 436

Stelcner, M., 443

Stember, C. H., 115

Stepick, A., 391

Stepick, C. D., 391

**Stereotypes** [1] Overgeneralizations that are
thought to apply to all members of a
groups:

American, 81–82e

as rationalization, 79–80

attribution theory and, 79–80

authoritarian personality theory and, 86

cognition/categorization of, 78–79

cognitive/emotional dimensions of, 80

definition of, 26, 78, 539

gender/minority, 82–83

new forms of, 133

of American Indians, 281

scapegoat hypothesis and, 84–85

selective perception and, 79

to control minority groups, 81

types of, 80–81

*See also* Modern racism; *specific minority
groups*

Stevens, G., 412, 413, 414, 415

Stoddard, E., 170

Stoll, M., 247

Stolzenberg, L., 130

**Stratification** [1] The unequal distribution of
valued goods and services (e.g., income,
job opportunities, prestige and fame,
education, health care) in society; the
social class system, 15–18, 539

**Structural assimilation** [2] *See also*
integration.

definition of, 38–39, 539

Structural integration, social class affect on,
44–45

**Structural mobility** [12] Rising occupational
and social-class standing that is the result
of changes in the overall structure of the
economy and labor market as opposed to
individual efforts:

continuing industrialization and, 450

definition of, 539

European immigrants and, 450

**Structural pluralism** [2] A situation in which
a group has acculturated but is not
integrated, 51, 172

definition of, 539

*See also* Segregation era, African Americans
and

Structural racism, 255, 256

Stuckey, S., 243

Student Nonviolent Coordinating Committee
(SNCC), 231

Stultz, B., 58e

**Subsistence technology** [1] The means by
which a society satisfies basic needs. An
agrarian society relies on labor-intensive
agriculture, whereas an industrial society
relies on machines and inanimate fuel
supplies:

definition of, 16, 539

dominant-minority group relations and,
496–497

Subsociety. *See* Chinatowns

Sung, B. L., 373

Suro, R., 57e, 325

Swedish immigrants, 431

Sweetman, A., 443

Swim, J., 127

Switzerland, peaceful pluralistic society of,
478–479

Symbolic ethnicity, 458–459

**Symbolic racism** [4] 125, 539. *See* modern
racism.

Taiwanese, 342, 359

Takaki, Ronald, 312, 349, 355, 380–381, 502–503

# Permission Credits

For permission to reprint from the following, grateful acknowledgment is made to the publishers and copyright holders.

## Chapter 1

Chapter photos: Judith J. Friedman.

Narrative Portrait: From Lawrence Hill's *Blackberry Sweet Juice.* Published by HarperCollins Publishers Ltd. Copyright © 2001 by Lawrence Hill. Reprinted with permission.

Current Debate, "The Argument for Genetic Differences is Deeply Flawed," copyright © New Statesman. All rights reserved. Reprinted with permission.

## Chapter 2

Chapter photos: Sidney Poitier, copyright © CORBIS; Stephanie Williams, copyright © AP/World Wide Photos; students at Randolph, copyright © AP/World Wide Photos; J.P. Loving & wife, copyright © AP/World Wide Photos; Halle Berry, copyright © AP/World Wide Photos.

Exhibit 2.5: From Alba, R., Logan, J., Luiz, A., & Stultz, B. (2002). "Only English by the third generation? Loss and preservation of the mother tongue among the grandchildren of contemporary immigrants," in *Demography, 39*(3), copyright © 2002, reprinted with permission.

Narrative Portrait: From Puzo, M., "Choosing a dream: Italians in Hell's Kitchen," in W. Brown & A. Ling (Eds.), *Visions of America.* Reprinted by permission of Donadio & Olson, Inc. Copyright © 1993 Brown and Ling.

Narrative Portrait: From Rodriguez, L., *Always Running: La Vida Loca,* copyright © 1993, reprinted with permission of Curbstone Press.

"Kilkelly" song lyrics reprinted by permission of Peter Jones.

Exhibit 2.6: From O'Sullivan, E., "Migration and Housing in Ireland: Report to the European Observatory on Homelessness," copyright © 2003, reprinted with permission of FEANTSA.

Current Debates: From Mujica, M., "Official English legislation: myths and realities," in *Human Events, 59,* copyright © 2003, reprinted with permission.

Current Debates: From Hurtado, A., & Vega, L., "Shift happens: Spanish and English transmission between parents and their children," in *Journal of Social Issues, 60*(1), copyright © 2004, reprinted with permission of Blackwell Publishing.

# Chapter 3

Exhibit 3.2: Karlins, M., Coffman, T., & Walters, G. (1969). "On the fading of social stereotypes: studies in three generations of college students," in *Journal of Personality and Social Psychology, 13.* Copyright © 1969 by the American Psychological Association. Adapted with permission.

Narrative Portrait: Reprinted with the permission of Scribner, a division of Simon & Schuster Adult Publishing Group, from *Kaffir Boy* by Mark Mathabane. Copyright © 1986 by Mark Mathabane. All rights reserved.

Current Debates: From Prosise, T., & Johnson, A., "Law enforcement and crime on 'Cops' and the 'World's Wildest Police Videos': anecdotal form and the justification of racial profiling," in *Western Journal of Communication, 68,* copyright © 2004, reprinted with permission of Taylor and Francis, Ltd. www.tandf.co.uk/journals

Current Debates: From Taylor, J. & Whitney, G., "Racial profiling: Is there an empirical basis?" in *Mankind Quarterly, 42,* copyright © 2002, reprinted with permission of The Council for Social and Economic Studies.

# Chapter 4

Chapter photos: U.S. Nazi meeting 1936, Otto Hagel/Hansel Meith; Alabama protest, National Archives; Tommie Smith & John Carlos raising fists, Corbis-Bettman; Cross-burning, Emery Smith; church burned, AP/World Wide Photos; nazi graffiti, AP/World Wide Photos; Aryan Nations, Emery Smith; Nazi graffiti, AP/World Wide Photos; Coors billboard, Ed Buryn/Jeroboam; mom & son, Emery Smith; skinhead, Emery Smith; white order couple, Emery Smith.

Narrative Portrait: Copyright © 1992 *Race: How Blacks and Whites Think and Feel About the American Obsession* by Studs Terkel. Reprinted by permission of The New Press, www.thenewpress.com

Current Debates: From Bobo, L., "Racial attitudes and relations at the close of the Twentieth Century," in N. Smelser, W. Wilson, & E. Mitchell (Eds.), *America Becoming: Racial Trends and Their Consequences, Vol. 1,* copyright © 2001, reprinted with permission of the National Academies Press, Washington, D.C.

Current Debates: From Zuriff, G. E., "Inventing racism," in *Public Interest, 146,* copyright © 2002, reprinted with permission of National Affairs, Inc.

# Chapter 5

Chapter photos: child & nurse, www.daguerre.org; Fannie Virginia Casseopia, Photographs & Prints Division, Schomberg Center for Research in Black Culture, NY Public Library; Renty, Peabody Museum of Archaeology and Ethnology; other images courtesy of the Library of Congress.

Narrative Portrait: From Osofsky, G., *Puttin' on Ole Massa,* copyright © 1969, reprinted with permission.

Narrative Portrait: Reprinted by permission of the publishers from *Incidents in the Life of a Slave Girl: Written by Herself* by Harriet Jacobs, edited and with an introduction by Jean Fagan Yellin, Harvard University Press, copyright © 1987, 2000 by the President and Fellows of Harvard College.

Current Debates: From *Ar'nt I a Woman?: Female Slaves in the Plantation South* by Deborah Gray White. Copyright © 1985 by Deborah Gray White. Used by permission of W.W. Norton & Company, Inc.

# Chapter 6

Chapter photos: courtesy of the collection of Eric Margolis.

Current Debates: From Sowell, T., "How affirmative action hurts blacks," in *Forbes, 160*, copyright © 1997 Forbes, Inc., reprinted by permission of Forbes Magazine.

Current Debates: From Patterson, O., *The Ordeal of Integration*, copyright © 1997 by Orlando Patterson. Reprinted by permission of Counterpoint Press, a member of Perseus Books, L.L.C.

# Chapter 7

Narrative Portrait: From Herstein, A., "Acorns to oaks: Condolezza Rice's journey from the Jim Crow South to the White House," in *American Clergy*, copyright © 2004, reprinted with permission of *American Clergy* magazine, www.americanclergy.com.

Current Debates: From Marable, M., "An idea whose time has come. . . . Whites have an obligation to recognize slavery's legacy," in *Newsweek*, 8/27, copyright © 2001 Newsweek, Inc., All rights reserved. Reprinted by permission.

Current Debates: From McWhorter, J., "Blood money, an analysis of slavery reparations," in *The American Enterprise, 12*(18), copyright © 2001, reprinted with permission of *The American Enterprise*, www.TAEmag.com.

# Chapter 8

Chapter photos: Apache prisoners and Chiricahua Apaches, Denver Public Library; Rough rock demonstration, Monty Roessel.

Narrative Portrait: From Crow Dog, M., *Lakota Woman*, copyright © 1990, reprinted with permission of Grove/Atlantic, Inc.

Narrative Portrait: Reprinted with the permission of Pocket Books, an imprint of Simon & Schuster Adult Publishing Group, from *Lame Deer, Seeker of Visions* by John (Fire) Lame Deer and Richard Erdoes. Copyright © 1972 by John (Fire) Deer and Richard Erdoes. All rights reserved.

Current Debates: Reprinted courtesy of *Sports Illustrated*: "The Indian Wars" by S. L. Price, March 4, 2002. Copyright © 2002, Time, Inc. All rights reserved.

Current Debates: Reprinted courtesy of *Sports Illustrated*: "Polls Apart" by Andrea Woo, March 4, 2002. Copyright © 2002, Time, Inc. All rights reserved.

Current Debates: From King, C.R., Staurowsky, E.J., Baca, L., Davis, R. & Pewewardy, C., "Of polls and race prejudice: *Sports Illustrated's* Errant 'Indian Wars,'" in *Journal of Sport and Social Issues, 26*, copyright © 2002, reprinted with permission of Sage Publications, Inc.

# Chapter 9

Chapter photos: Aultman collection, Colorado State Historical Society; High school graduates, L.A. Public Library; Main St., Lake County Museum; other images courtesy of the Library of Congress.

Narrative Portrait: From Guilbalt, Rose Del Castillo, "Americanization is tough on 'Macho,'" in *The San Francisco Chronicle*, copyright © 1989. Reprinted with permission via Copyright Clearance Center.

Narrative Portrait: From Cofer, Judith Ortiz, *The Latin Deli: Prose & Poetry*, copyright © 1993 by Judith Ortiz Cofer. Reprinted by permission of the University of Georgia Press.

Poem, "Stupid America" by Abelardo "Lalo" Berrientos Delgado, copyright © 1969, reprinted with permission.

Current Debates: From Fonte, J., "How to make an American," in *The American Enterprise, 15*, copyright © 2004, reprinted with permission of *The American Enterprise*, www.TAEmag.com.

Current Debates: From Fukuyama, F., "Identity crisis: whey we shouldn't worry about Mexican immigration," in http://slate.msn.com/id/2101756/#continuearticle. Reprinted with permission.

## Chapter 10

Chapter photos: cartoon, Denver Public Library

Current Debates: Reprinted by permission of the publisher from *Harvard Encyclopedia of American Ethnic Groups* edited by Stephan S. Thernstrom, Ann Orlov, and Oscar Handlin, pp. 570–571, Cambridge, Mass.: The Belknap Press of Harvard University Press, Copyright © 1980 by the President and Fellows of Harvard College.

Current Debates: From Portes, A. & Zhou, M, "Gaining the upper hand: economic mobility among immigrant and domestic minorities," in *Ethnic and Racial Studies, 15,* reprinted with permission of Taylor and Francis, Ltd. www.tandf.co.uk/journals.

Current Debates: From Takaki, R., *A Different Mirror,* copyright © 1993 by Ronald Takaki. Reprinted by permission of Little, Brown, and Co., Inc.

## Chapter 11

Photo essay: From Gold, S., *The Arab American Community in Detroit, Michigan.* Reprinted with permission of the University of California Press.

Narrative Portrait: "Vo Thi Tam, from Vietnam, 1979" and an excerpt from "Ho Yang, from China, 1920," reprinted from *American Mosaic: The Immigrant Experience in the Words of Those Who Lived It,* by Joan Morrison and Charlotte Fox Zabusky, copyright © 1980, 1993, by permission of the University of Pittsburgh Press.

Current Debates: From Brimelow, P., *Alien Nation,* copyright © 1995 by Peter Brimelow; maps & illustrations copyright © 1995 by John Grimwade. Used by permission of Random House, Inc.

Current Debates: From Farley, R., "New Americans," in *The New American Reality: Who We Are, How We Got There, Where We are Going.* Copyright © 1996 Russell Sage Foundation, 112 East 64th Street, New York, NY 10021. Reprinted with permission.

Current Debates: From Borjas, G. J., *Heaven's Door,* copyright © 1999 Princeton University Press. Reprinted by permission of Princeton University Press.

## Chapter 12

Chapter photos: Ellis island, NY Public Library; Labor agency, New York City, 1910, photo by Lewis Wickes Hine, NY Public Library; Church, Fred Hulstran History in Pictures Collection; Aultman collection, Colorado State Historical Society; Norwegian dancers, Minnesota Historical Society; other images courtesy of Farm Security Administration; Bob Sweeney & John McCormick, Minnesota Historical Society.

Narrative Portrait: From Gray, D. J., "Shadows of the past: The rise and fall of prejudice in an American city," in *American Journal of Economics and Sociology, 50,* copyright © 1991, reprinted with permission of Blackwell Publishing, Ltd.

Current Debates: From Dyer, R., "The matter of whiteness," in Rothenburg, P. (Ed.), *White Privilege,* copyright © 2002, reprinted with permission of Taylor and Francis.

Current Debates: From *Origins and Destinies, Immigration, Race, and Ethnicity in America, 1st edition* by Pedraza/Rumbaut. Copyright © 1996. Reprinted with permission of Wadsworth, a division of Thomson Learning: www.thomsonrights.com.

Disclaimer: The publisher has made every effort to obtain written permission for the use of the above material. In the event of an unintentional omission, please contact the publisher.

WARNER MEMORIAL LIBRARY
EASTERN UNIVERSITY
ST. DAVIDS, PA 19087-3696